Modern
Quantum Mechanics
Revised Edition

J. J. Sakurai
Late, University of California, Los Angeles

San Fu Tuan, Editor
University of Hawaii, Manoa

PEARSON
Education

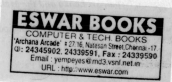

ISBN 81-7808-006-0

First ISE Reprint, 1999
Second Indian Reprint, 2000
Third Indian Reprint, 2001
Fourth Indian Reprint, 2002
Fifth Indian Reprint, 2003
Sixth Indian Reprint, 2004
Seventh Indian Reprint, 2004

This edition is manufactured in India and is authorized for sale only in India, Bangladesh, Bhutan, Pakistan, Nepal, Sri Lanka and the Maldives.

Published by Pearson Education (Singapore) Pte. Ltd., Indian Branch, 482 F.I.E. Patparganj, Delhi 110 092, India

Printed in India by Sheel Print N Pack

Foreword

J. J. Sakurai was always a very welcome guest here at CERN, for he was one of those rare theorists to whom the experimental facts are even more interesting than the theoretical game itself. Nevertheless, he delighted in theoretical physics and in its teaching, a subject on which he held strong opinions. He thought that much theoretical physics teaching was both too narrow and too remote from application: "...we see a number of sophisticated, yet uneducated, theoreticians who are conversant in the LSZ formalism of the Heisenberg field operators, but do not know why an excited atom radiates, or are ignorant of the quantum theoretic derivation of Rayleigh's law that accounts for the blueness of the sky." And he insisted that the student must be able to use what has been taught: "The reader who has read the book but cannot do the exercises has learned nothing."

He put these principles to work in his fine book *Advanced Quantum Mechanics* (1967) and in *Invariance Principles and Elementary Particles* (1964), both of which have been very much used in the CERN library. This new book, *Modern Quantum Mechanics*, should be used even more, by a larger and less specialized group. The book combines breadth of interest with a thorough practicality. Its readers will find here what they need to know, with a sustained and successful effort to make it intelligible.

J. J. Sakurai's sudden death on November 1, 1982 left this book unfinished. Reinhold Bertlmann and I helped Mrs. Sakurai sort out her husband's papers at CERN. Among them we found a rough, handwritten version of most of the book and a large collection of exercises. Though only three chapters had been completely finished, it was clear that the bulk of the creative work had been done. It was also clear that much work remained to fill in gaps, polish the writing, and put the manuscript in order.

That the book is now finished is due to the determination of Noriko Sakurai and the dedication of San Fu Tuan. Upon her husband's death, Mrs. Sakurai resolved immediately that his last effort should not go to waste. With great courage and dignity she became the driving force behind the project, overcoming all obstacles and setting the high standards to be maintained. San Fu Tuan willingly gave his time and energy to the editing and completion of Sakurai's work. Perhaps only others close to the hectic field of high-energy theoretical physics can fully appreciate the sacrifice involved.

For me personally, J. J. had long been far more than just a particularly distinguished colleague. It saddens me that we will never again laugh together at physics and physicists and life in general, and that he will not see the success of his last work. But I am happy that it has been brought to fruition.

John S. Bell
CERN, Geneva

Preface to the Revised Edition

Since 1989 the Editor has enthusiastically pursued a revised edition of Modern Quantum Mechanics by his late great friend J. J. Sakurai, in order to extend this text's usefulness into the twenty-first century. Much consultation took place with the panel of Sakurai friends who helped with the original edition, but in particular with Professor Yasuo Hara of Tsukuba University and Professor Akio Sakurai of Kyoto Sangyo University in Japan.

This book is intended for the first year graduate student who has studied quantum mechanics at the junior or senior level. It does not provide an introduction to quantum mechanics for the beginner. The reader should have had some experience in solving time-dependent and time-independent wave equations. A familiarity with the time evolution of the Gaussian wave packet in a force-free region is assumed, as is the ability to solve one-dimensional transmission-reflection problems. Some of the general properties of the energy eigenfunctions and the energy eigenvalues should also be known to the student who uses this text.

The major motivation for this project is to revise the main text. There are three important additions and/or changes to the revised edition, which otherwise preserves the original version unchanged. These include a reworking of certain portions of Section 5.2 on time-independent perturbation theory for the degenerate case by Professor Kenneth Johnson of M.I.T., taking into account a subtle point that has not been properly treated by a number of texts on quantum mechanics in this country. Professor Roger Newton of Indiana University contributed refinements on lifetime broadening in Stark effect, additional explanations of phase shifts at resonances, the optical theorem, and on non-normalizable state. These appear as "remarks by the editor" or "editor's note" in the revised edition. Professor Thomas Fulton of the Johns Hopkins University reworked his Coulomb Scattering contribution (Section 7.13) so that it now appears as a shorter text portion emphasizing the physics, with the mathematical details relegated to Appendix C.

Though not a major part of the text, some additions were deemed necessary to take into account developments in quantum mechanics that have become prominent since November, 1 1982. To this end, two supplements are included at the end of the text. Supplement I is on adiabatic change and geometrical phase (popularized by M. V. Berry since 1983) and is actually an English translation of the supplement on this subject written by Professor Akio Sakurai for the Japanese version of Modern Quantum Mechanics (copyright © Yoshioka-Shoten Publishing of Kyoto). Supplement II is on non-exponential decays written by my colleague here, Professor Xerxes Tata, and read over by Professor E. C. G. Sudarshan of the University of Texas at Austin. Though non-exponential decays have a long history theoretically, experimental work on transition rates that tests indirectly such decays was done only in 1990. Introduction of additional material is of course a subjective matter on the part of the Editor; the readers will evaluate for themselves its appropriateness. Thanks to Professor Akio Sakurai, the revised edition has been "finely toothcombed" for misprint errors of the first ten printings of the original edition. My colleague, Professor Sandip Pakvasa, provided overall guidance and encouragement to me throughout this process of revision.

In addition to the acknowledgments above, my former students Li Ping, Shi Xiaohong, and Yasunaga Suzuki provided the sounding board for ideas on the revised edition when taking may graduate quantum mechanics course at the University of Hawaii during the spring of 1992. Suzuki provided the initial translation from Japanese of Supplement I as a course term paper. Dr. Andy Acker provided me with computer graphic assistance. The Department of Physics and Astronomy and particularly the High Energy Physics Group of the University of Hawaii at Manoa provided again both the facilities and a conducive atmosphere for me to carry out my editorial task. Finally I wish to express my gratitude to Physics (and sponsoring) Senior Editor, Stuart Johnson, and his Editorial Assistant, Jennifer Duggan, as well as Senior Production Coordinator Amy Willcutt, of Addison-Wesley for their encouragement and optimism that the revised edition will indeed materialize.

San Fu TUAN
Honolulu, Hawaii

J. J. Sakurai 1933–1982

In Memoriam

Jun John Sakurai was born in 1933 in Tokyo and came to the United States as a high school student in 1949. He studied at Harvard and at Cornell, where he received his Ph.D. in 1958. He was then appointed assistant professor of Physics at the University of Chicago, and became a full professor in 1964. He stayed at Chicago until 1970 when he moved to the University of California at Los Angeles, where he remained until his death. During his lifetime he wrote 119 articles in theoretical physics of elementary particles as well as several books and monographs on both quantum and particle theory.

The discipline of theoretical physics has as its principal aim the formulation of theoretical descriptions of the physical world that are at once concise and comprehensive. Because nature is subtle and complex, the pursuit of theoretical physics requires bold and enthusiastic ventures to the frontiers of newly discovered phenomena. This is an area in which Sakurai reigned supreme with his uncanny physical insight and intuition and also his ability to explain these phenomena in illuminating physical terms to the unsophisticated. One has but to read his very lucid textbooks on *Invariance Principles and Elementary Particles* and *Advanced Quantum Mechanics* as well as his reviews and summer school lectures to appreciate this. Without exaggeration I could say that much of what I did understand in particle physics came from these and from his articles and private tutoring.

When Sakurai was still a graduate student, he proposed what is now known as the V-A theory of weak interactions, independently of (and simultaneously with) Richard Feynman, Murray Gell-Mann, Robert Marshak, and George Sudarshan. In 1960 he published in *Annals of Physics* a prophetic paper, probably his single most important one. It was concerned with the first serious attempt to construct a theory of strong interactions based on Abelian and non-Abelian (Yang-Mills) gauge invariance. This seminal work induced theorists to attempt an understanding of the mechanisms of mass generation for gauge (vector) fields, now realized as the Higgs mechanism. Above all it stimulated the search for a realistic unification of forces under the gauge principle, now crowned with success in the celebrated Glashow-Weinberg-Salam unification of weak and electromagnetic forces. On the phenomenological side, Şakurai pursued and vigorously advocated the vector mesons dominance model of hadron dynamics. He was the first to discuss the mixing of ω and ϕ meson states. Indeed, he made numerous important contributions to particle physics phenomenology in a much more general sense, as his heart was always close to experimental activities.

I knew Jun John for more than 25 years, and I had the greatest admiration not only for his immense powers as a theoretical physicist but also for the warmth and generosity of his spirit. Though a graduate student himself at Cornell during 1957–1958, he took time from his own pioneering research in K-nucleon dispersion relations to help me (via extensive correspondence) with my Ph.D. thesis on the same subject at Berkeley. Both Sandip Pakvasa and I were privileged to be associated with one of his last papers on weak couplings of heavy quarks, which displayed once more his infectious and intuitive style of doing physics. It is of course gratifying to us in retrospect that Jun John counted this paper among the score of his published works that he particularly enjoyed.

The physics community suffered a great loss at Jun John Sakurai's death. The personal sense of loss is a severe one for me. Hence I am profoundly thankful for the opportunity to edit and complete his manuscript on *Modern Quantum Mechanics* for publication. In my faith no greater gift can be given me than an opportunity to show my respect and love for Jun John through meaningful service.

San Fu Tuan

Contents

Modern Quantum Mechanics

CHAPTER 1

Fundamental Concepts

The revolutionary change in our understanding of microscopic phenomena that took place during the first 27 years of the twentieth century is unprecedented in the history of natural sciences. Not only did we witness severe limitations in the validity of classical physics, but we found the alternative theory that replaced the classical physical theories to be far richer in scope and far richer in its range of applicability.

The most traditional way to begin a study of quantum mechanics is to follow the historical developments—Planck's radiation law, the Einstein-Debye theory of specific heats, the Bohr atom, de Broglie's matter waves, and so forth—together with careful analyses of some key experiments such as the Compton effect, the Franck-Hertz experiment, and the Davisson-Germer-Thompson experiment. In that way we may come to appreciate how the physicists in the first quarter of the twentieth century were forced to abandon, little by little, the cherished concepts of classical physics and how, despite earlier false starts and wrong turns, the great masters—Heisenberg, Schrödinger, and Dirac, among others—finally succeeded in formulating quantum mechanics as we know it today.

However, we do not follow the historical approach in this book. Instead, we start with an example that illustrates, perhaps more than any other example, the inadequacy of classical concepts in a fundamental way. We hope that by exposing the reader to a "shock treatment" at the onset, he or she may be attuned to what we might call the "quantum-mechanical way of thinking" at a very early stage.

1.1. THE STERN-GERLACH EXPERIMENT

The example we concentrate on in this section is the Stern-Gerlach experiment, originally conceived by O. Stern in 1921 and carried out in Frankfurt by him in collaboration with W. Gerlach in 1922. This experiment illustrates in a dramatic manner the necessity for a radical departure from the concepts of classical mechanics. In the subsequent sections the basic formalism of quantum mechanics is presented in a somewhat axiomatic manner but always with the example of the Stern-Gerlach experiment in the back of our minds. In a certain sense, a two-state system of the Stern-Gerlach type is the least classical, most quantum-mechanical system. A solid understanding of problems involving two-state systems will turn out to be rewarding to any serious student of quantum mechanics. It is for this reason that we refer repeatedly to two-state problems throughout this book.

Description of the Experiment

We now present a brief discussion of the Stern-Gerlach experiment, which is discussed in almost any book on modern physics.* First, silver (Ag) atoms are heated in an oven. The oven has a small hole through which some of the silver atoms escape. As shown in Figure 1.1, the beam goes through a collimator and is then subjected to an inhomogeneous magnetic field produced by a pair of pole pieces, one of which has a very sharp edge.

We must now work out the effect of the magnetic field on the silver atoms. For our purpose the following oversimplified model of the silver atom suffices. The silver atom is made up of a nucleus and 47 electrons, where 46 out of the 47 electrons can be visualized as forming a spherically symmetrical electron cloud with no net angular momentum. If we ignore the nuclear spin, which is irrelevant to our discussion, we see that the atom as a whole does have an angular momentum, which is due solely to the spin—intrinsic as opposed to orbital—angular momentum of the single 47th ($5s$) electron. The 47 electrons are attached to the nucleus, which is $\sim 2 \times 10^5$ times heavier than the electron; as a result, the heavy atom as a whole possesses a magnetic moment equal to the spin magnetic moment of the 47th electron. In other words, the magnetic moment μ of the atom is

---

*For an elementary but enlightening discussion of the Stern-Gerlach experiment, see French and Taylor (1978, 432–38).

FIGURE 1.1. The Stern-Gerlach experiment.

proportional to the electron spin $\mathbf{S}$,

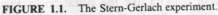

$$\boldsymbol{\mu} \propto \mathbf{S}, \tag{1.1.1}$$

where the precise proportionality factor turns out to be $e/m_e c$ ($e < 0$ in this book) to an accuracy of about 0.2%.

Because the interaction energy of the magnetic moment with the magnetic field is just $-\boldsymbol{\mu} \cdot \mathbf{B}$, the z-component of the force experienced by the atom is given by

$$F_z = \frac{\partial}{\partial z} (\boldsymbol{\mu} \cdot \mathbf{B}) \simeq \mu_z \frac{\partial B_z}{\partial z}, \tag{1.1.2}$$

where we have ignored the components of $\mathbf{B}$ in directions other than the z-direction. Because the atom as a whole is very heavy, we expect that the classical concept of trajectory can be legitimately applied, a point which can be justified using the Heisenberg uncertainty principle to be derived later. With the arrangement of Figure 1.1, the $\mu_z > 0$ ($S_z < 0$) atom experiences a downward force, while the $\mu_z < 0$ ($S_z > 0$) atom experiences an upward force. The beam is then expected to get split according to the values of μ_z. In other words, the SG (Stern-Gerlach) apparatus "measures" the z-component of $\boldsymbol{\mu}$ or, equivalently, the z-component of $\mathbf{S}$ up to a proportionality factor.

The atoms in the oven are randomly oriented; there is no preferred direction for the orientation of $\boldsymbol{\mu}$. If the electron were like a classical spinning object, we would expect all values of μ_z to be realized between $|\boldsymbol{\mu}|$ and $-|\boldsymbol{\mu}|$. This would lead us to expect a continuous bundle of beams coming out of the SG apparatus, as shown in Figure 1.2a. Instead, what we

(a)   **(b)**

FIGURE 1.2. Beams from the SG apparatus; (a) is expected from classical physics, while (b) is actually observed.

experimentally observe is more like the situation in Figure 1.2b. In other words, the SG apparatus splits the original silver beam from the oven into *two distinct* components, a phenomenon referred to in the early days of quantum theory as "space quantization." To the extent that μ can be identified within a proportionality factor with the electron spin **S**, only two possible values of the z-component of **S** are observed to be possible, S_z up and S_z down, which we call $S_z +$ and $S_z -$. The two possible values of S_z are multiples of some fundamental unit of angular momentum; numerically it turns out that $S_z = \hbar/2$ and $-\hbar/2$, where

$$\hbar = 1.0546 \times 10^{-27} \, \text{erg-s}$$

$$= 6.5822 \times 10^{-16} \, \text{eV-s} \tag{1.1.3}$$

This "quantization" of the electron spin angular momentum is the first important feature we deduce from the Stern-Gerlach experiment.

Of course, there is nothing sacred about the up-down direction or the z-axis. We could just as well have applied an inhomogeneous field in a horizontal direction, say in the x-direction, with the beam proceeding in the y-direction. In this manner we could have separated the beam from the oven into an $S_x +$ component and an $S_x -$ component.

Sequential Stern-Gerlach Experiments

Let us now consider a sequential Stern-Gerlach experiment. By this we mean that the atomic beam goes through two or more SG apparatuses in sequence. The first arrangement we consider is relatively straightforward. We subject the beam coming out of the oven to the arrangement shown in Figure 1.3a, where SG$\hat{z}$ stands for an apparatus with the inhomogeneous magnetic field in the z-direction, as usual. We then block the $S_z -$ compo-

FIGURE 1.3.   Sequential Stern-Gerlach experiments.

nent coming out of the first SGẑ apparatus and let the remaining S_z+ component be subjected to another SGẑ apparatus. This time there is only one beam component coming out of the second apparatus—just the S_z+ component. This is perhaps not so surprising; after all if the atom spins are up, they are expected to remain so, short of any external field that rotates the spins between the first and the second SGẑ apparatuses.

A little more interesting is the arrangement shown in Figure 1.3b. Here the first SG apparatus is the same as before but the second one (SGx̂) has an inhomogeneous magnetic field in the x-direction. The S_z+ beam that enters the second apparatus (SGx̂) is now split into two components, an S_x+ component and an S_x- component, with equal intensities. How can we explain this? Does it mean that 50% of the atoms in the S_z+ beam coming out of the first apparatus (SGẑ) are made up of atoms characterized by both S_z+ and S_x+, while the remaining 50% have both S_z+ and S_x-? It turns out that such a picture runs into difficulty, as will be shown below.

We now consider a third step, the arrangement shown in Figure 1.3(c), which most dramatically illustrates the peculiarities of quantum-mechanical systems. This time we add to the arrangement of Figure 1.3b yet a third apparatus, of the SGẑ type. It is observed experimentally that *two* components emerge from the third apparatus, not one; the emerging beams are seen to have *both* an S_z+ component and an S_z- component. This is a complete surprise because after the atoms emerged from the first apparatus, we made sure that the S_z- component was completely blocked. How is it possible that the S_z- component which, we thought, we eliminated earlier reappears? The model in which the atoms entering the third apparatus are visualized to have both S_z+ and S_x+ is clearly unsatisfactory.

This example is often used to illustrate that in quantum mechanics we cannot determine both S_z and S_x simultaneously. More precisely, we can say that the selection of the S_x+ beam by the second apparatus (SG$\hat{x}$) completely destroys any *previous* information about S_z.

It is amusing to compare this situation with that of a spinning top in classical mechanics, where the angular momentum

$$\mathbf{L} = I\omega \tag{1.1.4}$$

can be measured by determining the components of the angular-velocity vector ω. By observing how fast the object is spinning in which direction we can determine ω_x, ω_y, and ω_z simultaneously. The moment of inertia I is computable if we know the mass density and the geometric shape of the spinning top, so there is no difficulty in specifying both L_z and L_x in this classical situation.

It is to be clearly understood that the limitation we have encountered in determining S_z and S_x is not due to the incompetence of the experimentalist. By improving the experimental techniques we cannot make the S_z- component out of the third apparatus in Figure 1.3c disappear. The peculiarities of quantum mechanics are imposed upon us by the experiment itself. The limitation is, in fact, inherent in microscopic phenomena.

Analogy with Polarization of Light

Because this situation looks so novel, some analogy with a familiar classical situation may be helpful here. To this end we now digress to consider the polarization of light waves.

Consider a monochromatic light wave propagating in the z-direction. A linearly polarized (or plane polarized) light with a polarization vector in the x-direction, which we call for short an *x-polarized light*, has a space-time dependent electric field oscillating in the x-direction

$$\mathbf{E} = E_0\hat{x}\cos(kz - \omega t). \tag{1.1.5}$$

Likewise, we may consider a y-polarized light, also propagating in the z-direction,

$$\mathbf{E} = E_0\hat{y}\cos(kz - \omega t). \tag{1.1.6}$$

Polarized light beams of type (1.1.5) or (1.1.6) can be obtained by letting an unpolarized light beam go through a Polaroid filter. We call a filter that selects only beams polarized in the x-direction an *x-filter*. An x-filter, of course, becomes a y-filter when rotated by 90° about the propagation (z)

FIGURE 1.4. Light beams subjected to Polaroid filters.

direction. It is well known that when we let a light beam go through an x-filter and subsequently let it impinge on a y-filter, no light beam comes out provided, of course, we are dealing with 100% efficient Polaroids; see Figure 1.4a.

The situation is even more interesting if we insert between the x-filter and the y-filter yet another Polaroid that selects only a beam polarized in the direction—which we call the x'-direction—that makes an angle of 45° with the x-direction in the xy plane; see Figure 1.4b. This time, there is a light beam coming out of the y-filter despite the fact that right after the beam went through the x-filter it did not have any polarization component in the y-direction. In other words, once the x'-filter intervenes and selects the x'-polarized beam, it is immaterial whether the beam was previously x-polarized. The selection of the x'-polarized beam by the second Polaroid destroys any previous information on light polarization. Notice that this situation is quite analogous to the situation that we encountered earlier with the SG arrangement of Figure 1.3b, provided that the following correspondence is made:

$$S_z \pm \text{ atoms} \leftrightarrow x\text{-}, y\text{-polarized light}$$
$$S_x \pm \text{ atoms} \leftrightarrow x'\text{-}, y'\text{-polarized light},$$

(1.1.7)

where the x'- and the y'-axes are defined as in Figure 1.5.

Let us examine how we can quantitatively describe the behavior of 45°-polarized beams (x'- and y'-polarized beams) within the framework of

FIGURE 1.5. Orientations of the x'- and y'-axes.

classical electrodynamics. Using Figure 1.5 we obtain

$$E_0 \hat{\mathbf{x}}' \cos(kz - \omega t) = E_0 \left[\frac{1}{\sqrt{2}} \hat{\mathbf{x}} \cos(kz - \omega t) + \frac{1}{\sqrt{2}} \hat{\mathbf{y}} \cos(kz - \omega t) \right],$$

$$E_0 \hat{\mathbf{y}}' \cos(kz - \omega t) = E_0 \left[-\frac{1}{\sqrt{2}} \hat{\mathbf{x}} \cos(kz - \omega t) + \frac{1}{\sqrt{2}} \hat{\mathbf{y}} \cos(kz - \omega t) \right].$$

$$(1.1.8)$$

In the triple-filter arrangement of Figure 1.4b the beam coming out of the first Polaroid is an $\hat{\mathbf{x}}$-polarized beam, which can be regarded as a linear combination of an x'-polarized beam and a y'-polarized beam. The second Polaroid selects the x'-polarized beam, which can in turn be regarded as a linear combination of an x-polarized and a y-polarized beam. And finally, the third Polaroid selects the y-polarized component.

Applying correspondence (1.1.7) from the sequential Stern-Gerlach experiment of Figure 1.3c, to the triple-filter experiment of Figure 1.4b suggests that we might be able to represent the spin state of a silver atom by some kind of vector in a new kind of two-dimensional vector space, an abstract vector space not to be confused with the usual two-dimensional (xy) space. Just as $\hat{\mathbf{x}}$ and $\hat{\mathbf{y}}$ in (1.1.8) are the base vectors used to decompose the polarization vector $\hat{\mathbf{x}}'$ of the $\hat{\mathbf{x}}'$-polarized light, it is reasonable to represent the $S_x +$ state by a vector, which we call a *ket* in the Dirac notation to be developed fully in the next section. We denote this vector by

$|S_x; +\rangle$ and write it as a linear combination of two base vectors, $|S_z; +\rangle$ and $|S_z; -\rangle$, which correspond to the $S_z +$ and the $S_z -$ states, respectively. So we may conjecture

$$|S_x; +\rangle \stackrel{?}{=} \frac{1}{\sqrt{2}}|S_z; +\rangle + \frac{1}{\sqrt{2}}|S_z; -\rangle \qquad (1.1.9a)$$

$$|S_x; -\rangle \stackrel{?}{=} -\frac{1}{\sqrt{2}}|S_z; +\rangle + \frac{1}{\sqrt{2}}|S_z; -\rangle \qquad (1.1.9b)$$

in analogy with (1.1.8). Later we will show how to obtain these expressions using the general formalism of quantum mechanics.

Thus the unblocked component coming out of the second (SG$\hat{x}$) apparatus of Figure 1.3c is to be regarded as a superposition of $S_z +$ and $S_z -$ in the sense of (1.1.9a). It is for this reason that two components emerge from the third (SG$\hat{z}$) apparatus.

The next question of immediate concern is, How are we going to represent the $S_y \pm$ states? Symmetry arguments suggest that if we observe an $S_z \pm$ beam going in the x-direction and subject it to an SG$\hat{y}$ apparatus, the resulting situation will be very similar to the case where an $S_z \pm$ beam going in the y-direction is subjected to an SG$\hat{x}$ apparatus. The kets for $S_y \pm$ should then be regarded as a linear combination of $|S_z; \pm\rangle$, but it appears from (1.1.9) that we have already used up the available possibilities in writing $|S_x; \pm\rangle$. How can our vector space formalism distinguish $S_y \pm$ states from $S_x \pm$ states?

An analogy with polarized light again rescues us here. This time we consider a circularly polarized beam of light, which can be obtained by letting a linearly polarized light pass through a quarter-wave plate. When we pass such a circularly polarized light through an x-filter or a y-filter, we again obtain either an x-polarized beam or a y-polarized beam of equal intensity. Yet everybody knows that the circularly polarized light is totally different from the 45°-linearly polarized (x'-polarized or y'-polarized) light.

Mathematically, how do we represent a circularly polarized light? A right circularly polarized light is nothing more than a linear combination of an x-polarized light and a y-polarized light, where the oscillation of the electric field for the y-polarized component is 90° out of phase with that of the x-polarized component:*

$$\mathbf{E} = E_0\left[\frac{1}{\sqrt{2}}\hat{x}\cos(kz - \omega t) + \frac{1}{\sqrt{2}}\hat{y}\cos\left(kz - \omega t + \frac{\pi}{2}\right) \right]. \quad (1.1.10)$$

It is more elegant to use complex notation by introducing ϵ as follows:

$$\text{Re}(\epsilon) = \mathbf{E}/E_0. \qquad (1.1.11)$$

---

*Unfortunately, there is no unanimity in the definition of right versus left circularly polarized light in the literature.

For a right circularly polarized light, we can then write

$$\varepsilon = \left[\frac{1}{\sqrt{2}} \hat{x} e^{i(kz - \omega t)} + \frac{i}{\sqrt{2}} \hat{y} e^{i(kz - \omega t)} \right], \qquad (1.1.12)$$

where we have used $i = e^{i\pi/2}$.

We can make the following analogy with the spin states of silver atoms:

$$S_y + \text{atom} \leftrightarrow \text{right circularly polarized beam};$$
$$S_y - \text{atom} \leftrightarrow \text{left circularly polarized beam}. \qquad (1.1.13)$$

Applying this analogy to (1.1.12), we see that if we are allowed to make the coefficients preceding base kets complex, there is no difficulty in accommodating the $S_y \pm$ atoms in our vector space formalism:

$$|S_y; \pm\rangle \overset{?}{=} \frac{1}{\sqrt{2}} |S_z; +\rangle \pm \frac{i}{\sqrt{2}} |S_z; -\rangle, \qquad (1.1.14)$$

which are obviously different from (1.1.9). We thus see that the two-dimensional vector space needed to describe the spin states of silver atoms must be a *complex* vector space; an arbitrary vector in the vector space is written as a linear combination of the base vectors $|S_z; \pm\rangle$ with, in general, complex coefficients. The fact that the necessity of complex numbers is already apparent in such an elementary example is rather remarkable.

The reader must have noted by this time that we have deliberately avoided talking about photons. In other words, we have completely ignored the quantum aspect of light; nowhere did we mention the polarization states of individual photons. The analogy we worked out is between kets in an abstract vector space that describes the spin states of individual atoms with the polarization vectors of the *classical electromagnetic field*. Actually we could have made the analogy even more vivid by introducing the photon concept and talking about the probability of finding a circularly polarized photon in a linearly polarized state, and so forth; however, that is not needed here. Without doing so, we have already accomplished the main goal of this section: to introduce the idea that quantum-mechanical states are to be represented by vectors in an abstract complex vector space.*

1.2. KETS, BRAS, AND OPERATORS

In the preceding section we showed how analyses of the Stern-Gerlach experiment lead us to consider a complex vector space. In this and the

---

*The reader who is interested in grasping the basic concepts of quantum mechanics through a careful study of photon polarization may find Chapter 1 of Baym (1969) extremely illuminating.

following section we formulate the basic mathematics of vector spaces as used in quantum mechanics. Our notation throughout this book is the bra and ket notation developed by P. A. M. Dirac. The theory of linear vector spaces had, of course, been known to mathematicians prior to the birth of quantum mechanics, but Dirac's way of introducing vector spaces has many advantages, especially from the physicist's point of view.

Ket Space

We consider a complex vector space whose dimensionality is specified according to the nature of a physical system under consideration. In Stern-Gerlach–type experiments where the only quantum-mechanical degree of freedom is the spin of an atom, the dimensionality is determined by the number of alternative paths the atoms can follow when subjected to a SG apparatus; in the case of the silver atoms of the previous section, the dimensionality is just two, corresponding to the two possible values S_z can assume.* Later, in Section 1.6, we consider the case of continuous spectra—for example, the position (coordinate) or momentum of a particle —where the number of alternatives is nondenumerably infinite, in which case the vector space in question is known as a **Hilbert space** after D. Hilbert, who studied vector spaces in infinite dimensions.

In quantum mechanics a physical state, for example, a silver atom with a definite spin orientation, is represented by a **state vector** in a complex vector space. Following Dirac, we call such a vector a **ket** and denote it by $|\alpha\rangle$. This state ket is postulated to contain complete information about the physical state; everything we are allowed to ask about the state is contained in the ket. Two kets can be added:

$$|\alpha\rangle + |\beta\rangle = |\gamma\rangle. \tag{1.2.1}$$

The sum $|\gamma\rangle$ is just another ket. If we multiply $|\alpha\rangle$ by a complex number c, the resulting product $c|\alpha\rangle$ is another ket. The number c can stand on the left or on the right of a ket; it makes no difference:

$$c|\alpha\rangle = |\alpha\rangle c. \tag{1.2.2}$$

In the particular case where c is zero, the resulting ket is said to be a **null ket**.

One of the physics postulates is that $|\alpha\rangle$ and $c|\alpha\rangle$, with $c \neq 0$, represent the same physical state. In other words, only the "direction" in vector space is of significance. Mathematicians may prefer to say that we are here dealing with rays rather than vectors.

---

*For many physical systems the dimension of the state space is denumerably infinite. While we will usually indicate a finite number of dimensions, N, of the ket space, the results also hold for denumerably infinite dimensions.

An **observable**, such as momentum and spin components, can be represented by an **operator**, such as A, in the vector space in question. Quite generally, an operator acts on a ket *from the left*,

$$A \cdot (|\alpha\rangle) = A|\alpha\rangle, \tag{1.2.3}$$

which is yet another ket. There will be more on multiplication operations later.

In general, $A|\alpha\rangle$ is *not* a constant times $|\alpha\rangle$. However, there are particular kets of importance, known as **eigenkets** of operator A, denoted by

$$|a'\rangle, |a''\rangle, |a'''\rangle, \dots \tag{1.2.4}$$

with the property

$$A|a'\rangle = a'|a'\rangle, A|a''\rangle = a''|a''\rangle, \dots \tag{1.2.5}$$

where a', a'', ... are just numbers. Notice that applying A to an eigenket just reproduces the same ket apart from a multiplicative number. The set of numbers $\{a', a'', a''', \dots\}$, more compactly denoted by $\{a'\}$, is called the set of **eigenvalues** of operator A. When it becomes necessary to order eigenvalues in a specific manner, $\{a^{(1)}, a^{(2)}, a^{(3)}, \dots\}$ may be used in place of $\{a', a'', a''', \dots\}$.

The physical state corresponding to an eigenket is called an **eigenstate**. In the simplest case of spin $\frac{1}{2}$ systems, the eigenvalue-eigenket relation (1.2.5) is expressed as

$$S_z|S_z; +\rangle = \frac{\hbar}{2}|S_z; +\rangle, \qquad S_z|S_z; -\rangle = -\frac{\hbar}{2}|S_z; -\rangle, \tag{1.2.6}$$

where $|S_z; \pm\rangle$ are eigenkets of operator S_z with eigenvalues $\pm \hbar/2$. Here we could have used just $|\hbar/2\rangle$ for $|S_z; +\rangle$ in conformity with the notation $|a'\rangle$, where an eigenket is labeled by its eigenvalue, but the notation $|S_z; \pm\rangle$, already used in the previous section, is more convenient here because we also consider eigenkets of S_x:

$$S_x|S_x; \pm\rangle = \pm \frac{\hbar}{2}|S_x; \pm\rangle. \tag{1.2.7}$$

We remarked earlier that the dimensionality of the vector space is determined by the number of alternatives in Stern-Gerlach–type experiments. More formally, we are concerned with an N-dimensional vector space spanned by the N eigenkets of observable A. Any arbitrary ket $|\alpha\rangle$ can be written as

$$|\alpha\rangle = \sum_{a'} c_{a'}|a'\rangle, \tag{1.2.8}$$

with a', a'', ... up to $a^{(N)}$, where $c_{a'}$ is a complex coefficient. The question of the uniqueness of such an expansion will be postponed until we prove the orthogonality of eigenkets.

Bra Space and Inner Products

The vector space we have been dealing with is a ket space. We now introduce the notion of a **bra space**, a vector space "dual to" the ket space. We postulate that corresponding to every ket $|\alpha\rangle$ there exists a bra, denoted by $\langle\alpha|$, in this dual, or bra, space. The bra space is spanned by eigenbras $\{\langle a'|\}$ which correspond to the eigenkets $\{|a'\rangle\}$. There is a one-to-one correspondence between a ket space and a bra space:

$$|\alpha\rangle \overset{DC}{\leftrightarrow} \langle\alpha|$$

$$|a'\rangle, |a''\rangle, \ldots \overset{DC}{\leftrightarrow} \langle a'|, \langle a''|, \ldots \qquad (1.2.9)$$

$$|\alpha\rangle + |\beta\rangle \overset{DC}{\leftrightarrow} \langle\alpha| + \langle\beta|$$

where DC stands for **dual correspondence**. Roughly speaking, we can regard the bra space as some kind of mirror image of the ket space.

The bra dual to $c|\alpha\rangle$ is postulated to be $c^*\langle\alpha|$, *not* $c\langle\alpha|$, which is a very important point. More generally, we have

$$c_\alpha|\alpha\rangle + c_\beta|\beta\rangle \overset{DC}{\leftrightarrow} c_\alpha^*\langle\alpha| + c_\beta^*\langle\beta|. \qquad (1.2.10)$$

We now define the **inner product** of a bra and a ket.* The product is written as a bra standing on the left and a ket standing on the right, for example,

$$\langle\beta|\alpha\rangle = (\langle\beta|)\cdot(|\alpha\rangle). \qquad (1.2.11)$$
$$\underset{\text{bra}\,(c)\,\text{ket}}{}$$

This product is, in general, a complex number. Notice that in forming an inner product we always take one vector from the bra space and one vector from the ket space.

We postulate two fundamental properties of inner products. First,

$$\langle\beta|\alpha\rangle = \langle\alpha|\beta\rangle^*. \qquad (1.2.12)$$

In other words, $\langle\beta|\alpha\rangle$ and $\langle\alpha|\beta\rangle$ are complex conjugates of each other. Notice that even though the inner product is, in some sense, analogous to the familiar scalar product $\mathbf{a}\cdot\mathbf{b}$, $\langle\beta|\alpha\rangle$ must be clearly distinguished from $\langle\alpha|\beta\rangle$; the analogous distinction is not needed in real vector space because $\mathbf{a}\cdot\mathbf{b}$ is equal to $\mathbf{b}\cdot\mathbf{a}$. Using (1.2.12) we can immediately deduce that $\langle\alpha|\alpha\rangle$ must be a real number. To prove this just let $\langle\beta| \to \langle\alpha|$.

---

*In the literature an inner product is often referred to as a *scalar product* because it is analogous to $\mathbf{a}\cdot\mathbf{b}$ in Euclidean space; in this book, however, we reserve the term *scalar* for a quantity invariant under rotations in the usual three-dimensional space.

The second postulate on inner products is

$$\langle \alpha | \alpha \rangle \geq 0, \tag{1.2.13}$$

where the equality sign holds only if $|\alpha\rangle$ is a *null ket*. This is sometimes known as the postulate of **positive definite metric**. From a physicist's point of view, this postulate is essential for the probabilistic interpretation of quantum mechanics, as will become apparent later.*

Two kets $|\alpha\rangle$ and $|\beta\rangle$ are said to be **orthogonal** if

$$\langle \alpha | \beta \rangle = 0, \tag{1.2.14}$$

even though in the definition of the inner product the bra $\langle \alpha |$ appears. The orthogonality relation (1.2.14) also implies, via (1.2.12),

$$\langle \beta | \alpha \rangle = 0. \tag{1.2.15}$$

Given a ket which is not a null ket, we can form a **normalized ket** $|\tilde{\alpha}\rangle$, where

$$|\tilde{\alpha}\rangle = \left(\frac{1}{\sqrt{\langle \alpha | \alpha \rangle}} \right) |\alpha\rangle, \tag{1.2.16}$$

with the property

$$\langle \tilde{\alpha} | \tilde{\alpha} \rangle = 1. \tag{1.2.17}$$

Quite generally, $\sqrt{\langle \alpha | \alpha \rangle}$ is known as the **norm** of $|\alpha\rangle$, analogous to the magnitude of vector $\sqrt{\mathbf{a} \cdot \mathbf{a}} = |\vec{\mathbf{a}}|$ in Euclidean vector space. Because $|\alpha\rangle$ and $c|\alpha\rangle$ represent the same physical state, we might as well require that the kets we use for physical states be normalized in the sense of (1.2.17).†

Operators

As we remarked earlier, observables like momentum and spin components are to be represented by operators that can act on kets. We can consider a more general class of operators that act on kets; they will be denoted by X, Y, and so forth, while A, B, and so on will be used for a restrictive class of operators that correspond to observables.

An operator acts on a ket from the left side,

$$X \cdot (|\alpha\rangle) = X|\alpha\rangle, \tag{1.2.18}$$

and the resulting product is another ket. Operators X and Y are said to be **equal**,

$$X = Y, \tag{1.2.19}$$

---

*Attempts to abandon this postulate led to physical theories with "indefinite metric." We shall not be concerned with such theories in this book.

†For eigenkets of observables with continuous spectra, different normalization conventions will be used; see Section 1.6.

if

$$X|\alpha\rangle = Y|\alpha\rangle \qquad (1.2.20)$$

for an *arbitrary* ket in the ket space in question. Operator X is said to be the **null operator** if, for any *arbitrary* ket $|\alpha\rangle$, we have

$$X|\alpha\rangle = 0. \qquad (1.2.21)$$

Operators can be added; addition operations are commutative and associative:

$$X + Y = Y + X, \qquad (1.2.21a)$$
$$X + (Y + Z) = (X + Y) + Z. \qquad (1.2.21b)$$

With the single exception of the time-reversal operator to be considered in Chapter 4, the operators that appear in this book are all linear, that is,

$$X(c_\alpha|\alpha\rangle + c_\beta|\beta\rangle) = c_\alpha X|\alpha\rangle + c_\beta X|\beta\rangle. \qquad (1.2.22)$$

An operator X always acts on a bra from the *right* side

$$(\langle\alpha|)\cdot X = \langle\alpha|X, \qquad (1.2.23)$$

and the resulting product is another bra. The ket $X|\alpha\rangle$ and the bra $\langle\alpha|X$ are, in general, *not* dual to each other. We define the symbol $X^\dagger$ as

$$X|\alpha\rangle \overset{DC}{\leftrightarrow} \langle\alpha|X^\dagger. \qquad (1.2.24)$$

The operator $X^\dagger$ is called the **Hermitian adjoint**, or simply the adjoint, of X. An operator X is said to be Hermitian if

$$X = X^\dagger. \qquad (1.2.25)$$

Multiplication

Operators X and Y can be multiplied. Multiplication operations are, in general, *noncommutative*, that is,

$$XY \neq YX. \qquad (1.2.26)$$

Multiplication operations are, however, associative:

$$X(YZ) = (XY)Z = XYZ. \qquad (1.2.27)$$

We also have

$$X(Y|\alpha\rangle) = (XY)|\alpha\rangle = XY|\alpha\rangle, \qquad (\langle\beta|X)Y = \langle\beta|(XY) = \langle\beta|XY.$$

$$\qquad (1.2.28)$$

Notice that

$$(XY)^\dagger = Y^\dagger X^\dagger \qquad (1.2.29)$$

because

$$XY|\alpha\rangle = X(Y|\alpha\rangle) \overset{DC}{\leftrightarrow} (\langle\alpha|Y^\dagger)X^\dagger = \langle\alpha|Y^\dagger X^\dagger \tag{1.2.30}$$

So far, we have considered the following products: $\langle\beta|\alpha\rangle$, $X|\alpha\rangle$, $\langle\alpha|X$, and XY. Are there other products we are allowed to form? Let us multiply $|\beta\rangle$ and $\langle\alpha|$, in that order. The resulting product

$$(|\beta\rangle) \cdot (\langle\alpha|) = |\beta\rangle\langle\alpha| \tag{1.2.31}$$

is known as the **outer product** of $|\beta\rangle$ and $\langle\alpha|$. We will emphasize in a moment that $|\beta\rangle\langle\alpha|$ is to be regarded as an operator; hence it is fundamentally different from the inner product $\langle\beta|\alpha\rangle$, which is just a number.

There are also "illegal products." We have already mentioned that an operator must stand on the left of a ket or on the right of a bra. In other words, $|\alpha\rangle X$ and $X\langle\alpha|$ are examples of illegal products. They are neither kets, nor bras, nor operators; they are simply nonsensical. Products like $|\alpha\rangle|\beta\rangle$ and $\langle\alpha|\langle\beta|$ are also illegal when $|\alpha\rangle$ and $|\beta\rangle$ ($\langle\alpha|$ and $\langle\beta|$) are ket (bra) vectors belonging to the same ket (bra) space.*

The Associative Axiom

As is clear from (1.2.27), multiplication operations among operators are associative. Actually the associative property is postulated to hold quite generally as long as we are dealing with "legal" multiplications among kets, bras, and operators. Dirac calls this important postulate the **associative axiom of multiplication**.

To illustrate the power of this axiom let us first consider an outer product acting on a ket:

$$(|\beta\rangle\langle\alpha|) \cdot |\gamma\rangle. \tag{1.2.32}$$

Because of the associative axiom, we can regard this equally well as

$$|\beta\rangle \cdot (\langle\alpha|\gamma\rangle), \tag{1.2.33}$$

where $\langle\alpha|\gamma\rangle$ is just a number. So the outer product acting on a ket is just another ket; in other words, $|\beta\rangle\langle\alpha|$ can be regarded as an operator. Because (1.2.32) and (1.2.33) are equal, we may as well omit the dots and let $|\beta\rangle\langle\alpha|\gamma\rangle$ stand for the operator $|\beta\rangle\langle\alpha|$ acting on $|\gamma\rangle$ or, equivalently, the number $\langle\alpha|\gamma\rangle$ multiplying $|\beta\rangle$. (On the other hand, if (1.2.33) is written as $(\langle\alpha|\gamma\rangle) \cdot |\beta\rangle$, we cannot afford to omit the dot and brackets because the

---

*Later in the book we will encounter products like $|\alpha\rangle|\beta\rangle$, which are more appropriately written as $|\alpha\rangle \otimes |\beta\rangle$, but in such cases $|\alpha\rangle$ and $|\beta\rangle$ always refer to kets from *different* vector spaces. For instance, the first ket belongs to the vector space for electron spin, the second ket to the vector space for electron orbital angular momentum; or the first ket lies in the vector space of particle 1, the second ket in the vector space of particle 2, and so forth.

resulting expression would look illegal.) Notice that the operator $|\beta\rangle\langle\alpha|$ rotates $|\gamma\rangle$ into the direction of $|\beta\rangle$. It is easy to see that if

$$X = |\beta\rangle\langle\alpha|, \qquad (1.2.34)$$

then

$$X^\dagger = |\alpha\rangle\langle\beta|, \qquad (1.2.35)$$

which is left as an exercise.

In a second important illustration of the associative axiom, we note that

$$\underset{\text{bra}}{(\langle\beta|)} \cdot \underset{\text{ket}}{(X|\alpha\rangle)} = \underset{\text{bra}}{(\langle\beta|X)} \cdot \underset{\text{ket}}{(|\alpha\rangle)}. \qquad (1.2.36)$$

Because the two sides are equal, we might as well use the more compact notation

$$\langle\beta|X|\alpha\rangle \qquad (1.2.37)$$

to stand for either side of (1.2.36). Recall now that $\langle\alpha|X^\dagger$ is the bra that is dual to $X|\alpha\rangle$, so

$$\langle\beta|X|\alpha\rangle = \langle\beta|\cdot(X|\alpha\rangle)$$

$$= \{(\langle\alpha|X^\dagger)\cdot|\beta\rangle\}^*$$

$$= \langle\alpha|X^\dagger|\beta\rangle^*, \qquad (1.2.38)$$

where, in addition to the associative axiom, we used the fundamental property of the inner product (1.2.12). For a *Hermitian* X we have

$$\langle\beta|X|\alpha\rangle = \langle\alpha|X|\beta\rangle^*. \qquad (1.2.39)$$

1.3. BASE KETS AND MATRIX REPRESENTATIONS

Eigenkets of an Observable

Let us consider the eigenkets and eigenvalues of a Hermitian operator A. We use the symbol A, reserved earlier for an observable, because in quantum mechanics Hermitian operators of interest quite often turn out to be the operators representing some physical observables.

We begin by stating an important theorem:

Theorem. The eigenvalues of a Hermitian operator A are real; the eigenkets of A corresponding to different eigenvalues are orthogonal.

Proof. First, recall that

$$A|a'\rangle = a'|a'\rangle. \qquad (1.3.1)$$

Because A is Hermitian, we also have

$$\langle a''|A = a''^{*}\langle a''|, \tag{1.3.2}$$

where $a', a'' \ldots$ are eigenvalues of A. If we multiply both sides of (1.3.1) by $\langle a''|$ on the left, both sides of (1.3.2) by $|a'\rangle$ on the right, and subtract, we obtain

$$(a' - a''^{*})\langle a''|a'\rangle = 0. \tag{1.3.3}$$

Now a' and a'' can be taken to be either the same or different. Let us first choose them to be the same; we then deduce the reality condition (the first half of the theorem)

$$a' = a'^{*}, \tag{1.3.4}$$

where we have used the fact that $|a'\rangle$ is not a null ket. Let us now assume a' and a'' to be different. Because of the just-proved reality condition, the difference $a' - a''^{*}$ that appears in (1.3.3) is equal to $a' - a''$, which cannot vanish, by assumption. The inner product $\langle a''|a'\rangle$ must then vanish:

$$\langle a''|a'\rangle = 0, \quad (a' \neq a''), \tag{1.3.5}$$

which proves the orthogonality property (the second half of the theorem). $\square$

We expect on physical grounds that an observable has real eigenvalues, a point that will become clearer in the next section, where measurements in quantum mechanics will be discussed. The theorem just proved guarantees the reality of eigenvalues whenever the operator is Hermitian. That is why we talk about Hermitian observables in quantum mechanics.

It is conventional to normalize $|a'\rangle$ so the $\{|a'\rangle\}$ form a **orthonormal** set:

$$\langle a''|a'\rangle = \delta_{a''a'}. \tag{1.3.6}$$

We may logically ask, Is this set of eigenkets complete? Since we started our discussion by asserting that the whole ket space is spanned by the eigenkets of A, the eigenkets of A must therefore form a complete set by *construction* of our ket space.*

Eigenkets as Base Kets

We have seen that the normalized eigenkets of A form a complete orthonormal set. An arbitrary ket in the ket space can be expanded in terms

---

*The astute reader, already familiar with wave mechanics, may point out that the completeness of eigenfunctions we use can be proved by applying the Sturm-Liouville theory to the Schrödinger wave equation. But to "derive" the Schrödinger wave equation from our fundamental postulates, the completeness of the position eigenkets must be assumed.

of the eigenkets of A. In other words, the eigenkets of A are to be used as base kets in much the same way as a set of mutually orthogonal unit vectors is used as base vectors in Euclidean space.

Given an arbitrary ket $|\alpha\rangle$ in the ket space spanned by the eigenkets of A, let us attempt to expand it as follows:

$$|\alpha\rangle = \sum_{a'} c_{a'} |a'\rangle. \qquad (1.3.7)$$

Multiplying $\langle a''|$ on the left and using the orthonormality property (1.3.6), we can immediately find the expansion coefficient,

$$c_{a'} = \langle a'|\alpha\rangle. \qquad (1.3.8)$$

In other words, we have

$$|\alpha\rangle = \sum_{a'} |a'\rangle \langle a'|\alpha\rangle, \qquad (1.3.9)$$

which is analogous to an expansion of a vector $\mathbf{V}$ in (real) Euclidean space:

$$\mathbf{V} = \sum \hat{\mathbf{e}}_i (\hat{\mathbf{e}}_i \cdot \mathbf{V}), \qquad (1.3.10)$$

where $\{\hat{\mathbf{e}}_i\}$ form an orthogonal set of unit vectors. We now recall the associative axiom of multiplication: $|a'\rangle \langle a'|\alpha\rangle$ can be regarded either as the number $\langle a'|\alpha\rangle$ multiplying $|a'\rangle$ or, equivalently, as the operator $|a'\rangle \langle a'|$ acting on $|\alpha\rangle$. Because $|\alpha\rangle$ in (1.3.9) is an arbitrary ket, we must have

$$\sum_{a'} |a'\rangle \langle a'| = 1, \qquad (1.3.11)$$

where the 1 on the right-hand side is to be understood as the identity *operator*. Equation (1.3.11) is known as the **completeness relation** or **closure**.

It is difficult to overestimate the usefulness of (1.3.11). Given a chain of kets, operators, or bras multiplied in legal orders, we can insert, in any place at our convenience, the identity operator written in form (1.3.11). Consider, for example $\langle \alpha|\alpha\rangle$; by inserting the identity operator between $\langle \alpha|$ and $|\alpha\rangle$, we obtain

$$\langle \alpha|\alpha\rangle = \langle \alpha| \cdot \left(\sum_{a'} |a'\rangle \langle a'| \right) \cdot |\alpha\rangle$$

$$= \sum_{a'} |\langle a'|\alpha\rangle|^2. \qquad (1.3.12)$$

This, incidentally, shows that if $|\alpha\rangle$ is normalized, then the expansion coefficients in (1.3.7) must satisfy

$$\sum_{a'} |c_{a'}|^2 = \sum_{a'} |\langle a'|\alpha\rangle|^2 = 1. \qquad (1.3.13)$$

Let us now look at $|a'\rangle\langle a'|$ that appears in (1.3.11). Since this is an outer product, it must be an operator. Let it operate on $|\alpha\rangle$:

$$(|a'\rangle\langle a'|)\cdot|\alpha\rangle = |a'\rangle\langle a'|\alpha\rangle = c_{a'}|a'\rangle. \tag{1.3.14}$$

We see that $|a'\rangle\langle a'|$ selects that portion of the ket $|\alpha\rangle$ parallel to $|a'\rangle$, so $|a'\rangle\langle a'|$ is known as the **projection operator** along the base ket $|a'\rangle$ and is denoted by $\Lambda_{a'}$:

$$\Lambda_{a'} \equiv |a'\rangle\langle a'|. \tag{1.3.15}$$

The completeness relation (1.3.11) can now be written as

$$\sum_{a'} \Lambda_{a'} = 1. \tag{1.3.16}$$

Matrix Representations

Having specified the base kets, we now show how to represent an operator, say X, by a square matrix. First, using (1.3.11) twice, we write the operator X as

$$X = \sum_{a''}\sum_{a'} |a''\rangle\langle a''|X|a'\rangle\langle a'|. \tag{1.3.17}$$

There are altogether N^2 numbers of form $\langle a''|X|a'\rangle$, where N is the dimensionality of the ket space. We may arrange them into an $N \times N$ square matrix such that the column and row indices appear as follows:

$$\underset{\text{row} \quad \text{column}}{\langle a''| X |a'\rangle} . \tag{1.3.18}$$

Explicitly we may write the matrix as

$$X \doteq \begin{pmatrix} \langle a^{(1)}|X|a^{(1)}\rangle & \langle a^{(1)}|X|a^{(2)}\rangle & \cdots \\ \langle a^{(2)}|X|a^{(1)}\rangle & \langle a^{(2)}|X|a^{(2)}\rangle & \cdots \\ \vdots & \vdots & \ddots \end{pmatrix}, \tag{1.3.19}$$

where the symbol $\doteq$ stands for "is represented by." *

Using (1.2.38), we can write

$$\langle a''|X|a'\rangle = \langle a'|X^\dagger|a''\rangle^*. \tag{1.3.20}$$

At last, the Hermitian adjoint operation, originally defined by (1.2.24), has been related to the (perhaps more familiar) concept of *complex conjugate transposed*. If an operator B is Hermitian, we have

$$\langle a''|B|a'\rangle = \langle a'|B|a''\rangle^*. \tag{1.3.21}$$

---

*We do not use the equality sign here because the particular form of a matrix representation depends on the particular choice of base kets used. The operator is different from a representation of the operator just as the actress is different from a poster of the actress.

The way we arranged $\langle a''|X|a'\rangle$ into a square matrix is in conformity with the usual rule of matrix multiplication. To see this just note that the matrix representation of the operator relation

$$Z = XY \tag{1.3.22}$$

reads

$$\langle a''|Z|a'\rangle = \langle a''|XY|a'\rangle$$
$$= \sum_{a'''} \langle a''|X|a'''\rangle\langle a'''|Y|a'\rangle. \tag{1.3.23}$$

Again, all we have done is to insert the identity operator, written in form (1.3.11), between X and Y!

Let us now examine how the ket relation

$$|\gamma\rangle = X|\alpha\rangle \tag{1.3.24}$$

can be represented using our base kets. The expansion coefficients of $|\gamma\rangle$ can be obtained by multiplying $\langle a'|$ on the left:

$$\langle a'|\gamma\rangle = \langle a'|X|\alpha\rangle$$
$$= \sum_{a''} \langle a'|X|a''\rangle\langle a''|\alpha\rangle. \tag{1.3.25}$$

But this can be seen as an application of the rule for multiplying a square matrix with a column matrix representing once the expansion coefficients of $|\alpha\rangle$ and $|\gamma\rangle$ arrange themselves to form column matrices as follows:

$$|\alpha\rangle \doteq \begin{pmatrix} \langle a^{(1)}|\alpha\rangle \\ \langle a^{(2)}|\alpha\rangle \\ \langle a^{(3)}|\alpha\rangle \\ \vdots \end{pmatrix}, \quad |\gamma\rangle \doteq \begin{pmatrix} \langle a^{(1)}|\gamma\rangle \\ \langle a^{(2)}|\gamma\rangle \\ \langle a^{(3)}|\gamma\rangle \\ \vdots \end{pmatrix}. \tag{1.3.26}$$

Likewise, given

$$\langle\gamma| = \langle\alpha|X, \tag{1.3.27}$$

we can regard

$$\langle\gamma|a'\rangle = \sum_{a''} \langle\alpha|a''\rangle\langle a''|X|a'\rangle. \tag{1.3.28}$$

So a bra is represented by a row matrix as follows:

$$\langle\gamma| \doteq (\langle\gamma|a^{(1)}\rangle, \langle\gamma|a^{(2)}\rangle, \langle\gamma|a^{(3)}\rangle, \ldots)$$
$$= (\langle a^{(1)}|\gamma\rangle^*, \langle a^{(2)}|\gamma\rangle^*, \langle a^{(3)}|\gamma\rangle^*, \ldots). \tag{1.3.29}$$

Note the appearance of complex conjugation when the elements of the column matrix are written as in (1.3.29). The inner product $\langle\beta|\alpha\rangle$ can be written as the product of the row matrix representing $\langle\beta|$ with the column matrix representing $|\alpha\rangle$:

$$\langle\beta|\alpha\rangle = \sum_{a'}\langle\beta|a'\rangle\langle a'|\alpha\rangle$$

$$= (\langle a^{(1)}|\beta\rangle^*, \langle a^{(2)}|\beta\rangle^*, \dots)\begin{pmatrix}\langle a^{(1)}|\alpha\rangle \\ \langle a^{(2)}|\alpha\rangle \\ \vdots\end{pmatrix} \qquad (1.3.30)$$

If we multiply the row matrix representing $\langle\alpha|$ with the column matrix representing $|\beta\rangle$, then we obtain just the complex conjugate of the preceding expression, which is consistent with the fundamental property of the inner product (1.2.12). Finally, the matrix representation of the outer product $|\beta\rangle\langle\alpha|$ is easily seen to be

$$|\beta\rangle\langle\alpha| \doteq \begin{pmatrix} \langle a^{(1)}|\beta\rangle\langle a^{(1)}|\alpha\rangle^* & \langle a^{(1)}|\beta\rangle\langle a^{(2)}|\alpha\rangle^* & \cdots \\ \langle a^{(2)}|\beta\rangle\langle a^{(1)}|\alpha\rangle^* & \langle a^{(2)}|\beta\rangle\langle a^{(2)}|\alpha\rangle^* & \cdots \\ \vdots & \vdots & \end{pmatrix}.$$

$$(1.3.31)$$

The matrix representation of an observable A becomes particularly simple if the eigenkets of A themselves are used as the base kets. First, we have

$$A = \sum_{a''}\sum_{a'} |a''\rangle\langle a''|A|a'\rangle\langle a'|. \qquad (1.3.32)$$

But the square matrix $\langle a''|A|a'\rangle$ is obviously diagonal,

$$\langle a''|A|a'\rangle = \langle a'|A|a'\rangle\delta_{a'a''} = a'\delta_{a'a''}, \qquad (1.3.33)$$

so

$$A = \sum_{a'} a'|a'\rangle\langle a'|$$

$$= \sum_{a'} a'\Lambda_{a'}. \qquad (1.3.34)$$

Spin $\frac{1}{2}$ Systems

It is here instructive to consider the special case of spin $\frac{1}{2}$ systems. The base kets used are $|S_z; \pm\rangle$, which we denote, for brevity, as $|\pm\rangle$. The simplest operator in the ket space spanned by $|\pm\rangle$ is the identity operator, which, according to (1.3.11), can be written as

$$1 = |+\rangle\langle+| + |-\rangle\langle-|. \qquad (1.3.35)$$

According to (1.3.34), we must be able to write S_z as

$$S_z = (\hbar/2)[(|+\rangle\langle+|) - (|-\rangle\langle-|)]. \qquad (1.3.36)$$

The eigenket-eigenvalue relation

$$S_z|\pm\rangle = \pm(\hbar/2)|\pm\rangle \tag{1.3.37}$$

immediately follows from the orthonormality property of $|\pm\rangle$.

It is also instructive to look at two other operators,

$$S_+ \equiv \hbar|+\rangle\langle-|, \qquad S_- \equiv \hbar|-\rangle\langle+|, \tag{1.3.38}$$

which are both seen to be *non*-Hermitian. The operator S_+, acting on the spin-down ket $|-\rangle$, turns $|-\rangle$ into the spin-up ket $|+\rangle$ multiplied by $\hbar$. On the other hand, the spin-up ket $|+\rangle$, when acted upon by S_+, becomes a null ket. So the physical interpretation of S_+ is that it raises the spin component by one unit of $\hbar$; if the spin component cannot be raised any further, we automatically get a null state. Likewise, S_- can be interpreted as an operator that lowers the spin component by one unit of $\hbar$. Later we will show that $S_\pm$ can be written as $S_x \pm iS_y$.

In constructing the matrix representations of the angular momentum operators, it is customary to label the column (row) indices in *descending* order of angular momentum components, that is, the first entry corresponds to the maximum angular momentum component, the second, the next highest, and so forth. In our particular case of spin $\frac{1}{2}$ systems, we have

$$|+\rangle \doteq \begin{pmatrix} 1 \\ 0 \end{pmatrix}, \qquad |-\rangle \doteq \begin{pmatrix} 0 \\ 1 \end{pmatrix}, \tag{1.3.39a}$$

$$S_z \doteq \frac{\hbar}{2}\begin{pmatrix} 1 & 0 \\ 0 & -1 \end{pmatrix}, \qquad S_+ \doteq \hbar\begin{pmatrix} 0 & 1 \\ 0 & 0 \end{pmatrix}, \qquad S_- \doteq \hbar\begin{pmatrix} 0 & 0 \\ 1 & 0 \end{pmatrix}. \tag{1.3.39b}$$

We will come back to these explicit expressions when we discuss the Pauli two-component formalism in Chapter 3.

1.4. MEASUREMENTS, OBSERVABLES, AND THE UNCERTAINTY RELATIONS

Measurements

Having developed the mathematics of ket spaces, we are now in a position to discuss the quantum theory of measurement processes. This is not a particularly easy subject for beginners, so we first turn to the words of the great master, P. A. M. Dirac, for guidance (Dirac 1958, 36): "A measurement always causes the system to jump into an eigenstate of the dynamical variable that is being measured." What does all this mean? We interpret Dirac's words as follows: Before a measurement of observable A is made, the system is assumed to be represented by some linear combination

$$|\alpha\rangle = \sum_{a'} c_{a'}|a'\rangle = \sum_{a'} |a'\rangle\langle a'|\alpha\rangle. \tag{1.4.1}$$

When the measurement is performed, the system is "thrown into" one of the eigenstates, say $|a'\rangle$ of observable A. In other words,

$$|\alpha\rangle \xrightarrow{\quad A \text{ measurement} \quad} |a'\rangle. \tag{1.4.2}$$

For example, a silver atom with an arbitrary spin orientation will change into either $|S_z; +\rangle$ or $|S_z; -\rangle$ when subjected to a SG apparatus of type SG$\hat{z}$. Thus *a measurement usually changes the state*. The only exception is when the state is already in one of the eigenstates of the observable being measured, in which case

$$|a'\rangle \xrightarrow{\quad A \text{ measurement} \quad} |a'\rangle \tag{1.4.3}$$

with certainty, as will be discussed further. When the measurement causes $|\alpha\rangle$ to change into $|a'\rangle$, it is said that A is measured to be a'. It is in this sense that the result of a measurement yields one of the eigenvalues of the observable being measured.

Given (1.4.1), which is the state ket of a physical system before the measurement, we do not know in advance into which of the various $|a'\rangle$'s the system will be thrown as the result of the measurement. We do postulate, however, that the probability for jumping into some particular $|a'\rangle$ is given by

$$\text{Probability for } a' = |\langle a'|\alpha\rangle|^2, \tag{1.4.4}$$

provided that $|\alpha\rangle$ is normalized.

Although we have been talking about a single physical system, to determine probability (1.4.4) empirically, we must consider a great number of measurements performed on an ensemble—that is, a collection—of identically prepared physical systems, all characterized by the same ket $|\alpha\rangle$. Such an ensemble is known as a **pure ensemble**. (We will say more about ensembles in Chapter 3.) As an example, a beam of silver atoms which survive the first SG$\hat{z}$ apparatus of Figure 1.3 with the $S_z -$ component blocked is an example of a pure ensemble because every member atom of the ensemble is characterized by $|S_z; +\rangle$.

The probabilistic interpretation (1.4.4) for the squared inner product $|\langle a'|\alpha\rangle|^2$ is one of the fundamental postulates of quantum mechanics, so it cannot be proven. Let us note, however, that it makes good sense in extreme cases. Suppose the state ket is $|a'\rangle$ itself even before a measurement is made; then according to (1.4.4), the probability for getting a'—or, more precisely, for being thrown into $|a'\rangle$—as the result of the measurement is predicted to be 1, which is just what we expect. By measuring A once again, we, of course, get $|a'\rangle$ only; quite generally, repeated measurements of the same observable in succession yield the same result.* If, on the other hand, we are interested in the probability for the system initially characterized by $|a'\rangle$ to be thrown into some other eigenket $|a''\rangle$ with $a'' \neq a'$, then (1.4.4) gives zero because of the orthogonality between $|a'\rangle$ and $|a''\rangle$. From the point of view of measurement theory, orthogonal kets correspond to mutually exclusive alternatives; for example, if a spin $\frac{1}{2}$ system is in $|S_z; +\rangle$, it is not in $|S_z; -\rangle$ with certainty.

Quite generally, the probability for anything must be nonnegative. Furthermore, the probabilities for the various alternative possibilities must add up to unity. Both of these expectations are met by our probability postulate (1.4.4).

We define the **expectation value** of A taken with respect to state $|\alpha\rangle$ as

$$\langle A \rangle \equiv \langle \alpha | A | \alpha \rangle. \tag{1.4.5}$$

To make sure that we are referring to state $|\alpha\rangle$, the notation $\langle A \rangle_\alpha$ is sometimes used. Equation (1.4.5) is a definition; however, it agrees with our intuitive notion of *average measured value* because it can be written as

$$\langle A \rangle = \sum_{a'} \sum_{a''} \langle \alpha | a'' \rangle \langle a'' | A | a' \rangle \langle a' | \alpha \rangle$$

$$= \sum_{a'} \underset{\substack{\uparrow \\ \text{measured value } a'}}{a'} \underset{\text{probability for obtaining } a'}{\underbrace{|\langle a' | \alpha \rangle|^2}} \tag{1.4.6}$$

It is very important not to confuse eigenvalues with expectation values. For example, the expectation value of S_z for spin $\frac{1}{2}$ systems can assume *any* real value between $-\hbar/2$ and $+\hbar/2$, say $0.273\hbar$; in contrast, the eigenvalue of S_z assumes only two values, $\hbar/2$ and $-\hbar/2$.

To clarify further the meaning of measurements in quantum mechanics we introduce the notion of a **selective measurement**, or *filtration*. In Section 1.1 we considered a Stern-Gerlach arrangement where we let only one of the spin components pass out of the apparatus while we completely blocked the other component. More generally, we imagine a measurement process with a device that selects only one of the eigenkets of A, say $|a'\rangle$, and rejects all others; see Figure 1.6. This is what we mean by a selective measurement; it is also called filtration because only one of the A eigenkets filters through the ordeal. Mathematically we can say that such a selective

---

*Here successive measurements must be carried out immediately afterward. This point will become clear when we discuss the time evolution of a state ket in Chapter 2.

FIGURE 1.6. Selective measurement.

measurement amounts to applying the projection operator $\Lambda_{a'}$ to $|\alpha\rangle$:

$$\Lambda_{a'}|\alpha\rangle = |a'\rangle\langle a'|\alpha\rangle. \tag{1.4.7}$$

J. Schwinger has developed a formalism of quantum mechanics based on a thorough examination of selective measurements. He introduces a measurement symbol $M(a')$ in the beginning, which is identical to $\Lambda_{a'}$ or $|a'\rangle\langle a'|$ in our notation, and deduces a number of properties of $M(a')$ (and also of $M(b', a')$ which amount to $|b'\rangle\langle a'|$) by studying the outcome of various Stern-Gerlach–type experiments. In this way he motivates the entire mathematics of kets, bras, and operators. In this book we do not follow Schwinger's path; the interested reader may consult Gottfried's book. (Gottfried 1966, 192–9).

Spin $\frac{1}{2}$ Systems, Once Again

Before proceeding with a general discussion of observables, we once again consider spin $\frac{1}{2}$ systems. This time we show that the results of sequential Stern-Gerlach experiments, when combined with the postulates of quantum mechanics discussed so far, are sufficient to determine not only the $S_{x,y}$ eigenkets, $|S_x; \pm\rangle$ and $|S_y; \pm\rangle$, but also the operators S_x and S_y themselves.

First, we recall that when the $S_x +$ beam is subjected to an apparatus of type SG$\hat{z}$, the beam splits into two components with equal intensities. This means that the probability for the $S_x +$ state to be thrown into $|S_z; \pm\rangle$, simply denoted as $|\pm\rangle$, is $\frac{1}{2}$ each; hence,

$$|\langle +|S_x; +\rangle| = |\langle -|S_x; +\rangle| = \frac{1}{\sqrt{2}}. \tag{1.4.8}$$

We can therefore construct the $S_x +$ ket as follows:

$$|S_x; +\rangle = \frac{1}{\sqrt{2}}|+\rangle + \frac{1}{\sqrt{2}}e^{i\delta_1}|-\rangle, \tag{1.4.9}$$

with δ_1 real. In writing (1.4.9) we have used the fact that the *overall* phase (common to both $|+\rangle$ and $|-\rangle$) of a state ket is immaterial; the coefficient of $|+\rangle$ can be chosen to be real and positive by convention. The S_x- ket must be orthogonal to the S_x+ ket because the S_x+ alternative and S_x- alternative are mutually exclusive. This orthogonality requirement leads to

$$|S_x; -\rangle = \frac{1}{\sqrt{2}}|+\rangle - \frac{1}{\sqrt{2}}e^{i\delta_1}|-\rangle, \qquad (1.4.10)$$

where we have, again, chosen the coefficient of $|+\rangle$ to be real and positive by convention. We can now construct the operator S_x using (1.3.34) as follows:

$$S_x = \frac{\hbar}{2}\left[(|S_x; +\rangle\langle S_x; +|)-(|S_x; -\rangle\langle S_x; -|)\right]$$

$$= \frac{\hbar}{2}\left[e^{-i\delta_1}(|+\rangle\langle -|)+e^{i\delta_1}(|-\rangle\langle +|)\right]. \qquad (1.4.11)$$

Notice that the S_x we have constructed is Hermitian, just as it must be. A similar argument with S_x replaced by S_y leads to

$$|S_y; \pm\rangle = \frac{1}{\sqrt{2}}|+\rangle \pm \frac{1}{\sqrt{2}}e^{i\delta_2}|-\rangle, \qquad (1.4.12)$$

$$S_y = \frac{\hbar}{2}\left[e^{-i\delta_2}(|+\rangle\langle -|)+e^{i\delta_2}(|-\rangle\langle +|)\right]. \qquad (1.4.13)$$

Is there any way of determining δ_1 and δ_2? Actually there is one piece of information we have not yet used. Suppose we have a beam of spin $\frac{1}{2}$ atoms moving in the z-direction. We can consider a sequential Stern-Gerlach experiment with $SG\hat{x}$ followed by $SG\hat{y}$. The results of such an experiment are completely analogous to the earlier case leading to (1.4.8):

$$|\langle S_y; \pm|S_x; +\rangle| = |\langle S_y; \pm|S_x; -\rangle| = \frac{1}{\sqrt{2}}, \qquad (1.4.14)$$

which is not surprising in view of the invariance of physical systems under rotations. Inserting (1.4.10) and (1.4.12) into (1.4.14), we obtain

$$\frac{1}{2}|1 \pm e^{i(\delta_1 - \delta_2)}| = \frac{1}{\sqrt{2}}, \qquad (1.4.15)$$

which is satisfied only if

$$\delta_2 - \delta_1 = \pi/2 \quad \text{or} \quad -\pi/2. \qquad (1.4.16)$$

We thus see that the matrix elements of S_x and S_y cannot all be real. If the S_x matrix elements are real, the S_y matrix elements must be purely imaginary (and vice versa). Just from this extremely simple example, the introduction of complex numbers is seen to be an essential feature in quantum mechanics. It is convenient to take the S_x matrix elements to be real* and

* This can always be done by adjusting arbitrary phase factors in the definition of $|+\rangle$ and $|-\rangle$. This point will become clearer in Chapter 3, where the behavior of $|\pm\rangle$ under rotations will be discussed.

set $\delta_1 = 0$; if we were to choose $\delta_1 = \pi$, the positive x-axis would be oriented in the opposite direction. The second phase angle δ_2 must then be $-\pi/2$ or $\pi/2$. The fact that there is still an ambiguity of this kind is not surprising. We have not yet specified whether the coordinate system we are using is right-handed or left-handed; given the x- and the z-axes there is still a twofold ambiguity in the choice of the positive y-axis. Later we will discuss angular momentum as a generator of rotations using the right-handed coordinate system; it can then be shown that $\delta_2 = \pi/2$ is the correct choice.

To summarize, we have

$$|S_x; \pm\rangle = \frac{1}{\sqrt{2}}|+\rangle \pm \frac{1}{\sqrt{2}}|-\rangle, \tag{1.4.17a}$$

$$|S_y; \pm\rangle = \frac{1}{\sqrt{2}}|+\rangle \pm \frac{i}{\sqrt{2}}|-\rangle, \tag{1.4.17b}$$

and

$$S_x = \frac{\hbar}{2}[(|+\rangle\langle-|)+(|-\rangle\langle+|)], \tag{1.4.18a}$$

$$S_y = \frac{\hbar}{2}[-i(|+\rangle\langle-|)+i(|-\rangle\langle+|)]. \tag{1.4.18b}$$

The $S_x +$ and $S_y \pm$ eigenkets given here are seen to be in agreement with our earlier guesses (1.1.9) and (1.1.14) based on an analogy with linearly and circularly polarized light. (Note, in this comparison, that only the relative phase between the $|+\rangle$ and $|-\rangle$ components is of physical significance.) Furthermore, the non-Hermitian $S_\pm$ operators defined by (1.3.38) can now be written as

$$S_\pm = S_x \pm iS_y. \tag{1.4.19}$$

The operators S_x and S_y, together with S_z given earlier, can be readily shown to satisfy the commutation relations

$$[S_i, S_j] = i\varepsilon_{ijk}\hbar S_k, \tag{1.4.20}$$

and the anticommutation relations

$$\{S_i, S_j\} = \frac{1}{2}\hbar^2\delta_{ij}, \tag{1.4.21}$$

where the commutator [,] and the anticommutator { , } are defined by

$$[A, B] \equiv AB - BA, \tag{1.4.22a}$$

$$\{A, B\} \equiv AB + BA. \tag{1.4.22b}$$

The commutation relations in (1.4.20) will be recognized as the simplest realization of the angular momentum commutation relations, whose significance will be discussed in detail in Chapter 3. In contrast, the anticommutation relations in (1.4.21) turn out to be a *special* property of spin $\frac{1}{2}$ systems.

We can also define the operator $\mathbf{S} \cdot \mathbf{S}$, or $\mathbf{S}^2$ for short, as follows:

$$\mathbf{S}^2 = S_x^2 + S_y^2 + S_z^2. \qquad (1.4.23)$$

Because of (1.4.21), this operator turns out to be just a constant multiple of the identity operator

$$\mathbf{S}^2 = \left(\frac{3}{4}\right)\hbar^2. \qquad (1.4.24)$$

We obviously have

$$\left[\mathbf{S}^2, S_i\right] = 0. \qquad (1.4.25)$$

As will be shown in Chapter 3, for spins higher than $\frac{1}{2}$, $\mathbf{S}^2$ is no longer a multiple of the identity operator; however, (1.4.25) still holds.

Compatible Observables

Returning now to the general formalism, we will discuss compatible versus incompatible observables. Observables A and B are defined to be **compatible** when the corresponding operators commute,

$$[A, B] = 0, \qquad (1.4.26)$$

and **incompatible** when

$$[A, B] \neq 0, \qquad (1.4.27)$$

For example, $\mathbf{S}^2$ and S_z are compatible observables, while S_x and S_z are incompatible observables.

Let us first consider the case of compatible observables A and B. As usual, we assume that the ket space is spanned by the eigenkets of A. We may also regard the same ket space as being spanned by the eigenkets of B. We now ask, How are the A eigenkets related to the B eigenkets when A and B are compatible observables?

Before answering this question we must touch upon a very important point we have bypassed earlier—the concept of *degeneracy*. Suppose there are two (or more) linearly independent eigenkets of A having the same eigenvalue; then the eigenvalues of the two eigenkets are said to be **degenerate**. In such a case the notation $|a'\rangle$ that labels the eigenket by its eigenvalue alone does not give a complete description; furthermore, we may recall that our earlier theorem on the orthogonality of different eigenkets was proved under the assumption of no degeneracy. Even worse, the whole concept that the ket space is spanned by $\{|a'\rangle\}$ appears to run into difficulty when the dimensionality of the ket space is larger than the number of distinct eigenvalues of A. Fortunately, in practical applications in quantum mechanics, it is usually the case that in such a situation the eigenvalues of *some other* commuting observable, say B, can be used to label the degenerate eigenkets.

Now we are ready to state an important theorem.

Theorem. *Suppose that A and B are compatible observables, and the eigenvalues of A are nondegenerate. Then the matrix elements $\langle a''|B|a'\rangle$ are all diagonal. (Recall here that the matrix elements of A are already diagonal if $\{|a'\rangle\}$ are used as the base kets.)*

Proof. The proof of this important theorem is extremely simple. Using the definition (1.4.26) of compatible observables, we observe that

$$\langle a''|[A, B]|a'\rangle = (a'' - a')\langle a''|B|a'\rangle = 0. \qquad (1.4.28)$$

So $\langle a''|B|a'\rangle$ must vanish unless $a' = a''$, which proves our assertion. □

We can write the matrix elements of B as

$$\langle a''|B|a'\rangle = \delta_{a'a''}\langle a'|B|a'\rangle. \qquad (1.4.29)$$

So both A and B can be represented by diagonal matrices with the *same* set of base kets. Using (1.3.17) and (1.4.29) we can write B as

$$B = \sum_{a''} |a''\rangle\langle a''|B|a''\rangle\langle a''|. \qquad (1.4.30)$$

Suppose that this operator acts on an eigenket of A:

$$B|a'\rangle = \sum_{a''} |a''\rangle\langle a''|B|a''\rangle\langle a''|a'\rangle = (\langle a'|B|a'\rangle)|a'\rangle. \qquad (1.4.31)$$

But this is nothing other than the eigenvalue equation for the operator B with eigenvalue

$$b' \equiv \langle a'|B|a'\rangle. \qquad (1.4.32)$$

The ket $|a'\rangle$ is therefore a **simultaneous eigenket** of A and B. Just to be impartial to both operators, we may use $|a', b'\rangle$ to characterize this simultaneous eigenket.

We have seen that compatible observables have simultaneous eigenkets. Even though the proof given is for the case where the A eigenkets are nondegenerate, the statement holds even if there is an n-fold degeneracy, that is,

$$A|a'^{(i)}\rangle = a'|a'^{(i)}\rangle \quad \text{for } i = 1, 2, \ldots, n \qquad (1.4.33)$$

where $|a'^{(i)}\rangle$ are n mutually orthonormal eigenkets of A, all with the same eigenvalue a'. To see this, all we need to do is construct appropriate linear combinations of $|a'^{(i)}\rangle$ that diagonalize the B operator by following the diagonalization procedure to be discussed in Section 1.5.

A simultaneous eigenket of A and B, denoted by $|a', b'\rangle$, has the property

$$A|a', b'\rangle = a'|a', b'\rangle, \qquad (1.4.34a)$$

$$B|a', b'\rangle = b'|a', b'\rangle. \qquad (1.4.34b)$$

When there is no degeneracy, this notation is somewhat superfluous because it is clear from (1.4.32) that if we specify a', we necessarily know the b' that appears in $|a', b'\rangle$. The notation $|a', b'\rangle$ is much more powerful when there are degeneracies. A simple example may be used to illustrate this point.

Even though a complete discussion of orbital angular momentum will not appear in this book until Chapter 3, the reader may be familiar from his or her earlier training in elementary wave mechanics that the eigenvalues of $\mathbf{L}^2$ (orbital angular momentum squared) and L_z (the z-component of orbital angular momentum) are $\hbar^2 l(l + 1)$ and $m_l \hbar$, respectively, with l an integer and $m_l = -l, -l+1,...,+l$. To characterize an orbital angular momentum state completely, it is necessary to specify *both* l and m_l. For example, if we just say $l=1$, the m_l value can still be 0, +1, or −1; if we just say $m_l = 1$, l can be 1, 2, 3, 4, and so on. Only by specifying *both* l and m_l do we succeed in uniquely characterizing the orbital angular momentum state in question. Quite often a **collective index** K' is used to stand for (a', b'), so that

$$|K'\rangle = |a', b'\rangle. \qquad (1.4.35)$$

We can obviously generalize our considerations to a situation where there are several (more than two) mutually compatible observables, namely,

$$[A, B] = [B, C] = [A, C] = \cdots = 0. \qquad (1.4.36)$$

Assume that we have found a **maximal** set of commuting observables; that is, we cannot add any more observables to our list without violating (1.4.36). The eigenvalues of individual operators $A, B, C,...$ may have degeneracies, but if we specify a combination $(a', b', c',...)$, then the corresponding simultaneous eigenket of $A, B, C,...$ is uniquely specified. We can again use a collective index K' to stand for $(a', b', c',...)$. The orthonormality relation for

$$|K'\rangle = |a', b', c',...\rangle \qquad (1.4.37)$$

reads

$$\langle K''|K'\rangle = \delta_{K'K''} = \delta_{aa'}\delta_{bb'}\delta_{cc'} ..., \qquad (1.4.38)$$

while the completeness relation, or closure, can be written as

$$\sum_{K'} |K'\rangle\langle K'| = \sum_{a'}\sum_{b'}\sum_{c'} ... |a', b', c',...\rangle\langle a', b', c',...| = 1. \qquad (1.4.39)$$

We now consider measurements of A and B when they are compatible observables. Suppose we measure A first and obtain result a'. Subsequently, we may measure B and get result b'. Finally we measure A again. It follows from our measurement formalism that the third measurement always gives a' with certainty, that is, the second (B) measurement does not destroy the previous information obtained in the first (A) measurement. This is rather obvious when the eigenvalues of A are nondegenerate:

$$|\alpha\rangle \xrightarrow{\;A\text{ measurement}\;} |a', b'\rangle \xrightarrow{\;B\text{ measurement}\;} |a', b'\rangle \xrightarrow{\;A\text{ measurement}\;} |a', b'\rangle.$$

$$(1.4.40)$$

When there is degeneracy, the argument goes as follows: After the first (A) measurement, which yields a', the system is thrown into some linear combination

$$\sum_i^n c_{a'}^{(i)} |a', b^{(i)}\rangle, \qquad (1.4.41)$$

where n is the degree of degeneracy and the kets $|a', b^{(i)}\rangle$ all have the same eigenvalue a' as far as operator A is concerned. The second (B) measurement may select just one of the terms in the linear combination (1.4.41), say, $|a', b^{(j)}\rangle$, but the third (A) measurement applied to it still yields a'. Whether or not there is degeneracy, A measurements and B measurements do not interfere. The term *compatible* is indeed deemed appropriate.

Incompatible Observables

We now turn to incompatible observables, which are more nontrivial. The first point to be emphasized is that incompatible observables do not have a complete set of simultaneous eigenkets. To show this let us assume the converse to be true. There would then exist a set of simultaneous eigenkets with property (1.4.34a) and (1.4.34b). Clearly,

$$AB|a', b'\rangle = Ab'|a', b'\rangle = a'b'|a', b'\rangle. \qquad (1.4.42)$$

Likewise,

$$BA|a', b'\rangle = Ba'|a', b'\rangle = a'b'|a', b'\rangle; \qquad (1.4.43)$$

hence,

$$AB|a', b'\rangle = BA|a', b'\rangle, \qquad (1.4.44)$$

and thus $[A, B] = 0$ in contradiction to the assumption. So in general, $|a', b'\rangle$ does not make sense for incompatible observables. There is, however, an interesting exception; it may happen that there exists a subspace of the ket space such that (1.4.44) holds for all elements of this subspace, even though A and B are incompatible. An example from the theory of orbital angular momentum may be helpful here. Suppose we consider an $l = 0$ state (s-state). Even though L_x and L_z do *not* commute, this state *is* a simultaneous eigenstate of L_x and L_z (with eigenvalue zero for both operators). The subspace in this case is one-dimensional.

We already encountered some of the peculiarities associated with incompatible observables when we discussed sequential Stern-Gerlach experiments in Section 1.1. We now give a more general discussion of experiments of that type. Consider the sequence of selective measurements shown in Figure 1.7(a). The first (A) filter selects some particular $|a'\rangle$ and rejects all others, the second (B) filter selects some particular $|b'\rangle$ and rejects all others, and the third (C) filter selects some particular $|c'\rangle$ and rejects all others. We are interested in the probability of obtaining $|c'\rangle$ when the beam coming out of the first filter is normalized to unity. Because the probabilities are multiplicative, we obviously have

$$|\langle c'|b'\rangle|^2|\langle b'|a'\rangle|^2. \tag{1.4.45}$$

Now let us sum over b' to consider the total probability for going through all possible b' routes. Operationally this means that we first record the probability of obtaining c' with all but the first b' route blocked, then we repeat the procedure with all but the second b' blocked, and so on; then we sum the probabilities at the end and obtain

$$\sum_{b'} |\langle c'|b'\rangle|^2|\langle b'|a'\rangle|^2 = \sum_{b'} \langle c'|b'\rangle\langle b'|a'\rangle\langle a'|b'\rangle\langle b'|c'\rangle. \tag{1.4.46}$$

We now compare this with a different arrangement, where the B filter is absent (or not operative); see Figure 1.7b. Clearly, the probability is

(a)

(b)

FIGURE 1.7. Sequential selective measurements.

just $|\langle c'|a'\rangle|^2$, which can also be written as follows:

$$|\langle c'|a'\rangle|^2 = |\sum_{b'} \langle c'|b'\rangle\langle b'|a'\rangle|^2 = \sum_{b'}\sum_{b''} \langle c'|b'\rangle\langle b'|a'\rangle\langle a'|b''\rangle\langle b''|c'\rangle.$$

$$(1.4.47)$$

Notice that expressions (1.4.46) and (1.4.47) are different! This is remarkable because in both cases the pure $|a'\rangle$ beam coming out of the first (A) filter can be regarded as being made up of the B eigenkets

$$|a'\rangle = \sum_{b'} |b'\rangle\langle b'|a'\rangle, \qquad (1.4.48)$$

where the sum is over all possible values of b'. The crucial point to be noted is that the result coming out of the C filter depends on whether or not B measurements have actually been carried out. In the first case we experimentally ascertain which of the B eigenvalues are actually realized; in the second case, we merely imagine $|a'\rangle$ to be built up of the various $|b'\rangle$'s in the sense of (1.4.48). Put in another way, actually recording the probabilities of going through the various b' routes makes all the difference even though we sum over b' afterwards. Here lies the heart of quantum mechanics.

Under what conditions do the two expressions become equal? It is left as an exercise for the reader to show that for this to happen, in the absence of degeneracy, it is sufficient that

$$[A, B] = 0 \quad \text{or} \quad [B, C] = 0. \qquad (1.4.49)$$

In other words, the peculiarity we have illustrated is characteristic of incompatible observables.

The Uncertainty Relation

The last topic to be discussed in this section is the uncertainty relation. Given an observable A, we define an **operator**

$$\Delta A \equiv A - \langle A \rangle, \qquad (1.4.50)$$

where the expectation value is to be taken for a certain physical state under consideration. The expectation value of $(\Delta A)^2$ is known as the **dispersion** of A. Because we have

$$\langle (\Delta A)^2 \rangle = \langle (A^2 - 2A\langle A \rangle + \langle A \rangle^2) \rangle = \langle A^2 \rangle - \langle A \rangle^2, \qquad (1.4.51)$$

the last line of (1.4.51) may be taken as an alternative definition of dispersion. Sometimes the terms **variance** and **mean square deviation** are used for the same quantity. Clearly, the dispersion vanishes when the state in question is an eigenstate of A. Roughly speaking, the dispersion of an observable characterizes "fuzziness." For example, for the $S_z +$ state of a spin $\frac{1}{2}$ system, the dispersion of S_x can be computed to be

$$\langle S_x^2 \rangle - \langle S_x \rangle^2 = \hbar^2/4. \tag{1.4.52}$$

In contrast the dispersion $\langle (\Delta S_z)^2 \rangle$ obviously vanishes for the $S_z +$ state. So, for the $S_z +$ state, S_z is "sharp"—a vanishing dispersion for S_z—while S_x is fuzzy.

We now state the uncertainty relation, which is the generalization of the well-known x-p uncertainty relation to be discussed in Section 1.6. Let A and B be observables. Then for any state we must have the following inequality:

$$\langle (\Delta A)^2 \rangle \langle (\Delta B)^2 \rangle \geq \frac{1}{4} |\langle [A, B] \rangle|^2. \tag{1.4.53}$$

To prove this we first state three lemmas.

Lemma 1. *The Schwarz inequality*

$$\langle \alpha | \alpha \rangle \langle \beta | \beta \rangle \geq |\langle \alpha | \beta \rangle|^2, \tag{1.4.54}$$

which is analogous to

$$|\mathbf{a}|^2 |\mathbf{b}|^2 \geq |\mathbf{a} \cdot \mathbf{b}|^2 \tag{1.4.55}$$

in real Euclidian space.

Proof. First note

$$(\langle \alpha | + \lambda^* \langle \beta |) \cdot (|\alpha \rangle + \lambda |\beta \rangle) \geq 0, \tag{1.4.56}$$

where λ can be any complex number. This inequality must hold when λ is set equal to $-\langle \beta | \alpha \rangle / \langle \beta | \beta \rangle$:

$$\langle \alpha | \alpha \rangle \langle \beta | \beta \rangle - |\langle \alpha | \beta \rangle|^2 \geq 0, \tag{1.4.57}$$

which is the same as (1.4.54).   □

Lemma 2. *The expectation value of a Hermitian operator is purely real.*

Proof. The proof is trivial—just use (1.3.21).   □

Lemma 3. *The expectation value of an anti-Hermitian operator, defined by $C = -C^\dagger$, is purely imaginary.*

Proof. The proof is also trivial.   □

Armed with these lemmas, we are in a position to prove the uncertainty relation (1.4.53). Using Lemma 1 with

$$|\alpha \rangle = \Delta A | \; \rangle,$$
$$|\beta \rangle = \Delta B | \; \rangle, \tag{1.4.58}$$

where the blank ket $| \rangle$ emphasizes the fact that our consideration may be applied to *any* ket, we obtain

$$\langle (\Delta A)^2 \rangle \langle (\Delta B)^2 \rangle \geq |\langle \Delta A \Delta B \rangle|^2, \tag{1.4.59}$$

where the Hermiticity of ΔA and ΔB has been used. To evaluate the right-hand side of (1.4.59), we note

$$\Delta A \Delta B = \frac{1}{2}[\Delta A, \Delta B] + \frac{1}{2}\{\Delta A, \Delta B\}, \tag{1.4.60}$$

where the commutator $[\Delta A, \Delta B]$, which is equal to $[A, B]$, is clearly anti-Hermitian

$$([A, B])^\dagger = (AB - BA)^\dagger = BA - AB = -[A, B]. \tag{1.4.61}$$

In contrast, the anticommutator $\{\Delta A, \Delta B\}$ is obviously Hermitian, so

$$\langle \Delta A \Delta B \rangle = \underbrace{\frac{1}{2}\langle [A, B] \rangle}_{\substack{\text{purely} \\ \text{imaginary}}} + \underbrace{\frac{1}{2}\langle \{\Delta A, \Delta B\} \rangle}_{\substack{\text{purely} \\ \text{real}}}, \tag{1.4.62}$$

where Lemmas 2 and 3 have been used. The right-hand side of (1.4.59) now becomes

$$|\langle \Delta A \Delta B \rangle|^2 = \frac{1}{4}|\langle [A, B] \rangle|^2 + \frac{1}{4}|\langle \{\Delta A, \Delta B\} \rangle|^2. \tag{1.4.63}$$

The proof of (1.4.53) is now complete because the omission of the second (the anticommutator) term of (1.4.63) can only make the inequality relation stronger.*

Applications of the uncertainty relation to spin $\frac{1}{2}$ systems will be left as exercises. We come back to this topic when we discuss the fundamental x-p commutation relation in Section 1.6.

1.5. CHANGE OF BASIS

Transformation Operator

Suppose we have two incompatible observables A and B. The ket space in question can be viewed as being spanned either by the set $\{|a'\rangle\}$ or by the set $\{|b'\rangle\}$. For example, for spin $\frac{1}{2}$ systems $|S_z \pm \rangle$ may be used as our base kets; alternatively, $|S_x \pm \rangle$ may be used as our base kets. The two different sets of base kets, of course, span the same ket space. We are interested in finding out how the two descriptions are related. Changing the

---

*In the literature most authors use ΔA for our $\sqrt{\langle (\Delta A)^2 \rangle}$ so the uncertainty relation is written as $\Delta A \Delta B \geq \frac{1}{2}|\langle [A, B] \rangle|$. In this book, however, ΔA and ΔB are to be understood as operators [see (1.4.50)], not numbers.

set of base kets is referred to as a **change of basis** or a **change of representation**. The basis in which the base eigenkets are given by $\{|a'\rangle\}$ is called the A representation or, sometimes, the A diagonal representation because the square matrix corresponding to A is diagonal in this basis.

Our basic task is to construct a transformation operator that connects the old orthonormal set $\{|a'\rangle\}$ and the new orthonormal set $\{|b'\rangle\}$. To this end, we first show the following.

Theorem. Given two sets of base kets, both satisfying orthonormality and completeness, there exists a unitary operator U such that

$$|b^{(1)}\rangle = U|a^{(1)}\rangle, |b^{(2)}\rangle = U|a^{(2)}\rangle, \ldots, |b^{(N)}\rangle = U|a^{(N)}\rangle. \qquad (1.5.1)$$

By a **unitary operator** *we mean an operator fulfilling the conditions*

$$U^{\dagger}U = 1 \qquad (1.5.2)$$

as well as

$$UU^{\dagger} = 1. \qquad (1.5.3)$$

Proof. We prove this theorem by explicit construction. We assert that the operator

$$U = \sum_{k} |b^{(k)}\rangle\langle a^{(k)}| \qquad (1.5.4)$$

will do the job and we apply this U to $|a^{(l)}\rangle$. Clearly,

$$U|a^{(l)}\rangle = |b^{(l)}\rangle \qquad (1.5.5)$$

is guaranteed by the orthonormality of $\{|a'\rangle\}$. Furthermore, U is unitary:

$$U^{\dagger}U = \sum_{k}\sum_{l} |a^{(l)}\rangle\langle b^{(l)}|b^{(k)}\rangle\langle a^{(k)}| = \sum_{k} |a^{(k)}\rangle\langle a^{(k)}| = 1, \qquad (1.5.6)$$

where we have used the orthonormality of $\{|b'\rangle\}$ and the completeness of $\{|a'\rangle\}$. We obtain relation (1.5.3) in an analogous manner.   □

Transformation Matrix

It is instructive to study the matrix representation of the U operator in the old $\{|a'\rangle\}$ basis. We have

$$\langle a^{(k)}|U|a^{(l)}\rangle = \langle a^{(k)}|b^{(l)}\rangle, \qquad (1.5.7)$$

which is obvious from (1.5.5). In other words, the matrix elements of the U operator are built up of the inner products of old base bras and new base kets. We recall that the rotation matrix in three dimensions that changes one set of unit base vectors $(\hat{\mathbf{x}}, \hat{\mathbf{y}}, \hat{\mathbf{z}})$ into another set $(\hat{\mathbf{x}}', \hat{\mathbf{y}}', \hat{\mathbf{z}}')$ can be written as

(Goldstein 1980, 128–37, for example)

$$R = \begin{pmatrix} \hat{x}\cdot\hat{x}' & \hat{x}\cdot\hat{y}' & \hat{x}\cdot\hat{z}' \\ \hat{y}\cdot\hat{x}' & \hat{y}\cdot\hat{y}' & \hat{y}\cdot\hat{z}' \\ \hat{z}\cdot\hat{x}' & \hat{z}\cdot\hat{y}' & \hat{z}\cdot\hat{z}' \end{pmatrix} \tag{1.5.8}$$

The square matrix made up of $\langle a^{(k)}|U|a^{(l)}\rangle$ is referred to as the **transformation matrix** from the $\{|a'\rangle\}$ basis to the $\{|b'\rangle\}$ basis.

Given an arbitrary ket $|\alpha\rangle$ whose expansion coefficients $\langle a'|\alpha\rangle$ are known in the old basis,

$$|\alpha\rangle = \sum_{a'} |a'\rangle\langle a'|\alpha\rangle, \tag{1.5.9}$$

how can we obtain $\langle b'|\alpha\rangle$, the expansion coefficients in the new basis? The answer is very simple: Just multiply (1.5.9) (with a' replaced by $a^{(l)}$ to avoid confusion) by $\langle b^{(k)}|$

$$\langle b^{(k)}|\alpha\rangle = \sum_{l} \langle b^{(k)}|a^{(l)}\rangle\langle a^{(l)}|\alpha\rangle = \sum_{l} \langle a^{(k)}|U^{\dagger}|a^{(l)}\rangle\langle a^{(l)}|\alpha\rangle. \tag{1.5.10}$$

In matrix notation, (1.5.10) states that the column matrix for $|\alpha\rangle$ in the new basis can be obtained just by applying the square matrix $U^{\dagger}$ to the column matrix in the old basis:

$$(\text{New}) = (U^{\dagger})(\text{old}). \tag{1.5.11}$$

The relationships between the old matrix elements and the new matrix elements are also easy to obtain:

$$\langle b^{(k)}|X|b^{(l)}\rangle = \sum_{m}\sum_{n} \langle b^{(k)}|a^{(m)}\rangle\langle a^{(m)}|X|a^{(n)}\rangle\langle a^{(n)}|b^{(l)}\rangle$$

$$= \sum_{m}\sum_{n} \langle a^{(k)}|U^{\dagger}|a^{(m)}\rangle\langle a^{(m)}|X|a^{(n)}\rangle\langle a^{(n)}|U|a^{(l)}\rangle. \tag{1.5.12}$$

This is simply the well-known formula for a **similarity transformation** in matrix algebra,

$$X' = U^{\dagger}XU. \tag{1.5.13}$$

The **trace** of an operator X is defined as the sum of diagonal elements:

$$\text{tr}(X) = \sum_{a'} \langle a'|X|a'\rangle. \tag{1.5.14}$$

Even though a particular set of base kets is used in the definition, $\text{tr}(X)$

turns out to be independent of representation, as shown:

$$\sum_{a'} \langle a'|X|a' \rangle = \sum_{a'} \sum_{b'} \sum_{b''} \langle a'|b' \rangle \langle b'|X|b'' \rangle \langle b''|a' \rangle$$

$$= \sum_{b'} \sum_{b''} \langle b''|b' \rangle \langle b'|X|b'' \rangle$$

$$= \sum_{b'} \langle b'|X|b' \rangle. \qquad (1.5.15)$$

We can also prove

$$\text{tr}(XY) = \text{tr}(YX), \qquad (1.5.16a)$$

$$\text{tr}(U^\dagger XU) = \text{tr}(X), \qquad (1.5.16b)$$

$$\text{tr}(|a'\rangle\langle a''|) = \delta_{a'a''}, \qquad (1.5.16c)$$

$$\text{tr}(|b'\rangle\langle a'|) = \langle a'|b' \rangle. \qquad (1.5.16d)$$

Diagonalization

So far we have not discussed how to find the eigenvalues and eigenkets of an operator B whose matrix elements in the old $\{|a'\rangle\}$ basis are assumed to be known. This problem turns out to be equivalent to that of finding the unitary matrix that diagonalizes B. Even though the reader may already be familiar with the diagonalization procedure in matrix algebra, it is worth working out this problem using the Dirac bra-ket notation.

We are interested in obtaining the eigenvalue b' and the eigenket $|b'\rangle$ with the property

$$B|b'\rangle = b'|b'\rangle. \qquad (1.5.17)$$

First, we rewrite this as

$$\sum_{a'} \langle a''|B|a' \rangle \langle a'|b' \rangle = b'\langle a''|b' \rangle. \qquad (1.5.18)$$

When $|b'\rangle$ in (1.5.17) stands for the lth eigenket of operator B, we can write (1.5.18) in matrix notation as follows:

$$\begin{pmatrix} B_{11} & B_{12} & B_{13} & \cdots \\ B_{21} & B_{22} & B_{23} & \cdots \\ \vdots & \vdots & \vdots & \ddots \end{pmatrix} \begin{pmatrix} C_1^{(l)} \\ C_2^{(l)} \\ \vdots \end{pmatrix} = b^{(l)} \begin{pmatrix} C_1^{(l)} \\ C_2^{(l)} \\ \vdots \end{pmatrix}, \qquad (1.5.19)$$

with

$$B_{ij} = \langle a^{(i)}|B|a^{(j)} \rangle, \qquad (1.5.20a)$$

and

$$C_k^{(l)} = \langle a^{(k)}|b^{(l)} \rangle, \qquad (1.5.20b)$$

where i, j, k run up to N, the dimensionality of the ket space. As we know from linear algebra, nontrivial solutions for $C_k^{(l)}$ are possible only if the characteristic equation

$$\det(B - \lambda 1) = 0 \tag{1.5.21}$$

is satisfied. This is an Nth order algebraic equation for λ, and the N roots obtained are to be identified with the various $b^{(l)}$'s we are trying to determine. Knowing $b^{(l)}$ we can solve for the corresponding $C_k^{(l)}$'s up to an overall constant to be determined from the normalization condition. Comparing (1.5.20b) with (1.5.7), we see that the $C_k^{(l)}$'s are just the elements of the unitary matrix involved in the change of basis $\{|a'\rangle\} \rightarrow \{|b'\rangle\}$.

For this procedure the Hermiticity of B is important. For example, consider S_+ defined by (1.3.38) or (1.4.19). This operator is obviously non-Hermitian. The corresponding matrix, which reads in the S_z basis as

$$S_+ \doteq \hbar \begin{pmatrix} 0 & 1 \\ 0 & 0 \end{pmatrix}, \tag{1.5.22}$$

cannot be diagonalized by any unitary matrix. In Chapter 2 we will encounter eigenkets of a non-Hermitian operator in connection with a coherent state of a simple harmonic oscillator. Such eigenkets, however, are known *not* to form a complete orthonormal set, and the formalism we have developed in this section cannot be immediately applied.

Unitary Equivalent Observables

We conclude this section by discussing a remarkable theorem on the unitary transform of an observable.

Theorem.   *Consider again two sets of orthonormal basis* $\{|a'\rangle\}$ *and* $\{|b'\rangle\}$ *connected by the U operator* (1.5.4). *Knowing U, we may construct a* **unitary transform** *of A, UAU^{-1}; then A and UAU^{-1} are said to be* **unitary equivalent observables.** *The eigenvalue equation for A,*

$$A|a^{(l)}\rangle = a^{(l)}|a^{(l)}\rangle, \tag{1.5.23}$$

clearly implies that

$$UAU^{-1}U|a^{(l)}\rangle = a^{(l)}U|a^{(l)}\rangle. \tag{1.5.24}$$

But this can be rewritten as

$$(UAU^{-1})|b^{(l)}\rangle = a^{(l)}|b^{(l)}\rangle. \tag{1.5.25}$$

This deceptively simple result is quite profound. It tells us that the $|b'\rangle$'s are eigenkets of UAU^{-1} with *exactly the same eigenvalues* as the A

eigenvalues. In other words, *unitary equivalent observables have identical spectra.*

The eigenket $|b^{(l)}\rangle$, by definition, satisfies the relationship

$$B|b^{(l)}\rangle = b^{(l)}|b^{(l)}\rangle. \tag{1.5.26}$$

Comparing (1.5.25) and (1.5.26), we infer that B and UAU^{-1} are simultaneously diagonalizable. A natural question is, is UAU^{-1} the same as B itself? The answer quite often is yes in cases of physical interest. Take, for example, S_x and S_z. They are related by a unitary operator, which, as we will discuss in Chapter 3, is actually the rotation operator around the y-axis by angle $\pi/2$. In this case S_x itself is the unitary transform of S_z. Because we know that S_x and S_z exhibit the same set of eigenvalues—namely, $+ \hbar/2$ and $- \hbar/2$—we see that our theorem holds in this particular example.

1.6. POSITION, MOMENTUM, AND TRANSLATION

Continuous Spectra

The observables considered so far have all been assumed to exhibit discrete eigenvalue spectra. In quantum mechanics, however, there are observables with continuous eigenvalues. Take, for instance, p_z, the z-component of momentum. In quantum mechanics this is again represented by a Hermitian operator. In contrast to S_z, however, the eigenvalues of p_z (in appropriate units) can assume any real value between $- \infty$ and ∞.

The rigorous mathematics of a vector space spanned by eigenkets that exhibit a continuous spectrum is rather treacherous. The dimensionality of such a space is obviously infinite. Fortunately, many of the results we worked out for a finite-dimensional vector space with discrete eigenvalues can immediately be generalized. In places where straightforward generalizations do not hold, we indicate danger signals.

We start with the analogue of eigenvalue equation (1.2.5), which, in the continuous-spectrum case, is written as

$$\xi|\xi'\rangle = \xi'|\xi'\rangle, \tag{1.6.1}$$

where ξ is an operator and ξ' is simply a number. The ket $|\xi'\rangle$ is, in other words, an eigenket of operator ξ with eigenvalue ξ', just as $|a'\rangle$ is an eigenket of operator A with eigenvalue a'.

In pursuing this analogy we replace the Kronecker symbol by Dirac's δ-function—a discrete sum over the eigenvalues $\{a'\}$ by an integral over the *continuous variable* ξ' —so

$$\langle a'|a''\rangle = \delta_{a'a''} \rightarrow \langle \xi'|\xi''\rangle = \delta(\xi' - \xi''),\tag{1.6.2a}$$

$$\sum_{a'} |a'\rangle\langle a'| = 1 \rightarrow \int d\xi' |\xi'\rangle\langle \xi'| = 1,\tag{1.6.2b}$$

$$|\alpha\rangle = \sum_{a'} |a'\rangle\langle a'|\alpha\rangle \rightarrow |\alpha\rangle = \int d\xi' |\xi'\rangle\langle \xi'|\alpha\rangle,\tag{1.6.2c}$$

$$\sum_{a'} |\langle a'|\alpha\rangle|^2 = 1 \rightarrow \int d\xi' |\langle \xi'|\alpha\rangle|^2 = 1,\tag{1.6.2d}$$

$$\langle \beta|\alpha\rangle = \sum_{a'} \langle \beta|a'\rangle\langle a'|\alpha\rangle \rightarrow \langle \beta|\alpha\rangle = \int d\xi' \, \langle \beta|\xi'\rangle\langle \xi'|\alpha\rangle,\tag{1.6.2e}$$

$$\langle a''|A|a'\rangle = a'\delta_{a'a''} \rightarrow \langle \xi''|\xi|\xi'\rangle = \xi'\delta(\xi'' - \xi').\tag{1.6.2f}$$

Notice in particular how the completeness relation (1.6.2b) is used to obtain (1.6.2c) and (1.6.2e).

Position Eigenkets and Position Measurements

In Section 1.4 we emphasized that a measurement in quantum mechanics is essentially a filtering process. To extend this idea to measurements of observables exhibiting continuous spectra it is best to work with a specific example. To this end we consider the position (or coordinate) operator in one dimension.

The eigenkets $|x'\rangle$ of the position operator x satisfying

$$x|x'\rangle = x'|x'\rangle\tag{1.6.3}$$

are postulated to form a complete set. Here x' is just a number with the dimension of length 0.23 cm, for example, while x is an operator. The state ket for an arbitrary physical state can be expanded in terms of $\{|x'\rangle\}$:

$$|\alpha\rangle = \int_{-\infty}^{\infty} dx' |x'\rangle\langle x'|\alpha\rangle.\tag{1.6.4}$$

We now consider a highly idealized selective measurement of the position observable. Suppose we place a very tiny detector that clicks only when the particle is precisely at x' and nowhere else. Immediately after the detector clicks, we can say that the state in question is represented by $|x'\rangle$. In other words, when the detector clicks, $|\alpha\rangle$ abruptly "jumps into" $|x'\rangle$ in much the same way as an arbitrary spin state jumps into the $S_z +$ (or $S_z -$) state when subjected to an SG apparatus of the S_z type.

In practice the best the detector can do is to locate the particle within a narrow interval around x'. A realistic detector clicks when a particle is observed to be located within some narrow range $(x' - \Delta/2, x' + \Delta/2)$.

When a count is registered in such a detector, the state ket changes abruptly as follows:

$$|\alpha\rangle = \int_{-\infty}^{\infty} dx'' |x''\rangle\langle x''|\alpha\rangle \xrightarrow{\text{measurement}} \int_{x'-\Delta/2}^{x'+\Delta/2} dx'' |x''\rangle\langle x''|\alpha\rangle. \quad (1.6.5)$$

Assuming that $\langle x''|\alpha\rangle$ does not change appreciably within the narrow interval, the probability for the detector to click is given by

$$|\langle x'|\alpha\rangle|^2 dx', \quad (1.6.6)$$

where we have written dx' for Δ. This is analogous to $|\langle a'|\alpha\rangle|^2$ for the probability for $|\alpha\rangle$ to be thrown into $|a'\rangle$ when A is measured. The probability of recording the particle *somewhere* between $-\infty$ and ∞ is given by

$$\int_{-\infty}^{\infty} dx' |\langle x'|\alpha\rangle|^2, \quad (1.6.7)$$

which is normalized to unity if $|\alpha\rangle$ is normalized:

$$\langle\alpha|\alpha\rangle = 1 \Rightarrow \int_{-\infty}^{\infty} dx' \langle\alpha|x'\rangle\langle x'|\alpha\rangle = 1. \quad (1.6.8)$$

The reader familiar with wave mechanics may have recognized by this time that $\langle x'|\alpha\rangle$ is the wave function for the physical state represented by $|\alpha\rangle$. We will say more about this identification of the expansion coefficient with the x-representation of the wave function in Section 1.7.

The notion of a position eigenket can be extended to three dimensions. It is assumed in nonrelativistic quantum mechanics that the position eigenkets $|x'\rangle$ are complete. The state ket for a particle with internal degrees of freedom, such as spin, ignored can therefore be expanded in terms of $\{|x'\rangle\}$ as follows:

$$|\alpha\rangle = \int d^3x' |x'\rangle\langle x'|\alpha\rangle, \quad (1.6.9)$$

where x' stands for x', y', and z'; in other words, $|x'\rangle$ is a *simultaneous* eigenket of the observables x, y, and z in the sense of Section 1.4:

$$|x'\rangle \equiv |x', y', z'\rangle, \quad (1.6.10a)$$

$$x|x'\rangle = x'|x'\rangle, \qquad y|x'\rangle = y'|x'\rangle, \qquad z|x'\rangle = z'|x'\rangle. \quad (1.6.10b)$$

To be able to consider such a simultaneous eigenket at all, we are implicitly assuming that the three components of the position vector can be measured simultaneously to arbitrary degrees of accuracy; hence, we must have

$$[x_i, x_j] = 0, \quad (1.6.11)$$

where x_1, x_2, and x_3 stand for x, y, and z, respectively.

Translation

We now introduce the very important concept of translation, or spatial displacement. Suppose we start with a state that is well localized around $\mathbf{x}'$. Let us consider an operation that changes this state into another well-localized state, this time around $\mathbf{x}' + d\mathbf{x}'$ with everything else (for example, the spin direction) unchanged. Such an operation is defined to be an **infinitesimal translation** by $d\mathbf{x}'$, and the operator that does the job is denoted by $\mathscr{T}(d\mathbf{x}')$:

$$\mathscr{T}(d\mathbf{x}')|\mathbf{x}'\rangle = |\mathbf{x}' + d\mathbf{x}'\rangle, \tag{1.6.12}$$

where a possible arbitrary phase factor is set to unity by convention. Notice that the right-hand side of (1.6.12) is again a position eigenket, but this time with eigenvalue $\mathbf{x}' + d\mathbf{x}'$. Obviously $|\mathbf{x}'\rangle$ is *not* an eigenket of the infinitesimal translation operator.

By expanding an arbitrary state ket $|\alpha\rangle$ in terms of the position eigenkets we can examine the effect of infinitesimal translation on $|\alpha\rangle$:

$$|\alpha\rangle \rightarrow \mathscr{T}(d\mathbf{x}')|\alpha\rangle = \mathscr{T}(d\mathbf{x}')\int d^3x'|\mathbf{x}'\rangle\langle\mathbf{x}'|\alpha\rangle = \int d^3x'|\mathbf{x}' + d\mathbf{x}'\rangle\langle\mathbf{x}'|\alpha\rangle.$$

$$\tag{1.6.13}$$

We also write the right-hand side of (1.6.13) as

$$\int d^3x'|\mathbf{x}' + d\mathbf{x}'\rangle\langle\mathbf{x}'|\alpha\rangle = \int d^3x'|\mathbf{x}'\rangle\langle\mathbf{x}' - d\mathbf{x}'|\alpha\rangle \tag{1.6.14}$$

because the integration is over all space and $\mathbf{x}'$ is just an integration variable. This shows that the wave function of the translated state $\mathscr{T}(d\mathbf{x}')|\alpha\rangle$ is obtained by substituting $\mathbf{x}' - d\mathbf{x}'$ for $\mathbf{x}'$ in $\langle\mathbf{x}'|\alpha\rangle$.

There is an equivalent approach to translation that is often treated in the literature. Instead of considering an infinitesimal translation of the physical system itself, we consider a change in the coordinate system being used such that the origin is shifted in the *opposite* direction, $-d\mathbf{x}'$. Physically, in this alternative approach we are asking how the *same* state ket would look to another observer whose coordinate system is shifted by $-d\mathbf{x}'$. In this book we try not to use this approach. Obviously it is important that we do not mix the two approaches!

We now list the properties of the infinitesimal translation operator $\mathscr{T}(d\mathbf{x}')$. The first property we demand is the unitarity property imposed by probability conservation. It is reasonable to require that if the ket $|\alpha\rangle$ is normalized to unity, the translated ket $\mathscr{T}(d\mathbf{x}')|\alpha\rangle$ also be normalized to unity, so

$$\langle\alpha|\alpha\rangle = \langle\alpha|\mathscr{T}^\dagger(d\mathbf{x}')\mathscr{T}(d\mathbf{x}')|\alpha\rangle. \tag{1.6.15}$$

This condition is guaranteed by demanding that the infinitesimal translation be unitary:

$$\mathcal{T}^{\dagger}(d\mathbf{x}')\mathcal{T}(d\mathbf{x}')=1. \qquad (1.6.16)$$

Quite generally, the norm of a ket is preserved under unitary transformations. For the second property, suppose we consider two successive infinitesimal translations—first by $d\mathbf{x}'$ and subsequently by $d\mathbf{x}''$, where $d\mathbf{x}'$ and $d\mathbf{x}''$ need not be in the same direction. We expect the net result to be just a *single* translation operation by the vector sum $d\mathbf{x}'+d\mathbf{x}''$, so we demand that

$$\mathcal{T}(d\mathbf{x}'')\mathcal{T}(d\mathbf{x}') = \mathcal{T}(d\mathbf{x}'+d\mathbf{x}''). \qquad (1.6.17)$$

For the third property, suppose we consider a translation in the opposite direction; we expect the opposite-direction translation to be the same as the inverse of the original translation:

$$\mathcal{T}(-d\mathbf{x}') = \mathcal{T}^{-1}(d\mathbf{x}'). \qquad (1.6.18)$$

For the fourth property, we demand that as $d\mathbf{x}' \to 0$, the translation operation reduce to the identity operation

$$\lim_{d\mathbf{x}' \to 0} \mathcal{T}(d\mathbf{x}') = 1 \qquad (1.6.19)$$

and that the difference between $\mathcal{T}(d\mathbf{x}')$ and the identity operator be of first order in $d\mathbf{x}'$.

We now demonstrate that if we take the infinitesimal translation operator to be

$$\mathcal{T}(d\mathbf{x}') = 1 - i\mathbf{K}\cdot d\mathbf{x}' \qquad (1.6.20)$$

where the components of $\mathbf{K}$, K_x, K_y, and K_z, are **Hermitian operators**, then all the properties listed are satisfied. The first property, the unitarity of $\mathcal{T}(d\mathbf{x}')$, is checked as follows:

$$\mathcal{T}^{\dagger}(d\mathbf{x}')\mathcal{T}(d\mathbf{x}') = (1 + i\mathbf{K}^{\dagger}\cdot d\mathbf{x}')(1 - i\mathbf{K}\cdot d\mathbf{x}')$$
$$= 1 - i(\mathbf{K}-\mathbf{K}^{\dagger})\cdot d\mathbf{x}' + 0\left[(d\mathbf{x}')^2\right]$$
$$\simeq 1, \qquad (1.6.21)$$

where terms of second order in $d\mathbf{x}'$ have been ignored for an infinitesimal translation. The second property [(1.6.17)] can also be proved as follows:

$$\mathcal{T}(d\mathbf{x}'')\mathcal{T}(d\mathbf{x}') = (1 - i\mathbf{K}\cdot d\mathbf{x}'')(1 - i\mathbf{K}\cdot d\mathbf{x}')$$
$$\simeq 1 - i\mathbf{K}\cdot(d\mathbf{x}'+d\mathbf{x}'')$$
$$= \mathcal{T}(d\mathbf{x}'+d\mathbf{x}''). \qquad (1.6.22)$$

The third and fourth properties are obviously satisfied by (1.6.20).

Accepting (1.6.20) to be the correct form for $\mathcal{T}(d\mathbf{x}')$, we are in a position to derive an extremely fundamental relation between the $\mathbf{K}$ operator and the **x** operator. First, note that

$$\mathbf{x}\mathscr{T}(d\mathbf{x}')|\mathbf{x}'\rangle = \mathbf{x}|\mathbf{x}' + d\mathbf{x}'\rangle = (\mathbf{x}' + d\mathbf{x}')|\mathbf{x}' + d\mathbf{x}'\rangle \quad (1.6.23a)$$

and

$$\mathscr{T}(d\mathbf{x}')\mathbf{x}|\mathbf{x}'\rangle = \mathbf{x}'\mathscr{T}(d\mathbf{x}')|\mathbf{x}'\rangle = \mathbf{x}'|\mathbf{x}' + d\mathbf{x}'\rangle; \quad (1.6.23b)$$

hence,

$$[\mathbf{x}, \mathscr{T}(d\mathbf{x}')]|\mathbf{x}'\rangle = d\mathbf{x}'|\mathbf{x}' + d\mathbf{x}'\rangle \simeq d\mathbf{x}'|\mathbf{x}'\rangle, \quad (1.6.24)$$

where the error made in writing the last line of (1.6.24) is of second order in $d\mathbf{x}'$. Now $|\mathbf{x}'\rangle$ can be *any* position eigenket, and the position eigenkets are known to form a complete set. We must therefore have an **operator identity**

$$[\mathbf{x}, \mathscr{T}(d\mathbf{x}')] = d\mathbf{x}', \quad (1.6.25)$$

or

$$-i\mathbf{x}\mathbf{K}\cdot d\mathbf{x}' + i\mathbf{K}\cdot d\mathbf{x}'\mathbf{x} = d\mathbf{x}', \quad (1.6.26)$$

where on the right-hand sides of (1.6.25) and (1.6.26) $d\mathbf{x}'$ is understood to be the number $d\mathbf{x}'$ multiplied by the identity operator in the ket space spanned by $|\mathbf{x}'\rangle$. By choosing $d\mathbf{x}'$ in the direction of $\hat{\mathbf{x}}_j$ and forming the scalar product with $\hat{\mathbf{x}}_i$, we obtain

$$[x_i, K_j] = i\delta_{ij}, \quad (1.6.27)$$

where again δ_{ij} is understood to be multiplied by the identity operator.

Momentum as a Generator of Translation

Equation (1.6.27) is the fundamental commutation relation between the position operators x, y, z and the K operators K_x, K_y, K_z. Remember that so far the K operator is *defined* in terms of the infinitesimal translation operator by (1.6.20). What is the physical significance we can attach to **K**?

J. Schwinger, lecturing on quantum mechanics, once remarked, "... for fundamental properties we will borrow only names from classical physics." In the present case we would like to borrow from classical mechanics the notion that momentum is the generator of an infinitesimal translation. An infinitesimal translation in classical mechanics can be regarded as a canonical transformation,

$$\mathbf{x}_{\text{new}} \equiv \mathbf{X} = \mathbf{x} + d\mathbf{x}, \qquad \mathbf{p}_{\text{new}} \equiv \mathbf{P} = \mathbf{p}, \quad (1.6.28)$$

obtainable from the generating function (Goldstein 1980, 395 and 411)

$$F(\mathbf{x}, \mathbf{P}) = \mathbf{x}\cdot\mathbf{P} + \mathbf{p}\cdot d\mathbf{x}, \quad (1.6.29)$$

where **p** and **P** refer to the corresponding momenta.

This equation has a striking similarity to the infinitesimal translation operator (1.6.20) in quantum mechanics, particularly if we recall that $\mathbf{x}\cdot\mathbf{P}$ in

(1.6.29) is the generating function for the identity transformation ($\mathbf{X} = \mathbf{x}, \mathbf{P} = \mathbf{p}$). We are therefore led to speculate that the operator $\mathbf{K}$ is in some sense related to the momentum operator in quantum mechanics.

Can the K operator be identified with the momentum operator itself? Unfortunately the dimension is all wrong; the K operator has the dimension of $1/\text{length}$ because $\mathbf{K} \cdot d\mathbf{x}'$ must be dimensionless. But it appears legitimate to set

$$\mathbf{K} = \frac{\mathbf{p}}{\text{universal constant with the dimension of action}} . \qquad (1.6.30)$$

From the fundamental postulates of quantum mechanics there is no way to determine the actual numerical value of the universal constant. Rather, this constant is needed here because, historically, classical physics was developed before quantum mechanics using units convenient for describing macroscopic quantities—the circumference of the earth, the mass of 1 cc of water, the duration of a mean solar day, and so forth. Had microscopic physics been formulated before macroscopic physics, the physicists would have almost certainly chosen the basic units in such a way that the universal constant appearing in (1.6.30) would be unity.

An analogy from electrostatics may be helpful here. The interaction energy between two particles of charge e separated at a distance r is proportional to e^2/r; in unrationalized Gaussian units, the proportionality factor is just 1, but in rationalized mks units, which may be more convenient for electrical engineers, the proportionality factor is $1/4\pi\varepsilon_o$.

The universal constant that appears in (1.6.30) turns out to be the same as the constant $\hbar$ that appears in L. de Broglie's relation, written in 1924,

$$\frac{2\pi}{\lambda} = \frac{p}{\hbar}, \qquad (1.6.31)$$

where λ is the wavelength of a "particle wave." In other words, the K operator is the quantum mechanical operator that corresponds to the wave number—that is, 2π times the reciprocal wavelength, usually denoted by k. With this identification the infinitesimal translation operator $\mathscr{T}(d\mathbf{x}')$ reads

$$\mathscr{T}(d\mathbf{x}') = 1 - i\mathbf{p} \cdot d\mathbf{x}'/\hbar, \qquad (1.6.32)$$

where $\mathbf{p}$ is the momentum operator. The commutation relation (1.6.27) now becomes

$$[x_i, p_j] = i\hbar\delta_{ij}. \qquad (1.6.33)$$

The commutation relations (1.6.33) imply, for example, that x and p_x (but not x and p_y) are incompatible observables. It is therefore impossible to find simultaneous eigenkets of x and p_x. The general formalism of

Section 1.4 can be applied here to obtain the **position-momentum uncertainty relation** of W. Heisenberg:

$$\langle (\Delta x)^2 \rangle \langle (\Delta p_x)^2 \rangle \geq \hbar^2/4. \qquad (1.6.34)$$

Some applications of (1.6.34) will appear in Section 1.7.

So far we have concerned ourselves with infinitesimal translations. A finite translation—that is, a spatial displacement by a finite amount—can be obtained by successively compounding infinitesimal translations. Let us consider a finite translation in the x-direction by an amount $\Delta x'$:

$$\mathcal{T}(\Delta x' \hat{\mathbf{x}})|x'\rangle = |x' + \Delta x' \hat{\mathbf{x}}\rangle. \qquad (1.6.35)$$

By compounding N infinitesimal translations, each of which is characterized by a spatial displacement $\Delta x'/N$ in the x-direction, and letting $N \to \infty$, we obtain

$$\mathcal{T}(\Delta x' \hat{\mathbf{x}}) = \lim_{N \to \infty} \left(1 - \frac{ip_x \Delta x'}{N\hbar} \right)^N$$

$$= \exp\left(- \frac{ip_x \Delta x'}{\hbar} \right). \qquad (1.6.36)$$

Here $\exp(-ip_x \Delta x'/\hbar)$ is understood to be a function of the *operator* p_x; generally, for any operator X we have

$$\exp(X) \equiv 1 + X + \frac{X^2}{2!} + \cdots. \qquad (1.6.37)$$

A fundamental property of translations is that successive translations in different directions, say in the x- and y-directions, commute. We see this clearly in Figure 1.8; in shifting from A and B it does not matter whether we go via C or via D. Mathematically,

$$\mathcal{T}(\Delta y' \hat{\mathbf{y}})\mathcal{T}(\Delta x' \hat{\mathbf{x}}) = \mathcal{T}(\Delta x' \hat{\mathbf{x}} + \Delta y' \hat{\mathbf{y}}),$$
$$\mathcal{T}(\Delta x' \hat{\mathbf{x}})\mathcal{T}(\Delta y' \hat{\mathbf{y}}) = \mathcal{T}(\Delta x' \hat{\mathbf{x}} + \Delta y' \hat{\mathbf{y}}). \qquad (1.6.38)$$

FIGURE 1.8. Successive translations in different directions.

This point is not so trivial as it may appear; we will show in Chapter 3 that rotations about different axes do *not* commute. Treating $\Delta x'$ and $\Delta y'$ up to second order, we obtain

$$[\mathcal{T}(\Delta y'\hat{y}), \mathcal{T}(\Delta x'\hat{x})] = \left[\left(1 - \frac{ip_y\Delta y'}{\hbar} - \frac{p_y^2(\Delta y')^2}{2\hbar^2} + \cdots\right),\right.$$
$$\left.\left(1 - \frac{ip_x\Delta x'}{\hbar} - \frac{p_x^2(\Delta x')^2}{2\hbar^2} + \cdots\right)\right]$$

$$\approx -\frac{(\Delta x')(\Delta y')[p_y, p_x]}{\hbar^2}. \tag{1.6.39}$$

Because $\Delta x'$ and $\Delta y'$ are arbitrary, requirement (1.6.38), or

$$[\mathcal{T}(\Delta y'\hat{y}), \mathcal{T}(\Delta x'\hat{x})] = 0, \tag{1.6.40}$$

immediately leads to

$$[p_x, p_y] = 0, \tag{1.6.41}$$

or, more generally,

$$[p_i, p_j] = 0. \tag{1.6.42}$$

This commutation relation is a direct consequence of the fact that translations in different directions commute. Whenever the generators of transformations commute, the corresponding group is said to be **Abelian**. The translation group in three dimensions is Abelian.

Equation (1.6.42) implies that p_x, p_y, and p_z are mutually compatible observables. We can therefore conceive of a simultaneous eigenket of p_x, p_y, p_z, namely,

$$|\mathbf{p}'\rangle \equiv |p_x', p_y', p_z'\rangle, \tag{1.6.43a}$$

$$p_x|\mathbf{p}'\rangle = p_x'|\mathbf{p}'\rangle, \, p_y|\mathbf{p}'\rangle = p_y'|\mathbf{p}'\rangle, \, p_z|\mathbf{p}'\rangle = p_z'|\mathbf{p}'\rangle. \tag{1.6.43b}$$

It is instructive to work out the effect of $\mathcal{T}(d\mathbf{x}')$ on such a momentum eigenket:

$$\mathcal{T}(d\mathbf{x}')|\mathbf{p}'\rangle = \left(1 - \frac{i\mathbf{p}\cdot d\mathbf{x}'}{\hbar}\right)|\mathbf{p}'\rangle = \left(1 - \frac{i\mathbf{p}'\cdot d\mathbf{x}'}{\hbar}\right)|\mathbf{p}'\rangle. \tag{1.6.44}$$

We see that the momentum eigenket remains the same even though it suffers a slight phase change, so unlike $|\mathbf{x}'\rangle$, $|\mathbf{p}'\rangle$ *is* an eigenket of $\mathcal{T}(d\mathbf{x}')$, which we anticipated because

$$[\mathbf{p}, \mathcal{T}(d\mathbf{x}')] = 0. \tag{1.6.45}$$

Notice, however, that the eigenvalue of $\mathcal{T}(d\mathbf{x}')$ is complex; we do not expect a real eigenvalue here because $\mathcal{T}(d\mathbf{x}')$, though unitary, is not Hermitian.

The Canonical Commutation Relations

We summarize the commutator relations we inferred by studying the properties of translation:

$$[x_i, x_j] = 0, \qquad [p_i, p_j] = 0, \qquad [x_i, p_j] = i\hbar\delta_{ij}. \qquad (1.6.46)$$

These relations form the cornerstone of quantum mechanics; in his book, P. A. M. Dirac calls them the "fundamental quantum conditions." More often they are known as the **canonical commutation relations**, or the **fundamental commutation relations**.

Historically it was W. Heisenberg who, in 1925, showed that the combination rule for atomic transition lines known at that time could best be understood if one associated arrays of numbers obeying certain multiplication rules with these frequencies. Immediately afterward M. Born and P. Jordan pointed out that Heisenberg's multiplication rules are essentially those of matrix algebra, and a theory was developed based on the matrix analogues of (1.6.46), which is now known as **matrix mechanics.***

Also in 1925, P. A. M. Dirac observed that the various quantum-mechanical relations can be obtained from the corresponding classical relations just by replacing classical Poisson brackets by commutators, as follows:

$$[\ ,\ ]_{\text{classical}} \rightarrow \frac{[\ ,\ ]}{i\hbar}, \qquad (1.6.47)$$

where we may recall that the classical Poisson brackets are defined for functions of q's and p's as

$$[A(q, p), B(q, p)]_{\text{classical}} \equiv \sum_s \left(\frac{\partial A}{\partial q_s} \frac{\partial B}{\partial p_s} - \frac{\partial A}{\partial p_s} \frac{\partial B}{\partial q_s} \right). \qquad (1.6.48)$$

For example, in classical mechanics, we have

$$[x_i, p_j]_{\text{classical}} = \delta_{ij}, \qquad (1.6.49)$$

which in quantum mechanics turns into (1.6.33).

Dirac's rule (1.6.47) is plausible because the classical Poisson brackets and quantum-mechanical commutators satisfy similar algebraic properties. In particular, the following relations can be proved regardless of whether [,] is understood as a classical Poisson bracket or as a quantum-

---

*Appropriately, $pq - qp = h/2\pi i$ is inscribed on the gravestone of M. Born in Göttingen.

mechanical commutator:

$$[A, A] = 0 \tag{1.6.50a}$$

$$[A, B] = -[B, A] \tag{1.6.50b}$$

$$[A, c] = 0 \quad (c \text{ is just a number}) \tag{1.6.50c}$$

$$[A + B, C] = [A, C] + [B, C] \tag{1.6.50d}$$

$$[A, BC] = [A, B]C + B[A, C] \tag{1.6.50e}$$

$$[A, [B, C]] + [B, [C, A]] + [C, [A, B]] = 0, \tag{1.6.50f}$$

where the last relation is known as the **Jacobi identity**.* However, there are important differences. First, the dimension of the classical Poisson bracket differs from that of the quantum-mechanical commutator because of the differentiations with respect to q and p appearing in (1.6.48). Second, the Poisson bracket of real functions of q's and p's is purely real, while the commutator of two Hermitian operators is anti-Hermitian (see Lemma 3 of Section 1.4). To take care of these differences the factor $i\hbar$ is inserted in (1.6.47).

We have deliberately avoided exploiting Dirac's analogy in obtaining the canonical commutation relations. Our approach to the commutation relations is based solely on (1) the properties of translations and (2) the identification of the generator of translation with the momentum operator modulo a universal constant with the dimension of action. We believe that this approach is more powerful because it can be generalized to situations where observables have no classical analogues. For example, the spin-angular-momentum components we encountered in Section 1.4 having nothing to do with the p's and q's of classical mechanics; yet, as we will show in Chapter 3, the spin-angular-momentum commutation relations can be derived using the properties of rotations just as we derived the canonical commutation relations using the properties of translations.

1.7. WAVE FUNCTIONS IN POSITION AND MOMENTUM SPACE

Position-Space Wave Function

In this section we present a systematic study of the properties of wave functions in both position and momentum space. For simplicity let us return to the one-dimensional case. The base kets used are the position kets

---

*It is amusing that the Jacobi identity in quantum mechanics is much easier to prove than its classical analogue.

satisfying

$$x|x'\rangle = x'|x'\rangle,\tag{1.7.1}$$

normalized in such a way that the orthogonality condition reads

$$\langle x''|x'\rangle = \delta(x'' - x').\tag{1.7.2}$$

We have already remarked that the ket representing a physical state can be expanded in terms of $|x'\rangle$,

$$|\alpha\rangle = \int dx'\,|x'\rangle\langle x'|\alpha\rangle,\tag{1.7.3}$$

and that the expansion coefficient $\langle x'|\alpha\rangle$ is interpreted in such a way that

$$|\langle x'|\alpha\rangle|^2\,dx'\tag{1.7.4}$$

is the probability for the particle to be found in a narrow interval dx' around x'. In our formalism the inner product $\langle x'|\alpha\rangle$ is what is usually referred to as the **wave function** $\psi_\alpha(x')$ for state $|\alpha\rangle$:

$$\langle x'|\alpha\rangle = \psi_\alpha(x').\tag{1.7.5}$$

In elementary wave mechanics the probabilistic interpretations for the expansion coefficient $c_{a'}$ ($=\langle a'|\alpha\rangle$) and for the wave function $\psi_\alpha(x')$ ($=\langle x'|\alpha\rangle$) are often presented as separate postulates. One of the major advantages of our formalism, originally due to Dirac, is that the two kinds of probabilistic interpretations are unified; $\psi_\alpha(x')$ *is* an expansion coefficient [see (1.7.3)] in much the same way as $c_{a'}$ is. By following the footsteps of Dirac we come to appreciate the unity of quantum mechanics.

Consider the inner product $\langle\beta|\alpha\rangle$. Using the completeness of $|x'\rangle$, we have

$$\langle\beta|\alpha\rangle = \int dx'\,\langle\beta|x'\rangle\langle x'|\alpha\rangle$$

$$= \int dx'\,\psi_\beta^*(x')\psi_\alpha(x'),\tag{1.7.6}$$

so $\langle\beta|\alpha\rangle$ characterizes the overlap between the two wave functions. Note that we are not defining $\langle\beta|\alpha\rangle$ as the overlap integral; the identification of $\langle\beta|\alpha\rangle$ with the overlap integral *follows* from our completeness postulate for $|x'\rangle$. The more general interpretation of $\langle\beta|\alpha\rangle$, *independent of representations*, is that it represents the probability amplitude for state $|\alpha\rangle$ to be found in state $|\beta\rangle$.

This time let us interpret the expansion

$$|\alpha\rangle = \sum_{a'} |a'\rangle\langle a'|\alpha\rangle\tag{1.7.7}$$

using the language of wave functions. We just multiply both sides of (1.7.7) by the position eigenbra $\langle x'|$ on the left. Thus

$$\langle x'|\alpha\rangle = \sum_{a'} \langle x'|a'\rangle\langle a'|\alpha\rangle. \qquad (1.7.8)$$

In the usual notation of wave mechanics this is recognized as

$$\psi_\alpha(x') = \sum_{a'} c_{a'} u_{a'}(x'),$$

where we have introduced an **eigenfunction** of operator A with eigenvalue a':

$$u_{a'}(x') = \langle x'|a'\rangle. \qquad (1.7.9)$$

Let us now examine how $\langle\beta|A|\alpha\rangle$ can be written using the wave functions for $|\alpha\rangle$ and $|\beta\rangle$. Clearly, we have

$$\langle\beta|A|\alpha\rangle = \int dx' \int dx'' \langle\beta|x'\rangle\langle x'|A|x''\rangle\langle x''|\alpha\rangle$$

$$= \int dx' \int dx'' \psi_\beta^*(x')\langle x'|A|x''\rangle\psi_\alpha(x''). \qquad (1.7.10)$$

So to be able to evaluate $\langle\beta|A|\alpha\rangle$, we must know the matrix element $\langle x'|A|x''\rangle$, which is, in general, a function of the two variables x' and x''.

An enormous simplification takes place if observable A is a function of the position operator x. In particular, consider

$$A = x^2, \qquad (1.7.11)$$

which actually appears in the Hamiltonian for the simple harmonic oscillator problem to be discussed in Chapter 2. We have

$$\langle x'|x^2|x''\rangle = (\langle x'|)\cdot(x''^2|x''\rangle) = x'^2\delta(x' - x''), \qquad (1.7.12)$$

where we have used (1.7.1) and (1.7.2). The double integral (1.7.10) is now reduced to a *single* integral:

$$\langle\beta|x^2|\alpha\rangle = \int dx' \langle\beta|x'\rangle x'^2\langle x'|\alpha\rangle$$

$$= \int dx' \psi_\beta^*(x')x'^2\psi_\alpha(x'). \qquad (1.7.13)$$

In general,

$$\langle\beta|f(x)|\alpha\rangle = \int dx' \psi_\beta^*(x')f(x')\psi_\alpha(x'). \qquad (1.7.14)$$

Note that the $f(x)$ on the left-hand side of (1.7.14) is an operator, while the $f(x')$ on the right-hand side is not an operator.

Momentum Operator in the Position Basis

We now examine how the momentum operator may look in the x-basis—that is, in the representation where the position eigenkets are used as base kets. Our starting point is the definition of momentum as the generator of infinitesimal translations:

$$\left(1 - \frac{ip\Delta x'}{\hbar}\right)|\alpha\rangle = \int dx' \, \mathcal{T}(\Delta x')|x'\rangle\langle x'|\alpha\rangle$$

$$= \int dx' \, |x' + \Delta x'\rangle\langle x'|\alpha\rangle$$

$$= \int dx' \, |x'\rangle\langle x' - \Delta x'|\alpha\rangle$$

$$= \int dx' \, |x'\rangle\left(\langle x'|\alpha\rangle - \Delta x' \frac{\partial}{\partial x'}\langle x'|\alpha\rangle\right). \quad (1.7.15)$$

Comparison of both sides yields

$$p|\alpha\rangle = \int dx' \, |x'\rangle\left(-i\hbar \frac{\partial}{\partial x'}\langle x'|\alpha\rangle\right) \quad (1.7.16)$$

or

$$\langle x'|p|\alpha\rangle = -i\hbar \frac{\partial}{\partial x'}\langle x'|\alpha\rangle, \quad (1.7.17)$$

where we have used the orthogonality property (1.7.2). For the matrix element p in the x-representation, we obtain

$$\langle x'|p|x''\rangle = -i\hbar \frac{\partial}{\partial x'}\delta(x' - x''). \quad (1.7.18)$$

From (1.7.16) we get a very important identity:

$$\langle \beta|p|\alpha\rangle = \int dx' \, \langle \beta|x'\rangle\left(-i\hbar \frac{\partial}{\partial x'}\langle x'|\alpha\rangle\right)$$

$$= \int dx' \, \psi_\beta^*(x')\left(-i\hbar \frac{\partial}{\partial x'}\right)\psi_\alpha(x'). \quad (1.7.19)$$

In our formalism (1.7.19) is not a postulate; rather, it has been *derived* using the basic properties of momentum. By repeatedly applying (1.7.17), we can also obtain

$$\langle x'|p^n|\alpha\rangle = (-i\hbar)^n \frac{\partial^n}{\partial x'^n}\langle x'|\alpha\rangle, \quad (1.7.20)$$

$$\langle \beta|p^n|\alpha\rangle = \int dx' \, \psi_\beta^*(x')(-i\hbar)^n \frac{\partial^n}{\partial x'^n}\psi_\alpha(x'). \quad (1.7.21)$$

Momentum-Space Wave Function

So far we have worked exclusively in the x-basis. There is actually a complete symmetry between x and p—apart from occasional minus signs—which we can infer from the canonical commutation relations. Let us now work in the p-basis, that is, in the momentum representation.

For simplicity we continue working in one-space. The base eigenkets in the p-basis specify

$$p|p'\rangle = p'|p'\rangle \tag{1.7.22}$$

and

$$\langle p'|p''\rangle = \delta(p' - p''). \tag{1.7.23}$$

The momentum eigenkets $\{|p'\rangle\}$ span the ket space in much the same way as the position eigenkets $\{|x'\rangle\}$. An arbitrary state ket $|\alpha\rangle$ can therefore be expanded as follows:

$$|\alpha\rangle = \int dp' |p'\rangle\langle p'|\alpha\rangle. \tag{1.7.24}$$

We can give a probabilistic interpretation for the expansion coefficient $\langle p'|\alpha\rangle$; the probability that a measurement of p gives eigenvalue p' within a narrow interval dp' is $|\langle p'|\alpha\rangle|^2 dp'$. It is customary to call $\langle p'|\alpha\rangle$ the **momentum-space wave function**; the notation $\phi_\alpha(p')$ is often used:

$$\langle p'|\alpha\rangle = \phi_\alpha(p'). \tag{1.7.25}$$

If $|\alpha\rangle$ is normalized, we obtain

$$\int dp' \langle\alpha|p'\rangle\langle p'|\alpha\rangle = \int dp' |\phi_\alpha(p')|^2 = 1. \tag{1.7.26}$$

Let us now establish the connection between the x-representation and the p-representation. We recall that in the case of the discrete spectra, the change of basis from the old set $\{|a'\rangle\}$ to the new set $\{|b'\rangle\}$ is characterized by the transformation matrix (1.5.7). Likewise, we expect that the desired information is contained in $\langle x'|p'\rangle$, which is a function of x' and p', usually called the **transformation function** from the x-representation to the p-representation. To derive the explicit form of $\langle x'|p'\rangle$, first recall (1.7.17); letting $|\alpha\rangle$ be the momentum eigenket $|p'\rangle$, we obtain

$$\langle x'|p|p'\rangle = -i\hbar \frac{\partial}{\partial x'}\langle x'|p'\rangle \tag{1.7.27}$$

or

$$p'\langle x'|p'\rangle = -i\hbar \frac{\partial}{\partial x'}\langle x'|p'\rangle. \tag{1.7.28}$$

The solution to this differential equation for $\langle x'|p'\rangle$ is

$$\langle x'|p'\rangle = N\exp\left(\frac{ip'x'}{\hbar}\right),\qquad(1.7.29)$$

where N is the normalization constant to be determined in a moment. Even though the transformation function $\langle x'|p'\rangle$ is a function of two variables, x' and p', we can temporarily regard it as a function of x' with p' fixed. It can then be viewed as the probability amplitude for the momentum eigenstate specified by p' to be found at position x'; in other words, it is just the wave function for the momentum eigenstate $|p'\rangle$, often referred to as the momentum eigenfunction (still in the x-space). So (1.7.29) simply says that the wave function of a momentum eigenstate is a plane wave. It is amusing that we have obtained this plane-wave solution without solving the Schrödinger equation (which we have not yet written down).

To get the normalization constant N let us first consider

$$\langle x'|x''\rangle = \int dp'\,\langle x'|p'\rangle\langle p'|x''\rangle.\qquad(1.7.30)$$

The left-hand side is just $\delta(x'-x'')$; the right-hand side can be evaluated using the explicit form of $\langle x'|p'\rangle$:

$$\delta(x'-x'') = |N|^2\int dp'\exp\left[\frac{ip'(x'-x'')}{\hbar}\right]$$

$$= 2\pi\hbar|N|^2\delta(x'-x'').\qquad(1.7.31)$$

Choosing N to be purely real and positive by convention, we finally have

$$\langle x'|p'\rangle = \frac{1}{\sqrt{2\pi\hbar}}\exp\left(\frac{ip'x'}{\hbar}\right).\qquad(1.7.32)$$

We can now demonstrate how the position-space wave function is related to the momentum-space wave function. All we have to do is rewrite

$$\langle x'|\alpha\rangle = \int dp'\langle x'|p'\rangle\langle p'|\alpha\rangle\qquad(1.7.33a)$$

and

$$\langle p'|\alpha\rangle = \int dx'\langle p'|x'\rangle\langle x'|\alpha\rangle\qquad(1.7.33b)$$

as

$$\psi_\alpha(x') = \left[\frac{1}{\sqrt{2\pi\hbar}}\right]\int dp'\exp\left(\frac{ip'x'}{\hbar}\right)\phi_\alpha(p')\qquad(1.7.34a)$$

and

$$\phi_\alpha(p') = \left[\frac{1}{\sqrt{2\pi\hbar}}\right]\int dx'\exp\left(\frac{-ip'x'}{\hbar}\right)\psi_\alpha(x').\qquad(1.7.34b)$$

This pair of equations is just what one expects from Fourier's inversion theorem. Apparently the mathematics we have developed somehow "knows" Fourier's work on integral transforms.

Gaussian Wave Packets

It is instructive to look at a physical example to illustrate our basic formalism. We consider what is known as a **Gaussian wave packet**, whose x-space wave function is given by

$$\langle x'|\alpha\rangle = \left[\frac{1}{\pi^{1/4}\sqrt{d}}\right]\exp\left[ikx' - \frac{x'^2}{2d^2}\right]. \tag{1.7.35}$$

This is a plane wave with wave number k modulated by a Gaussian profile centered on the origin. The probability of observing the particle vanishes very rapidly for $|x'| > d$; more quantitatively, the probability density $|\langle x'|\alpha\rangle|^2$ has a Gaussian shape with width d.

We now compute the expectation values of x, x^2, p, and p^2. The expectation value of x is clearly zero by symmetry:

$$\langle x\rangle = \int_{-\infty}^{\infty} dx'\langle\alpha|x'\rangle x'\langle x'|\alpha\rangle = \int_{-\infty}^{\infty} dx'|\langle x'|\alpha\rangle|^2 x' = 0. \tag{1.7.36}$$

For x^2 we obtain

$$\begin{aligned}
\langle x^2\rangle &= \int_{-\infty}^{\infty} dx'\, x'^2|\langle x'|\alpha\rangle|^2 \\
&= \left(\frac{1}{\sqrt{\pi}\,d}\right)\int_{-\infty}^{\infty} dx'\, x'^2\exp\left[\frac{-x'^2}{d^2}\right] \\
&= \frac{d^2}{2},
\end{aligned} \tag{1.7.37}$$

which leads to

$$\langle(\Delta x)^2\rangle = \langle x^2\rangle - \langle x\rangle^2 = \frac{d^2}{2} \tag{1.7.38}$$

for the dispersion of the position operator. The expectation values of p and p^2 can also be computed as follows:

$$\langle p\rangle = \hbar k \tag{1.7.39a}$$

$$\langle p^2\rangle = \frac{\hbar^2}{2d^2} + \hbar^2 k^2, \tag{1.7.39b}$$

which is left as an exercise. The momentum dispersion is therefore given by

$$\langle(\Delta p)^2\rangle = \langle p^2\rangle - \langle p\rangle^2 = \frac{\hbar^2}{2d^2}. \tag{1.7.40}$$

Armed with (1.7.38) and (1.7.40), we can check the Heisenberg uncertainty
relation (1.6.34); in this case the uncertainty product is given by

$$\langle(\Delta x)^2\rangle\langle(\Delta p)^2\rangle = \frac{\hbar^2}{4}, \tag{1.7.41}$$

independent of d, so for a Gaussian wave packet we actually have an
equality relation rather than the more general inequality relation (1.6.34).
For this reason a Gaussian wave packet is often called a *minimum uncertainty wave packet.*

We now go to momentum space. By a straightforward
integration—just completing the square in the exponent—we obtain

$$\langle p'|\alpha\rangle = \left(\frac{1}{\sqrt{2\pi\hbar}}\right)\left(\frac{1}{\pi^{1/4}\sqrt{d}}\right)\int_{-\infty}^{\infty} dx' \exp\left(\frac{-ip'x'}{\hbar} + ikx' - \frac{x'^2}{2d^2}\right)$$

$$= \sqrt{\frac{d}{\hbar\sqrt{\pi}}} \exp\left[\frac{-(p'-\hbar k)^2 d^2}{2\hbar^2}\right]. \tag{1.7.42}$$

This momentum-space wave function provides an alternative method for
obtaining $\langle p\rangle$ and $\langle p^2\rangle$, which is also left as an exercise.

The probability of finding the particle with momentum p' is
Gaussian (in momentum space) centered on $\hbar k$, just as the probability of
finding the particle at x' is Gaussian (in position space) centered on zero.
Furthermore, the widths of the two Gaussians are inversely proportional to
each other, which is just another way of expressing the constancy of the
uncertainty product $\langle(\Delta x)^2\rangle\langle\Delta p)^2\rangle$ explicitly computed in (1.7.41). The
wider the spread in the p-space, the narrower the spread in the x-space, and
vice versa.

As an extreme example, suppose we let $d \to \infty$. The position-space
wave function (1.7.35) then becomes a plane wave extending over all space;
the probability of finding the particle is just constant, independent of x'. In
contrast, the momentum-space wave function is δ-function-like and is
sharply peaked at $\hbar k$. In the opposite extreme, by letting $d \to 0$, we obtain a
position-space wave function localized like the δ-function, but the momentum-space wave function (1.7.42) is just constant, independent of p'.

We have seen that an extremely well localized (in the x-space) state is
to be regarded as a superposition of momentum eigenstates with all possible
values of momenta. Even those momentum eigenstates whose momenta are
comparable to or exceed mc must be included in the superposition. However, at such high values of momentum, a description based on nonrelativistic quantum mechanics is bound to break down.* Despite this limitation

---

*It turns out that the concept of a localized state in relativistic quantum mechanics is far
more intricate because of the possibility of "negative energy states," or pair creation (Sakurai
1967, 118–19).

our formalism, based on the existence of the position eigenket $|x'\rangle$, has a wide domain of applicability.

Generalization to Three Dimensions

So far in this section we have worked exclusively in one-space for simplicity, but everything we have done can be generalized to three-space, if the necessary changes are made. The base kets to be used can be taken as either the position eigenkets satisfying

$$\mathbf{x}|\mathbf{x}'\rangle = \mathbf{x}'|\mathbf{x}'\rangle \tag{1.7.43}$$

or the momentum eigenkets satisfying

$$\mathbf{p}|\mathbf{p}'\rangle = \mathbf{p}'|\mathbf{p}'\rangle. \tag{1.7.44}$$

They obey the normalization conditions

$$\langle \mathbf{x}'|\mathbf{x}''\rangle = \delta^3(\mathbf{x}' - \mathbf{x}'') \tag{1.7.45a}$$

and

$$\langle \mathbf{p}'|\mathbf{p}''\rangle = \delta^3(\mathbf{p}' - \mathbf{p}''), \tag{1.7.45b}$$

where δ^3 stands for the three-dimensional δ-function

$$\delta^3(\mathbf{x}' - \mathbf{x}'') = \delta(x' - x'')\delta(y' - y'')\delta(z' - z''). \tag{1.7.46}$$

The completeness relations read

$$\int d^3x' |\mathbf{x}'\rangle\langle\mathbf{x}'| = 1 \tag{1.7.47a}$$

and

$$\int d^3p' |\mathbf{p}'\rangle\langle\mathbf{p}'| = 1, \tag{1.7.47b}$$

which can be used to expand an arbitrary state ket:

$$|\alpha\rangle = \int d^3x' |\mathbf{x}'\rangle\langle\mathbf{x}'|\alpha\rangle, \tag{1.7.48a}$$

$$|\alpha\rangle = \int d^3p' |\mathbf{p}'\rangle\langle\mathbf{p}'|\alpha\rangle. \tag{1.7.48b}$$

The expansion coefficients $\langle\mathbf{x}'|\alpha\rangle$ and $\langle\mathbf{p}'|\alpha\rangle$ are identified with the wave functions $\psi_\alpha(\mathbf{x}')$ and $\phi_\alpha(\mathbf{p}')$ in position and momentum space, respectively.

The momentum operator, when taken between $|\beta\rangle$ and $|\alpha\rangle$, becomes

$$\langle\beta|\mathbf{p}|\alpha\rangle = \int d^3x' \psi_\beta^*(\mathbf{x}')(-i\hbar\nabla)\psi_\alpha(\mathbf{x}'). \tag{1.7.49}$$

The transformation function analogous to (1.7.32) is

$$\langle \mathbf{x}'|\mathbf{p}'\rangle = \left[\frac{1}{(2\pi\hbar)^{3/2}}\right]\exp\left(\frac{i\mathbf{p}'\cdot\mathbf{x}'}{\hbar}\right), \tag{1.7.50}$$

so that

$$\psi_\alpha(\mathbf{x}') = \left[\frac{1}{(2\pi\hbar)^{3/2}}\right]\int d^3p'\exp\left(\frac{i\mathbf{p}'\cdot\mathbf{x}'}{\hbar}\right)\phi_\alpha(\mathbf{p}') \tag{1.7.51a}$$

and

$$\phi_\alpha(\mathbf{p}') = \left[\frac{1}{(2\pi\hbar)^{3/2}}\right]\int d^3x'\exp\left(\frac{-i\mathbf{p}'\cdot\mathbf{x}'}{\hbar}\right)\psi_\alpha(\mathbf{x}'). \tag{1.7.51b}$$

It is interesting to check the dimension of the wave functions. In one-dimensional problems the normalization requirement (1.6.8) implies that $|\langle x'|\alpha\rangle|^2$ has the dimension of inverse length, so the wave function itself must have the dimension of $(\text{length})^{-1/2}$. In contrast, the wave function in three-dimensional problems must have the dimension of $(\text{length})^{-3/2}$ because $|\langle \mathbf{x}'|\alpha\rangle|^2$ integrated over all spatial volume must be unity (dimensionless).

Problems

1. Prove

$$[AB,CD] = -AC\{D,B\}+A\{C,B\}D-C\{D,A\}B+\{C,A\}DB.$$

2. Suppose a 2×2 matrix X (not necessarily Hermitian, nor unitary) is written as

$$X = a_0 + \boldsymbol{\sigma}\cdot\mathbf{a},$$

where a_0 and $a_{1,2,3}$ are numbers.
   a. How are a_0 and a_k $(k=1,2,3)$ related to $\text{tr}(X)$ and $\text{tr}(\sigma_k X)$?
   b. Obtain a_0 and a_k in terms of the matrix elements X_{ij}.
3. Show that the determinant of a 2×2 matrix $\boldsymbol{\sigma}\cdot\mathbf{a}$ is invariant under

$$\boldsymbol{\sigma}\cdot\mathbf{a} \rightarrow \boldsymbol{\sigma}\cdot\mathbf{a}' \equiv \exp\left(\frac{i\boldsymbol{\sigma}\cdot\hat{\mathbf{n}}\phi}{2}\right)\boldsymbol{\sigma}\cdot\mathbf{a}\exp\left(\frac{-i\boldsymbol{\sigma}\cdot\hat{\mathbf{n}}\phi}{2}\right).$$

Find a_k' in terms of a_k when $\hat{\mathbf{n}}$ is in the positive z-direction and interpret your result.
4. Using the rules of bra-ket algebra, prove or evaluate the following:
   a. $\text{tr}(XY) = \text{tr}(YX)$, where X and Y are operators;
   b. $(XY)^\dagger = Y^\dagger X^\dagger$, where X and Y are operators;
   c. $\exp[if(A)] = ?$ in ket-bra form, where A is a Hermitian operator whose eigenvalues are known;
   d. $\sum_{a'}\psi_{a'}^*(\mathbf{x}')\psi_{a'}(\mathbf{x}'')$, where $\psi_{a'}(\mathbf{x}') = \langle \mathbf{x}'|a'\rangle$.

5. a. Consider two kets $|\alpha\rangle$ and $|\beta\rangle$. Suppose $\langle a'|\alpha\rangle$, $\langle a''|\alpha\rangle$,... and $\langle a'|\beta\rangle$, $\langle a''|\beta\rangle$,... are all known, where $|a'\rangle$, $|a''\rangle$,... form a complete set of base kets. Find the matrix representation of the operator $|\alpha\rangle\langle\beta|$ in that basis.

  b. We now consider a spin $\frac{1}{2}$ system and let $|\alpha\rangle$ and $|\beta\rangle$ be $|s_z = \hbar/2\rangle$ and $|s_x = \hbar/2\rangle$, respectively. Write down explicitly the square matrix that corresponds to $|\alpha\rangle\langle\beta|$ in the usual (s_z diagonal) basis.

6. Suppose $|i\rangle$ and $|j\rangle$ are eigenkets of some Hermitian operator A. Under what condition can we conclude that $|i\rangle + |j\rangle$ is also an eigenket of A? Justify your answer.

7. Consider a ket space spanned by the eigenkets $\{|a'\rangle\}$ of a Hermitian operator A. There is no degeneracy.

  a. Prove that

$$\prod_{a'}(A - a')$$

  is the null operator.

  b. What is the significance of

$$\prod_{a'' \neq a'} \frac{(A - a'')}{(a' - a'')}?$$

  c. Illustrate (a) and (b) using A set equal to S_z of a spin $\frac{1}{2}$ system.

8. Using the orthonormality of $|+\rangle$ and $|-\rangle$, prove

$$\left[S_i, S_j\right] = i\varepsilon_{ijk}\hbar S_k, \qquad \{S_i, S_j\} = \left(\frac{\hbar^2}{2}\right)\delta_{ij},$$

where

$$S_x = \frac{\hbar}{2}(|+\rangle\langle-| + |-\rangle\langle+|), \qquad S_y = \frac{i\hbar}{2}(-|+\rangle\langle-| + |-\rangle\langle+|),$$

$$S_z = \frac{\hbar}{2}(|+\rangle\langle+| - |-\rangle\langle-|).$$

9. Construct $|\mathbf{S}\cdot\hat{\mathbf{n}}; +\rangle$ such that

$$\mathbf{S}\cdot\hat{\mathbf{n}}|\mathbf{S}\cdot\hat{\mathbf{n}}; +\rangle = \left(\frac{\hbar}{2}\right)|\mathbf{S}\cdot\hat{\mathbf{n}}; +\rangle$$

where $\hat{\mathbf{n}}$ is characterized by the angles shown in the figure. Express your answer as a linear combination of $|+\rangle$ and $|-\rangle$. [*Note*: The answer is

$$\cos\left(\frac{\beta}{2}\right)|+\rangle + \sin\left(\frac{\beta}{2}\right)e^{i\alpha}|-\rangle.$$

But do not just verify that this answer satisfies the above eigenvalue equation. Rather, treat the problem as a straightforward eigenvalue

problem. Also do not use rotation operators, which we will introduce
later in this book.]

10. The Hamiltonian operator for a two-state system is given by

$$H = a(|1\rangle\langle 1| - |2\rangle\langle 2| + |1\rangle\langle 2| + |2\rangle\langle 1|),$$

where a is a number with the dimension of energy. Find the energy
eigenvalues and the corresponding energy eigenkets (as linear combina-
tions of $|1\rangle$ and $|2\rangle$).

11. A two-state system is characterized by the Hamiltonian

$$H = H_{11}|1\rangle\langle 1| + H_{22}|2\rangle\langle 2| + H_{12}[|1\rangle\langle 2| + |2\rangle\langle 1|]$$

where H_{11}, H_{22}, and H_{12} are real numbers with the dimension of
energy, and $|1\rangle$ and $|2\rangle$ are eigenkets of some observable ($\neq H$). Find
the energy eigenkets and corresponding energy eigenvalues. Make sure
that your answer makes good sense for $H_{12} = 0$. (You need not solve
this problem from scratch. The following fact may be used without
proof:

$$(\mathbf{S}\cdot\hat{\mathbf{n}})|\hat{\mathbf{n}}; +\rangle = \frac{\hbar}{2}|\hat{\mathbf{n}}; +\rangle,$$

with $|\hat{\mathbf{n}}; +\rangle$ given by

$$|\hat{\mathbf{n}}; +\rangle = \cos\frac{\beta}{2}|+\rangle + e^{i\alpha}\sin\frac{\beta}{2}|-\rangle,$$

where β and α are the polar and azimuthal angles, respectively, that
characterize $\hat{\mathbf{n}}$.)

12. A spin $\frac{1}{2}$ system is known to be in an eigenstate of $\mathbf{S}\cdot\hat{\mathbf{n}}$ with eigenvalue
$\hbar/2$, where $\hat{\mathbf{n}}$ is a unit vector lying in the xz-plane that makes an angle
γ with the positive z-axis.

a. Suppose S_x is measured. What is the probability of getting $+\hbar/2$?

b. Evaluate the dispersion in S_y, that is,

$$\langle (S_x - \langle S_x \rangle)^2 \rangle.$$

(For your own peace of mind check your answers for the special cases $\gamma = 0$, $\pi/2$, and π.)

13. A beam of spin $\frac{1}{2}$ atoms goes through a series of Stern-Gerlach–type measurements as follows:

a. The first measurement accepts $s_z = \hbar/2$ atoms and rejects $s_z = -\hbar/2$ atoms.

b. The second measurement accepts $s_n = \hbar/2$ atoms and rejects $s_n = -\hbar/2$ atoms, where s_n is the eigenvalue of the operator $\mathbf{S} \cdot \hat{\mathbf{n}}$, with $\hat{\mathbf{n}}$ making an angle β in the xz-plane with respect to the z-axis.

c. The third measurement accepts $s_z = -\hbar/2$ atoms and rejects $s_z = \hbar/2$ atoms.

What is the intensity of the final $s_z = -\hbar/2$ beam when the $s_z = \hbar/2$ beam surviving the first measurement is normalized to unity? How must we orient the second measuring apparatus if we are to maximize the intensity of the final $s_z = -\hbar/2$ beam?

14. A certain observable in quantum mechanics has a 3×3 matrix representation as follows:

$$\frac{1}{\sqrt{2}} \begin{pmatrix} 0 & 1 & 0 \\ 1 & 0 & 1 \\ 0 & 1 & 0 \end{pmatrix}.$$

a. Find the normalized eigenvectors of this observable and the corresponding eigenvalues. Is there any degeneracy?

b. Give a physical example where all this is relevant.

15. Let A and B be observables. Suppose the simultaneous eigenkets of A and B $\{|a', b'\rangle\}$ form a *complete* orthonormal set of base kets. Can we always conclude that

$$[A, B] = 0?$$

If your answer is yes, prove the assertion. If your answer is no, give a counterexample.

16. Two Hermitian operators anticommute:

$$\{A, B\} = AB + BA = 0.$$

Is it possible to have a simultaneous (that is, common) eigenket of A and B? Prove or illustrate your assertion.

17. Two observables A_1 and A_2, which do not involve time explicitly, are known not to commute,

$$[A_1, A_2] \neq 0,$$

yet we also know that A_1 and A_2 both commute with the Hamiltonian:

$$[A_1, H] = 0, \qquad [A_2, H] = 0.$$

Prove that the energy eigenstates are, in general, degenerate. Are there exceptions? As an example, you may think of the central-force problem $H = \mathbf{p}^2/2m + V(r)$, with $A_1 \to L_z$, $A_2 \to L_x$.

18. a. The simplest way to derive the Schwarz inequality goes as follows. First, observe

$$(\langle \alpha | + \lambda^* \langle \beta |) \cdot (| \alpha \rangle + \lambda | \beta \rangle) \geq 0$$

for any complex number λ; then choose λ in such a way that the preceding inequality reduces to the Schwarz inequality.

b. Show that the equality sign in the generalized uncertainty relation holds if the state in question satisfies

$$\Delta A | \alpha \rangle = \lambda \, \Delta B | \alpha \rangle$$

with λ purely *imaginary*.

c. Explicit calculations using the usual rules of wave mechanics show that the wave function for a Gaussian wave packet given by

$$\langle x' | \alpha \rangle = (2 \pi d^2)^{-1/4} \exp \left[\frac{i \langle p \rangle x'}{\hbar} - \frac{(x' - \langle x \rangle)^2}{4d^2} \right]$$

satisfies the minimum uncertainty relation

$$\sqrt{\langle (\Delta x)^2 \rangle} \, \sqrt{\langle (\Delta p)^2 \rangle} = \frac{\hbar}{2}.$$

Prove that the requirement

$$\langle x' | \Delta x | \alpha \rangle = (\text{imaginary number}) \langle x' | \Delta p | \alpha \rangle$$

is indeed satisfied for such a Gaussian wave packet, in agreement with (b).

19. a. Compute

$$\langle (\Delta S_x)^2 \rangle \equiv \langle S_x^2 \rangle - \langle S_x \rangle^2,$$

where the expectation value is taken for the $S_z +$ state. Using your result, check the generalized uncertainty relation

$$\langle (\Delta A)^2 \rangle \langle (\Delta B)^2 \rangle \geq \frac{1}{4} |\langle [A, B] \rangle|^2,$$

with $A \to S_x$, $B \to S_y$.

b. Check the uncertainty relation with $A \to S_x$, $B \to S_y$ for the $S_x +$ state.

20. Find the linear combination of $|+\rangle$ and $|-\rangle$ kets that maximizes the

uncertainty product

$$\langle (\Delta S_x)^2 \rangle \langle (\Delta S_y)^2 \rangle.$$

Verify explicitly that for the linear combination you found, the uncertainty relation for S_x and S_y is not violated.

21. Evaluate the x-p uncertainty product $\langle (\Delta x)^2 \rangle \langle (\Delta p)^2 \rangle$ for a one-dimensional particle confined between two rigid walls

$$V = \begin{cases} 0 & \text{for } 0 < x < a, \\ \infty & \text{otherwise.} \end{cases}$$

Do this for both the ground and excited states.

22. Estimate the rough order of magnitude of the length of time that an ice pick can be balanced on its point if the only limitation is that set by the Heisenberg uncertainty principle. Assume that the point is sharp and that the point and the surface on which it rests are hard. You may make approximations which do not alter the general order of magnitude of the result. Assume reasonable values for the dimensions and weight of the ice pick. Obtain an approximate numerical result and express it *in seconds*.

23. Consider a three-dimensional ket space. If a certain set of orthonormal kets—say, $|1\rangle$, $|2\rangle$, and $|3\rangle$—are used as the base kets, the operators A and B are represented by

$$A \doteq \begin{pmatrix} a & 0 & 0 \\ 0 & -a & 0 \\ 0 & 0 & -a \end{pmatrix}, \qquad B \doteq \begin{pmatrix} b & 0 & 0 \\ 0 & 0 & -ib \\ 0 & ib & 0 \end{pmatrix}$$

with a and b both real.

a. Obviously A exhibits a degenerate spectrum. Does B also exhibit a degenerate spectrum?

b. Show that A and B commute.

c. Find a new set of orthonormal kets which are simultaneous eigenkets of both A and B. Specify the eigenvalues of A and B for each of the three eigenkets. Does your specification of eigenvalues completely characterize each eigenket?

24. a. Prove that $(1/\sqrt{2})(1 + i\sigma_x)$ acting on a two-component spinor can be regarded as the matrix representation of the rotation operator about the x-axis by angle $-\pi/2$. (The minus sign signifies that the rotation is clockwise.)

b. Construct the matrix representation of S_z when the eigenkets of S_y are used as base vectors.

25. Some authors define an *operator* to be real when every member of its matrix elements $\langle b'|A|b'' \rangle$ is real in some representation ($\{|b'\rangle\}$ basis in this case). Is this concept representation independent, that is, do the

matrix elements remain real even if some basis other than $\{|b'\rangle\}$ is used? Check your assertion using familiar operators such as S_y and S_z (see Problem 24) or x and p_x.

26. Construct the transformation matrix that connects the S_z diagonal basis to the S_x diagonal basis. Show that your result is consistent with the general relation

$$U = \sum_r |b^{(r)}\rangle\langle a^{(r)}|.$$

27. a. Suppose that $f(A)$ is a function of a Hermitian operator A with the property $A|a'\rangle = a'|a'\rangle$. Evaluate $\langle b''|f(A)|b'\rangle$ when the transformation matrix from the a' basis to the b' basis is known.

   b. Using the continuum analogue of the result obtained in (a), evaluate

   $$\langle \mathbf{p}''|F(r)|\mathbf{p}'\rangle.$$

   Simplify your expression as far as you can. Note that r is $\sqrt{x^2 + y^2 + z^2}$, where x, y, and z are *operators*.

28. a. Let x and p_x be the coordinate and linear momentum in one dimension. Evaluate the classical Poisson bracket

   $$[x, F(p_x)]_{\text{classical}}.$$

   b. Let x and p_x be the corresponding quantum-mechanical operators this time. Evaluate the commutator

   $$\left[x, \exp\left(\frac{ip_x a}{\hbar}\right)\right].$$

   c. Using the result obtained in (b), prove that

   $$\exp\left(\frac{ip_x a}{\hbar}\right)|x'\rangle, \qquad (x|x'\rangle = x'|x'\rangle)$$

   is an eigenstate of the coordinate operator x. What is the corresponding eigenvalue?

29. a. On page 247, Gottfried (1966) states that

   $$[x_i, G(\mathbf{p})] = i\hbar \frac{\partial G}{\partial p_i}, \qquad [p_i, F(\mathbf{x})] = -i\hbar \frac{\partial F}{\partial x_i}$$

   can be "easily derived" from the fundamental commutation relations for all functions of F and G that can be expressed as power series in their arguments. Verify this statement.

   b. Evaluate $[x^2, p^2]$. Compare your result with the classical Poisson bracket $[x^2, p^2]_{\text{classical}}$.

30. The translation operator for a finite (spatial) displacement is given by

$$\mathscr{T}(\mathbf{l}) = \exp\left(\frac{-i\mathbf{p} \cdot \mathbf{l}}{\hbar}\right),$$

where **p** is the momentum *operator*.

a. Evaluate

$$[x_i, \mathscr{T}(\mathbf{l})].$$

b. Using (a) (or otherwise), demonstrate how the expectation value $\langle \mathbf{x} \rangle$ changes under translation.

31. In the main text we discussed the effect of $\mathscr{T}(d\mathbf{x}')$ on the position and momentum eigenkets and on a more general state ket $|\alpha\rangle$. We can also study the behavior of expectation values $\langle \mathbf{x} \rangle$ and $\langle \mathbf{p} \rangle$ under infinitesimal translation. Using (1.6.25), (1.6.45), and $|\alpha\rangle \to \mathscr{T}(d\mathbf{x}')|\alpha\rangle$ only, prove $\langle \mathbf{x} \rangle \to \langle \mathbf{x} \rangle + d\mathbf{x}', \langle \mathbf{p} \rangle \to \langle \mathbf{p} \rangle$ under infinitesimal translation.

32. a. Verify (1.7.39a) and (1.7.39b) for the expectation value of p and p^2 from the Gaussian wave packet (1.7.35).

b. Evaluate the expectation value of p and p^2 using the momentum-space wave function (1.7.42).

33. a. Prove the following:

(i) $$\langle p'|x|\alpha\rangle = i\hbar \frac{\partial}{\partial p'} \langle p'|\alpha\rangle,$$

(ii) $$\langle \beta|x|\alpha\rangle = \int dp' \, \phi_\beta^*(p') i\hbar \frac{\partial}{\partial p'} \phi_\alpha(p'),$$

where $\phi_\alpha(p') = \langle p'|\alpha\rangle$ and $\phi_\beta(p') = \langle p'|\beta\rangle$ are momentum-space wave functions.

b. What is the physical significance of

$$\exp\left(\frac{ix\Xi}{\hbar}\right),$$

where x is the position operator and Ξ is some number with the dimension of momentum? Justify your answer.

CHAPTER 2

Quantum Dynamics

So far we have not discussed how physical systems change with time. This chapter is devoted exclusively to the dynamic development of state kets and/or observables. In other words, we are concerned here with the quantum mechanical analogue of Newton's (or Lagrange's or Hamilton's) equations of motion.

2.1. TIME EVOLUTION AND THE SCHRODINGER EQUATION

The first important point we should keep in mind is that time is just a parameter in quantum mechanics, *not* an operator. In particular, time is not an observable in the language of the previous chapter. It is nonsensical to talk about the time operator in the same sense as we talk about the position operator. Ironically, in the historical development of wave mechanics both L. de Broglie and E. Schrödinger were guided by a kind of covariant analogy between energy and time on the one hand and momentum and position (spatial coordinate) on the other. Yet when we now look at quantum mechanics in its finished form, there is no trace of a symmetrical treatment between time and space. The relativistic quantum theory of fields does treat the time and space coordinates on the same footing, but it does so only at the expense of demoting position from the status of being an observable to that of being just a parameter.

Time Evolution Operator

Our basic concern in this section is, How does a state ket change with time? Suppose we have a physical system whose state ket at t_0 is represented by $|\alpha\rangle$. At later times, we do not, in general, expect the system to remain in the same state $|\alpha\rangle$. Let us denote the ket corresponding to the state at some later time by

$$|\alpha, t_0; t\rangle, \quad (t > t_0), \tag{2.1.1}$$

where we have written α, t_0 to remind ourselves that the system *used to be* in state $|\alpha\rangle$ at some earlier reference time t_0. Because time is assumed to be a continuous parameter, we expect

$$\lim_{t \to t_0} |\alpha, t_0; t\rangle = |\alpha\rangle \tag{2.1.2}$$

and we may as well use a shorthand notation,

$$|\alpha, t_0; t_0\rangle = |\alpha, t_0\rangle, \tag{2.1.3}$$

for this. Our basic task is to study the time evolution of a state ket:

$$|\alpha, t_0\rangle = |\alpha\rangle \xrightarrow{\text{time evolution}} |\alpha, t_0; t\rangle. \tag{2.1.4}$$

Put in another way, we are interested in asking how the state ket changes under a time displacement $t_0 \to t$.

As in the case of translation, the two kets are related by an operator which we call the **time-evolution operator** $\mathscr{U}(t, t_0)$:

$$|\alpha, t_0; t\rangle = \mathscr{U}(t, t_0)|\alpha, t_0\rangle. \tag{2.1.5}$$

What are some of the properties we would like to ascribe to the time-evolution operator? The first important property is the unitary requirement for $\mathscr{U}(t, t_0)$ that follows from probability conservation. Suppose that at t_0 the state ket is expanded in terms of the eigenkets of some observable A:

$$|\alpha, t_0\rangle = \sum_{a'} c_{a'}(t_0)|a'\rangle. \tag{2.1.6}$$

Likewise, at some later time, we have

$$|\alpha, t_0; t\rangle = \sum_{a'} c_{a'}(t)|a'\rangle. \tag{2.1.7}$$

In general, we do not expect the modulus of the individual expansion coefficient to remain the same:*

$$|c_{a'}(t)| \neq |c_{a'}(t_0)|. \tag{2.1.8}$$

For instance, consider a spin $\frac{1}{2}$ system with its spin magnetic moment

---

*We later show, however, that if the Hamiltonian commutes with A, then $|c_{a'}(t)|$ is indeed equal to $|c_{a'}(t_0)|$.

subjected to a uniform magnetic field in the z-direction. To be specific, suppose that at t_0 the spin is in the positive x-direction; that is, the system is found in an eigenstate of S_x with eigenvalue $\hbar/2$. As time goes on, the spin precesses in the xy-plane, as will be quantitatively demonstrated later in this section. This means that the probability for observing S_x+ is no longer unity at $t > t_0$; there is a finite probability for observing S_x- as well. Yet the *sum* of the probabilities for S_x+ and S_x- remains unity at all times. Generally, in the notation of (2.1.6) and (2.1.7), we must have

$$\sum_{a'} |c_{a'}(t_0)|^2 = \sum_{a'} |c_{a'}(t)|^2 \qquad (2.1.9)$$

despite (2.1.8) for the individual expansion coefficients. Stated another way, if the state ket is initially normalized to unity, it must remain normalized to unity at all later times:

$$\langle \alpha, t_0 | \alpha, t_0 \rangle = 1 \Rightarrow \langle \alpha, t_0; t | \alpha, t_0; t \rangle = 1. \qquad (2.1.10)$$

As in the translation case, this property is guaranteed if the time-evolution operator is taken to be unitary. For this reason we take unitarity,

$$\mathcal{U}^\dagger(t, t_0) \mathcal{U}(t, t_0) = 1, \qquad (2.1.11)$$

to be one of the fundamental properties of the $\mathcal{U}$ operator. It is no coincidence that many authors regard unitarity as being synonymous with probability conservation.

Another feature we require of the $\mathcal{U}$ operator is the composition property:

$$\mathcal{U}(t_2, t_0) = \mathcal{U}(t_2, t_1) \mathcal{U}(t_1, t_0), \quad (t_2 > t_1 > t_0). \qquad (2.1.12)$$

This equation says that if we are interested in obtaining time evolution from t_0 to t_2, then we can obtain the same result by first considering time evolution from t_0 to t_1, then from t_1 to t_2—a reasonable requirement. Note that we read (2.1.12) from right to left!

It also turns out to be advantageous to consider an infinitesimal time-evolution operator $\mathcal{U}(t_0 + dt, t_0)$:

$$|\alpha, t_0; t_0 + dt\rangle = \mathcal{U}(t_0 + dt, t_0)|\alpha, t_0\rangle. \qquad (2.1.13)$$

Because of continuity [see (2.1.2)], the infinitesimal time-evolution operator must reduce to the identity operator as dt goes to zero,

$$\lim_{dt \to 0} \mathcal{U}(t_0 + dt, t_0) = 1, \qquad (2.1.14)$$

and as in the translation case, we expect the difference between $\mathcal{U}(t_0 + dt, t_0)$ and 1 to be of first order in dt.

We assert that all these requirements are satisfied by

$$\mathcal{U}(t_0 + dt, t_0) = 1 - i\Omega \, dt, \qquad (2.1.15)$$

where Ω is a Hermitian operator,*

$$\Omega^\dagger = \Omega. \tag{2.1.16}$$

With (2.1.15) the infinitesimal time-displacement operator satisfies the composition property

$$\mathscr{U}(t_0 + dt_1 + dt_2, t_0) = \mathscr{U}(t_0 + dt_1 + dt_2, t_0 + dt_1)\mathscr{U}(t_0 + dt_1, t_0); \tag{2.1.17}$$

it differs from the identity operator by a term of order dt. The unitarity property can also be checked as follows:

$$\mathscr{U}^\dagger(t_0 + dt, t_0)\mathscr{U}(t_0 + dt, t_0) = (1 + i\Omega^\dagger dt)(1 - i\Omega\, dt) \simeq 1, \tag{2.1.18}$$

to the extent that terms of order $(dt)^2$ or higher can be ignored.

The operator Ω has the dimension of frequency or inverse time. Is there any familiar observable with the dimension of frequency? We recall that in the old quantum theory, angular frequency ω is postulated to be related to energy by the Planck-Einstein relation

$$E = \hbar\omega. \tag{2.1.19}$$

Let us now borrow from classical mechanics the idea that the Hamiltonian is the generator of time evolution (Goldstein 1980, 407–8). It is then natural to relate Ω to the Hamiltonian operator H:

$$\Omega = \frac{H}{\hbar}. \tag{2.1.20}$$

To sum up, the infinitesimal time-evolution operator is written as

$$\mathscr{U}(t_0 + dt, t_0) = 1 - \frac{iH\, dt}{\hbar}, \tag{2.1.21}$$

where H, the Hamiltonian operator, is assumed to be Hermitian. The reader may ask whether the $\hbar$ introduced here is the same as the $\hbar$ that appears in the expression for the translation operator (1.6.32). This question can be answered by comparing the quantum-mechanical equation of motion we derive later with the classical equation of motion. It turns out that unless the two $\hbar$'s are taken to be the same, we are unable to obtain a relation like

$$\frac{d\mathbf{x}}{dt} = \frac{\mathbf{p}}{m} \tag{2.1.22}$$

as the classical limit of the corresponding quantum-mechanical relation.

The Schrödinger Equation

We are now in a position to derive the fundamental differential equation for the time-evolution operator $\mathscr{U}(t, t_0)$. We exploit the composi-

---

*If the Ω operator depends on time explicitly, it must be evaluated at t_0.

tion property of the time-evolution operator by letting $t_1 \rightarrow t$, $t_2 \rightarrow t + dt$ in (2.1.12):

$$\mathscr{U}(t + dt, t_0) = \mathscr{U}(t + dt, t)\mathscr{U}(t, t_0) = \left(1 - \frac{iH\,dt}{\hbar}\right)\mathscr{U}(t, t_0),$$

(2.1.23)

where the time difference $t - t_0$ need not be infinitesimal. We have

$$\mathscr{U}(t + dt, t_0) - \mathscr{U}(t, t_0) = -i\left(\frac{H}{\hbar}\right) dt\,\mathscr{U}(t, t_0), \qquad (2.1.24)$$

which can be written in differential equation form:

$$i\hbar\frac{\partial}{\partial t}\mathscr{U}(t, t_0) = H\mathscr{U}(t, t_0). \qquad (2.1.25)$$

This is the **Schrödinger equation for the time-evolution operator**. Everything that has to do with time development follows from this fundamental equation.

Equation (2.1.25) immediately leads to the Schrodinger equation for a state ket. Multiplying both sides of (2.1.25) by $|\alpha, t_0\rangle$ on the right, we obtain

$$i\hbar\frac{\partial}{\partial t}\mathscr{U}(t, t_0)|\alpha, t_0\rangle = H\mathscr{U}(t, t_0)|\alpha, t_0\rangle. \qquad (2.1.26)$$

But $|\alpha, t_0\rangle$ does not depend on t, so this is the same as

$$i\hbar\frac{\partial}{\partial t}|\alpha, t_0; t\rangle = H|\alpha, t_0; t\rangle, \qquad (2.1.27)$$

where (2.1.5) has been used.

If we are given $\mathscr{U}(t, t_0)$ and, in addition, know how $\mathscr{U}(t, t_0)$ acts on the initial state ket $|\alpha, t_0\rangle$, it is not necessary to bother with the Schrödinger equation for the state ket (2.1.27). All we have to do is apply $\mathscr{U}(t, t_0)$ to $|\alpha, t_0\rangle$; in this manner we can obtain a state ket at any t. Our first task is therefore to derive formal solutions to the Schrödinger equation for the time evolution operator (2.1.25). There are three cases to be treated separately:

Case 1. The Hamiltonian operator is independent of time. By this we mean that even when the parameter t is changed, the H operator remains unchanged. The Hamiltonian for a spin-magnetic moment interacting with a time-independent magnetic field is an example of this. The solution to (2.1.25) in such a case is given by

$$\mathscr{U}(t, t_0) = \exp\left[\frac{-iH(t - t_0)}{\hbar}\right]. \qquad (2.1.28)$$

To prove this let us expand the exponential as follows:

$$\exp\left[\frac{-iH(t - t_0)}{\hbar}\right] = 1 - \frac{iH(t - t_0)}{\hbar} + \left[\frac{(-i)^2}{2}\right]\left[\frac{H(t - t_0)}{\hbar}\right]^2 + \cdots.$$

(2.1.29)

Because the time derivative of this expansion is given by

$$\frac{\partial}{\partial t} \exp\left[\frac{-iH(t-t_0)}{\hbar} \right] = \frac{-iH}{\hbar} + \left[\frac{(-i)^2}{2} \right] 2\left(\frac{H}{\hbar} \right)^2 (t-t_0) + \cdots ,$$

$$(2.1.30)$$

expression (2.1.28) obviously satisfies differential equation (2.1.25). The boundary condition is also satisfied because as $t \to t_0$, (2.1.28) reduces to the identity operator. An alternative way to obtain (2.1.28) is to compound successively infinitesimal time-evolution operators just as we did to obtain (1.6.36) for finite translation:

$$\lim_{N \to \infty} \left[1 - \frac{(iH/\hbar)(t-t_0)}{N} \right]^N = \exp\left[\frac{-iH(t-t_0)}{\hbar} \right]. \quad (2.1.31)$$

Case 2.   The Hamiltonian operator H is time-dependent but the H's at different times commute. As an example, let us consider the spin-magnetic moment subjected to a magnetic field whose strength varies with time but whose direction is always unchanged. The formal solution to (2.1.25) in this case is

$$\mathcal{U}(t, t_0) = \exp\left[-\left(\frac{i}{\hbar} \right) \int_{t_0}^{t} dt' H(t') \right]. \quad (2.1.32)$$

This can be proved in a similar way. We simply replace $H(t - t_0)$ in (2.1.29) and (2.1.30) by $\int_{t_0}^{t} dt' H(t')$.

Case 3.   The H's at different times do *not* commute. Continuing with the example involving spin-magnetic moment, we suppose, this time, that the magnetic field direction also changes with time: at $t = t_1$ in the x-direction, at $t = t_2$ in the y-direction, and so forth. Because S_x and S_y do not commute, $H(t_1)$ and $H(t_2)$, which go like $\mathbf{S} \cdot \mathbf{B}$, do not commute either. The formal solution in such a situation is given by

$$\mathcal{U}(t, t_0) = 1 + \sum_{n=1}^{\infty} \left(\frac{-i}{\hbar} \right)^n \int_{t_0}^{t} dt_1 \int_{t_0}^{t_1} dt_2 \cdots \int_{t_0}^{t_{n-1}} dt_n\, H(t_1) H(t_2) \cdots H(t_n),$$

$$(2.1.33)$$

which is sometimes known as the **Dyson series**, after F. J. Dyson, who developed a perturbation expansion of this form in quantum field theory. We do not prove (2.1.33) now because the proof is very similar to the one presented in Chapter 5 for the time-evolution operator in the interaction picture.

In elementary applications, only case 1 is of practical interest. In the remaining part of this chapter we assume that the H operator is time-independent. We will encounter time-dependent Hamiltonians in Chapter 5.

Energy Eigenkets

To be able to evaluate the effect of the time-evolution operator (2.1.28) on a general initial ket $|\alpha\rangle$, we must first know how it acts on the base kets used in expanding $|\alpha\rangle$. This is particularly straightforward if the base kets used are eigenkets of A such that

$$[A, H] = 0; \tag{2.1.34}$$

then the eigenkets of A are also eigenkets of H, called **energy eigenkets**, whose eigenvalues are denoted by $E_{a'}$:

$$H|a'\rangle = E_{a'}|a'\rangle. \tag{2.1.35}$$

We can now expand the time-evolution operator in terms of $|a'\rangle\langle a'|$. Taking $t_0 = 0$ for simplicity, we obtain

$$\exp\left(\frac{-iHt}{\hbar}\right) = \sum_{a'}\sum_{a''}|a''\rangle\langle a''|\exp\left(\frac{-iHt}{\hbar}\right)|a'\rangle\langle a'|$$

$$= \sum_{a'}|a'\rangle\exp\left(\frac{-iE_{a'}t}{\hbar}\right)\langle a'|. \tag{2.1.36}$$

The time-evolution operator written in this form enables us to solve any initial-value problem once the expansion of the initial ket in terms of $\{|a'\rangle\}$ is known. As an example, suppose that the initial ket expansion reads

$$|\alpha, t_0 = 0\rangle = \sum_{a'}|a'\rangle\langle a'|\alpha\rangle = \sum_{a'}c_{a'}|a'\rangle. \tag{2.1.37}$$

We then have

$$|\alpha, t_0 = 0; t\rangle = \exp\left(\frac{-iHt}{\hbar}\right)|\alpha, t_0 = 0\rangle = \sum_{a'}|a'\rangle\langle a'|\alpha\rangle\exp\left(\frac{-iE_{a'}t}{\hbar}\right). \tag{2.1.38}$$

In other words, the expansion coefficient changes with time as

$$c_{a'}(t = 0) \rightarrow c_{a'}(t) = c_{a'}(t = 0)\exp\left(\frac{-iE_{a'}t}{\hbar}\right) \tag{2.1.39}$$

with its modulus unchanged. Notice that the relative phases among various components do vary with time because the oscillation frequencies are different.

A special case of interest is where the initial state happens to be one of $\{|a'\rangle\}$ itself. We have

$$|\alpha, t_0 = 0\rangle = |a'\rangle \tag{2.1.40}$$

initially, and at a later time

$$|\alpha, t_0 = 0; t\rangle = |a'\rangle \exp\left(\frac{-iE_a \cdot t}{\hbar}\right), \tag{2.1.41}$$

so if the system is initially a simultaneous eigenstate of A and H, it remains so at all times. The most that can happen is the phase modulation, $\exp(-iE_a \cdot t/\hbar)$. It is in this sense that an observable compatible with H [see (2.1.34)] is a *constant of the motion*. We will encounter this connection once again in a different form when we discuss the Heisenberg equation of motion.

In the foregoing discussion the basic task in quantum dynamics is reduced to finding an observable that commutes with H and evaluating its eigenvalues. Once that is done, we expand the initial ket in terms of the eigenkets of that observable and just apply the time-evolution operator. This last step merely amounts to changing the phase of each expansion coefficient, as indicated by (2.1.39).

Even though we worked out the case where there is just one observable A that commutes with H, our considerations can easily be generalized when there are several mutually compatible observables all also commuting with H:

$$[A, B] = [B, C] = [A, C] = \cdots = 0,$$
$$[A, H] = [B, H] = [C, H] = \cdots = 0. \tag{2.1.42}$$

Using the collective index notation of Section 1.4 [see (1.4.37)], we have

$$\exp\left(\frac{-iHt}{\hbar}\right) = \sum_{K'} |K'\rangle \exp\left(\frac{-iE_{K'} \cdot t}{\hbar}\right)\langle K'|, \tag{2.1.43}$$

where $E_{K'}$ is uniquely specified once $a', b', c', \ldots$ are specified. It is therefore of fundamental importance to find *a complete set of mutually compatible observables that also commute with H*. Once such a set is found, we express the initial ket as a superposition of the simultaneous eigenkets of $A, B, C, \ldots$ and H. The final step is just to apply the time-evolution operator, written as (2.1.43). In this manner we can solve the most general initial-value problem with a time-independent H.

Time Dependence of Expectation Values

It is instructive to study how the expectation value of an observable changes as a function of time. Suppose that at $t = 0$ the initial state is one of the eigenstates of an observable A that commutes with H, as in (2.1.40). We now look at the expectation value of some other observable B, which need not commute with A nor with H. Because at a later time we have

$$|a', t_0 = 0; t\rangle = \mathcal{U}(t, 0)|a'\rangle \tag{2.1.44}$$

for the state ket, $\langle B \rangle$ is given by

$$\langle B \rangle = \left(\langle a' | \mathcal{U}^\dagger(t,0) \right) \cdot B \cdot \left(\mathcal{U}(t,0) | a' \rangle \right)$$

$$= \langle a' | \exp\left(\frac{iE_{a'}t}{\hbar} \right) B \exp\left(\frac{-iE_{a'}t}{\hbar} \right) | a' \rangle$$

$$= \langle a' | B | a' \rangle, \tag{2.1.45}$$

which is *independent of t*. So the expectation value of an observable taken with respect to an energy eigenstate does not change with time. For this reason an energy eigenstate is often referred to as a **stationary state**.

The situation is more interesting when the expectation value is taken with respect to a *superposition* of energy eigenstates, or a **nonstationary state**. Suppose that initially we have

$$| \alpha, t_0 = 0 \rangle = \sum_{a'} c_{a'} | a' \rangle. \tag{2.1.46}$$

We easily compute the expectation value of B to be

$$\langle B \rangle = \left[\sum_{a'} c_{a'}^* \langle a' | \exp\left(\frac{iE_{a'}t}{\hbar} \right) \right] \cdot B \cdot \left[\sum_{a''} c_{a''} \exp\left(\frac{-iE_{a''}t}{\hbar} \right) | a'' \rangle \right]$$

$$= \sum_{a'} \sum_{a''} c_{a'}^* c_{a''} \langle a' | B | a'' \rangle \exp\left[\frac{-i(E_{a''} - E_{a'})t}{\hbar} \right]. \tag{2.1.47}$$

So this time the expectation value consists of oscillating terms whose angular frequencies are determined by N. Bohr's frequency condition

$$\omega_{a''a'} = \frac{(E_{a''} - E_{a'})}{\hbar}. \tag{2.1.48}$$

Spin Precession

It is appropriate to treat an example here. We consider an extremely simple system which, however, illustrates the basic formalism we have developed.

We start with a Hamiltonian of a spin $\frac{1}{2}$ system with magnetic moment $e\hbar/2m_e c$ subjected to an external magnetic field **B**:

$$H = -\left(\frac{e}{m_e c} \right) \mathbf{S} \cdot \mathbf{B} \tag{2.1.49}$$

($e < 0$ for the electron). Furthermore, we take **B** to be a static, uniform magnetic field in the z-direction. We can then write H as

$$H = -\left(\frac{eB}{m_e c} \right) S_z. \tag{2.1.50}$$

Because S_z and H differ just by a multiplicative constant, they obviously commute. The S_z eigenstates are also energy eigenstates, and the corresponding energy eigenvalues are

$$E_\pm = \mp \frac{e\hbar B}{2m_e c}, \quad \text{for } S_z \pm. \tag{2.1.51}$$

It is convenient to define ω in such a way that the difference in the two energy eigenvalues is $\hbar\omega$:

$$\omega \equiv \frac{|e|B}{m_e c}. \tag{2.1.52}$$

We can then rewrite the H operator simply as

$$H = \omega S_z. \tag{2.1.53}$$

All the information on time development is contained in the time-evolution operator

$$\mathcal{U}(t,0) = \exp\left(\frac{-i\omega S_z t}{\hbar}\right). \tag{2.1.54}$$

We apply this to the initial state. The base kets we must use in expanding the initial ket are obviously the S_z eigenkets, $|+\rangle$ and $|-\rangle$, which are also energy eigenkets. Suppose that at $t=0$ the system is characterized by

$$|\alpha\rangle = c_+|+\rangle + c_-|-\rangle. \tag{2.1.55}$$

Upon applying (2.1.54), we see that the state ket at some later time is

$$|\alpha, t_0 = 0; t\rangle = c_+ \exp\left(\frac{-i\omega t}{2}\right)|+\rangle + c_- \exp\left(\frac{+i\omega t}{2}\right)|-\rangle, \tag{2.1.56}$$

where we have used

$$H|\pm\rangle = \left(\frac{\pm \hbar\omega}{2}\right)|\pm\rangle. \tag{2.1.57}$$

Specifically, let us suppose that the initial ket $|\alpha\rangle$ represents the spin-up (or, more precisely, $S_z +$) state $|+\rangle$, which means that

$$c_+ = 1, \quad c_- = 0. \tag{2.1.58}$$

At a later time, (2.1.56) tells us that it is still in the spin-up state, which is no surprise because this is a stationary state.

Next, let us suppose that initially the system is in the $S_x +$ state. Comparing (1.4.17a) with (2.1.55), we see that

$$c_+ = c_- = \frac{1}{\sqrt{2}}. \tag{2.1.59}$$

It is straightforward to work out the probabilities for the system to be found in the $S_x \pm$ state at some later time t:

$$|\langle S_x \pm | \alpha, t_0 = 0; t\rangle|^2 = \left| \left[\left(\frac{1}{\sqrt{2}} \right)\langle + | \pm \left(\frac{1}{\sqrt{2}} \right)\langle - | \right] \cdot \left[\left(\frac{1}{\sqrt{2}} \right)\exp\left(\frac{-i\omega t}{2} \right)| + \rangle \right. \right.$$

$$\left. \left. + \left(\frac{1}{\sqrt{2}} \right)\exp\left(\frac{+i\omega t}{2} \right)| - \rangle \right] \right|^2$$

$$= \left| \frac{1}{2}\exp\left(\frac{-i\omega t}{2} \right) \pm \frac{1}{2}\exp\left(\frac{+i\omega t}{2} \right) \right|^2$$

$$= \begin{cases} \cos^2\dfrac{\omega t}{2}, & \text{for } S_x +, \\[2mm] \sin^2\dfrac{\omega t}{2}, & \text{for } S_x -. \end{cases}$$

(2.1.60a)

(2.1.60b)

Even though the spin is initially in the positive x-direction, the magnetic field in the z-direction causes it to rotate; as a result, we obtain a finite probability for finding $S_x -$ at some later time. The sum of the two probabilities is seen to be unity at all times, in agreement with the unitarity property of the time-evolution operator.

Using (1.4.6), we can write the expectation value of S_x as

$$\langle S_x \rangle = \left(\frac{\hbar}{2} \right)\cos^2\left(\frac{\omega t}{2} \right) + \left(\frac{-\hbar}{2} \right)\sin^2\left(\frac{\omega t}{2} \right)$$

$$= \left(\frac{\hbar}{2} \right)\cos \omega t,$$

(2.1.61)

so this quantity oscillates with an angular frequency corresponding to the difference of the two energy eigenvalues divided by $\hbar$, in agreement with our general formula (2.1.47). Similar exercises with S_y and S_z show that

$$\langle S_y \rangle = \left(\frac{\hbar}{2} \right)\sin \omega t$$

(2.1.62a)

and

$$\langle S_z \rangle = 0.$$

(2.1.62b)

Physically this means that the spin precesses in the xy-plane. We will comment further on spin precession when we discuss rotation operators in Chapter 3.

Correlation Amplitude and the Energy-Time Uncertainty Relation

We conclude this section by asking how state kets at different times are correlated with each other. Suppose the initial state ket at $t = 0$ of a physical system is given by $|\alpha\rangle$. With time it changes into $|\alpha, t_0 = 0; t\rangle$, which we obtain by applying the time-evolution operator. We are concerned with the extent to which the state ket at a later time t is similar to the state ket at $t = 0$; we therefore construct the inner product between the two state kets at different times:

$$C(t) \equiv \langle \alpha | \alpha, t_0 = 0; t \rangle$$
$$= \langle \alpha | \mathscr{U}(t,0) | \alpha \rangle, \qquad (2.1.63)$$

which is known as the **correlation amplitude**. The modulus of $C(t)$ provides a quantitative measure of the "resemblance" between the state kets at different times.

As an extreme example, consider the very special case where the initial ket $|\alpha\rangle$ is an eigenket of H; we then have

$$C(t) = \langle a' | a', t_0 = 0; t \rangle = \exp\left(\frac{-iE_{a'}t}{\hbar} \right), \qquad (2.1.64)$$

so the modulus of the correlation amplitude is unity at all times—which is not surprising for a stationary state. In the more general situation where the initial ket is represented by a superposition of $\{|a'\rangle\}$, as in (2.1.37), we have

$$C(t) = \left(\sum_{a'} c_{a'}^* \langle a' | \right) \left[\sum_{a''} c_{a''} \exp\left(\frac{-iE_{a''}t}{\hbar} \right) | a'' \rangle \right]$$
$$= \sum_{a'} |c_{a'}|^2 \exp\left(\frac{-iE_{a'}t}{\hbar} \right). \qquad (2.1.65)$$

As we sum over many terms with oscillating time dependence of different frequencies, a strong cancellation is possible for moderately large values of t. We expect the correlation amplitude that starts with unity at $t = 0$ to decrease in magnitude with time.

To estimate (2.1.65) in a more concrete manner, let us suppose that the state ket can be regarded as a superposition of so many energy eigenkets with similar energies that we can regard them as exhibiting essentially a quasi-continuous spectrum. It is then legitimate to replace the sum by the integral

$$\sum_{a'} \rightarrow \int dE\, \rho(E), \qquad c_{a'} \rightarrow g(E)\Big|_{E \simeq E_{a'}}, \qquad (2.1.66)$$

where $\rho(E)$ characterizes the density of energy eigenstates. Expression (2.1.65) now becomes

$$C(t) = \int dE\, |g(E)|^2 \rho(E) \exp\left(\frac{-iEt}{\hbar} \right), \qquad (2.1.67)$$

subject to the normalization condition

$$\int dE\, |g(E)|^2 \rho(E) = 1. \qquad (2.1.68)$$

In a realistic physical situation $|g(E)|^2\rho(E)$ may be peaked around $E = E_0$ with width ΔE. Writing (2.1.67) as

$$C(t) = \exp\left(\frac{-iE_0 t}{\hbar}\right) \int dE |g(E)|^2 \rho(E) \exp\left[\frac{-i(E - E_0)t}{\hbar}\right],$$

(2.1.69)

we see that as t becomes large, the integrand oscillates very rapidly unless the energy interval $|E - E_0|$ is small compared with $\hbar/t$. If the interval for which $|E - E_0| \simeq \hbar/t$ holds is much narrower than ΔE —the width of $|g(E)|^2\rho(E)$—we get essentially no contribution to $C(t)$ because of strong cancellations. The characteristic time at which the modulus of the correlation amplitude starts becoming appreciably different from 1 is given by

$$t \simeq \frac{\hbar}{\Delta E}.$$

(2.1.70)

Even though this equation is obtained for a superposition state with a quasi-continuous energy spectrum, it also makes sense for a two-level system; in the spin-precession problem considered earlier, the state ket, which is initially $|S_x + \rangle$, starts losing its identity after $\sim 1/\omega = \hbar/(E_+ - E_-)$, as is evident from (2.1.60).

To summarize, as a result of time evolution the state ket of a physical system ceases to retain its original form after a time interval of order $\hbar/\Delta E$. In the literature this point is often said to illustrate the *time-energy uncertainty relation*

$$\Delta t \, \Delta E \simeq \hbar.$$

(2.1.71)

However, it is to be clearly understood that this time-energy uncertainty relation is of a very different nature from the uncertainty relation between two incompatible observables discussed in Section 1.4. In Chapter 5 we will come back to (2.1.71) in connection with time-dependent perturbation theory.

2.2. THE SCHRÖDINGER VERSUS THE HEISENBERG PICTURE

Unitary Operators

In the previous section we introduced the concept of time development by considering the time-evolution operator that affects state kets; that approach to quantum dynamics is known as the **Schrödinger picture**. There is another formulation of quantum dynamics where observables, rather than state kets, vary with time; this second approach is known as the **Heisenberg picture**. Before discussing the differences between the two approaches in detail, we digress to make some general comments on unitary operators.

Unitary operators are used for many different purposes in quantum mechanics. In this book we introduced (Section 1.5) an operator satisfying the unitarity property. In that section we were concerned with the question of how the base kets in one representation are related to those in some other representations. The state kets themselves are assumed not to change as we switch to a different set of base kets even though the numerical values of the expansion coefficients for $|\alpha\rangle$ are, of course, different in different representations. Subsequently we introduced two unitary operators that actually change the state kets, the translation operator of Section 1.6 and the time-evolution operator of Section 2.1. We have

$$|\alpha\rangle \to U|\alpha\rangle, \tag{2.2.1}$$

where U may stand for $\mathcal{T}(d\mathbf{x})$ or $\mathcal{U}(t, t_0)$. Here $U|\alpha\rangle$ is the state ket corresponding to a physical system that actually has undergone translation or time evolution.

It is important to keep in mind that under a unitary transformation that changes the state kets, the inner product of a state bra and a state ket remains unchanged:

$$\langle\beta|\alpha\rangle \to \langle\beta|U^\dagger U|\alpha\rangle = \langle\beta|\alpha\rangle. \tag{2.2.2}$$

Using the fact that these transformations affect the state kets but not operators, we can infer how $\langle\beta|X|\alpha\rangle$ must change:

$$\langle\beta|X|\alpha\rangle \to (\langle\beta|U^\dagger)\cdot X\cdot(U|\alpha\rangle) = \langle\beta|U^\dagger X U|\alpha\rangle. \tag{2.2.3}$$

We now make a very simple mathematical observation that follows from the associative axiom of multiplication:

$$(\langle\beta|U^\dagger)\cdot X\cdot(U|\alpha\rangle) = \langle\beta|\cdot(U^\dagger X U)\cdot|\alpha\rangle. \tag{2.2.4}$$

Is there any physics in this observation? This mathematical identity suggests two approaches to unitary transformations:

Approach 1:

$$|\alpha\rangle \to U|\alpha\rangle, \quad \text{with operators unchanged}, \tag{2.2.5a}$$

Approach 2:

$$X \to U^\dagger X U, \quad \text{with state kets unchanged}. \tag{2.2.5b}$$

In classical physics we do not introduce state kets, yet we talk about translation, time evolution, and the like. This is possible because these operations actually change quantities such as x and L, which are observables of classical mechanics. We therefore conjecture that a closer connection with classical physics may be established if we follow approach 2.

A simple example may be helpful here. We go back to the infinitesimal translation operator $\mathcal{T}(d\mathbf{x}')$. The formalism presented in Section 1.6 is based on approach 1; $\mathcal{T}(d\mathbf{x}')$ affects the state kets, not the position operator:

$$|\alpha\rangle \to \left(1 - \frac{i\mathbf{p}\cdot d\mathbf{x}'}{\hbar}\right)|\alpha\rangle,$$

$$\mathbf{x} \to \mathbf{x}. \tag{2.2.6}$$

In contrast, if we follow approach 2, we obtain

$$|\alpha\rangle \to |\alpha\rangle,$$

$$\mathbf{x} \to \left(1 + \frac{i\mathbf{p}\cdot d\mathbf{x}'}{\hbar}\right)\mathbf{x}\left(1 - \frac{i\mathbf{p}\cdot d\mathbf{x}'}{\hbar}\right)$$

$$= \mathbf{x} + \left(\frac{i}{\hbar}\right)[\mathbf{p}\cdot d\mathbf{x}', \mathbf{x}]$$

$$= \mathbf{x} + d\mathbf{x}'. \tag{2.2.7}$$

We leave it as an exercise for the reader to show that both approaches lead to the same result for the expectation value of $\mathbf{x}$:

$$\langle \mathbf{x} \rangle \to \langle \mathbf{x} \rangle + \langle d\mathbf{x}' \rangle. \tag{2.2.8}$$

State Kets and Observables in the Schrödinger and the Heisenberg Pictures

We now return to the time-evolution operator $\mathcal{U}(t, t_0)$. In the previous section we examined how state kets evolve with time. This means that we were following approach 1, known as the **Schrödinger picture** when applied to time evolution. Alternatively we may follow approach 2, known as the **Heisenberg picture** when applied to time evolution.

In the Schrödinger picture the operators corresponding to observables like x, p_y, and S_z are fixed in time, while state kets vary with time, as indicated in the previous section. In contrast, in the Heisenberg picture the operators corresponding to observables vary with time; the state kets are fixed, frozen so to speak, at what they were at t_0. It is convenient to set t_0 in $\mathcal{U}(t, t_0)$ to zero for simplicity and work with $\mathcal{U}(t)$, which is defined by

$$\mathcal{U}(t, t_0 = 0) \equiv \mathcal{U}(t) = \exp\left(\frac{-iHt}{\hbar}\right). \tag{2.2.9}$$

Motivated by (2.2.5b) of approach 2, we define the Heisenberg picture observable by

$$A^{(H)}(t) \equiv \mathcal{U}^\dagger(t) A^{(S)} \mathcal{U}(t), \tag{2.2.10}$$

where the superscripts H and S stand for Heisenberg and Schrödinger, respectively. At $t = 0$, the Heisenberg picture observable and the corresponding Schrödinger picture observable coincide:

$$A^{(H)}(0) = A^{(S)}. \tag{2.2.11}$$

The state kets also coincide between the two pictures at $t = 0$; at later t the Heisenberg picture state ket is frozen to what it was at $t = 0$:

$$|\alpha, t_0 = 0; t\rangle_H = |\alpha, t_0 = 0\rangle, \qquad (2.2.12)$$

independent of t. This is in dramatic contrast with the Schrödinger-picture state ket,

$$|\alpha, t_0 = 0; t\rangle_S = \mathcal{U}(t)|\alpha, t_0 = 0\rangle. \qquad (2.2.13)$$

The expectation value $\langle A \rangle$ is obviously the same in both pictures:

$$_S\langle \alpha, t_0 = 0; t|A^{(S)}|\alpha, t_0 = 0; t\rangle_S = \langle \alpha, t_0 = 0|\mathcal{U}^\dagger A^{(S)}\mathcal{U}|\alpha, t_0 = 0\rangle$$
$$= {}_H\langle \alpha, t_0 = 0; t|A^{(H)}(t)|\alpha, t_0 = 0; t\rangle_H. \qquad (2.2.14)$$

The Heisenberg Equation of Motion

We now derive the fundamental equation of motion in the Heisenberg picture. Assuming that $A^{(S)}$ does not depend explicitly on time, which is the case in most physical situations of interest, we obtain [by differentiating (2.2.10)]

$$\frac{dA^{(H)}}{dt} = \frac{\partial \mathcal{U}^\dagger}{\partial t} A^{(S)}\mathcal{U} + \mathcal{U}^\dagger A^{(S)} \frac{\partial \mathcal{U}}{\partial t}$$

$$= -\frac{1}{i\hbar}\mathcal{U}^\dagger H \mathcal{U} \mathcal{U}^\dagger A^{(S)}\mathcal{U} + \frac{1}{i\hbar}\mathcal{U}^\dagger A^{(S)}\mathcal{U}\mathcal{U}^\dagger H \mathcal{U}$$

$$= \frac{1}{i\hbar}[A^{(H)}, \mathcal{U}^\dagger H \mathcal{U}], \qquad (2.2.15)$$

where we have used [see (2.1.25)]

$$\frac{\partial \mathcal{U}}{\partial t} = \frac{1}{i\hbar}H\mathcal{U}, \qquad (2.2.16a)$$

$$\frac{\partial \mathcal{U}^\dagger}{\partial t} = -\frac{1}{i\hbar}\mathcal{U}^\dagger H. \qquad (2.2.16b)$$

Because H was originally introduced in the Schrödinger picture, we may be tempted to define

$$H^{(H)} = \mathcal{U}^\dagger H \mathcal{U} \qquad (2.2.17)$$

in accordance with (2.2.10). But in elementary applications where $\mathcal{U}$ is given by (2.2.9), $\mathcal{U}$ and H obviously commute; as a result,

$$\mathcal{U}^\dagger H \mathcal{U} = H, \qquad (2.2.18)$$

so it is all right to write (2.2.15) as

$$\frac{dA^{(H)}}{dt} = \frac{1}{i\hbar}[A^{(H)}, H]. \qquad (2.2.19)$$

This equation is known as the **Heisenberg equation of motion**. Notice that we have derived it using the properties of the time-evolution operator and the defining equation for $A^{(H)}$.

It is instructive to compare (2.2.19) with the classical equation of motion in Poisson bracket form. In classical physics, for a function A of q's and p's that does not involve time explicitly, we have (Goldstein 1980, 405-6)

$$\frac{dA}{dt} = [A, H]_{\text{classical}}. \tag{2.2.20}$$

Again, we see that Dirac's quantization rule (1.6.47) leads to the correct equation in quantum mechanics. Indeed, historically (2.2.19) was first written by P. A. M. Dirac, who—with his characteristic modesty—called it the Heisenberg equation of motion. It is worth noting, however, that (2.2.19) makes sense whether or not $A^{(H)}$ has a classical analogue. For example, the spin operator in the Heisenberg picture satisfies

$$\frac{dS_i^{(H)}}{dt} = \frac{1}{i\hbar}\left[S_i^{(H)}, H\right], \tag{2.2.21}$$

which can be used to discuss spin precession, but this equation has no classical counterpart because S_z *cannot* be written as a function of q's and p's. Rather than insisting on Dirac's rule, (1.6.47), we may argue that for quantities possessing classical counterparts, the correct classical equation can be obtained from the corresponding quantum-mechanical equation via the ansatz,

$$\frac{[\ ,\ ]}{i\hbar} \rightarrow [\ ,\ ]_{\text{classical}}. \tag{2.2.22}$$

Classical mechanics can be derived from quantum mechanics, but the opposite is not true.*

Free Particles; Ehrenfest's Theorem

Whether we work in the Schrödinger picture or in the Heisenberg picture, to be able to use the equations of motion we must first learn how to construct the appropriate Hamiltonian operator. For a physical system with classical analogues, we assume the Hamiltonian to be of the same form as in classical physics; we merely replace the classical x_i's and p_i's by the corresponding operators in quantum mechanics. With this assumption we can reproduce the correct classical equations in the classical limit. Whenever

---

*In this book we follow the order: the Schrödinger picture → the Heisenberg picture → classical. For an enlightening treatment of the same subject in opposite order, classical → the Heisenberg picture → the Schrödinger picture, see Finkelstein (1973), 68–70 and 109.

an ambiguity arises because of noncommuting observables, we attempt to resolve it by requiring H to be Hermitian; for instance, we write the quantum-mechanical analogue of the classical product xp as $\frac{1}{2}(xp + px)$. When the physical system in question has no classical analogues, we can only guess the structure of the Hamiltonian operator. We try various forms until we get the Hamiltonian that leads to results agreeing with empirical observation.

In practical applications it is often necessary to evaluate the commutator of x_i (or p_i) with functions of x_j and p_j. To this end the following formulas are found to be useful:

$$[x_i, F(\mathbf{p})] = i\hbar \frac{\partial F}{\partial p_i} \qquad (2.2.23a)$$

and

$$[p_i, G(\mathbf{x})] = -i\hbar \frac{\partial G}{\partial x_i}, \qquad (2.2.23b)$$

where F and G are functions that can be expanded in powers of p_j's and x_j's, respectively. We can easily prove both formulas by repeatedly applying (1.6.50e).

We are now in a position to apply the Heisenberg equation of motion to a free particle of mass m. The Hamiltonian is taken to be of the same form as in classical mechanics:

$$H = \frac{\mathbf{p}^2}{2m} = \frac{\left(p_x^2 + p_y^2 + p_z^2\right)}{2m}. \qquad (2.2.24)$$

We look at the observables p_i and x_i, which are understood to be the momentum and the position operator in the Heisenberg picture even though we omit the superscript (H). Because p_i commutes with any function of p_j's, we have

$$\frac{dp_i}{dt} = \frac{1}{i\hbar}[p_i, H] = 0. \qquad (2.2.25)$$

Thus for a free particle, the momentum operator is a constant of the motion, which means that $p_i(t)$ is the same as $p_i(0)$ at all times. Quite generally, it is evident from the Heisenberg equation of motion (2.2.19) that whenever $A^{(H)}$ commutes with the Hamiltonian, $A^{(H)}$ is a constant of the motion. Next,

$$\frac{dx_i}{dt} = \frac{1}{i\hbar}[x_i, H] = \frac{1}{i\hbar}\frac{1}{2m}i\hbar\frac{\partial}{\partial p_i}\left(\sum_{j=1}^{3} p_j^2\right)$$

$$= \frac{p_i}{m} = \frac{p_i(0)}{m}, \qquad (2.2.26)$$

where we have taken advantage of (2.2.23a), so we have the solution

$$x_i(t) = x_i(0) + \left(\frac{p_i(0)}{m}\right)t, \tag{2.2.27}$$

which is reminiscent of the classical trajectory equation for a uniform rectilinear motion. It is important to note that even though we have

$$\left[x_i(0), x_j(0)\right] = 0 \tag{2.2.28}$$

at equal times, the commutator of the x_i's at *different* times does *not* vanish; specifically,

$$\left[x_i(t), x_i(0)\right] = \left[\frac{p_i(0)t}{m}, x_i(0)\right] = \frac{-i\hbar t}{m}. \tag{2.2.29}$$

Applying the uncertainty relation (1.4.53) to this commutator, we obtain

$$\langle(\Delta x_i)^2\rangle_t \langle(\Delta x_i)^2\rangle_{t=0} \geq \frac{\hbar^2 t^2}{4m^2}. \tag{2.2.30}$$

Among other things, this relation implies that even if the particle is well localized at $t = 0$, its position becomes more and more uncertain with time, a conclusion which can also be obtained by studying the time-evolution behavior of free-particle wave packets in wave mechanics.

We now add a potential $V(\mathbf{x})$ to our earlier free-particle Hamiltonian:

$$H = \frac{\mathbf{p}^2}{2m} + V(\mathbf{x}). \tag{2.2.31}$$

Here $V(\mathbf{x})$ is to be understood as a function of the x-, y-, and z-operators. Using (2.2.23b) this time, we obtain

$$\frac{dp_i}{dt} = \frac{1}{i\hbar}\left[p_i, V(\mathbf{x})\right] = -\frac{\partial}{\partial x_i}V(\mathbf{x}). \tag{2.2.32}$$

On the other hand, we see that

$$\frac{dx_i}{dt} = \frac{p_i}{m} \tag{2.2.33}$$

still holds because x_i commutes with the newly added term $V(\mathbf{x})$. We can use the Heisenberg equation of motion once again to deduce

$$\frac{d^2 x_i}{dt^2} = \frac{1}{i\hbar}\left[\frac{dx_i}{dt}, H\right] = \frac{1}{i\hbar}\left[\frac{p_i}{m}, H\right]$$

$$= \frac{1}{m}\frac{dp_i}{dt}. \tag{2.2.34}$$

Combining this with (2.2.32), we finally obtain in vectorial form

$$m\frac{d^2\mathbf{x}}{dt^2} = -\nabla V(\mathbf{x}). \tag{2.2.35}$$

This is the quantum-mechanical analogue of Newton's second law. By taking the expectation values of both sides with respect to a Heisenberg state ket that does *not* move with time, we obtain

$$m\frac{d^2}{dt^2}\langle \mathbf{x} \rangle = \frac{d\langle \mathbf{p} \rangle}{dt} = -\langle \nabla V(\mathbf{x}) \rangle. \qquad (2.2.36)$$

This is known as the **Ehrenfest theorem** after P. Ehrenfest, who derived it in 1927 using the formalism of wave mechanics. When written in this expectation form, its validity is independent of whether we are using the Heisenberg or the Schrödinger picture; after all, the expectation values are the same in the two pictures. In contrast, the operator form (2.2.35) is meaningful only if we understand $\mathbf{x}$ and $\mathbf{p}$ to be Heisenberg-picture operators.

We note that in (2.2.36) the $\hbar$'s have completely disappeared. It is therefore not surprising that the center of a wave packet moves like a *classical* particle subjected to $V(\mathbf{x})$.

Base Kets and Transition Amplitudes

So far we have avoided asking how the base kets evolve in time. A common misconception is that as time goes on, all kets move in the Schrödinger picture and are stationary in the Heisenberg picture. This is *not* the case, as we will make clear shortly. The important point is to distinguish the behavior of state kets from that of base kets.

We started our discussion of ket spaces in Section 1.2 by remarking that the eigenkets of observables are to be used as base kets. What happens to the defining eigenvalue equation

$$A|a'\rangle = a'|a'\rangle \qquad (2.2.37)$$

with time? In the Schrödinger picture, A does not change, so the base kets, obtained as the solutions to this eigenvalue equation at $t = 0$, for instance, must remain unchanged. Unlike state kets, the base kets do *not* change in the Schrödinger picture.

The whole situation is very different in the Heisenberg picture, where the eigenvalue equation we must study is for the time-dependent operator

$$A^{(H)}(t) = \mathcal{U}^\dagger A(0)\mathcal{U}. \qquad (2.2.38)$$

From (2.2.37) evaluated at $t = 0$, when the two pictures coincide, we deduce

$$\mathcal{U}^\dagger A(0)\mathcal{U}\mathcal{U}^\dagger|a'\rangle = a'\mathcal{U}^\dagger|a'\rangle, \qquad (2.2.39)$$

which implies an eigenvalue equation for $A^{(H)}$:

$$A^{(H)}(\mathcal{U}^\dagger|a'\rangle) = a'(\mathcal{U}^\dagger|a'\rangle). \qquad (2.2.40)$$

If we continue to maintain the view that the eigenkets of observables form the base kets, then $\{\mathcal{U}^\dagger|a'\rangle\}$ must be used as the base kets in the Heisenberg picture. As time goes on, the Heisenberg-picture base kets, denoted by $|a', t\rangle_H$, move as follows:

$$|a', t\rangle_H = \mathcal{U}^\dagger |a'\rangle. \tag{2.2.41}$$

Because of the appearance of $\mathcal{U}^\dagger$ rather than $\mathcal{U}$ in (2.2.41), the Heisenberg-picture base kets are seen to rotate oppositely when compared with the Schrödinger-picture state kets; specifically, $|a', t\rangle_H$ satisfies the "wrong-sign Schrödinger equation"

$$i\hbar \frac{\partial}{\partial t} |a', t\rangle_H = - H |a', t\rangle_H. \tag{2.2.42}$$

As for the eigenvalues themselves, we see from (2.2.40) that they are unchanged with time. This is consistent with the theorem on unitary equivalent observables discussed in Section 1.5. Notice also the following expansion for $A^{(H)}(t)$ in terms of the base kets and bras of the Heisenberg picture:

$$
\begin{aligned}
A^{(H)}(t) &= \sum_{a'} |a', t\rangle_H a'_H \langle a', t| \\
&= \sum_{a'} \mathcal{U}^\dagger |a'\rangle a' \langle a'| \mathcal{U} \\
&= \mathcal{U}^\dagger A^{(S)} \mathcal{U},
\end{aligned}
\tag{2.2.43}
$$

which shows that everything is quite consistent provided that the Heisenberg base kets change as in (2.2.41).

We see that the expansion coefficients of a state ket in terms of base kets are the same in both pictures:

$$c_{a'}(t) = \underbrace{\langle a'|}_{\text{base bra}} \cdot \underbrace{(\mathcal{U}|\alpha, t_0 = 0\rangle)}_{\text{state ket}} \quad \text{(the Schrödinger picture)} \tag{2.2.44a}$$

$$c_{a'}(t) = \underbrace{(\langle a'|\mathcal{U})}_{\text{base bra}} \cdot \underbrace{|\alpha, t_0 = 0\rangle}_{\text{state ket}} \quad \text{(the Heisenberg picture)}. \tag{2.2.44b}$$

Pictorially, we may say that the cosine of the angle between the state ket and the base ket is the same whether we rotate the state ket counterclockwise or the base ket clockwise. These considerations apply equally well to base kets that exhibit a continuous spectrum; in particular, the wave function $\langle x'|\alpha\rangle$ can be regarded either as (1) the inner product of the stationary position eigenbra with the moving state ket (the Schrödinger picture) or as (2) the inner product of the moving position eigenbra with the stationary state ket (the Heisenberg picture). We will discuss the time dependence of the wave function in Section 2.4, where we will derive the celebrated wave equation of Schrödinger.

To illustrate further the equivalence between the two pictures, we study transition amplitudes, which will play a fundamental role in Section

TABLE 2.1. The Schrödinger Picture Versus the Heisenberg Picture

	Schrödinger picture	Heisenberg picture
State ket	Moving: (2.1.5), (2.1.27)	Stationary
Observable	Stationary	Moving: (2.2.10), (2.2.19)
Base ket	Stationary	Moving oppositely: (2.2.41), (2.2.42)

2.5. Suppose there is a physical system prepared at $t = 0$ to be in an eigenstate of observable A with eigenvalue a'. At some later time t we may ask, What is the probability amplitude, known as the **transition amplitude**, for the system to be found in an eigenstate of observable B with eigenvalue b'? Here A and B can be the same or different. In the Schrödinger picture the state ket at t is given by $\mathscr{U}|a'\rangle$, while the base kets $|a'\rangle$ and $|b'\rangle$ do not vary with time; so we have

$$\underbrace{\langle b'|}_{\text{base bra}} \cdot \underbrace{(\mathscr{U}|a'\rangle)}_{\text{state ket}} \qquad (2.2.45)$$

for this transition amplitude. In contrast, in the Heisenberg picture the state ket is stationary, that is, it remains as $|a'\rangle$ at all times, but the base kets evolve oppositely. So the transition amplitude is

$$\underbrace{(\langle b'|\mathscr{U})}_{\text{base bra}} \cdot \underbrace{|a'\rangle}_{\text{state ket}} . \qquad (2.2.46)$$

Obviously (2.2.45) and (2.2.46) are the same. They can both be written as

$$\langle b'|\mathscr{U}(t,0)|a'\rangle. \qquad (2.2.47)$$

In some loose sense this is the transition amplitude for "going" from state $|a'\rangle$ to state $|b'\rangle$.

To conclude this section let us summarize the differences between the Schrödinger picture and the Heisenberg picture; see Table 2.1.

2.3. SIMPLE HARMONIC OSCILLATOR

The simple harmonic oscillator is one of the most important problems in quantum mechanics. From a pedagogical point of view it can be used to illustrate the basic concepts and methods in quantum mechanics. From a practical point of view it has applications in a variety of branches of modern physics—molecular spectroscopy, solid state physics, nuclear structure, quantum field theory, quantum optics, quantum statistical mechanics, and so forth. From a historical point of view it was M. Planck's proposal to associate discrete units of energy with radiation oscillators that led to the birth of quantum concepts. A thorough understanding of the properties of quantum-mechanical oscillators is indispensable for any serious student of modern physics.

Energy Eigenkets and Energy Eigenvalues

We begin our discussion with Dirac's elegant operator method, which is based on the earlier work of M. Born and N. Wiener, to obtain the energy eigenkets and energy eigenvalues of the simple harmonic oscillator. The basic Hamiltonian is

$$H = \frac{p^2}{2m} + \frac{m\omega^2 x^2}{2}, \tag{2.3.1}$$

where ω is the angular frequency of the classical oscillator related to the spring constant k in Hooke's law via $\omega = \sqrt{k/m}$. The operators x and p are, of course, Hermitian. It is convenient to define two non-Hermitian operators,

$$a = \sqrt{\frac{m\omega}{2\hbar}} \left(x + \frac{ip}{m\omega} \right), \qquad a^\dagger = \sqrt{\frac{m\omega}{2\hbar}} \left(x - \frac{ip}{m\omega} \right), \tag{2.3.2}$$

known as the **annihilation operator** and the **creation operator**, respectively, for reasons that will become evident shortly. Using the canonical commutation relations, we readily obtain

$$[a, a^\dagger] = \left(\frac{1}{2\hbar} \right) (-i[x, p] + i[p, x]) = 1. \tag{2.3.3}$$

We also define the number operator

$$N = a^\dagger a, \tag{2.3.4}$$

which is obviously Hermitian. It is straightforward to show that

$$a^\dagger a = \left(\frac{m\omega}{2\hbar} \right) \left(x^2 + \frac{p^2}{m^2\omega^2} \right) + \left(\frac{i}{2\hbar} \right) [x, p]$$

$$= \frac{H}{\hbar\omega} - \frac{1}{2}, \tag{2.3.5}$$

so we have an important relation between the number operator and the Hamiltonian operator:

$$H = \hbar\omega \left(N + \tfrac{1}{2} \right). \tag{2.3.6}$$

Because H is just a linear function of N, N can be diagonalized simultaneously with H. We denote an energy eigenket of N by its eigenvalue n, so

$$N|n\rangle = n|n\rangle. \tag{2.3.7}$$

We will later show that n must be a nonnegative integer. Because of (2.3.6) we also have

$$H|n\rangle = \left(n + \tfrac{1}{2} \right) \hbar\omega |n\rangle, \tag{2.3.8}$$

which means that the energy eigenvalues are given by

$$E_n = (n + \tfrac{1}{2})\hbar\omega. \tag{2.3.9}$$

To appreciate the physical significance of a, $a^\dagger$, and N, let us first note that

$$[N, a] = [a^\dagger a, a] = a^\dagger[a, a] + [a^\dagger, a]a = -a, \tag{2.3.10}$$

where we have used (2.3.3). Likewise, we can derive

$$[N, a^\dagger] = a^\dagger. \tag{2.3.11}$$

As a result, we have

$$Na^\dagger|n\rangle = ([N, a^\dagger] + a^\dagger N)|n\rangle$$
$$= (n+1)a^\dagger|n\rangle \tag{2.3.12a}$$

and

$$Na|n\rangle = ([N, a] + aN)|n\rangle$$
$$= (n-1)a|n\rangle. \tag{2.3.12b}$$

These relations imply that $a^\dagger|n\rangle(a|n\rangle)$ is also an eigenket of N with eigenvalue increased (decreased) by one. Because the increase (decrease) of n by one amounts to the creation (annihilation) of one quantum unit of energy $\hbar\omega$, the term *creation operator* (*annihilation operator*) for $a^\dagger(a)$ is deemed appropriate.

Equation (2.3.12b) implies that $a|n\rangle$ and $|n-1\rangle$ are the same up to a multiplicative constant. We write

$$a|n\rangle = c|n-1\rangle, \tag{2.3.13}$$

where c is a numerical constant to be determined from the requirement that both $|n\rangle$ and $|n-1\rangle$ be normalized. First, note that

$$\langle n|a^\dagger a|n\rangle = |c|^2. \tag{2.3.14}$$

We can evaluate the left-hand side of (2.3.14) by noting that $a^\dagger a$ is just the number operator, so

$$n = |c|^2. \tag{2.3.15}$$

Taking c to be real and positive by convention, we finally obtain

$$a|n\rangle = \sqrt{n}\,|n-1\rangle. \tag{2.3.16}$$

Similarly, it is easy to show that

$$a^\dagger|n\rangle = \sqrt{n+1}\,|n+1\rangle. \tag{2.3.17}$$

Suppose that we keep on applying the annihilation operator a to both sides of (2.3.16):

$$a^2|n\rangle = \sqrt{n(n-1)}\,|n-2\rangle,$$
$$a^3|n\rangle = \sqrt{n(n-1)(n-2)}\,|n-3\rangle, \tag{2.3.18}$$

We can obtain numerical operator eigenkets with smaller and smaller n until the sequence terminates, which is bound to happen whenever we start with a positive integer n. One may argue that if we start with a noninteger n, the sequence will not terminate, leading to eigenkets with a negative value of n. But we also have the positivity requirement for the norm of $a|n\rangle$:

$$n = \langle n|N|n\rangle = \left(\langle n|a^{\dagger}\right)\cdot\left(a|n\rangle\right) \ge 0, \qquad (2.3.19)$$

which implies that n can never be negative! So we conclude that the sequence must terminate with $n = 0$ and that the allowed values of n are nonnegative integers.

Because the smallest possible value of n is zero, the ground state of the harmonic oscillator has

$$E_0 = \tfrac{1}{2}\hbar\omega. \qquad (2.3.20)$$

We can now successively apply the creation operator $a^{\dagger}$ to the ground state $|0\rangle$. Using (2.3.17), we obtain

$$|1\rangle = a^{\dagger}|0\rangle,$$

$$|2\rangle = \left(\frac{a^{\dagger}}{\sqrt{2}}\right)|1\rangle = \left[\frac{(a^{\dagger})^2}{\sqrt{2}}\right]|0\rangle,$$

$$|3\rangle = \left(\frac{a^{\dagger}}{\sqrt{3}}\right)|2\rangle = \left[\frac{(a^{\dagger})^3}{\sqrt{3!}}\right]|0\rangle, \qquad (2.3.21)$$

$$\vdots$$

$$|n\rangle = \left[\frac{(a^{\dagger})^n}{\sqrt{n!}}\right]|0\rangle.$$

In this way we have succeeded in constructing simultaneous eigenkets of N and H with energy eigenvalues

$$E_n = \left(n + \tfrac{1}{2}\right)\hbar\omega, \quad (n = 0,1,2,3,\dots). \qquad (2.3.22)$$

From (2.3.16), (2.3.17), and the orthonormality requirement for $\{|n\rangle\}$, we obtain the matrix elements

$$\langle n'|a|n\rangle = \sqrt{n}\,\delta_{n',n-1}, \qquad \langle n'|a^{\dagger}|n\rangle = \sqrt{n+1}\,\delta_{n',n+1}. \qquad (2.3.23)$$

Using these together with

$$x = \sqrt{\frac{\hbar}{2m\omega}}\,(a + a^{\dagger}), \qquad p = i\sqrt{\frac{m\hbar\omega}{2}}\,(-a + a^{\dagger}), \qquad (2.3.24)$$

we derive the matrix elements of the x and p operators:

$$\langle n'|x|n\rangle = \sqrt{\frac{\hbar}{2m\omega}}\,\left(\sqrt{n}\,\delta_{n',n-1} + \sqrt{n+1}\,\delta_{n',n+1}\right), \qquad (2.3.25a)$$

$$\langle n'|p|n\rangle = i\sqrt{\frac{m\hbar\omega}{2}}\,\left(-\sqrt{n}\,\delta_{n',n-1} + \sqrt{n+1}\,\delta_{n',n+1}\right). \qquad (2.3.25b)$$

Notice that neither x nor p is diagonal in the N-representation we are using. This is not surprising because x and p, like a and $a^\dagger$, do not commute with N.

The operator method can also be used to obtain the energy eigenfunctions in position space. Let us start with the ground state defined by

$$a|0\rangle = 0, \qquad (2.3.26)$$

which, in the x-representation, reads

$$\langle x'|a|0\rangle = \sqrt{\frac{m\omega}{2\hbar}} \, \langle x'|\left(x + \frac{ip}{m\omega} \right)|0\rangle = 0. \qquad (2.3.27)$$

Recalling (1.7.17), we can regard this as a differential equation for the ground-state wave function $\langle x'|0\rangle$:

$$\left(x' + x_0^2 \frac{d}{dx'} \right)\langle x'|0\rangle = 0, \qquad (2.3.28)$$

where we have introduced

$$x_0 \equiv \sqrt{\frac{\hbar}{m\omega}} \, , \qquad (2.3.29)$$

which sets the length scale of the oscillator. We see that the normalized solution to (2.3.28) is

$$\langle x'|0\rangle = \left(\frac{1}{\pi^{1/4}\sqrt{x_0}} \right)\exp\left[-\frac{1}{2}\left(\frac{x'}{x_0} \right)^2 \right]. \qquad (2.3.30)$$

We can also obtain the energy eigenfunctions for excited states by evaluating

$$\langle x'|1\rangle = \langle x'|a^\dagger|0\rangle = \left(\frac{1}{\sqrt{2}\,x_0} \right)\left(x' - x_0^2 \frac{d}{dx'} \right)\langle x'|0\rangle,$$

$$\langle x'|2\rangle = \left(\frac{1}{\sqrt{2}} \right)\langle x'|(a^\dagger)^2|0\rangle = \left(\frac{1}{\sqrt{2!}} \right)\left(\frac{1}{\sqrt{2}\,x_0} \right)^2\left(x' - x_0^2 \frac{d}{dx'} \right)^2\langle x'|0\rangle, \ldots$$

$$(2.3.31)$$

In general, we obtain

$$\langle x'|n\rangle = \left(\frac{1}{\pi^{1/4}\sqrt{2^n n!}} \right)\left(\frac{1}{x_0^{n+1/2}} \right)\left(x' - x_0^2 \frac{d}{dx'} \right)^n\exp\left[-\frac{1}{2}\left(\frac{x'}{x_0} \right)^2 \right].$$

$$(2.3.32)$$

It is instructive to look at the expectation values of x^2 and p^2 for the ground state. First, note that

$$x^2 = \left(\frac{\hbar}{2m\omega}\right)(a^2 + a^{\dagger 2} + a^\dagger a + aa^\dagger). \qquad (2.3.33)$$

When we take the expectation value of x^2, only the last term in (2.3.33) yields a nonvanishing contribution:

$$\langle x^2 \rangle = \frac{\hbar}{2m\omega} = \frac{x_0^2}{2}. \qquad (2.3.34)$$

Likewise,

$$\langle p^2 \rangle = \frac{\hbar m\omega}{2}. \qquad (2.3.35)$$

It follows that the expectation values of the kinetic and the potential energies are, respectively,

$$\left\langle \frac{p^2}{2m} \right\rangle = \frac{\hbar\omega}{4} = \frac{\langle H \rangle}{2} \quad \text{and} \quad \left\langle \frac{m\omega^2 x^2}{2} \right\rangle = \frac{\hbar\omega}{4} = \frac{\langle H \rangle}{2}, \qquad (2.3.36)$$

as expected from the virial theorem. From (2.3.25a) and (2.3.25b), it follows that

$$\langle x \rangle = \langle p \rangle = 0, \qquad (2.3.37)$$

which also holds for the excited states. We therefore have

$$\langle (\Delta x)^2 \rangle = \langle x^2 \rangle = \frac{\hbar}{2m\omega} \quad \text{and} \quad \langle (\Delta p)^2 \rangle = \langle p^2 \rangle = \frac{\hbar m\omega}{2}, \qquad (2.3.38)$$

and we see that the uncertainty relation is satisfied in the minimum uncertainty product form:

$$\langle (\Delta x)^2 \rangle \langle (\Delta p)^2 \rangle = \frac{\hbar^2}{4}. \qquad (2.3.39)$$

This is not surprising because the ground-state wave function has a Gaussian shape. In contrast, the uncertainty products for the excited states are larger:

$$\langle (\Delta x)^2 \rangle \langle (\Delta p)^2 \rangle = \left(n + \tfrac{1}{2}\right)^2 \hbar^2, \qquad (2.3.40)$$

as the reader may easily verify.

Time Development of the Oscillator

So far we have not discussed the time evolution of oscillator state kets nor of observables like x and p. Everything we have done is supposed to hold at some instant of time, say at $t = 0$; the operators x, p, a, and $a^\dagger$ are to be regarded either as Schrödinger-picture operators (at all t) or as Heisenberg-picture operators at $t = 0$. In the remaining part of this section, we work exclusively in the Heisenberg picture, which means that x, p, a, and $a^\dagger$ are all time-dependent even though we do not explicitly write $x^{(H)}(t)$, and so forth.

The Heisenberg equations of motion for p and x are, from (2.2.32) and (2.2.33),

$$\frac{dp}{dt} = -m\omega^2 x \qquad (2.3.41a)$$

and

$$\frac{dx}{dt} = \frac{p}{m}. \qquad (2.3.41b)$$

This pair of coupled differential equations is equivalent to two uncoupled differential equations for a and $a^\dagger$, namely,

$$\frac{da}{dt} = \sqrt{\frac{m\omega}{2\hbar}}\left(\frac{p}{m} - i\omega x\right) = -i\omega a \qquad (2.3.42a)$$

and

$$\frac{da^\dagger}{dt} = i\omega a^\dagger, \qquad (2.3.42b)$$

whose solutions are

$$a(t) = a(0)\exp(-i\omega t) \quad \text{and} \quad a^\dagger(t) = a^\dagger(0)\exp(i\omega t). \qquad (2.3.43)$$

Incidentally, these relations explicitly show that N and H are *time-independent* operators even in the Heisenberg picture, as they must be. In terms of x and p, we can rewrite (2.3.43) as

$$x(t) + \frac{ip(t)}{m\omega} = x(0)\exp(-i\omega t) + i\left[\frac{p(0)}{m\omega}\right]\exp(-i\omega t),$$

$$x(t) - \frac{ip(t)}{m\omega} = x(0)\exp(i\omega t) - i\left[\frac{p(0)}{m\omega}\right]\exp(i\omega t). \qquad (2.3.44)$$

Equating the Hermitian and anti-Hermitian parts of both sides separately, we deduce

$$x(t) = x(0)\cos\omega t + \left[\frac{p(0)}{m\omega}\right]\sin\omega t \qquad (2.3.45a)$$

and

$$p(t) = -m\omega x(0)\sin\omega t + p(0)\cos\omega t. \qquad (2.3.45b)$$

These look the same as the classical equations of motion. We see that the x and p operators "oscillate" just like their classical analogues.

For pedagogical reasons we now present an alternative derivation of (2.3.45a). Instead of solving the Heisenberg equation of motion, we attempt to evaluate

$$x(t) = \exp\left(\frac{iHt}{\hbar}\right)x(0)\exp\left(\frac{-iHt}{\hbar}\right). \qquad (2.3.46)$$

To this end we record a very useful formula:

$$\exp(iG\lambda)A\exp(-iG\lambda) = A + i\lambda[G,A] + \left(\frac{i^2\lambda^2}{2!}\right)[G,[G,A]] +$$

$$\cdots + \left(\frac{i^n\lambda^n}{n!}\right)[G,[G,[G,\ldots.[G,A]]].\ldots] + \cdots,$$

$$(2.3.47)$$

where G is a Hermitian operator and λ is a real parameter. We leave the proof of this formula, known as the **Baker-Hausdorff lemma** as an exercise. Applying this formula to (2.3.46), we obtain

$$\exp\left(\frac{iHt}{\hbar}\right)x(0)\exp\left(\frac{-iHt}{\hbar}\right)$$

$$= x(0) + \left(\frac{it}{\hbar}\right)[H,x(0)] + \left(\frac{i^2t^2}{2!\hbar^2}\right)[H,[H,x(0)]] + \cdots. \qquad (2.3.48)$$

Each term on the right-hand side can be reduced to either x or p by repeatedly using

$$[H,x(0)] = \frac{-i\hbar p(0)}{m} \qquad (2.3.49a)$$

and

$$[H,p(0)] = i\hbar m\omega^2 x(0). \qquad (2.3.49b)$$

Thus

$$\exp\left(\frac{iHt}{\hbar}\right)x(0)\exp\left(\frac{-iHt}{\hbar}\right) = x(0) + \left[\frac{p(0)}{m}\right]t - \left(\frac{1}{2!}\right)t^2\omega^2 x(0)$$

$$- \left(\frac{1}{3!}\right)\frac{t^3\omega^2 p(0)}{m} + \cdots$$

$$= x(0)\cos\omega t + \left[\frac{p(0)}{m\omega}\right]\sin\omega t, \qquad (2.3.50)$$

in agreement with (2.3.45a).

From (2.3.45a) and (2.3.45b), one may be tempted to conclude that $\langle x \rangle$ and $\langle p \rangle$ always oscillate with angular frequency ω. However, this inference is not correct. Take any energy eigenstate characterized by a definite value of n; the expectation value $\langle n|x(t)|n \rangle$ vanishes because the operators $x(0)$ and $p(0)$ change n by ± 1 and $|n\rangle$ and $|n \pm 1\rangle$ are orthogonal. This point is also obvious from our earlier conclusion (see Section 2.1) that the expectation value of an observable taken with respect to a stationary state does not vary with time. To observe oscillations reminiscent of the classical oscillator, we must look at a *superposition* of energy eigenstates such as

$$|\alpha\rangle = c_0|0\rangle + c_1|1\rangle. \qquad (2.3.51)$$

The expectation value of $x(t)$ taken with respect to (2.3.51) does oscillate, as the reader may readily verify.

We have seen that an energy eigenstate does not behave like the classical oscillator—in the sense of oscillating expectation values for x and p—no matter how large n may be. We may logically ask, How can we construct a superposition of energy eigenstates that most closely imitates the classical oscillator? In wave-function language, we want a wave packet that bounces back and forth without spreading in shape. It turns out that a *coherent state* defined by the eigenvalue equation for the non-Hermitian annihilation operator a,

$$a|\lambda\rangle = \lambda|\lambda\rangle, \qquad (2.3.52)$$

with, in general, a complex eigenvalue λ does the desired job. The coherent state has many other remarkable properties:

1. When expressed as a superposition of energy (or N) eigenstates,

$$|\lambda\rangle = \sum_{n=0}^{\infty} f(n)|n\rangle, \qquad (2.3.53)$$

the distribution of $|f(n)|^2$ with respect to n is of the Poisson type about some mean value $\bar{n}$:

$$|f(n)|^2 = \left(\frac{\bar{n}^n}{n!}\right)\exp(-\bar{n}). \qquad (2.3.54)$$

2. It can be obtained by translating the oscillator ground state by some finite distance.
3. It satisfies the minimum uncertainty product relation at all times.

A systematic study of coherent states, pioneered by R. Glauber, is very rewarding; the reader is urged to work out an exercise on this subject at the end of this chapter.*

2.4. SCHRÖDINGER'S WAVE EQUATION

Time-Dependent Wave Equation

We now turn to the Schrödinger picture and examine the time evolution of $|\alpha, t_0; t\rangle$ in the x-representation. In other words, our task is to study the behavior of the wave function

$$\psi(\mathbf{x}', t) = \langle \mathbf{x}'|\alpha, t_0; t\rangle \qquad (2.4.1)$$

as a function of time, where $|\alpha, t_0; t\rangle$ is a state ket in the Schrödinger

---

*For applications to laser physics, see Sargent, Scully, and Lamb (1974).

picture at time t, and $\langle x'|$ is a time-independent position eigenbra with eigenvalue x'. The Hamiltonian operator is taken to be

$$H = \frac{\mathbf{p}^2}{2m} + V(\mathbf{x}). \qquad (2.4.2)$$

The potential $V(\mathbf{x})$ is a Hermitian operator; it is also local in the sense that in the x-representation we have

$$\langle \mathbf{x}''|V(\mathbf{x})|\mathbf{x}'\rangle = V(\mathbf{x}')\delta^3(\mathbf{x}' - \mathbf{x}''), \qquad (2.4.3)$$

where $V(\mathbf{x}')$ is a real function of $\mathbf{x}'$. Later in this book we will consider more-complicated Hamiltonians—a time-dependent potential $V(\mathbf{x}, t)$; a nonlocal but separable potential where the right-hand side of (2.4.3) is replaced by $v_1(\mathbf{x}'')v_2(\mathbf{x}')$; a momentum-dependent interaction of the form $\mathbf{p} \cdot \mathbf{A} + \mathbf{A} \cdot \mathbf{p}$, where $\mathbf{A}$ is the vector potential in electrodynamics, and so on.

We now derive Schrödinger's time-dependent wave equation. We first write the Schrödinger equation for a state ket (2.1.27) in the x-representation:

$$i\hbar \frac{\partial}{\partial t} \langle \mathbf{x}'|\alpha, t_0; t \rangle = \langle \mathbf{x}'|H|\alpha, t_0; t \rangle, \qquad (2.4.4)$$

where we have used the fact that the position eigenbras in the Schrödinger picture do not change with time. Using (1.7.20), we can write the kinetic-energy contribution to the right-hand side of (2.4.4) as

$$\left\langle \mathbf{x}' \left| \frac{\mathbf{p}^2}{2m} \right| \alpha, t_0; t \right\rangle = -\left(\frac{\hbar^2}{2m} \right) \nabla'^2 \langle \mathbf{x}'|\alpha, t_0; t \rangle. \qquad (2.4.5)$$

As for $V(\mathbf{x})$, we simply use

$$\langle \mathbf{x}'|V(\mathbf{x}) = \langle \mathbf{x}'|V(\mathbf{x}'), \qquad (2.4.6)$$

where $V(\mathbf{x}')$ is no longer an operator. Combining everything, we deduce

$$i\hbar \frac{\partial}{\partial t} \langle \mathbf{x}'|\alpha, t_0; t \rangle = -\left(\frac{\hbar^2}{2m} \right) \nabla'^2 \langle \mathbf{x}'|\alpha, t_0; t \rangle + V(\mathbf{x}')\langle \mathbf{x}'|\alpha, t_0; t \rangle,$$

$$(2.4.7)$$

which we recognize to be the celebrated time-dependent wave equation of E. Schrödinger, usually written as

$$i\hbar \frac{\partial}{\partial t} \psi(\mathbf{x}', t) = -\left(\frac{\hbar^2}{2m} \right) \nabla'^2 \psi(\mathbf{x}', t) + V(\mathbf{x}')\psi(\mathbf{x}', t). \qquad (2.4.8)$$

The quantum mechanics based on wave equation (2.4.8) is known as **wave mechanics**. This equation is, in fact, the starting point of many textbooks on quantum mechanics. In our formalism, however, this is just the Schrödinger equation for a state ket written explicitly in the x-basis when the Hamiltonian operator is taken to be (2.4.2).

The Time-Independent Wave Equation

We now derive the partial differential equation satisfied by energy eigenfunctions. We showed in Section 2.1 that the time dependence of a stationary state is given by $\exp(-iE_{a'}t/\hbar)$. This enables us to write its wave function as

$$\langle \mathbf{x}'|a', t_0; t \rangle = \langle \mathbf{x}'|a' \rangle \exp\left(\frac{-iE_{a'}t}{\hbar} \right), \qquad (2.4.9)$$

where it is understood that initially the system is prepared in a simultaneous eigenstate of A and H with eigenvalues a' and $E_{a'}$, respectively. Let us now substitute (2.4.9) into the time-dependent Schrödinger equation (2.4.7). We are then led to

$$-\left(\frac{\hbar^2}{2m} \right) \nabla'^2 \langle \mathbf{x}'|a' \rangle + V(\mathbf{x}')\langle \mathbf{x}'|a' \rangle = E_{a'}\langle \mathbf{x}'|a' \rangle. \qquad (2.4.10)$$

This partial differential equation is satisfied by the energy eigenfunction $\langle \mathbf{x}'|a' \rangle$ with energy eigenvalue $E_{a'}$. Actually, in wave mechanics where the Hamiltonian operator is given as a function of $\mathbf{x}$ and $\mathbf{p}$, as in (2.4.2), it is not necessary to refer explicitly to observable A that commutes with H because we can always choose A to be that function of the observables $\mathbf{x}$ and $\mathbf{p}$ which coincides with H itself. We may therefore omit reference to a' and simply write (2.4.10) as the partial differential equation to be satisfied by the energy eigenfunction $u_E(\mathbf{x}')$:

$$-\left(\frac{\hbar^2}{2m} \right) \nabla'^2 u_E(\mathbf{x}') + V(\mathbf{x}')u_E(\mathbf{x}') = Eu_E(\mathbf{x}'). \qquad (2.4.11)$$

This is the **time-independent wave equation** of E. Schrödinger—announced in the first of four monumental papers, all written in the first half of 1926—that laid the foundations of wave mechanics. In the same paper he immediately applied (2.4.11) to derive the energy spectrum of the hydrogen atom.

To solve (2.4.11) some boundary condition has to be imposed. Suppose we seek a solution to (2.4.11) with

$$E < \lim_{|\mathbf{x}'| \to \infty} V(\mathbf{x}'), \qquad (2.4.12)$$

where the inequality relation is to hold for $|\mathbf{x}'| \to \infty$ in any direction. The appropriate boundary condition to be used in this case is

$$u_E(\mathbf{x}') \to 0 \quad \text{as } |\mathbf{x}'| \to \infty. \qquad (2.4.13)$$

Physically this means that the particle is bound or confined within a finite region of space. We know from the theory of partial differential equations that (2.4.11) subject to boundary condition (2.4.13) allows nontrivial solutions only for a discrete set of values of E. It is in this sense that the time-independent Schrödinger equation (2.4.11) yields the *quantization of energy levels*.* Once the partial differential equation (2.4.11) is written, the problem of finding the energy levels of microscopic physical systems is as straightforward as that of finding the characteristic frequencies of vibrating strings or membranes. In both cases we solve boundary-value problems in mathematical physics.

A short digression on the history of quantum mechanics is in order here. The fact that exactly soluble eigenvalue problems in the theory of partial differential equations can also be treated using matrix methods was already known to mathematicians in the first quarter of the twentieth century. Furthermore, theoretical physicists like M. Born frequently consulted great mathematicians of the day—D. Hilbert and H. Weyl, in particular. Yet when matrix mechanics was born in the summer of 1925, it did not immediately occur to the theoretical physicists or to the mathematicians to reformulate it using the language of partial differential equations. Six months after Heisenberg's pioneering paper, wave mechanics was proposed by Schrödinger. However, a close inspection of his papers shows that he was not at all influenced by the earlier works of Heisenberg, Born, and Jordan. Instead, the train of reasoning that led Schrödinger to formulate wave mechanics has its roots in W. R. Hamilton's analogy between optics and mechanics, on which we will comment later, and the particle-wave hypothesis of L. de Broglie. Once wave mechanics was formulated, many people, including Schrödinger himself, showed the equivalence between wave mechanics and matrix mechanics.

It is assumed that the reader of this book has some experience in solving the time-dependent and time-independent wave equations. He or she should be familiar with the time evolution of a Gaussian wave packet in a force-free region; should be able to solve one-dimensional transmission-reflection problems involving a rectangular potential barrier, and the like; should have seen derived some simple solutions of the time-independent wave equation—a particle in a box, a particle in a square well, the simple harmonic oscillator, the hydrogen atom, and so on—and should also be familiar with some general properties of the energy eigenfunctions and energy eigenvalues, such as (1) the fact that the energy levels exhibit a discrete or continuous spectrum depending on whether or not (2.4.12) is satisfied and (2) the property that the energy eigenfunction in one dimension is *sinusoidal* or *damped* depending on whether $E - V(x')$ is positive or negative. In this book we will not cover these topics. A brief summary of elementary solutions to Schrödinger's equations is presented in Appendix A.

---

*Schrödinger's paper that announced (2.4.11) is appropriately entitled *Quantisierung als Eigenwertproblem* (*Quantization as an Eigenvalue Problem*).

Interpretations of the Wave Function

We now turn to discussions of the physical interpretations of the wave function. In Section 1.7 we commented on the probabilistic interpretation of $|\psi|^2$ that follows from the fact that $\langle \mathbf{x}'|\alpha, t_0; t \rangle$ is to be regarded as an expansion coefficient of $|\alpha, t_0; t \rangle$ in terms of the position eigenkets $\{|\mathbf{x}'\rangle\}$. The quantity $\rho(\mathbf{x}', t)$ defined by

$$\rho(\mathbf{x}', t) = |\psi(\mathbf{x}', t)|^2 = |\langle \mathbf{x}'|\alpha, t_0; t \rangle|^2 \qquad (2.4.14)$$

is therefore regarded as the **probability density** in wave mechanics. Specifically, when we use a detector that ascertains the presence of the particle within a small volume element d^3x' around $\mathbf{x}'$, the probability of recording a positive result at time t is given by $\rho(\mathbf{x}', t)\, d^3x'$.

In the remainder of this section we use $\mathbf{x}$ for $\mathbf{x}'$ because the position operator will not appear. Using Schrödinger's time-dependent wave equation, it is straightforward to derive the continuity equation

$$\frac{\partial \rho}{\partial t} + \nabla \cdot \mathbf{j} = 0, \qquad (2.4.15)$$

where $\rho(\mathbf{x}, t)$ stands for $|\psi|^2$ as before, and $\mathbf{j}(\mathbf{x}, t)$, known as the **probability flux**, is given by

$$\mathbf{j}(\mathbf{x}, t) = -\left(\frac{i\hbar}{2m} \right) \left[\psi^* \nabla \psi - (\nabla \psi^*) \psi \right]$$

$$= \left(\frac{\hbar}{m} \right) \text{Im}(\psi^* \nabla \psi). \qquad (2.4.16)$$

The reality of the potential V (or the Hermiticity of the V operator) has played a crucial role in our obtaining this result. Conversely, a complex potential can phenomenologically account for the disappearance of a particle; such a potential is often used for nuclear reactions where incident particles get absorbed by nuclei.

We may intuitively expect that the probability flux $\mathbf{j}$ is related to momentum. This is indeed the case for $\mathbf{j}$ *integrated over all space*. From (2.4.16) we obtain

$$\int d^3x\, \mathbf{j}(\mathbf{x}, t) = \frac{\langle \mathbf{p} \rangle_t}{m}, \qquad (2.4.17)$$

where $\langle \mathbf{p} \rangle_t$ is the expectation value of the momentum operator at time t.

Equation (2.4.15) is reminiscent of the continuity equation in fluid dynamics that characterizes a hydrodynamic flow of a fluid in a source-free, sink-free region. Indeed, historically Schrödinger was first led to interpret $|\psi|^2$ as the actual matter density, or $e|\psi|^2$ as the actual electric charge density. If we adopt such a view, we are led to face some bizarre consequences.

A typical argument for a position measurement might go as follows. An atomic electron is to be regarded as a continuous distribution of matter filling up a finite region of space around the nucleus; yet, when a measurement is made to make sure that the electron is at some particular point, this continuous distribution of matter suddenly shrinks to a pointlike particle with no spatial extension. The more satisfactory *statistical interpretation* of $|\psi|^2$ as the probability density was first given by M. Born.

To understand the physical significance of the wave function, let us write it as

$$\psi(\mathbf{x}, t) = \sqrt{\rho(\mathbf{x}, t)} \exp\left[\frac{iS(\mathbf{x}, t)}{\hbar}\right], \qquad (2.4.18)$$

with S real and $\rho > 0$, which can always be done for any complex function of $\mathbf{x}$ and t. The meaning of ρ has already been given. What is the physical interpretation of S? Noting

$$\psi^* \nabla \psi = \sqrt{\rho}\, \nabla\left(\sqrt{\rho}\right) + \left(\frac{i}{\hbar}\right)\rho\nabla S, \qquad (2.4.19)$$

we can write the probability flux as [see (2.4.16)]

$$\mathbf{j} = \frac{\rho\nabla S}{m}. \qquad (2.4.20)$$

We now see that there is more to the wave function than the fact that $|\psi|^2$ is the probability density; the gradient of the phase S contains a vital piece of information. From (2.4.20) we see that the *spatial variation of the phase* of the wave function characterizes the probability flux; the stronger the phase variation, the more intense the flux. The direction of $\mathbf{j}$ at some point $\mathbf{x}$ is seen to be normal to the surface of a constant phase that goes through that point. In the particularly simple example of a plane wave (a momentum eigenfunction)

$$\psi(\mathbf{x}, t) \propto \exp\left(\frac{i\mathbf{p}\cdot\mathbf{x}}{\hbar} - \frac{iEt}{\hbar}\right), \qquad (2.4.21)$$

where $\mathbf{p}$ stands for the eigenvalue of the momentum operator. All this is evident because

$$\nabla S = \mathbf{p}. \qquad (2.4.22)$$

More generally, it is tempting to regard $\nabla S/m$ as some kind of "velocity,"

$$\text{"}\mathbf{v}\text{"} = \frac{\nabla S}{m}, \qquad (2.4.23)$$

and to write the continuity equation (2.4.15) as

$$\frac{\partial \rho}{\partial t} + \nabla\cdot(\rho\text{"}\mathbf{v}\text{"}) = 0, \qquad (2.4.24)$$

just as in fluid dynamics. However, we would like to caution the reader against a too literal interpretation of $\mathbf{j}$ as ρ times the velocity defined at every point in space, because a simultaneous precision measurement of position and velocity would necessarily violate the uncertainty principle.

The Classical Limit

We now discuss the classical limit of wave mechanics. First, we substitute ψ written in form (2.4.18) into both sides of the time-dependent wave equation. Straightforward differentiations lead to

$$-\left(\frac{\hbar^2}{2m}\right)$$

$$\times\left[\nabla^2\sqrt{\rho} + \left(\frac{2i}{\hbar}\right)(\nabla\sqrt{\rho})\cdot(\nabla S) - \left(\frac{1}{\hbar^2}\right)\sqrt{\rho}\,|\nabla S|^2 + \left(\frac{i}{\hbar}\right)\sqrt{\rho}\,\nabla^2 S\right] + \sqrt{\rho}\,V$$

$$= i\hbar\left[\frac{\partial\sqrt{\rho}}{\partial t} + \left(\frac{i}{\hbar}\right)\sqrt{\rho}\,\frac{\partial S}{\partial t}\right]. \tag{2.4.25}$$

So far everything has been exact. Let us suppose now that $\hbar$ can, in some sense, be regarded as a small quantity. The precise physical meaning of this approximation, to which we will come back later, is not evident now, but let us assume

$$\hbar|\nabla^2 S| \ll |\nabla S|^2, \tag{2.4.26}$$

and so forth. We can then collect terms in (2.4.25) that do not explicitly contain $\hbar$ to obtain a nonlinear partial differential equation for S:

$$\frac{1}{2m}|\nabla S(\mathbf{x},t)|^2 + V(\mathbf{x}) + \frac{\partial S(\mathbf{x},t)}{\partial t} = 0. \tag{2.4.27}$$

We recognize this to be the **Hamilton-Jacobi equation** in classical mechanics, first written in 1836, where $S(\mathbf{x},t)$ stands for Hamilton's principal function. So, not surprisingly, in the $\hbar \to 0$ limit, classical mechanics is contained in Schrödinger's wave mechanics. We have a semiclassical interpretation of the phase of the wave function: $\hbar$ times the phase is equal to Hamilton's principal function provided that $\hbar$ can be regarded as a small quantity.

Let us now look at a stationary state with time dependence $\exp(-iEt/\hbar)$. This time dependence is anticipated from the fact that for a classical system with a constant Hamiltonian, Hamilton's principal function S is separable:

$$S(x,t) = W(x) - Et, \tag{2.4.28}$$

where $W(x)$ is called **Hamilton's characteristic function** (Goldstein 1980, 445–46). As time goes on, a surface of a constant S advances in much the same way as a surface of a constant phase in wave optics—a "wave front" —advances. The momentum in the classical Hamilton-Jacobi theory is given by

$$\mathbf{p}_{\text{class}} = \nabla S = \nabla W, \qquad (2.4.29)$$

which is consistent with our earlier identification of $\nabla S/m$ with some kind of velocity. In classical mechanics the velocity vector is tangential to the particle trajectory, and as a result we can trace the trajectory by following continuously the direction of the velocity vector. The particle trajectory is like a ray in geometric optics because the ∇S that traces the trajectory is normal to the wave front defined by a constant S. In this sense geometrical optics is to wave optics what classical mechanics is to wave mechanics.

One might wonder, in hindsight, why this optical-mechanical analogy was not fully exploited in the nineteenth century. The reason is that there was no motivation for regarding Hamilton's principal function as the phase of some traveling wave; the wave nature of a material particle did not become apparent until the 1920s. Besides, the basic unit of action $\hbar$, which must enter into (2.4.18) for dimensional reasons, was missing in the physics of the nineteenth century.

Semiclassical (WKB) Approximation

Let us now restrict ourselves to one dimension and obtain an approximate stationary-state solution to Schrödinger's wave equation. This can easily be accomplished by noting that the corresponding solution of the classical Hamilton-Jacobi equation is

$$S(x,t) = W(x) - Et$$
$$= \pm \int^{x} dx' \sqrt{2m[E - V(x')]} - Et. \qquad (2.4.30)$$

For a stationary state we must have

$$\frac{\partial \rho}{\partial t} = 0, \quad (\text{all } x), \qquad (2.4.31)$$

which, because of the continuity equation [see (2.4.24)]

$$\frac{\partial \rho}{\partial t} + \frac{1}{m} \frac{\partial}{\partial x}\left(\rho \frac{\partial S}{\partial x}\right) = 0 \qquad (2.4.32)$$

implies

$$\rho \frac{dW}{dx} = \pm \rho \sqrt{2m[E - V(x)]} = \text{constant}; \qquad (2.4.33)$$

hence,

$$\sqrt{\rho} = \frac{\text{constant}}{[E - V(x)]^{1/4}} \propto \frac{1}{\sqrt{v_{\text{classical}}}}. \qquad (2.4.34)$$

This makes good sense because classically the probability for finding the particle at a given point should be inversely proportional to the velocity. Combining everything, we obtain an approximate solution:

$$\psi(x,t) \simeq \left\{ \frac{\text{constant}}{[E - V(x)]^{1/4}} \right\}$$

$$\times \exp\left[\pm \left(\frac{i}{\hbar} \right) \int^{x} dx' \sqrt{2m[E - V(x')]} - \frac{iEt}{\hbar} \right]. \quad (2.4.35)$$

This is known as the WKB solution, after G. Wentzel, A. Kramers, and L. Brillouin.*

Having obtained (2.4.35), let us return to the question of what we mean when we say that $\hbar$ is small. Our derivation of the Hamilton-Jacobi equation from the Schrödinger equation rested on (2.4.26), which, in one-dimensional problems, is equivalent to

$$\hbar \left| \frac{d^2 W}{dx^2} \right| \ll \left| \frac{dW}{dx} \right|^2. \quad (2.4.36)$$

In terms of the de Broglie wavelength divided by 2π, this condition amounts to

$$\lambda = \frac{\hbar}{\sqrt{2m[E - V(x)]}} \ll \frac{2[E - V(x)]}{|dV/dx|}. \quad (2.4.37)$$

In other words, λ must be small compared with the characteristic distance over which the potential varies appreciably. Roughly speaking, the potential must be essentially constant over many wavelengths. Thus we see that the semiclassical picture is reliable *in the short-wavelength limit*.

Solution (2.4.35) has been derived for the classically allowed region where $E - V(x)$ is positive. We now consider the classically forbidden region where $E - V(x)$ is negative. The classical Hamilton-Jacobi theory does not make sense in this case, so our approximate solution (2.4.35), which is valid for $E > V$, must therefore be modified. Fortunately an analogous solution exists in the $E < V$ region; by direct substitution we can check that

$$\psi(x,t) \simeq \left\{ \frac{\text{constant}}{[V(x) - E]^{1/4}} \right\} \exp\left[\pm \left(\frac{1}{\hbar} \right) \int^{x} dx' \sqrt{2m[V(x') - E]} - \frac{iEt}{\hbar} \right]$$

$$(2.4.38)$$

---

*A similar technique was used earlier by H. Jeffreys; this solution is referred to as the JWKB solution in some English books.

satisfies the wave equation provided that $\hbar/\sqrt{2m(V-E)}$ is small compared with the characteristic distance over which the potential varies.

Neither (2.4.35) nor (2.4.38) makes sense near the classical turning point defined by the value of x for which

$$V(x) = E \tag{2.4.39}$$

because λ (or its purely imaginary analogue) becomes infinite at that point, leading to a violent violation of (2.4.37). In fact, it is a nontrivial task to match the two solutions across the classical turning point. The standard procedure is based on the following steps:

1. Make a linear approximation to the potential $V(x)$ near the turning point x_0, defined by the root of (2.4.39).
2. Solve the differential equation

$$\frac{d^2 u_E}{dx^2} - \left(\frac{2m}{\hbar^2}\right)\left(\frac{dV}{dx}\right)_{x=x_0}(x-x_0)u_E = 0 \tag{2.4.40}$$

exactly to obtain a third solution involving the Bessel function of order $\pm\frac{1}{3}$, valid near x_0.
3. Match this solution to the other two solutions by choosing appropriately various constants of integration.

We do not discuss these steps in detail, as they are discussed in many places (Schiff 1968, 268–76, for example). Instead, we content ourselves to present the results of such an analysis for a potential well, schematically shown in Figure 2.1, with two turning points, x_1 and x_2. The wave function must behave like (2.4.35) in region II and like (2.4.38) in regions I and III. The correct matching from region I into region II can be shown to be

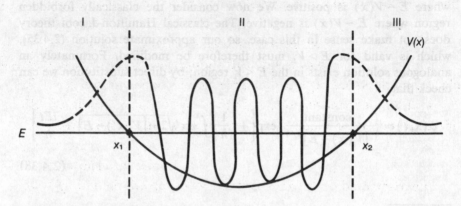

FIGURE 2.1. Schematic diagram for behavior of wave function $u_E(x)$ in potential well $V(x)$ with turning points x_1 and x_2.

accomplished by choosing the integration constants in such a way that*

$$\left\{ \frac{1}{[V(x)-E]^{1/4}} \right\} \exp\left[-\left(\frac{1}{\hbar}\right) \int_x^{x_1} dx' \sqrt{2m[V(x')-E]} \right]$$

$$\rightarrow \left\{ \frac{2}{[E-V(x)]^{1/4}} \right\} \cos\left[\left(\frac{1}{\hbar}\right) \int_{x_1}^x dx' \sqrt{2m[E-V(x')]} - \frac{\pi}{4} \right].$$

(2.4.41)

Likewise, from region III into region II we have

$$\left\{ \frac{1}{[V(x)-E]^{1/4}} \right\} \exp\left[-\left(\frac{1}{\hbar}\right) \int_{x_2}^x dx' \sqrt{2m[V(x')-E]} \right]$$

$$\rightarrow \left\{ \frac{2}{[E-V(x)]^{1/4}} \right\} \cos\left[-\left(\frac{1}{\hbar}\right) \int_x^{x_2} dx' \sqrt{2m[E-V(x')]} + \frac{\pi}{4} \right].$$

(2.4.42)

The uniqueness of the wave function in region II implies that the arguments of the cosine in (2.4.41) and (2.4.42) must differ at most by an integer multiple of π [not of 2π, because the signs of both sides of (2.4.42) can be reversed]. In this way we obtain a very interesting consistency condition,

$$\int_{x_1}^{x_2} dx \sqrt{2m[E-V(x)]} = (n+\tfrac{1}{2})\pi\hbar \quad (n=0,1,2,3,\dots). \quad (2.4.43)$$

Apart from the difference between $n+\tfrac{1}{2}$ and n, this equation is simply the quantization condition of the old quantum theory due to A. Sommerfeld and W. Wilson, originally written in 1915 as

$$\oint p\, dq = nh, \quad (2.4.44)$$

where h is Planck's h, not Dirac's $\hbar$, and the integral is evaluated over one whole period of classical motion, from x_1 to x_2 and back.

Equation (2.4.43) can be used to obtain approximate expressions for the energy levels of a particle confined in a potential well. As an example, we consider the energy spectrum of a ball bouncing up and down over a

---

*A quick way to understand the appearance of $\pi/4$ in (2.4.41) is as follows. The correctly matched pair of solutions in region I and region II, of the form (2.4.38) and (2.4.35), respectively, must be related to each other by analytic continuation in a *complex* x-plane. An excursion into the complex x-plane enables us to change the sign of $V(x)-E \simeq (dV/dx)_{x=x_1}(x-x_1)$ without going through the dangerous region with $x \simeq x_1$. We now observe that under such an analytic continuation, the $1/[V(x)-E]^{1/4}$ factor in (2.4.38) picks up a phase: $[(dV/dx)_{x=x_1}(x-x_1)]^{1/4} \rightarrow [(dV/dx)_{x=x_1}(x_1-x)]^{1/4}e^{i\pi/4}$.

hard surface:

$$V = \begin{cases} mgx, & \text{for } x > 0 \\ \infty, & \text{for } x < 0, \end{cases} \tag{2.4.45}$$

where x stands for the height of the ball measured from the hard surface. One might be tempted to use (2.4.43) directly with

$$x_1 = 0, \qquad x_2 = \frac{E}{mg}, \tag{2.4.46}$$

which are the classical turning points of this problem. We note, however, that (2.4.43) was derived under the assumption that the WKB wave function "leaks into" the $x < x_1$ region, while in our problem the wave function must strictly vanish for $x \le x_1 = 0$. A much more satisfactory approach to this problem is to consider the *odd-parity solutions*—guaranteed to vanish at $x = 0$—of a modified problem defined by

$$V(x) = mg|x| \quad (-\infty < x < \infty) \tag{2.4.47}$$

whose turning points are

$$x_1 = -\frac{E}{mg}, \qquad x_2 = \frac{E}{mg}. \tag{2.4.48}$$

The energy spectrum of the odd-parity states for this modified problem must clearly be the same as that of the original problem. The quantization condition then becomes

$$\int_{-E/mg}^{E/mg} dx \sqrt{2m(E - mg|x|)} = \left(n_{odd} + \tfrac{1}{2}\right)\pi\hbar, \quad (n_{odd} = 1, 3, 5, \dots) \tag{2.4.49}$$

or, equivalently,

$$\int_{0}^{E/mg} dx \sqrt{2m(E - mgx)} = \left(n - \tfrac{1}{4}\right)\pi\hbar, \quad (n = 1, 2, 3, 4, \dots). \tag{2.4.50}$$

This integral is elementary, and we obtain

$$E_n = \left\{ \frac{\left[3\left(n - \tfrac{1}{4}\right)\pi\right]^{2/3}}{2} \right\} (mg^2\hbar^2)^{1/3} \tag{2.4.51}$$

for the quantized energy levels of the bouncing ball.

It is known that this problem is soluble analytically without any approximation. The energy eigenvalues turn out to be expressible in terms of the zeros of the Airy function

$$Ai(-\lambda_n) = 0 \tag{2.4.52}$$

TABLE 2.2.   The Quantized Energies of a Bouncing Ball
in Units of $(mg^2\hbar^2/2)^{1/3}$

n	WKB	Exact
1	2.320	2.338
2	4.082	4.088
3	5.517	5.521
4	6.784	6.787
5	7.942	7.944
6	9.021	9.023
7	10.039	10.040
8	11.008	11.009
9	11.935	11.936
10	12.828	12.829

as

$$E_n = \left(\frac{\lambda_n}{2^{1/3}} \right) \left(mg^2\hbar^2 \right)^{1/3}. \qquad (2.4.53)$$

The two approaches are compared numerically in Table 2.2 for the first 10 energy levels. We see that agreement is excellent even for small values of n and essentially exact for $n \simeq 10$.

The quantum-theoretical treatment of a bouncing ball may appear to have little to do with the real world. It turns out, however, that a potential of type (2.4.45) is actually of practical interest in studying the energy spectrum of a quark-antiquark bound system, called **quarkonium**. To go from a bouncing ball to a quarkonium, the x in (2.4.45) is replaced by the quark-antiquark separation distance r. The analogue of the downward gravitational force mg is a constant (that is, r-independent) force believed to be operative between a quark and an antiquark. This force is empirically estimated to be in the neighborhood of

$$1 \text{ GeV/fm} \simeq 1.6 \times 10^5 \text{ N}, \qquad (2.4.54)$$

which corresponds to about 16 tons. This contrasts with the gravitational force of 0.98 N on a ball of 0.1 kg.

2.5. PROPAGATORS AND FEYNMAN PATH INTEGRALS

Propagators in Wave Mechanics

In Section 2.1 we showed how the most general time-evolution problem with a time-independent Hamiltonian can be solved once we expand the initial ket in terms of the eigenkets of an observable that commutes with H. Let us translate this statement into the language of wave mechanics. We start with

$$|\alpha, t_0; t\rangle = \exp\left[\frac{-iH(t-t_0)}{\hbar}\right]|\alpha, t_0\rangle$$

$$= \sum_{a'}|a'\rangle\langle a'|\alpha, t_0\rangle\exp\left[\frac{-iE_{a'}(t-t_0)}{\hbar}\right]. \qquad (2.5.1)$$

Multiplying both sides by $\langle \mathbf{x}'|$ on the left, we have

$$\langle \mathbf{x}'|\alpha, t_0; t\rangle = \sum_{a'}\langle \mathbf{x}'|a'\rangle\langle a'|\alpha, t_0\rangle\exp\left[\frac{-iE_{a'}(t-t_0)}{\hbar}\right], \qquad (2.5.2)$$

which is of the form

$$\psi(\mathbf{x}', t) = \sum_{a'}c_{a'}(t_0)u_{a'}(\mathbf{x}')\exp\left[\frac{-iE_{a'}(t-t_0)}{\hbar}\right], \qquad (2.5.3)$$

with

$$u_{a'}(\mathbf{x}') = \langle \mathbf{x}'|a'\rangle \qquad (2.5.4)$$

standing for the eigenfunction of operator A with eigenvalue a'. Note also that

$$\langle a'|\alpha, t_0\rangle = \int d^3x'\langle a'|\mathbf{x}'\rangle\langle \mathbf{x}'|\alpha, t_0\rangle, \qquad (2.5.5)$$

which we recognize as the usual rule in wave mechanics for getting the expansion coefficients of the initial state:

$$c_{a'}(t_0) = \int d^3x'u_{a'}^*(\mathbf{x}')\psi(\mathbf{x}', t_0). \qquad (2.5.6)$$

All this should be straightforward and familiar. Now (2.5.2) together with (2.5.5) can also be visualized as some kind of integral operator acting on the initial wave function to yield the final wave function:

$$\psi(\mathbf{x}'', t) = \int d^3x' K(\mathbf{x}'', t; \mathbf{x}', t_0)\psi(\mathbf{x}', t_0). \qquad (2.5.7)$$

Here the kernel of the integral operator, known as the **propagator** in wave mechanics, is given by

$$K(\mathbf{x}'', t; \mathbf{x}', t_0) = \sum_{a'}\langle \mathbf{x}''|a'\rangle\langle a'|\mathbf{x}'\rangle\exp\left[\frac{-iE_{a'}(t-t_0)}{\hbar}\right]. \qquad (2.5.8)$$

In any given problem the propagator depends only on the potential and is independent of the initial wave function. It can be constructed once the energy eigenfunctions and their eigenvalues are given.

Clearly, the time evolution of the wave function is completely predicted if $K(\mathbf{x}'', t; \mathbf{x}', t_0)$ is known and $\psi(\mathbf{x}', t_0)$ is given initially. In this sense Schrödinger's wave mechanics is a *perfectly causal theory*. The time development of a wave function subjected to some potential is as "deterministic" as anything else in classical mechanics *provided that the system is left undisturbed*. The only peculiar feature, if any, is that when a measurement intervenes, the wave function changes abruptly, in an uncontrollable way, into one of the eigenfunctions of the observable being measured.

There are two properties of the propagator worth recording here. First, for $t > t_0$, $K(\mathbf{x}'', t; \mathbf{x}', t_0)$ satisfies Schrödinger's time-dependent wave equation in the variables $\mathbf{x}''$ and t, with $\mathbf{x}'$ and t_0 fixed. This is evident from (2.5.8) because $\langle \mathbf{x}''|a'\rangle \exp[-iE_{a'}(t - t_0)/\hbar]$, being the wave function corresponding to $\mathscr{U}(t, t_0)|a'\rangle$, satisfies the wave equation. Second,

$$\lim_{t \to t_0} K(\mathbf{x}'', t; \mathbf{x}', t_0) = \delta^3(\mathbf{x}'' - \mathbf{x}'), \tag{2.5.9}$$

which is also obvious; as $t \to t_0$, because of the completeness of $\{|a'\rangle\}$, sum (2.5.8) just reduces to $\langle \mathbf{x}''|\mathbf{x}'\rangle$.

Because of these two properties, the propagator (2.5.8), regarded as a function of $\mathbf{x}''$, is simply the wave function at t of a particle which was localized *precisely* at $\mathbf{x}'$ at some earlier time t_0. Indeed, this interpretation follows, perhaps more elegantly, from noting that (2.5.8) can also be written as

$$K(\mathbf{x}'', t; \mathbf{x}', t_0) = \langle \mathbf{x}''|\exp\left[\frac{-iH(t - t_0)}{\hbar}\right]|\mathbf{x}'\rangle, \tag{2.5.10}$$

where the time-evolution operator acting on $|\mathbf{x}'\rangle$ is just the state ket at t of a system that was localized precisely at $\mathbf{x}'$ at time t_0 ($< t$). If we wish to solve a more general problem where the initial wave function extends over a finite region of space, all we have to do is multiply $\psi(\mathbf{x}', t_0)$ by the propagator $K(\mathbf{x}'', t; \mathbf{x}', t_0)$ and integrate over all space (that is, over $\mathbf{x}'$). In this manner we can add the various contributions from different positions ($\mathbf{x}'$). This situation is analogous to one in electrostatics; if we wish to find the electrostatic potential due to a general charge distribution $\rho(\mathbf{x}')$, we first solve the point-charge problem, multiply the point-charge solution with the charge distribution, and integrate:

$$\phi(\mathbf{x}) = \int d^3x' \frac{\rho(\mathbf{x}')}{|\mathbf{x} - \mathbf{x}'|}. \tag{2.5.11}$$

The reader familiar with the theory of the Green's functions must have recognized by this time that the propagator is simply the Green's function for the time-dependent wave equation satisfying

$$\left[-\left(\frac{\hbar^2}{2m}\right)\nabla''^2 + V(\mathbf{x}'') - i\hbar\frac{\partial}{\partial t}\right]K(\mathbf{x}'', t; \mathbf{x}', t_0) = -i\hbar\delta^3(\mathbf{x}'' - \mathbf{x}')\delta(t - t_0)$$

$$\tag{2.5.12}$$

with the boundary condition

$$K(\mathbf{x}'', t; \mathbf{x}', t_0) = 0, \quad \text{for } t < t_0. \tag{2.5.13}$$

The delta function $\delta(t - t_0)$ is needed on the right-hand side of (2.5.12) because K varies discontinuously at $t = t_0$.

The particular form of the propagator is, of course, dependent on the particular potential to which the particle is subjected. Consider, as an example, a free particle in one dimension. The obvious observable that commutes with H is momentum; $|p'\rangle$ is a simultaneous eigenket of the operators p and H:

$$p|p'\rangle = p'|p'\rangle \qquad H|p'\rangle = \left(\frac{p'^2}{2m}\right)|p'\rangle. \tag{2.5.14}$$

The momentum eigenfunction is just the transformation function of Section 1.7 [see (1.7.32)] which is of the plane-wave form. Combining everything, we have

$$K(x'', t; x', t_0) = \left(\frac{1}{2\pi\hbar}\right)\int_{-\infty}^{\infty} dp' \exp\left[\frac{ip'(x''-x')}{\hbar} - \frac{ip'^2(t-t_0)}{2m\hbar}\right]. \tag{2.5.15}$$

The integral can be evaluated by completing the square in the exponent. Here we simply record the result:

$$K(x'', t; x', t_0) = \sqrt{\frac{m}{2\pi i\hbar(t-t_0)}} \exp\left[\frac{im(x''-x')^2}{2\hbar(t-t_0)}\right]. \tag{2.5.16}$$

This expression may be used, for example, to study how a Gaussian wave packet spreads out as a function of time.

For the simple harmonic oscillator, where the wave function of an energy eigenstate is given by

$$u_n(x)\exp\left(\frac{-iE_n t}{\hbar}\right) = \left(\frac{1}{2^{n/2}\sqrt{n!}}\right)\left(\frac{m\omega}{\pi\hbar}\right)^{1/4}\exp\left(\frac{-m\omega x^2}{2\hbar}\right)$$

$$\times H_n\left(\sqrt{\frac{m\omega}{\hbar}}\, x\right)\exp\left[-i\omega\left(n+\frac{1}{2}\right)t\right], \tag{2.5.17}$$

the propagator is given by

$$K(x'', t; x', t_0) = \sqrt{\frac{m\omega}{2\pi i\hbar \sin[\omega(t-t_0)]}} \exp\left[\left\{\frac{im\omega}{2\hbar \sin[\omega(t-t_0)]}\right\}\right.$$

$$\left. \times \left\{(x''^2 + x'^2)\cos[\omega(t-t_0)] - 2x''x'\right\}\right]. \tag{2.5.18}$$

One way to prove this is to use

$$\left(\frac{1}{\sqrt{1-\zeta^2}}\right)\exp\left[\frac{-(\xi^2+\eta^2-2\xi\eta\zeta)}{(1-\zeta^2)}\right]$$

$$= \exp\left[-(\xi^2+\eta^2)\right]\sum_{n=0}\left(\frac{\zeta^n}{2^n n!}\right)H_n(\xi)H_n(\eta), \qquad (2.5.19)$$

which is found in books on special functions (Morse and Feshbach 1953, 786). It can also be obtained using the $a, a^\dagger$ operator method (Saxon 1968, 144–45) or, alternatively, the path-integral method to be described later. Notice that (2.5.18) is a periodic function of t with angular frequency ω, the classical oscillator frequency. This means, among other things, that a particle initially localized precisely at x' will return to its original position with certainty at $2\pi/\omega$ $(4\pi/\omega$, and so forth) later.

Certain space and time integrals derivable from $K(\mathbf{x}'', t; \mathbf{x}', t_0)$ are of considerable interest. Without loss of generality we set $t_0 = 0$ in the following. The first integral we consider is obtained by setting $\mathbf{x}'' = \mathbf{x}'$ and integrating over all space. We have

$$G(t) \equiv \int d^3x'\, K(\mathbf{x}', t; \mathbf{x}', 0)$$

$$= \int d^3x' \sum_{a'} |\langle \mathbf{x}'|a'\rangle|^2 \exp\left(\frac{-iE_{a'}t}{\hbar}\right)$$

$$= \sum_{a'} \exp\left(\frac{-iE_{a'}t}{\hbar}\right). \qquad (2.5.20)$$

This result is anticipated; recalling (2.5.10), we observe that setting $\mathbf{x}' = \mathbf{x}''$ and integrating are equivalent to taking the trace of the time-evolution operator in the $\mathbf{x}$-representation. But the trace is independent of representations; it can be evaluated more readily using the $\{|a'\rangle\}$ basis where the time-evolution operator is diagonal, which immediately leads to the last line of (2.5.20). Now we see that (2.5.20) is just the "sum over states," reminiscent of the partition function in statistical mechanics. In fact, if we analytically continue in the t variable and make t purely imaginary, with β defined by

$$\beta = \frac{it}{\hbar} \qquad (2.5.21)$$

real and positive, we can identify (2.5.20) with the partition function itself:

$$Z = \sum_{a'} \exp(-\beta E_{a'}). \qquad (2.5.22)$$

For this reason some of the techniques encountered in studying propagators in quantum mechanics are also useful in statistical mechanics.

Next, let us consider the Laplace-Fourier transform of $G(t)$:

$$\tilde{G}(E) \equiv -i \int_0^\infty dt\, G(t)\exp(iEt/\hbar)/\hbar$$

$$= -i \int_0^\infty dt \sum_{a'} \exp(-iE_{a'}t/\hbar)\exp(iEt/\hbar)/\hbar. \qquad (2.5.23)$$

The integrand here oscillates indefinitely. But we can make the integral meaningful by letting E acquire a small positive imaginary part:

$$E \to E + i\varepsilon. \qquad (2.5.24)$$

We then obtain, in the limit $\varepsilon \to 0$,

$$\tilde{G}(E) = \sum_{a'} \frac{1}{E - E_{a'}}. \qquad (2.5.25)$$

Observe now that the complete energy spectrum is exhibited as simple poles of $\tilde{G}(E)$ in the complex E-plane. If we wish to know the energy spectrum of a physical system, it is sufficient to study the analytic properties of $\tilde{G}(E)$.

Propagator as a Transition Amplitude

To gain further insight into the physical meaning of the propagator, we wish to relate it to the concept of transition amplitudes introduced in Section 2.2. But first, recall that the wave function which is the inner product of the fixed position bra $\langle \mathbf{x}'|$ with the moving state ket $|\alpha, t_0; t\rangle$ can also be regarded as the inner product of the Heisenberg-picture position bra $\langle \mathbf{x}', t|$, which moves "oppositely" with time, with the Heisenberg-picture state ket $|\alpha, t_0\rangle$, which is fixed in time. Likewise, the propagator can also be written as

$$K(\mathbf{x}'', t; \mathbf{x}', t_0) = \sum_{a'} \langle \mathbf{x}''|a'\rangle \langle a'|\mathbf{x}'\rangle \exp\left[\frac{-iE_{a'}(t - t_0)}{\hbar}\right]$$

$$= \sum_{a'} \langle \mathbf{x}''|\exp\left(\frac{-iHt}{\hbar}\right)|a'\rangle \langle a'|\exp\left(\frac{iHt_0}{\hbar}\right)|\mathbf{x}'\rangle$$

$$= \langle \mathbf{x}'', t|\mathbf{x}', t_0\rangle, \qquad (2.5.26)$$

where $|\mathbf{x}', t_0\rangle$ and $\langle \mathbf{x}'', t|$ are to be understood as an eigenket and an eigenbra of the position operator in the Heisenberg picture. In Section 2.1 we showed that $\langle b', t|a'\rangle$, in the Heisenberg-picture notation, is the probability amplitude for a system originally prepared to be an eigenstate of A with eigenvalue a' at some initial time $t_0 = 0$ to be found at a later time t in an eigenstate of B with eigenvalue b', and we called it the transition amplitude for going from state $|a'\rangle$ to state $|b'\rangle$. Because there is nothing special about the choice of t_0—only the time difference $t - t_0$ is relevant—we can identify $\langle \mathbf{x}'', t | \mathbf{x}', t_0 \rangle$ as the probability amplitude for the particle prepared at t_0 with position eigenvalue $\mathbf{x}'$ to be found at a later time t at $\mathbf{x}''$. Roughly speaking, $\langle \mathbf{x}'', t | \mathbf{x}', t_0 \rangle$ is the amplitude for the particle to go from a space-time point $(\mathbf{x}', t_0)$ to another space-time point $(\mathbf{x}'', t)$, so the term *transition amplitude* for this expression is quite appropriate. This interpretation is, of course, in complete accord with the interpretation we gave earlier for $K(\mathbf{x}'', t; \mathbf{x}', t_0)$.

Yet another way to interpret $\langle \mathbf{x}'', t | \mathbf{x}', t_0 \rangle$ is as follows. As we emphasized earlier, $|\mathbf{x}', t_0\rangle$ is the position eigenket at t_0 with the eigenvalue $\mathbf{x}'$ in the Heisenberg picture. Because at any given time the Heisenberg-picture eigenkets of an observable can be chosen as base kets, we can regard $\langle \mathbf{x}'', t | \mathbf{x}', t_0 \rangle$ as the transformation function that connects the two sets of base kets at *different* times. So in the Heisenberg picture, time evolution can be viewed as a *unitary transformation*, in the sense of changing bases, that connects one set of base kets formed by $\{|\mathbf{x}', t_0\rangle\}$ to another formed by $\{|\mathbf{x}'', t\rangle\}$. This is reminiscent of classical physics, in which the time development of a classical dynamic variable such as $\mathbf{x}(t)$ is viewed as a canonical (or contact) transformation generated by the classical Hamiltonian (Goldstein 1980, 407–8).

It turns out to be convenient to use a notation that treats the space and time coordinates more symmetrically. To this end we write $\langle \mathbf{x}'', t'' | \mathbf{x}', t' \rangle$ in place of $\langle \mathbf{x}'', t | \mathbf{x}', t_0 \rangle$. Because at any given time the position kets in the Heisenberg picture form a complete set, it is legitimate to insert the identity operator written as

$$\int d^3 x'' |\mathbf{x}'', t''\rangle \langle \mathbf{x}'', t''| = 1 \qquad (2.5.27)$$

at any place we desire. For example, consider the time evolution from t' to t'''; by dividing the time interval (t', t''') into two parts, (t', t'') and (t'', t'''), we have

$$\langle \mathbf{x}''', t''' | \mathbf{x}', t' \rangle = \int d^3 x'' \langle \mathbf{x}''', t''' | \mathbf{x}'', t'' \rangle \langle \mathbf{x}'', t'' | \mathbf{x}', t' \rangle,$$

$$(t''' > t'' > t'). \quad (2.5.28)$$

We call this the **composition property** of the transition amplitude.* Clearly, we can divide the time interval into as many smaller subintervals as we wish. We have

$$\langle \mathbf{x}'''', t'''' | \mathbf{x}', t' \rangle = \int d^3 x''' \int d^3 x'' \langle \mathbf{x}'''', t'''' | \mathbf{x}''', t''' \rangle \langle \mathbf{x}''', t''' | \mathbf{x}'', t'' \rangle$$

$$\times \langle \mathbf{x}'', t'' | \mathbf{x}', t' \rangle, \quad (t'''' > t''' > t'' > t'), \qquad (2.5.29)$$

---

*The analogue of (2.5.28) in probability theory is known as the Chapman-Kolmogoroff equation, and in diffusion theory, the Smoluchowsky equation.

and so on. If we somehow guess the form of $\langle x'', t'' | x', t' \rangle$ for an *infinitesimal* time interval (between t' and $t'' = t' + dt$), we should be able to obtain the amplitude $\langle x'', t'' | x', t' \rangle$ for a finite time interval by compounding the appropriate transition amplitudes for infinitesimal time intervals in a manner analogous to (2.5.29). This kind of reasoning leads to an *independent formulation* of quantum mechanics due to R. P. Feynman, published in 1948, to which we now turn our attention.

Path Integrals as the Sum Over Paths

Without loss of generality we restrict ourselves to one-dimensional problems. Also, we avoid awkward expressions like

$$\underbrace{x'''' \cdots x'''}_{N \text{ times}}$$

by using notation such as x_N. With this notation we consider the transition amplitude for a particle going from the initial space-time point (x_1, t_1) to the final space-time point (x_N, t_N). The entire time interval between t_1 and t_N is divided into $N-1$ equal parts:

$$t_j - t_{j-1} = \Delta t = \frac{(t_N - t_1)}{(N-1)}. \tag{2.5.30}$$

Exploiting the composition property, we obtain

$$\langle x_N, t_N | x_1, t_1 \rangle = \int dx_{N-1} \int dx_{N-2} \cdots \int dx_2 \langle x_N, t_N | x_{N-1}, t_{N-1} \rangle$$
$$\times \langle x_{N-1}, t_{N-1} | x_{N-2}, t_{N-2} \rangle \cdots \langle x_2, t_2 | x_1, t_1 \rangle. \tag{2.5.31}$$

To visualize this pictorially, we consider a space-time plane, as shown in Figure 2.2. The initial and final space-time points are fixed to be (x_1, t_1) and (x_N, t_N), respectively. For each time segment, say between t_{n-1} and t_n, we are instructed to consider the transition amplitude to go from (x_{n-1}, t_{n-1}) to (x_n, t_n); we then integrate over $x_2, x_3, \ldots, x_{N-1}$. This means that we must *sum over all possible paths* in the space-time plane with the end points fixed.

Before proceeding further, it is profitable to review here how paths appear in classical mechanics. Suppose we have a particle subjected to a force field derivable from a potential $V(x)$. The *classical* Lagrangian is written as

$$L_{\text{classical}}(x, \dot{x}) = \frac{m\dot{x}^2}{2} - V(x). \tag{2.5.32}$$

Given this Lagrangian with the end points (x_1, t_1) and (x_N, t_N) specified, we do *not* consider just any path joining (x_1, t_1) and (x_N, t_N) in classical mechanics. On the contrary, there exists a *unique path* that corresponds to

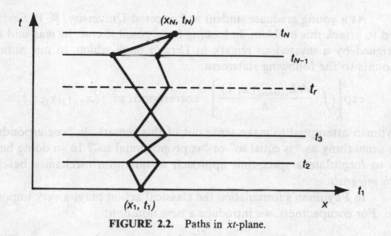

FIGURE 2.2. Paths in xt-plane.

the actual motion of the classical particle. For example, given

$$V(x) = mgx, \qquad (x_1, t_1) = (h, 0), \qquad (x_N, t_N) = \left(0, \sqrt{\frac{2h}{g}}\right),$$

(2.5.33)

where h may stand for the height of the Leaning Tower of Pisa, the classical path in the xt-plane can *only* be

$$x = h - \frac{gt^2}{2}.$$

(2.5.34)

More generally, according to Hamilton's principle, the unique path is that which minimizes the action, defined as the time integral of the classical Lagrangian:

$$\delta \int_{t_1}^{t_2} dt\, L_{\text{classical}}(x, \dot{x}) = 0,$$

(2.5.35)

from which Lagrange's equation of motion can be obtained.

Feynman's Formulation

The basic difference between classical mechanics and quantum mechanics should now be apparent. In classical mechanics a definite path in the xt-plane is associated with the particle's motion; in contrast, in quantum mechanics all possible paths must play roles including those which do not bear any resemblance to the classical path. Yet we must somehow be able to reproduce classical mechanics in a smooth manner in the limit $\hbar \to 0$. How are we to accomplish this?

As a young graduate student at Princeton University, R. P. Feynman tried to attack this problem. In looking for a possible clue, he was said to be intrigued by a mysterious remark in Dirac's book which, in our notation, amounts to the following statement:

$$\exp\left[i\int_{t_1}^{t_2} \frac{dt\,L_{\text{classical}}(x, \dot{x})}{\hbar}\right] \quad \text{corresponds to} \quad \langle x_2, t_2 | x_1, t_1 \rangle.$$

Feynman attempted to make sense out of this remark. Is "corresponds to" the same thing as "is equal to" or "is proportional to"? In so doing he was led to formulate a space-time approach to quantum mechanics based on *path integrals*.

In Feynman's formulation the classical action plays a very important role. For compactness, we introduce a new notation:

$$S(n, n-1) \equiv \int_{t_{n-1}}^{t_n} dt\,L_{\text{classical}}(x, \dot{x}). \tag{2.5.36}$$

Because $L_{\text{classical}}$ is a function of x and $\dot{x}$, $S(n, n-1)$ is defined only after a definite path is specified along which the integration is to be carried out. So even though the path dependence is not explicit in this notation, it is understood that we are considering a particular path in evaluating the integral. Imagine now that we are following some prescribed path. We concentrate our attention on a small segment along that path, say between (x_{n-1}, t_{n-1}) and (x_n, t_n). According to Dirac, we are instructed to associate $\exp[iS(n, n-1)/\hbar]$ with that segment. Going along the definite path we are set to follow, we successively multiply expressions of this type to obtain

$$\prod_{n=2}^{N} \exp\left[\frac{iS(n, n-1)}{\hbar}\right] = \exp\left[\left(\frac{i}{\hbar}\right)\sum_{n=2}^{N} S(n, n-1)\right] = \exp\left[\frac{iS(N, 1)}{\hbar}\right]. \tag{2.5.37}$$

This does not yet give $\langle x_N, t_N | x_1, t_1 \rangle$; rather, this equation is the contribution to $\langle x_N, t_N | x_1, t_1 \rangle$ arising from the particular path we have considered. We must still integrate over $x_2, x_3, \ldots, x_{N-1}$. At the same time, exploiting the composition property, we let the time interval between t_{n-1} and t_n be infinitesimally small. Thus our candidate expression for $\langle x_N, t_N | x_1, t_1 \rangle$ may be written, in some loose sense, as

$$\langle x_N, t_N | x_1, t_1 \rangle \sim \sum_{\text{all paths}} \exp\left[\frac{iS(N, 1)}{\hbar}\right], \tag{2.5.38}$$

where the sum is to be taken over an innumerably infinite set of paths!

Before presenting a more precise formulation, let us see whether considerations along this line make sense in the classical limit. As $\hbar \to 0$, the exponential in (2.5.38) oscillates very violently, so there is a tendency for cancellation among various contributions from neighboring paths. This is because $\exp[iS/\hbar]$ for some definite path and $\exp[iS/\hbar]$ for a slightly different path have very different phases because of the smallness of $\hbar$. So most paths do *not* contribute when $\hbar$ is regarded as a small quantity. However, there is an important exception.

Suppose that we consider a path that satisfies

$$\delta S(N, 1) = 0, \tag{2.5.39}$$

where the change in S is due to a slight deformation of the path with the end points fixed. This is precisely the classical path by virtue of Hamilton's principle. We denote the S that satisfies (2.5.39) by $S_{\min}$. We now attempt to deform the path a little bit from the classical path. The resulting S is still equal to $S_{\min}$ to first order in deformation. This means that the phase of $\exp[iS/\hbar]$ does not vary very much as we deviate slightly from the classical path even if $\hbar$ is small. As a result, as long as we stay near the classical path, constructive interference between neighboring paths is possible. In the $\hbar \to 0$ limit, the major contributions must then arise from a very narrow strip (or a tube in higher dimensions) containing the classical path, as shown in Figure 2.3. Our (or Feynman's) guess based on Dirac's mysterious remark makes good sense because the classical path gets singled out in the $\hbar \to 0$ limit.

To formulate Feynman's conjecture more precisely, let us go back to $\langle x_n, t_n | x_{n-1}, t_{n-1} \rangle$, where the time difference $t_n - t_{n-1}$ is assumed to be infinitesimally small. We write

$$\langle x_n, t_n | x_{n-1}, t_{n-1} \rangle = \left[\frac{1}{w(\Delta t)} \right] \exp\left[\frac{iS(n, n-1)}{\hbar} \right], \tag{2.5.40}$$

where we evaluate $S(n, n-1)$ in a moment in the $\Delta t \to 0$ limit. Notice that we have inserted a weight factor, $1/w(\Delta t)$, which is assumed to depend only on the time interval $t_n - t_{n-1}$ and not on $V(x)$. That such a factor is needed is clear from dimensional considerations; according to the way we

(x_N, t_N)

(x_1, t_1)

FIGURE 2.3.   Paths important in the $\hbar \to 0$ limit.

normalized our position eigenkets, $\langle x_n, t_n | x_{n-1}, t_{n-1} \rangle$ must have the dimension of 1/length.

We now look at the exponential in (2.5.40). Our task is to evaluate the $\Delta t \to 0$ limit of $S(n, n-1)$. Because the time interval is so small, it is legitimate to make a straight-line approximation to the path joining (x_{n-1}, t_{n-1}) and (x_n, t_n) as follows:

$$S(n, n-1) = \int_{t_{n-1}}^{t_n} dt \left[\frac{m\dot{x}^2}{2} - V(x) \right]$$

$$= \Delta t \left\{ \left(\frac{m}{2} \right) \left[\frac{(x_n - x_{n-1})}{\Delta t} \right]^2 - V\left(\frac{(x_n + x_{n-1})}{2} \right) \right\}.$$

$$(2.5.41)$$

As an example, we consider specifically the free-particle case, $V = 0$. Equation (2.5.40) now becomes

$$\langle x_n, t_n | x_{n-1}, t_{n-1} \rangle = \left[\frac{1}{w(\Delta t)} \right] \exp \left[\frac{im(x_n - x_{n-1})^2}{2\hbar \Delta t} \right]. \quad (2.5.42)$$

We see that the exponent appearing here is completely identical to the one in the expression for the free-particle propagator (2.5.16). The reader may work out a similar comparison for the simple harmonic oscillator.

We remarked earlier that the weight factor $1/w(\Delta t)$ appearing in (2.5.40) is assumed to be independent of $V(x)$, so we may as well evaluate it for the free particle. Noting the orthonormality, in the sense of δ-function, of Heisenberg-picture position eigenkets at equal times,

$$\langle x_n, t_n | x_{n-1}, t_{n-1} \rangle |_{t_n = t_{n-1}} = \delta(x_n - x_{n-1}), \quad (2.5.43)$$

we obtain

$$\frac{1}{w(\Delta t)} = \sqrt{\frac{m}{2\pi i\hbar \Delta t}}, \quad (2.5.44)$$

where we have used

$$\int_{-\infty}^{\infty} d\xi \exp \left(\frac{im\xi^2}{2\hbar \Delta t} \right) = \sqrt{\frac{2\pi i\hbar \Delta t}{m}} \quad (2.5.45a)$$

and

$$\lim_{\Delta t \to 0} \sqrt{\frac{m}{2\pi i\hbar \Delta t}} \exp \left(\frac{im\xi^2}{2\hbar \Delta t} \right) = \delta(\xi). \quad (2.5.45b)$$

This weight factor is, of course, anticipated from the expression for the free-particle propagator (2.5.16).

To summarize, as $\Delta t \to 0$, we are led to

$$\langle x_n, t_n | x_{n-1}, t_{n-1} \rangle = \sqrt{\frac{m}{2\pi i\hbar \Delta t}} \exp \left[\frac{iS(n, n-1)}{\hbar} \right]. \quad (2.5.46)$$

The final expression for the transition amplitude with $t_N - t_1$ finite is

$$\langle x_N, t_N | x_1, t_1 \rangle = \lim_{N \to \infty} \left(\frac{m}{2\pi i\hbar \Delta t} \right)^{(N-1)/2}$$

$$\times \int dx_{N-1} \int dx_{N-2} \cdots \int dx_2 \prod_{n=2}^{N} \exp\left[\frac{iS(n, n-1)}{\hbar} \right],$$

(2.5.47)

where the $N \to \infty$ limit is taken with x_N and t_N fixed. It is customary here to define a new kind of multidimensional (in fact, infinite-dimensional) integral operator

$$\int_{x_1}^{x_N} \mathscr{D}[x(t)] \equiv \lim_{N \to \infty} \left(\frac{m}{2\pi i\hbar \Delta t} \right)^{(N-1)/2} \int dx_{N-1} \int dx_{N-2} \cdots \int dx_2$$

(2.5.48)

and write (2.5.47) as

$$\langle x_N, t_N | x_1, t_1 \rangle = \int_{x_1}^{x_N} \mathscr{D}[x(t)] \exp\left[i \int_{t_1}^{t_N} dt \frac{L_{\text{classical}}(x, \dot{x})}{\hbar} \right].$$ (2.5.49)

This expression is known as **Feynman's path integral**. Its meaning as the sum over all possible paths should be apparent from (2.5.47).

Our steps leading to (2.5.49) are not meant to be a derivation. Rather, we (or Feynman) have attempted a new formulation of quantum mechanics based on the concept of paths, motivated by Dirac's mysterious remark. The only ideas we borrowed from the conventional form of quantum mechanics are (1) the superposition principle (used in summing the contributions from various alternate paths), (2) the composition property of the transition amplitude, and (3) classical correspondence in the $\hbar \to 0$ limit.

Even though we obtained the same result as the conventional theory for the free-particle case, it is now obvious, from what we have done so far, that Feynman's formulation is completely equivalent to Schrödinger's wave mechanics. We conclude this section by proving that Feynman's expression for $\langle x_N, t_N | x_1, t_1 \rangle$ indeed satisfies Schrödinger's time-dependent wave equation in the variables x_N, t_N, just as the propagator defined by (2.5.8).

We start with

$$\langle x_N, t_N | x_1, t_1 \rangle = \int dx_{N-1} \langle x_N, t_N | x_{N-1}, t_{N-1} \rangle \langle x_{N-1}, t_{N-1} | x_1, t_1 \rangle$$

$$= \int_{-\infty}^{\infty} dx_{N-1} \sqrt{\frac{m}{2\pi i\hbar \Delta t}} \exp\left[\left(\frac{im}{2\hbar} \right) \frac{(x_N - x_{N-1})^2}{\Delta t} - \frac{iV\Delta t}{\hbar} \right]$$

$$\times \langle x_{N-1}, t_{N-1} | x_1, t_1 \rangle,$$ (2.5.50)

where we have assumed $t_N - t_{N-1}$ to be infinitesimal. Introducing

$$\xi = x_N - x_{N-1} \tag{2.5.51}$$

and letting $x_N \to x$ and $t_N \to t + \Delta t$, we obtain

$$\langle x, t + \Delta t | x_1, t_1 \rangle = \sqrt{\frac{m}{2\pi i\hbar\,\Delta t}} \int_{-\infty}^{\infty} d\xi \exp\left(\frac{im\xi^2}{2\hbar\,\Delta t} - \frac{iV\Delta t}{\hbar}\right) \langle x - \xi, t | x_1, t_1 \rangle.$$

$$\tag{2.5.52}$$

As is evident from (2.5.45b), in the limit $\Delta t \to 0$, the major contribution to this integral comes from the $\xi \simeq 0$ region. It is therefore legitimate to expand $\langle x - \xi, t | x_1, t_1 \rangle$ in powers of ξ. We also expand $\langle x, t + \Delta t | x_1, t_1 \rangle$ and $\exp(-iV\Delta t/\hbar)$ in powers of Δt, so

$$\langle x, t | x_1, t_1 \rangle + \Delta t \frac{\partial}{\partial t} \langle x, t | x_1, t_1 \rangle$$

$$= \sqrt{\frac{m}{2\pi i\hbar\,\Delta t}} \int_{-\infty}^{\infty} d\xi \exp\left(\frac{im\xi^2}{2\hbar\,\Delta t}\right)\left(1 - \frac{iV\Delta t}{\hbar} + \cdots\right)$$

$$\times \left[\langle x, t | x_1, t_1 \rangle + \left(\frac{\xi^2}{2}\right)\frac{\partial^2}{\partial x^2}\langle x, t | x_1, t_1 \rangle + \cdots\right],$$

$$\tag{2.5.53}$$

where we have dropped a term linear in ξ because it vanishes when integrated with respect to ξ. The $\langle x, t | x_1, t_1 \rangle$ term on the left-hand side just matches the leading term on the right-hand side because of (2.5.45a). Collecting terms first order in Δt, we obtain

$$\Delta t \frac{\partial}{\partial t}\langle x, t | x_1, t_1 \rangle = \left(\sqrt{\frac{m}{2\pi i\hbar\,\Delta t}}\right)(\sqrt{2\pi})\left(\frac{i\hbar\,\Delta t}{m}\right)^{3/2}\frac{1}{2}\frac{\partial^2}{\partial x^2}\langle x, t | x_1, t_1 \rangle$$

$$- \left(\frac{i}{\hbar}\right)\Delta t\, V\langle x, t | x_1, t_1 \rangle, \tag{2.5.54}$$

where we have used

$$\int_{-\infty}^{\infty} d\xi\, \xi^2 \exp\left(\frac{im\xi^2}{2\hbar\,\Delta t}\right) = \sqrt{2\pi}\left(\frac{i\hbar\,\Delta t}{m}\right)^{3/2}, \tag{2.5.55}$$

obtained by differentiating (2.5.45a) with respect to Δt. In this manner we see that $\langle x, t | x_1, t_1 \rangle$ satisfies Schrödinger's time-dependent wave equation:

$$i\hbar\frac{\partial}{\partial t}\langle x, t | x_1, t_1 \rangle = -\left(\frac{\hbar^2}{2m}\right)\frac{\partial^2}{\partial x^2}\langle x, t | x_1, t_1 \rangle + V\langle x, t | x_1, t_1 \rangle. \tag{2.5.56}$$

Thus we can conclude that $\langle x, t | x_1, t_1 \rangle$ constructed according to Feynman's prescription is the same as the propagator in Schrödinger's wave mechanics.

Feynman's space-time approach based on path integrals is not too convenient for attacking practical problems in nonrelativistic quantum mechanics. Even for the simple harmonic oscillator it is rather cumbersome to evaluate explicitly the relevant path integral.* However, his approach is extremely gratifying from a conceptual point of view. By imposing a certain set of sensible requirements on a physical theory, we are inevitably led to a formalism equivalent to the usual formulation of quantum mechanics. It makes us wonder whether it is at all possible to construct a sensible alternative theory that is equally successful in accounting for microscopic phenomena.

Methods based on path integrals have been found to be very powerful in other branches of modern physics, such as quantum field theory and statistical mechanics. In this book the path-integral method will appear again when we discuss the Aharonov-Bohm effect.[†]

2.6. POTENTIALS AND GAUGE TRANSFORMATIONS

Constant Potentials

In classical mechanics it is well known that the zero point of the potential energy is of no physical significance. The time development of dynamic variables such as $\mathbf{x}(t)$ and $\mathbf{L}(t)$ is independent of whether we use $V(\mathbf{x})$ or $V(\mathbf{x}) + V_0$ with V_0 constant both in space and time. The force that appears in Newton's second law depends only on the gradient of the potential; an additive constant is clearly irrelevant. What is the analogous situation in quantum mechanics?

We look at the time evolution of a Schrödinger-picture state ket subject to some potential. Let $|\alpha, t_0; t\rangle$ be a state ket in the presence of $V(\mathbf{x})$, and $|\tilde{\alpha}, t_0; t\rangle$, the corresponding state ket appropriate for

$$\tilde{V}(\mathbf{x}) = V(\mathbf{x}) + V_0. \qquad (2.6.1)$$

To be precise let us agree that the initial conditions are such that both kets coincide with $|\alpha\rangle$ at $t = t_0$. If they represent the same physical situation, this can always be done by a suitable choice of the phase. Recalling that the state ket at t can be obtained by applying the time-evolution operator

---

*The reader is challenged to solve the simple harmonic oscillator problem using the Feynman path integral method in Problem 2-31.

[†] The reader who is interested in the fundamentals and applications of path integrals may consult Feynman and Hibbs 1965.

$\mathcal{U}(t, t_0)$ to the state ket at t_0, we obtain

$$|\alpha, t_0; t\rangle = \exp\left[-i\left(\frac{\mathbf{p}^2}{2m} + V(x) + V_0\right)\frac{(t - t_0)}{\hbar}\right]|\alpha\rangle$$

$$= \exp\left[\frac{-iV_0(t - t_0)}{\hbar}\right]|\alpha, t_0; t\rangle. \tag{2.6.2}$$

In other words, the ket computed under the influence of $\tilde{V}$ has a time dependence different only by a phase factor $\exp[-iV_0(t - t_0)/\hbar]$. For stationary states, this means that if the time dependence computed with $V(\mathbf{x})$ is $\exp[-iE(t - t_0)/\hbar]$, then the corresponding time dependence computed with $V(\mathbf{x}) + V_0$ is $\exp[-i(E + V_0)(t - t_0)/\hbar]$. In other words, the use of $\tilde{V}$ in place of V just amounts to the following change:

$$E \to E + V_0, \tag{2.6.3}$$

which the reader probably guessed immediately. Observable effects such as the time evolution of expectation values of $\langle \mathbf{x} \rangle$ and $\langle \mathbf{S} \rangle$ always depend on energy *differences* [see (2.1.47)]; the Bohr frequencies that characterize the sinusoidal time dependence of expectation values are the same whether we use $V(\mathbf{x})$ or $V(\mathbf{x}) + V_0$. In general, there can be no difference in the expectation values of observables if every state ket in the world is multiplied by a common factor $\exp[-iV_0(t - t_0)/\hbar]$.

Trivial as it may seem, we see here the first example of a class of transformations known as **gauge transformations**. The change in our convention for the zero-point energy of the potential

$$V(\mathbf{x}) \to V(\mathbf{x}) + V_0 \tag{2.6.4}$$

must be accompanied by a change in the state ket

$$|\alpha, t_0; t\rangle \to \exp\left[\frac{-iV_0(t - t_0)}{\hbar}\right]|\alpha, t_0; t\rangle. \tag{2.6.5}$$

Of course, this change implies the following change in the wave function:

$$\psi(\mathbf{x}', t) \to \exp\left[\frac{-iV_0(t - t_0)}{\hbar}\right]\psi(\mathbf{x}', t). \tag{2.6.6}$$

Next we consider V_0 that is spatially uniform but dependent on time. We then easily see that the analogue of (2.6.5) is

$$|\alpha, t_0; t\rangle \to \exp\left[-i\int_{t_0}^{t} dt' \frac{V_0(t')}{\hbar}\right]|\alpha, t_0; t\rangle. \tag{2.6.7}$$

Physically, the use of $V(\mathbf{x}) + V_0(t)$ in place of $V(\mathbf{x})$ simply means that we are choosing a new zero point of the energy scale at each instant of time.

FIGURE 2.4. Quantum-mechanical interference to detect a potential difference.

Even though the choice of the absolute scale of the potential is arbitrary, *potential differences* are of nontrivial physical significance and, in fact, can be detected in a very striking way. To illustrate this point, let us consider the arrangement shown in Figure 2.4. A beam of charged particles is split into two parts, each of which enters a metallic cage. If we so desire, we can maintain a finite potential difference between the two cages by turning on a switch, as shown. A particle in the beam can be visualized as a wave packet whose dimension is much smaller than the dimension of the cage. Suppose we switch on the potential difference only after the wave packets enter the cages and switch it off before the wave packets leave the cages. The particle in the cage experiences *no force* because inside the cage the potential is spatially uniform; hence no electric field is present. Now let us recombine the two beam components in such a way that they meet in the interference region of Figure 2.4. Because of the existence of the potential, each beam component suffers a phase change, as indicated by (2.6.7). As a result, there is an observable interference term in the beam intensity in the interference region, namely,

$$\cos(\phi_1 - \phi_2), \qquad \sin(\phi_1 - \phi_2), \tag{2.6.8}$$

where

$$\phi_1 - \phi_2 = \left(\frac{1}{\hbar}\right)\int_{t_i}^{t_f} dt \, [V_2(t) - V_1(t)]. \tag{2.6.9}$$

So despite the fact that the particle experiences no force, there is an observable effect that depends on whether $V_2(t) - V_1(t)$ has been applied. Notice that this effect is *purely quantum mechanical*; in the limit $\hbar \to 0$, the interesting interference effect gets washed out because the oscillation of the cosine becomes infinitely rapid.*

---

*This gedanken experiment is the Minkowski-rotated form of the Aharonov-Bohm experiment to be discussed later in this section.

Gravity in Quantum Mechanics

There is an experiment that exhibits in a striking manner how a gravitational effect appears in quantum mechanics. Before describing it, we first comment on the role of gravity in both classical and quantum mechanics.

Consider the classical equation of motion for a purely falling body:

$$m\ddot{\mathbf{x}} = -m\nabla\Phi_{\text{grav}} = -mg\hat{\mathbf{z}}. \tag{2.6.10}$$

The mass term drops out; so in the absence of air resistance, a feather and a stone would behave in the same way—à la Galileo—under the influence of gravity. This is, of course, a direct consequence of the equality of the gravitational and the inertial masses. Because the mass does not appear in the equation of a particle trajectory, gravity in classical mechanics is often said to be a purely geometric theory.

The situation is rather different in quantum mechanics. In the wave-mechanical formulation, the analogue of (2.6.10) is

$$\left[-\left(\frac{\hbar^2}{2m}\right)\nabla^2 + m\Phi_{\text{grav}}\right]\psi = i\hbar\frac{\partial\psi}{\partial t}. \tag{2.6.11}$$

The mass no longer cancels; instead it appears in the combination $\hbar/m$, so in a problem where $\hbar$ appears, m is also expected to appear. We can see this point also using the Feynman path-integral formulation of a falling body based on

$$\langle \mathbf{x}_n, t_n | \mathbf{x}_{n-1}, t_{n-1} \rangle = \sqrt{\frac{m}{2\pi i\hbar\Delta t}}\ \exp\left[i\int_{t_{n-1}}^{t_n} dt\ \frac{\left(\frac{1}{2}m\dot{\mathbf{x}}^2 - mgz\right)}{\hbar}\right],$$

$$(t_n - t_{n-1} = \Delta t \to 0). \tag{2.6.12}$$

Here again we see that m appears in the combination $m/\hbar$. This is in sharp contrast with Hamilton's classical approach, based on

$$\delta\int_{t_1}^{t_2} dt\left(\frac{m\dot{\mathbf{x}}^2}{2} - mgz\right) = 0, \tag{2.6.13}$$

where m can be eliminated in the very beginning.

Starting with the Schrödinger equation (2.6.11), we may derive the Ehrenfest theorem

$$\frac{d^2}{dt^2}\langle\mathbf{x}\rangle = -g\hat{\mathbf{z}}. \tag{2.6.14}$$

However, $\hbar$ does not appear here, nor does m. To see a *nontrivial* quantum-mechanical effect of gravity, we must study effects in which $\hbar$ appears explicitly—and consequently where we expect the mass to appear—in contrast with purely gravitational phenomena in classical mechanics.

Until 1975, there had been no direct experiment that established the presence of the $m\Phi_{grav}$ term in (2.6.11). To be sure, a free fall of an elementary particle had been observed, but the classical equation of motion —or the Ehrenfest theorem (2.6.14), where $\hbar$ does not appear—sufficed to account for this. The famous "weight of photon" experiment of V. Pound and collaborators did not test gravity in the quantum domain either because they measured a frequency shift where $\hbar$ does not explicitly appear.

On the microscopic scale, gravitational forces are too weak to be readily observable. To appreciate the difficulty involved in seeing gravity in bound-state problems, let us consider the ground state of an electron and a neutron bound by gravitational forces. This is the gravitational analogue of the hydrogen atom, where an electron and a proton are bound by Coulomb forces. At the same distance, the gravitational force between the electron and the neutron is weaker than the Coulomb force between the electron and the proton by a factor of $\sim 2 \times 10^{39}$. The Bohr radius involved here can be obtained simply:

$$a_0 = \frac{\hbar^2}{e^2 m_e} \rightarrow \frac{\hbar^2}{G_N m_e^2 m_n}, \tag{2.6.15}$$

where G_N is Newton's gravitational constant. If we substitute numbers in the equation, the Bohr radius of this gravitationally bound system turns out to be $\sim 10^{31}$ cm, or $\sim 10^{13}$ light years, which is larger than the estimated radius of the universe by a few orders of magnitude!

We now discuss a remarkable phenomenon known as **gravity-induced quantum interference**. A nearly monoenergetic beam of particles—in practice, thermal neutrons—is split into two parts and then brought together as shown in Figure 2.5. In actual experiments the neutron beam is split and bent by silicon crystals, but the details of this beautiful art of neutron interferometry do not concern us here. Because the size of the wave packet can be assumed to be much smaller than the macroscopic dimension of the loop formed by the two alternate paths, we can apply the concept of a classical trajectory. Let us first suppose that path $A \rightarrow B \rightarrow D$ and path $A \rightarrow C \rightarrow D$ lie in a horizontal plane. Because the absolute zero of the potential due to gravity is of no significance, we can set $V = 0$ for any phenomenon that takes place in this plane; in other words, it is legitimate to ignore gravity altogether. The situation is very different if the plane formed by the two alternate paths is rotated around segment AC by angle δ. This time the potential at level BD is higher than that at level AC by $mgl_2\sin\delta$, which means that the state ket associated with path BD "rotates faster." This leads to a gravity-induced phase difference between the amplitudes for the two wave packets arriving at D. Actually there is also a gravity-induced phase change associated with AB and also with CD, but the effects cancel as we compare the two alternate paths. The net result is that the wave packet

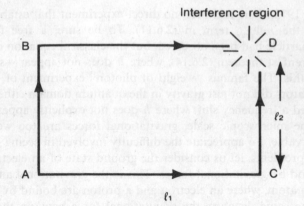

FIGURE 2.5. Experiment to detect gravity-induced quantum interference.

arriving at D via path ABD suffers a phase change

$$\exp\left[\frac{-im_n g l_2 \sin\delta\, T}{\hbar}\right] \qquad (2.6.16)$$

relative to that of the wave packet arriving at D via path ACD, where T is the time spent for the wave packet to go from B to D (or from A to C) and m_n, the neutron mass. We can control this phase difference by rotating the plane of Figure 2.5; δ can change from 0 to $\pi/2$, or from 0 to $-\pi/2$. Expressing the time spent T, or $l_1/v_{\text{wave packet}}$, in terms of λ, the de Broglie wavelength of the neutron, we obtain the following expression for the phase difference:

$$\phi_{ABD} - \phi_{ACD} = -\frac{\left(m_n^2 g l_1 l_2 \lambda \sin\delta\right)}{\hbar^2}. \qquad (2.6.17)$$

In this manner we predict an observable interference effect that depends on angle δ, which is reminiscent of fringes in Michelson-type interferometers in optics.

An alternative, more wave-mechanical way to understand (2.6.17) follows. Because we are concerned with a time-independent potential, the sum of the kinetic energy and the potential energy is constant:

$$\frac{\mathbf{p}^2}{2m} + mgz = E. \qquad (2.6.18)$$

The difference in height between level BD and level AC implies a slight difference in $\mathbf{p}$, or λ. As a result, there is an accumulation of phase differences due to the λ difference. It is left as an exercise to show that this wave-mechanical approach also leads to result (2.6.17).

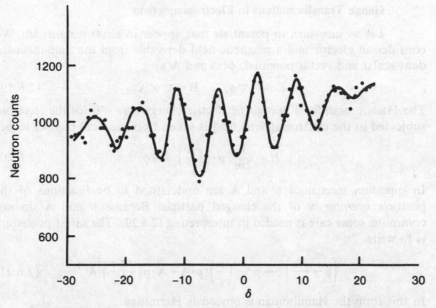

FIGURE 2.6. Dependence of gravity-induced phase on the angle of rotation δ.

What is interesting about expression (2.6.17) is that its magnitude is neither too small nor too large; it is just right for this interesting effect to be detected with thermal neutrons traveling through paths of "table-top" dimensions. For $\lambda = 1.42$ Å (comparable to interatomic spacing in silicon) and $l_1 l_2 = 10$ cm^2, we obtain 55.6 for $m_n^2 g l_1 l_2 \lambda / \hbar^2$. As we rotate the loop plane gradually by 90°, we predict the intensity in the interference region to exhibit a series of maxima and minima; quantitatively we should see $55.6/2\pi \simeq 9$ oscillations. It is extraordinary that such an effect has indeed been observed experimentally; see Figure 2.6 taken from a 1975 experiment of R. Colella, A. Overhauser, and S. A. Werner. The phase shift due to gravity is seen to be verified to well within 1%.

We emphasize that this effect is purely quantum mechanical because as $\hbar \to 0$, the interference pattern gets washed out. The gravitational potential has been shown to enter into the Schrödinger equation just as expected. This experiment also shows that gravity is not purely geometric at the quantum level because the effect depends on $(m/\hbar)^2$.*

---

*However, this does not imply that the equivalence principle is unimportant in understanding an effect of this sort. If the gravitational mass (m_{grav}) and inertial mass (m_{inert}) were unequal, $(m/\hbar)^2$ would have to be replaced by $m_{grav} m_{inert}/\hbar^2$. The fact that we could correctly predict the interference pattern without making a distinction between m_{grav} and m_{inert} shows some support for the equivalence principle at the quantum level.

Gauge Transformations in Electromagnetism

Let us now turn to potentials that appear in electromagnetism. We consider an electric and a magnetic field derivable from the time-independent scalar and vector potential, $\phi(\mathbf{x})$ and $\mathbf{A}(\mathbf{x})$:

$$\mathbf{E} = -\nabla\phi, \qquad \mathbf{B} = \nabla \times \mathbf{A}. \tag{2.6.19}$$

The Hamiltonian for a particle of electric charge e ($e < 0$ for the electron) subjected to the electromagnetic field is taken from classical physics to be

$$H = \frac{1}{2m}\left(\mathbf{p} - \frac{e\mathbf{A}}{c}\right)^2 + e\phi. \tag{2.6.20}$$

In quantum mechanics ϕ and $\mathbf{A}$ are understood to be functions of the position *operator* $\mathbf{x}$ of the charged particle. Because $\mathbf{p}$ and $\mathbf{A}$ do not commute, some care is needed in interpreting (2.6.20). The safest procedure is to write

$$\left(\mathbf{p} - \frac{e\mathbf{A}}{c}\right)^2 \rightarrow p^2 - \left(\frac{e}{c}\right)(\mathbf{p}\cdot\mathbf{A} + \mathbf{A}\cdot\mathbf{p}) + \left(\frac{e}{c}\right)^2 \mathbf{A}^2. \tag{2.6.21}$$

In this form the Hamiltonian is obviously Hermitian.

To study the dynamics of a charged particle subjected to ϕ and $\mathbf{A}$, let us first proceed in the Heisenberg picture. We can evaluate the time derivative of $\mathbf{x}$ in a straightforward manner as

$$\frac{dx_i}{dt} = \frac{[x_i, H]}{i\hbar} = \frac{(p_i - eA_i/c)}{m}, \tag{2.6.22}$$

which shows that the operator $\mathbf{p}$, defined in this book to be the generator of translation, is not the same as $m\,d\mathbf{x}/dt$. Quite often $\mathbf{p}$ is called **canonical momentum**, as distinguished from **kinematical** (or mechanical) **momentum**, denoted by $\mathbf{\Pi}$:

$$\mathbf{\Pi} \equiv m\frac{d\mathbf{x}}{dt} = \mathbf{p} - \frac{e\mathbf{A}}{c}. \tag{2.6.23}$$

Even though we have

$$[p_i, p_j] = 0 \tag{2.6.24}$$

for canonical momentum, the analogous commutator does not vanish for mechanical momentum. Instead we have

$$[\Pi_i, \Pi_j] = \left(\frac{i\hbar e}{c}\right)\varepsilon_{ijk}B_k, \tag{2.6.25}$$

as the reader may easily verify. Rewriting the Hamiltonian as

$$H = \frac{\Pi^2}{2m} + e\phi \tag{2.6.26}$$

and using the fundamental commutation relation, we can derive the quantum-mechanical version of the **Lorentz force**, namely,

$$m\frac{d^2\mathbf{x}}{dt^2} = \frac{d\mathbf{\Pi}}{dt} = e\left[\mathbf{E} + \frac{1}{2c}\left(\frac{d\mathbf{x}}{dt}\times\mathbf{B} - \mathbf{B}\times\frac{d\mathbf{x}}{dt}\right)\right]. \qquad (2.6.27)$$

This then is Ehrenfest's theorem, written in the Heisenberg picture, for the charged particle in the presence of **E** and **B**.

We now study Schrödinger's wave equation with ϕ and **A**. Our first task is to sandwich H between $\langle\mathbf{x}'|$ and $|\alpha, t_0; t\rangle$. The only term with which we have to be careful is

$$\langle\mathbf{x}'|\left[\mathbf{p} - \frac{e\mathbf{A}(\mathbf{x})}{c}\right]^2|\alpha, t_0; t\rangle$$

$$= \left[-i\hbar\nabla' - \frac{e\mathbf{A}(\mathbf{x}')}{c}\right]\langle\mathbf{x}'|\left[\mathbf{p} - \frac{e\mathbf{A}(\mathbf{x})}{c}\right]|\alpha, t_0; t\rangle$$

$$= \left[-i\hbar\nabla' - \frac{e\mathbf{A}(\mathbf{x}')}{c}\right]\cdot\left[-i\hbar\nabla' - \frac{e\mathbf{A}(\mathbf{x}')}{c}\right]\langle\mathbf{x}'|\alpha, t_0; t\rangle.$$

$$\qquad (2.6.28)$$

It is important to emphasize that the first ∇' in the last line can differentiate *both* $\langle\mathbf{x}'|\alpha, t_0; t\rangle$ *and* $\mathbf{A}(\mathbf{x}')$. Combining everything, we have

$$\frac{1}{2m}\left[-i\hbar\nabla' - \frac{e\mathbf{A}(\mathbf{x}')}{c}\right]\cdot\left[-i\hbar\nabla' - \frac{e\mathbf{A}(\mathbf{x}')}{c}\right]\langle\mathbf{x}'|\alpha, t_0; t\rangle$$

$$+ e\phi(\mathbf{x}')\langle\mathbf{x}'|\alpha, t_0; t\rangle = i\hbar\frac{\partial}{\partial t}\langle\mathbf{x}'|\alpha, t_0; t\rangle. \qquad (2.6.29)$$

From this expression we readily obtain the continuity equation

$$\frac{\partial\rho}{\partial t} + \nabla'\cdot\mathbf{j} = 0, \qquad (2.6.30)$$

where ρ is $|\psi|^2$ as before, with $\langle\mathbf{x}'|\alpha, t_0; t\rangle$ written as ψ, but for the probability flux **j** we have

$$\mathbf{j} = \left(\frac{\hbar}{m}\right)\text{Im}(\psi^*\nabla\psi) - \left(\frac{e}{mc}\right)\mathbf{A}|\psi|^2, \qquad (2.6.31)$$

which is just what we expect from the substitution

$$\nabla' \to \nabla' - \left(\frac{ie}{\hbar c}\right)\mathbf{A}. \qquad (2.6.32)$$

Writing the wave function of $\sqrt{\rho}\,\exp(iS/\hbar)$ [see (2.4.18)], we obtain an alternative form for **j**, namely,

$$\mathbf{j} = \left(\frac{\rho}{m}\right)\left(\nabla S - \frac{e\mathbf{A}}{c}\right), \qquad (2.6.33)$$

which is to be compared with (2.4.20). We will find this form to be convenient in discussing superconductivity, flux quantization, and so on. We also note that the space integral of $\mathbf{j}$ is the expectation value of kinematical momentum (not canonical momentum) apart from $1/m$:

$$\int d^3x' \mathbf{j} = \frac{\langle \mathbf{p} - e\mathbf{A}/c \rangle}{m} = \langle \mathbf{\Pi} \rangle / m. \tag{2.6.34}$$

We are now in a position to discuss the subject of **gauge transformations** in electromagnetism. First, consider

$$\phi \rightarrow \phi + \lambda, \qquad \mathbf{A} \rightarrow \mathbf{A}, \tag{2.6.35}$$

with λ constant, that is, independent of $\mathbf{x}$ and t. Both $\mathbf{E}$ and $\mathbf{B}$ obviously remain unchanged. This transformation just amounts to a change in the zero point of the energy scale, a possibility treated in the beginning of this section; we just replace V by $e\phi$. We have already discussed the accompanying change needed for the state ket [see (2.6.5)], so we do not dwell on this transformation any further.

Much more interesting is the transformation

$$\phi \rightarrow \phi, \qquad \mathbf{A} \rightarrow \mathbf{A} + \nabla \Lambda, \tag{2.6.36}$$

where Λ is a function of $\mathbf{x}$. The static electromagnetic fields $\mathbf{E}$ and $\mathbf{B}$ are unchanged under (2.6.36). Both (2.6.35) and (2.6.36) are special cases of

$$\phi \rightarrow \phi - \frac{1}{c} \frac{\partial \Lambda}{\partial t}, \qquad \mathbf{A} \rightarrow \mathbf{A} + \nabla \Lambda, \tag{2.6.37}$$

which leave $\mathbf{E}$ and $\mathbf{B}$, given by

$$\mathbf{E} = -\nabla \phi - \frac{1}{c} \frac{\partial \mathbf{A}}{\partial t}, \qquad \mathbf{B} = \nabla \times \mathbf{A}, \tag{2.6.38}$$

unchanged, but in the following we do not consider time-dependent fields and potentials. In the remaining part of this section the term *gauge transformation* refers to (2.6.36).

In classical physics observable effects such as the trajectory of a charged particle are independent of the gauge used, that is, of the particular choice of Λ we happen to adopt. Consider a charged particle in a uniform magnetic field in the z-direction

$$\mathbf{B} = B\hat{\mathbf{z}}. \tag{2.6.39}$$

This magnetic field may be derived from

$$A_x = \frac{-By}{2}, \qquad A_y = \frac{Bx}{2}, \qquad A_z = 0 \tag{2.6.40}$$

or also from

$$A_x = -By, \qquad A_y = 0, \qquad A_z = 0. \tag{2.6.41}$$

The second form is obtained from the first by

$$\mathbf{A} \to \mathbf{A} - \nabla\left(\frac{Bxy}{2}\right), \tag{2.6.42}$$

which is indeed of the form of (2.6.36). Regardless of which $\mathbf{A}$ we may use, the trajectory of the charged particle with a given set of initial conditions is the same; it is just a helix—a uniform circular motion when projected in the xy-plane, superposed with a uniform rectilinear motion in the z-direction. Yet if we look at p_x and p_y, the results are very different. For one thing, p_x is a constant of the motion when (2.6.41) is used but not when (2.6.40) is used.

Recall Hamilton's equations of motion:

$$\frac{dp_x}{dt} = -\frac{\partial H}{\partial x}, \qquad \frac{dp_y}{dt} = -\frac{\partial H}{\partial y}, \dots \tag{2.6.43}$$

In general, the canonical momentum $\mathbf{p}$ is *not* a gauge-invariant quantity; its numerical value depends on the particular gauge used even when we are referring to the same physical situation. In contrast, the *kinematic* momentum Π, or $m d\mathbf{x}/dt$, that traces the trajectory of the particle *is* a gauge-invariant quantity, as one may explicitly verify. Because $\mathbf{p}$ and $m d\mathbf{x}/dt$ are related via (2.6.23), $\mathbf{p}$ must change to compensate for the change in $\mathbf{A}$ given by (2.6.42).

We now return to quantum mechanics. We believe that it is reasonable to demand that the expectation values in quantum mechanics behave in a manner similar to the corresponding classical quantities under gauge transformations, so $\langle \mathbf{x} \rangle$ and $\langle \Pi \rangle$ are *not* to change under gauge transformations, while $\langle \mathbf{p} \rangle$ is expected to change.

Let us denote by $|\alpha\rangle$ the state ket in the presence of $\mathbf{A}$; the state ket for the same physical situation when

$$\tilde{\mathbf{A}} = \mathbf{A} + \nabla\Lambda \tag{2.6.44}$$

is used in place of $\mathbf{A}$ is denoted by $|\tilde{\alpha}\rangle$. Here Λ, as well as $\mathbf{A}$, is a function of the position operator $\mathbf{x}$. Our basic requirements are

$$\langle \alpha | \mathbf{x} | \alpha \rangle = \langle \tilde{\alpha} | \mathbf{x} | \tilde{\alpha} \rangle \tag{2.6.45a}$$

and

$$\left\langle \alpha \left| \left(\mathbf{p} - \frac{e\mathbf{A}}{c} \right) \right| \alpha \right\rangle = \left\langle \tilde{\alpha} \left| \left(\mathbf{p} - \frac{e\tilde{\mathbf{A}}}{c} \right) \right| \tilde{\alpha} \right\rangle. \tag{2.6.45b}$$

In addition, we require, as usual, the norm of the state ket to be preserved:

$$\langle \alpha | \alpha \rangle = \langle \tilde{\alpha} | \tilde{\alpha} \rangle. \tag{2.6.46}$$

We must construct an operator $\mathscr{G}$ that relates $|\tilde{\alpha}\rangle$ to $|\alpha\rangle$:

$$|\tilde{\alpha}\rangle = \mathscr{G}|\alpha\rangle. \tag{2.6.47}$$

Invariance properties (2.6.45a) and (2.6.45b) are guaranteed if

$$\mathcal{G}^{\dagger}\mathbf{x}\mathcal{G} = \mathbf{x} \qquad (2.6.48a)$$

and

$$\mathcal{G}^{\dagger}\left(\mathbf{p} - \frac{e\mathbf{A}}{c} - \frac{e\nabla\Lambda}{c}\right)\mathcal{G} = \mathbf{p} - \frac{e\mathbf{A}}{c}. \qquad (2.6.48b)$$

We assert that

$$\mathcal{G} = \exp\left[\frac{ie\Lambda(\mathbf{x})}{\hbar c}\right] \qquad (2.6.49)$$

will do the job. First, $\mathcal{G}$ is unitary, so (2.6.46) is all right. Second, (2.6.48a) is obviously satisfied because $\mathbf{x}$ commutes with any function of $\mathbf{x}$. As for (2.6.48b), just note that

$$\exp\left(\frac{-ie\Lambda}{\hbar c}\right)\mathbf{p}\exp\left(\frac{ie\Lambda}{\hbar c}\right) = \exp\left(\frac{-ie\Lambda}{\hbar c}\right)\left[\mathbf{p}, \exp\left(\frac{ie\Lambda}{\hbar c}\right)\right] + \mathbf{p}$$

$$= -\exp\left(\frac{-ie\Lambda}{\hbar c}\right)i\hbar\nabla\left[\exp\left(\frac{ie\Lambda}{\hbar c}\right)\right] + \mathbf{p}$$

$$= \mathbf{p} + \frac{e\nabla\Lambda}{c}, \qquad (2.6.50)$$

where we have used (2.2.23b).

The invariance of quantum mechanics under gauge transformations can also be demonstrated by looking directly at the Schrödinger equation. Let $|\alpha, t_0; t\rangle$ be a solution to the Schrödinger equation in the presence of $\mathbf{A}$:

$$\left[\frac{(\mathbf{p} - e\mathbf{A}/c)^2}{2m} + e\phi\right]|\alpha, t_0; t\rangle = i\hbar\frac{\partial}{\partial t}|\alpha, t_0; t\rangle. \qquad (2.6.51)$$

The corresponding solution in the presence of $\tilde{\mathbf{A}}$ must satisfy

$$\left[\frac{(\mathbf{p} - e\mathbf{A}/c - e\nabla\Lambda/c)^2}{2m} + e\phi\right]\widetilde{|\alpha, t_0; t\rangle} = i\hbar\frac{\partial}{\partial t}\widetilde{|\alpha, t_0; t\rangle}. \qquad (2.6.52)$$

We see that if the new ket is taken to be

$$\widetilde{|\alpha, t_0; t\rangle} = \exp\left(\frac{ie\Lambda}{\hbar c}\right)|\alpha, t_0; t\rangle \qquad (2.6.53)$$

in accordance with (2.6.49), then the new Schrödinger equation (2.6.52) will be satisfied; all we have to note is that

$$\exp\left(\frac{-ie\Lambda}{\hbar c}\right)\left(\mathbf{p} - \frac{e\mathbf{A}}{c} - \frac{e\nabla\Lambda}{c}\right)^2\exp\left(\frac{ie\Lambda}{\hbar c}\right) = \left(\mathbf{p} - \frac{e\mathbf{A}}{c}\right)^2, \qquad (2.6.54)$$

which follows from applying (2.6.50) twice.

Equation (2.6.53) also implies that the corresponding wave equations are related via

$$\bar{\psi}(\mathbf{x}',t) = \exp\left[\frac{ie\Lambda(\mathbf{x}')}{\hbar c}\right]\psi(\mathbf{x}',t), \qquad (2.6.55)$$

where $\Lambda(\mathbf{x}')$ is now a real function of the position vector eigenvalue $\mathbf{x}'$. This can, of course, be verified also by directly substituting (2.6.55) into Schrödinger's wave equation with $\mathbf{A}$ replaced by $\mathbf{A}+\nabla\Lambda$. In terms of ρ and S, we see that ρ is unchanged but S is modified as follows:

$$S \to S + \frac{e\Lambda}{c}. \qquad (2.6.56)$$

This is highly satisfactory because we see that the probability flux given by (2.6.33) is then gauge invariant.

To summarize, when vector potentials in different gauges are used for the same physical situation, the corresponding state kets (or wave functions) must necessarily be different. However, only a simple change is needed; we can go from a gauge specified by $\mathbf{A}$ to another specified by $\mathbf{A}+\nabla\Lambda$ by merely multiplying the old ket (the old wave function) by $\exp[ie\Lambda(\mathbf{x})/\hbar c]$ ($\exp[ie\Lambda(\mathbf{x}')/\hbar c]$). The **canonical momentum**, defined as the generator of translation, is manifestly *gauge dependent* in the sense that its expectation value depends on the particular gauge chosen, while the **kinematic momentum** and the probability flux are *gauge invariant*.

The reader may wonder why invariance under (2.6.49) is called *gauge invariance*. This word is the translation of the German *Eichinvarianz*, where *Eich* means *gauge*. There is a historical anecdote that goes with the origin of this term.

Consider some function of position at $\mathbf{x}$: $F(\mathbf{x})$. At a neighboring point we obviously have

$$F(\mathbf{x}+d\mathbf{x}) \simeq F(\mathbf{x}) + (\nabla F)\cdot d\mathbf{x}. \qquad (2.6.57)$$

But suppose we apply a scale change as we go from $\mathbf{x}$ to $\mathbf{x}+d\mathbf{x}$ as follows:

$$1\big|_{\text{at }\mathbf{x}} \to [1 + \Sigma(\mathbf{x})\cdot d\mathbf{x}]\big|_{\text{at }\mathbf{x}+d\mathbf{x}}. \qquad (2.6.58)$$

We must then rescale $F(\mathbf{x})$ as follows:

$$F(\mathbf{x}+d\mathbf{x})\big|_{\text{rescaled}} \simeq F(\mathbf{x}) + [(\nabla + \Sigma)F]\cdot d\mathbf{x} \qquad (2.6.59)$$

instead of (2.6.57). The combination $\nabla + \Sigma$ is similar to the gauge-invariant combination

$$\nabla - \left(\frac{ie}{\hbar c}\right)\mathbf{A} \qquad (2.6.60)$$

encountered in (2.6.32) except for the absence of i. Historically, H. Weyl unsuccessfully attempted to construct a geometric theory of electromagnetism based on *Eichinvarianz* by identifying the scale function $\Sigma(\mathbf{x})$ in

(2.6.58) and (2.6.59) with the vector potential **A** itself. With the birth of quantum mechanics, V. Fock and F. London realized the importance of the gauge-invariant combination (2.6.60), and they recalled Weyl's earlier work by comparing Σ with i times **A**. We are stuck with the term *gauge invariance* even though the quantum-mechanical analogue of (2.6.58)

$$1\bigg|_{\text{at x}} \rightarrow \left[1 - \left(\frac{ie}{\hbar c}\right)\mathbf{A} \cdot d\mathbf{x}\right]\bigg|_{\text{at x} + d\mathbf{x}} \tag{2.6.61}$$

would actually correspond to "phase change" rather than to "scale change."

The Aharonov-Bohm Effect

The use of vector potential in quantum mechanics has many far-reaching consequences, some of which we are now ready to discuss. We start with a relatively innocuous-looking problem.

Consider a hollow cylindrical shell, as shown in Figure 2.7a. We assume that a particle of charge e can be completely confined to the interior of the shell with rigid walls. The wave function is required to vanish on the inner ($\rho = \rho_a$) and outer ($\rho = \rho_b$) walls as well as at the top and the bottom. It is a straightforward boundary-value problem in mathematical physics to obtain the energy eigenvalues.

Let us now consider a modified arrangement where the cylindrical shell encloses a uniform magnetic field, as shown in Figure 2.7b. Specifi-

(a)

(b)

FIGURE 2.7. Hollow cylindrical shell (a) without a magnetic field, (b) with a uniform magnetic field.

cally, you may imagine fitting a very long solenoid into the hole in the middle in such a way that no magnetic field leaks into the region $\rho \geq \rho_a$. The boundary conditions for the wave function are taken to be the same as before; the walls are assumed to be just as rigid. Intuitively we may conjecture that the energy spectrum is unchanged because the region with $\mathbf{B} \neq 0$ is completely inaccessible to the charged particle trapped inside the shell. However, quantum mechanics tells us that this conjecture is *not* correct.

Even though the magnetic field vanishes in the interior, the vector potential $\mathbf{A}$ is nonvanishing there; using Stokes's theorem we can infer that the vector potential needed to produce the magnetic field $\mathbf{B}$ ($= B\hat{z}$) is

$$\mathbf{A} = \left(\frac{B\rho_a^2}{2\rho}\right)\hat{\phi}, \tag{2.6.62}$$

where $\hat{\phi}$ is the unit vector in the direction of increasing azimuthal angle. In attempting to solve the Schrödinger equation to find the energy eigenvalues for this new problem, we need only to replace the gradient ∇ by $\nabla - (ie/\hbar c)\mathbf{A}$; we can accomplish this in cylindrical coordinates by replacing the partial derivative with respect to ϕ as follows:

$$\frac{\partial}{\partial \phi} \rightarrow \frac{\partial}{\partial \phi} - \left(\frac{ie}{\hbar c}\right)\frac{B\rho_a^2}{2}; \tag{2.6.63}$$

recall the expression for gradient in cylindrical coordinates:

$$\nabla = \hat{\rho}\frac{\partial}{\partial \rho} + \hat{z}\frac{\partial}{\partial z} + \hat{\phi}\frac{1}{\rho}\frac{\partial}{\partial \phi}. \tag{2.6.64}$$

The replacement (2.6.63) results in an *observable* change in the energy spectrum, as the reader may verify explicitly. This is quite remarkable because the particle never "touches" the magnetic field; the Lorentz force the particle experiences is identically zero in this problem, yet the energy levels depend on whether or not the magnetic field is finite in the hole region inaccessible to the particle.

The problem we have just treated is the bound-state version of what is commonly referred to as the *Aharonov-Bohm effect.** We are now in a position to discuss the original form of the Aharonov-Bohm effect itself. Consider a particle of charge e going above or below a very long impenetrable cylinder, as shown in Figure 2.8. Inside the cylinder is a magnetic field parallel to the cylinder axis, taken to be normal to the plane of Figure 2.8. So the particle paths above and below enclose a magnetic flux. Our object is to study how the probability of finding the particle in the interference region B depends on the magnetic flux.

---

*After a 1959 paper by Y. Aharonov and D. Bohm. Essentially the same effect was discussed 10 years earlier by W. Ehrenberg and R. E. Siday.

Even though this problem can be attacked by comparing the solutions to the Schrödinger equation in the presence and absence of **B**, for pedagogical reasons we prefer to use the Feynman path-integral method. Let x_1 and x_N be typical points in source region A and interference region B, respectively. We recall from classical mechanics that the Lagrangian in the presence of the magnetic field can be obtained from that in the absence of the magnetic field, denoted by $L_{classical}^{(0)}$, as follows:

$$L_{classical}^{(0)} = \frac{m}{2}\left(\frac{d\mathbf{x}}{dt}\right)^2 \rightarrow L_{classical}^{(0)} + \frac{e}{c}\frac{d\mathbf{x}}{dt}\cdot\mathbf{A}. \qquad (2.6.65)$$

The corresponding change in the action for some definite path segment going from $(\mathbf{x}_{n-1}, t_{n-1})$ to $(\mathbf{x}_n, t_n)$ is then given by

$$S^{(0)}(n, n-1) \rightarrow S^{(0)}(n, n-1) + \frac{e}{c}\int_{t_{n-1}}^{t_n} dt\left(\frac{d\mathbf{x}}{dt}\right)\cdot\mathbf{A}. \qquad (2.6.66)$$

But this last integral can be written as

$$\frac{e}{c}\int_{t_{n-1}}^{t_n} dt\left(\frac{d\mathbf{x}}{dt}\right)\cdot\mathbf{A} = \frac{e}{c}\int_{\mathbf{x}_{n-1}}^{\mathbf{x}_n} \mathbf{A}\cdot d\mathbf{s}, \qquad (2.6.67)$$

where $d\mathbf{s}$ is the differential line element along the path segment, so when we consider the entire contribution from $\mathbf{x}_1$ to $\mathbf{x}_N$, we have the following change:

$$\Pi\exp\left[\frac{iS^{(0)}(n, n-1)}{\hbar}\right] \rightarrow \left\{\Pi\exp\left[\frac{iS^{(0)}(n, n-1)}{\hbar}\right]\right\}\exp\left(\frac{ie}{\hbar c}\int_{\mathbf{x}_1}^{\mathbf{x}_N}\mathbf{A}\cdot d\mathbf{s}\right). \qquad (2.6.68)$$

All this is for a particular path, such as going above the cylinder. We must still sum over all possible paths, which may appear to be a formidable task. Fortunately, we know from the theory of electromagnetism that the line integral $\int\mathbf{A}\cdot d\mathbf{s}$ is independent of paths, that is, it is dependent only on the end points, as long as the loop formed by a pair of different paths does not enclose a magnetic flux. As a result, the contributions due to $\mathbf{A}\neq 0$ to all paths going above the cylinder are given by a *common* phase factor;

FIGURE 2.8. The Aharonov-Bohm effect.

similarly, the contributions from all paths going below the cylinder are multiplied by another common phase factor. In the path-integral notation we have, for the entire transition amplitude,

$$\int_{above} \mathscr{D}[\mathbf{x}(t)]\exp\left[\frac{iS^{(0)}(N,1)}{\hbar}\right] + \int_{below} \mathscr{D}[\mathbf{x}(t)]\exp\left[\frac{iS^{(0)}(N,1)}{\hbar}\right]$$

$$\rightarrow \int_{above} \mathscr{D}[\mathbf{x}(t)]\exp\left[\frac{iS^{(0)}(N,1)}{\hbar}\right]\left\{\exp\left[\left(\frac{ie}{\hbar c}\right)\int_{\mathbf{x}_1}^{\mathbf{x}_N}\mathbf{A}\cdot d\mathbf{s}\right]_{above}\right\}$$

$$+ \int_{below} \mathscr{D}[\mathbf{x}(t)]\exp\left[\frac{iS^{(0)}(N,1)}{\hbar}\right]\cdot\left\{\exp\left[\left(\frac{ie}{\hbar c}\right)\int_{\mathbf{x}_1}^{\mathbf{x}_N}\mathbf{A}\cdot d\mathbf{s}\right]_{below}\right\}$$

$$(2.6.69)$$

The probability for finding the particle in the interference region B depends on the modulus squared of the entire transition amplitude and hence on the phase difference between the contribution from the paths going above and below. The phase difference due to the presence of **B** is just

$$\left[\left(\frac{e}{\hbar c}\right)\int_{\mathbf{x}_1}^{\mathbf{x}_N}\mathbf{A}\cdot d\mathbf{s}\right]_{above} - \left[\left(\frac{e}{\hbar c}\right)\int_{\mathbf{x}_1}^{\mathbf{x}_N}\mathbf{A}\cdot d\mathbf{s}\right]_{below} = \left(\frac{e}{\hbar c}\right)\oint\mathbf{A}\cdot d\mathbf{s}$$

$$= \left(\frac{e}{\hbar c}\right)\Phi_B, \quad (2.6.70)$$

where Φ_B stands for the magnetic flux inside the impenetrable cylinder. This means that as we change the magnetic field strength, there is a sinusoidal component in the probability for observing the particle in region B with a period given by a *fundamental unit of magnetic flux*, namely,

$$\frac{2\pi\hbar c}{|e|} = 4.135\times10^{-7} \quad \text{Gauss-cm}^2. \quad (2.6.71)$$

We emphasize that the interference effect discussed here is purely quantum mechanical. Classically, the motion of a charged particle is determined solely by Newton's second law supplemented by the force law of Lorentz. Here, as in the previous bound-state problem, the particle can never enter the region in which **B** is finite; the Lorentz force is identically zero in all regions where the particle wave function is finite. Yet there is a striking interference pattern that depends on the presence or absence of a magnetic field inside the impenetrable cylinder. This point has led some people to conclude that in quantum mechanics it is **A** rather than **B** that is fundamental. It is to be noted, however, that the observable effects in both examples depend only on Φ_B, which is directly expressible in terms of **B**. Experiments to verify the Aharonov-Bohm effect have been performed using a thin magnetized iron filament called a *whisker*.*

---

*One such recent experiment is that of A. Tonomura et al., *Phys. Rev. Lett.* **48** (1982): 1443.

Magnetic Monopole

We conclude this section with one of the most remarkable predict-ions of quantum physics, which has yet to be verified experimentally. An astute student of classical electrodynamics may be struck by the fact that there is a strong symmetry between $\mathbf{E}$ and $\mathbf{B}$, yet a magnetic charge—com-monly referred to as a **magnetic monopole**—analogous to electric charge is peculiarly absent in Maxwell's equations. The source of a magnetic field observed in nature is either a moving electric charge or a static magnetic dipole, never a static magnetic charge. Instead of

$$\nabla \cdot \mathbf{B} = 4\pi\rho_M \qquad (2.6.72)$$

analogous to

$$\nabla \cdot \mathbf{E} = 4\pi\rho, \qquad (2.6.73)$$

$\nabla \cdot \mathbf{B}$ actually vanishes in the usual way of writing Maxwell's equations. Quantum mechanics does not predict that a magnetic monopole must exist. However, it unambiguously requires that if a magnetic monopole is ever found in nature, the magnitude of magnetic charge must be quantized in terms of e, $\hbar$, and c, as we now demonstrate.

Suppose there is a point magnetic monopole, situated at the origin, of strength e_M analogous to a point electric charge. The static magnetic field is then given by

$$\mathbf{B} = \left(\frac{e_M}{r^2} \right)\hat{\mathbf{r}}. \qquad (2.6.74)$$

At first sight it may appear that the magnetic field (2.6.74) can be derived from

$$\mathbf{A} = \left[\frac{e_M(1-\cos\theta)}{r\sin\theta} \right]\hat{\boldsymbol{\phi}}. \qquad (2.6.75)$$

Recall the expression for curl in spherical coordinates:

$$\nabla \times \mathbf{A} = \hat{\mathbf{r}}\left[\frac{1}{r\sin\theta} \frac{\partial}{\partial\theta}(A_\phi\sin\theta) - \frac{\partial A_\theta}{\partial\phi} \right]$$

$$+ \hat{\boldsymbol{\theta}}\frac{1}{r}\left[\frac{1}{\sin\theta}\frac{\partial A_r}{\partial\phi} - \frac{\partial}{\partial r}(rA_\phi) \right] + \hat{\boldsymbol{\phi}}\frac{1}{r}\left[\frac{\partial}{\partial r}(rA_\theta) - \frac{\partial A_r}{\partial\theta} \right]. \qquad (2.6.76)$$

But vector potential (2.6.75) has one difficulty—it is singular on the negative z-axis ($\theta = \pi$). In fact, it turns out to be impossible to construct a singular-ity-free potential valid everywhere for this problem. To see this we first note "Gauss's law"

$$\int_{\text{closed surface}} \mathbf{B} \cdot d\boldsymbol{\sigma} = 4\pi e_M \qquad (2.6.77)$$

FIGURE 2.9. Regions of validity for the potentials $\mathbf{A}^{(I)}$ and $\mathbf{A}^{(II)}$.

for any surface boundary enclosing the origin at which the magnetic monopole is located. On the other hand, if $\mathbf{A}$ were nonsingular, we would have

$$\nabla \cdot (\nabla \times \mathbf{A}) = 0 \qquad (2.6.78)$$

everywhere; hence,

$$\int_{\text{closed surface}} \mathbf{B} \cdot d\boldsymbol{\sigma} = \int_{\text{volume inside}} \nabla \cdot (\nabla \times \mathbf{A}) d^3 x = 0, \qquad (2.6.79)$$

in contradiction with (2.6.77).

However, one might argue that because the vector potential is just a device for obtaining $\mathbf{B}$, we need not insist on having a single expression for $\mathbf{A}$ valid everywhere. Suppose we construct a pair of potentials,

$$\mathbf{A}^{(I)} = \left[\frac{e_M(1-\cos\theta)}{r\sin\theta} \right] \hat{\boldsymbol{\phi}}, \qquad (\theta < \pi - \varepsilon) \qquad (2.6.80a)$$

$$\mathbf{A}^{(II)} = -\left[\frac{e_M(1+\cos\theta)}{r\sin\theta} \right] \hat{\boldsymbol{\phi}}, \qquad (\theta > \varepsilon), \qquad (2.6.80b)$$

such that the potential $\mathbf{A}^{(I)}$ can be used everywhere except inside the cone defined by $\theta = \pi - \varepsilon$ around the negative z-axis; likewise, the potential $\mathbf{A}^{(II)}$ can be used everywhere except inside the cone $\theta = \varepsilon$ around the positive z-axis; see Figure 2.9. Together they lead to the correct expression for $\mathbf{B}$ everywhere.*

---

*An alternative approach to this problem uses $\mathbf{A}^{(I)}$ everywhere, but taking special care of the string of singularities, known as a **Dirac string**, along the negative z-axis.

Consider now what happens in the overlap region $\varepsilon < \theta < \pi - \varepsilon$, where we may use either $\mathbf{A}^{(I)}$ or $\mathbf{A}^{(II)}$. Because the two potentials lead to the same magnetic field, they must be related to each other by a gauge transformation. To find Λ appropriate for this problem we first note that

$$\mathbf{A}^{(II)} - \mathbf{A}^{(I)} = -\left(\frac{2e_M}{r\sin\theta}\right)\hat{\boldsymbol{\phi}}. \tag{2.6.81}$$

Recalling the expression for gradient in spherical coordinates,

$$\nabla\Lambda = \hat{\mathbf{r}}\frac{\partial\Lambda}{\partial r} + \hat{\boldsymbol{\theta}}\frac{1}{r}\frac{\partial\Lambda}{\partial\theta} + \hat{\boldsymbol{\phi}}\frac{1}{r\sin\theta}\frac{\partial\Lambda}{\partial\phi}, \tag{2.6.82}$$

we deduce that

$$\Lambda = -2e_M\phi \tag{2.6.83}$$

will do the job.

Next, we consider the wave function of an electrically charged particle of charge e subjected to magnetic field (2.6.74). As we emphasized earlier, the particular form of the wave function depends on the particular gauge used. In the overlap region where we may use either $\mathbf{A}^{(I)}$ or $\mathbf{A}^{(II)}$, the corresponding wave functions are, according to (2.6.55), related to each other by

$$\psi^{(II)} = \exp\left(\frac{-2iee_M\phi}{\hbar c}\right)\psi^{(I)}. \tag{2.6.84}$$

Wave functions $\psi^{(I)}$ and $\psi^{(II)}$ must each be *single-valued* because once we choose particular gauge, the expansion of the state ket in terms of the position eigenkets must be *unique*. After all, as we have repeatedly emphasized, the wave function is simply an expansion coefficient for the state ket in terms of the position eigenkets.

Let us now examine the behavior of wave function $\psi^{(II)}$ on the equator $\theta = \pi/2$ with some definite radius r, which is a constant. When we increase the azimuthal angle ϕ along the equator and go around once, say from $\phi = 0$ to $\phi = 2\pi$, $\psi^{(II)}$, as well as $\psi^{(I)}$, must return to its original value because each is single-valued. According to (2.6.84), this is possible only if

$$\frac{2ee_M}{\hbar c} = \pm N, \quad N = 0, \pm 1, \pm 2, \ldots. \tag{2.6.85}$$

So we reach a very far-reaching conclusion: The magnetic charges must be *quantized* in units of

$$\frac{\hbar c}{2|e|} \approx \left(\frac{137}{2}\right)|e|. \tag{2.6.86}$$

The smallest magnetic charge possible is $\hbar c/2|e|$, where e is the electronic charge. It is amusing that once a magnetic monopole is assumed to exist, we can use (2.6.85) backward, so to speak, to explain why the electric charges are quantized, for example, why the proton charge cannot be 0.999972 times $|e|$.*

We repeat once again that quantum mechanics does not require magnetic monopoles to exist. However, it unambiguously predicts that a magnetic charge, if it is ever found in nature, must be quantized in units of $\hbar c/2|e|$. The quantization of magnetic charges in quantum mechanics was first shown in 1931 by P. A. M. Dirac. The derivation given here is due to T. T. Wu and C. N. Yang.

PROBLEMS

1. Consider the spin-precession problem discussed in the text. It can also be solved in the Heisenberg picture. Using the Hamiltonian

$$H = -\left(\frac{eB}{mc}\right)S_z = \omega S_z,$$

    write the Heisenberg equations of motion for the time-dependent operators $S_x(t)$, $S_y(t)$, and $S_z(t)$. Solve them to obtain $S_{x,y,z}$ as functions of time.

2. Look again at the Hamiltonian of Chapter 1, Problem 11. Suppose the typist made an error and wrote H as

$$H = H_{11}|1\rangle\langle 1| + H_{22}|2\rangle\langle 2| + H_{12}|1\rangle\langle 2|.$$

    What principle is now violated? Illustrate your point explicitly by attempting to solve the most general time-dependent problem using an illegal Hamiltonian of this kind. (You may assume $H_{11} = H_{22} = 0$ for simplicity.)

3. An electron is subject to a uniform, time-independent magnetic field of strength B in the positive z-direction. At $t = 0$ the electron is known to be in an eigenstate of $\mathbf{S} \cdot \hat{\mathbf{n}}$ with eigenvalue $\hbar/2$, where $\hat{\mathbf{n}}$ is a unit vector, lying in the xz-plane, that makes an angle β with the z-axis.
    a. Obtain the probability for finding the electron in the $s_x = \hbar/2$ state as a function of time.
    b. Find the expectation value of S_x as a function of time.
    c. For your own peace of mind show that your answers make good sense in the extreme cases (i) $\beta \to 0$ and (ii) $\beta \to \pi/2$.

4. Let $x(t)$ be the coordinate operator for a free particle in one dimension in the Heisenberg picture. Evaluate

$$[x(t), x(0)]$$

---

*Empirically the equality in magnitude between the electron charge and the proton charge is established to an accuracy of four parts in 10^{19}.

5. Consider a particle in one dimension whose Hamiltonian is given by

$$H = \frac{p^2}{2m} + V(x).$$

By calculating $[[H, x], x]$ prove

$$\sum_{a'} |\langle a''|x|a'\rangle|^2 (E_{a'} - E_{a''}) = \frac{\hbar^2}{2m},$$

where $|a'\rangle$ is an energy eigenket with eigenvalue $E_{a'}$.

6. Consider a particle in three dimensions whose Hamiltonian is given by

$$H = \frac{\mathbf{p}^2}{2m} + V(\mathbf{x}).$$

By calculating $[\mathbf{x} \cdot \mathbf{p}, H]$ obtain

$$\frac{d}{dt}\langle \mathbf{x} \cdot \mathbf{p} \rangle = \left\langle \frac{\mathbf{p}^2}{m} \right\rangle - \langle \mathbf{x} \cdot \nabla V \rangle.$$

To identify the preceding relation with the quantum-mechanical analogue of the virial theorem it is essential that the left-hand side vanish. Under what condition would this happen?

7. Consider a free-particle wave packet in one dimension. At $t = 0$ it satisfies the minimum uncertainty relation

$$\langle (\Delta x)^2 \rangle \langle (\Delta p)^2 \rangle = \frac{\hbar^2}{4} \quad (t = 0).$$

In addition, we know

$$\langle x \rangle = \langle p \rangle = 0 \quad (t = 0).$$

Using the Heisenberg picture, obtain $\langle (\Delta x)^2 \rangle_t$ as a function of $t (t \geq 0)$ when $\langle (\Delta x)^2 \rangle_{t=0}$ is given. (Hint: Take advantage of the property of the minimum-uncertainty wave packet you worked out in Chapter 1, Problem 18).

8. Let $|a'\rangle$ and $|a''\rangle$ be eigenstates of a Hermitian operator A with eigenvalues a' and a'', respectively $(a' \neq a'')$. The Hamiltonian operator is given by

$$H = |a'\rangle \delta \langle a''| + |a''\rangle \delta \langle a'|,$$

where δ is just a real number.

a. Clearly, $|a'\rangle$ and $|a''\rangle$ are not eigenstates of the Hamiltonian. Write down the eigenstates of the Hamiltonian. What are their energy eigenvalues?

b. Suppose the system is known to be in state $|a'\rangle$ at $t = 0$. Write down the state vector in the Schrödinger picture for $t > 0$.

c. What is the probability for finding the system in $|a''\rangle$ for $t > 0$ if the system is known to be in state $|a'\rangle$ at $t = 0$?

d. Can you think of a physical situation corresponding to this problem?

9. A box containing a particle is divided into a right and left compartment by a thin partition. If the particle is known to be on the right (left) side with certainty, the state is represented by the position eigenket $|R\rangle(|L\rangle)$, where we have neglected spatial variations within each half of the box. The most general state vector can then be written as

$$|\alpha\rangle = |R\rangle\langle R|\alpha\rangle + |L\rangle\langle L|\alpha\rangle,$$

where $\langle R|\alpha\rangle$ and $\langle L|\alpha\rangle$ can be regarded as "wave functions." The particle can tunnel through the partition; this tunneling effect is characterized by the Hamiltonian

$$H = \Delta(|L\rangle\langle R| + |R\rangle\langle L|),$$

where Δ is a real number with the dimension of energy.

a. Find the normalized energy eigenkets. What are the corresponding energy eigenvalues?

b. In the Schrödinger picture the base kets $|R\rangle$ and $|L\rangle$ are fixed, and the state vector moves with time. Suppose the system is represented by $|\alpha\rangle$ as given above at $t = 0$. Find the state vector $|\alpha, t_0 = 0; t\rangle$ for $t > 0$ by applying the appropriate time-evolution operator to $|\alpha\rangle$.

c. Suppose at $t = 0$ the particle is on the right side with certainty. What is the probability for observing the particle on the left side as a function of time?

d. Write down the coupled Schrödinger equations for the wave functions $\langle R|\alpha, t_0 = 0; t\rangle$ and $\langle L|\alpha, t_0 = 0; t\rangle$. Show that the solutions to the coupled Schrödinger equations are just what you expect from (b).

e. Suppose the printer made an error and wrote H as

$$H = \Delta|L\rangle\langle R|.$$

By explicitly solving the most general time-evolution problem with this Hamiltonian, show that probability conservation is violated.

10. Using the one-dimensional simple harmonic oscillator as an example, illustrate the difference between the Heisenberg picture and the Schrödinger picture. Discuss in particular how (a) the dynamic variables x and p and (b) the most general state vector evolve with time in each of the two pictures.

11. Consider a particle subject to a one-dimensional simple harmonic oscillator potential. Suppose at $t = 0$ the state vector is given by

$$\exp\left(\frac{-ipa}{\hbar}\right)|0\rangle,$$

where p is the momentum operator and a is some number with dimension of length. Using the Heisenberg picture, evaluate the expectation value $\langle x \rangle$ for $t \geq 0$.

12. a. Write down the wave function (in coordinate space) for the state specified in Problem 11 at $t = 0$. You may use

$$\langle x'|0\rangle = \pi^{-1/4} x_0^{-1/2} \exp\left[-\frac{1}{2}\left(\frac{x'}{x_0}\right)^2\right], \quad \left(x_0 \equiv \left(\frac{\hbar}{m\omega}\right)^{1/2}\right).$$

   b. Obtain a simple expression for the probability that the state is found in the ground state at $t = 0$. Does this probability change for $t > 0$?

13. Consider a one-dimensional simple harmonic oscillator.

   a. Using

$$\left.\begin{matrix} a \\ a^\dagger \end{matrix}\right\} = \sqrt{\frac{m\omega}{2\hbar}}\left(x \pm \frac{ip}{m\omega}\right), \quad \left.\begin{matrix} a|n\rangle \\ a^\dagger|n\rangle \end{matrix}\right\} = \left\{\begin{matrix} \sqrt{n}\,|n-1\rangle \\ \sqrt{n+1}\,|n+1\rangle, \end{matrix}\right.$$

   evaluate $\langle m|x|n\rangle$, $\langle m|p|n\rangle$, $\langle m|\{x, p\}|n\rangle$, $\langle m|x^2|n\rangle$, and $\langle m|p^2|n\rangle$.

   b. Check that the virial theorem holds for the expectation values of the kinetic and the potential energy taken with respect to an energy eigenstate.

14. a. Using

$$\langle x'|p'\rangle = (2\pi\hbar)^{-1/2} e^{ip'x'/\hbar} \quad \text{(one dimension)}$$

   prove

$$\langle p'|x|\alpha\rangle = i\hbar \frac{\partial}{\partial p'}\langle p'|\alpha\rangle.$$

   b. Consider a one-dimensional simple harmonic oscillator. Starting with the Schrödinger equation for the state vector, derive the Schrödinger equation for the *momentum-space* wave function. (Make sure to distinguish the operator p from the eigenvalue p'.) Can you guess the energy eigenfunctions in momentum space?

15. Consider a function, known as the **correlation function**, defined by

$$C(t) = \langle x(t)x(0)\rangle,$$

   where $x(t)$ is the position operator in the Heisenberg picture. Evaluate the correlation function explicitly for the ground state of a one-dimensional simple harmonic oscillator.

16. Consider again a one-dimensional simple harmonic oscillator. Do the following algebraically, that is, without using wave functions.

   a. Construct a linear combination of $|0\rangle$ and $|1\rangle$ such that $\langle x\rangle$ is as large as possible.

   b. Suppose the oscillator is in the state constructed in (a) at $t = 0$. What is the state vector for $t > 0$ in the Schrödinger picture? Evaluate the expectation value $\langle x\rangle$ as a function of time for $t > 0$ using (i) the Schrödinger picture and (ii) the Heisenberg picture.

   c. Evaluate $\langle(\Delta x)^2\rangle$ as a function of time using either picture.

17. Show for the one-dimensional simple harmonic oscillator

$$\langle 0|e^{ikx}|0\rangle = \exp\left[-k^2\langle 0|x^2|0\rangle/2\right],$$

where x is the position *operator*.

18. A coherent state of a one-dimensional simple harmonic oscillator is defined to be an eigenstate of the (non-Hermitian) annihilation operator a:

$$a|\lambda\rangle = \lambda|\lambda\rangle,$$

where λ is, in general, a complex number.

a. Prove that

$$|\lambda\rangle = e^{-|\lambda|^2/2}e^{\lambda a^\dagger}|0\rangle$$

is a normalized coherent state.

b. Prove the minimum uncertainty relation for such a state.

c. Write $|\lambda\rangle$ as

$$|\lambda\rangle = \sum_{n=0}^{\infty} f(n)|n\rangle.$$

Show that the distribution of $|f(n)|^2$ with respect to n is of the Poisson form. Find the most probable value of n, hence of E.

d. Show that a coherent state can also be obtained by applying the translation (finite-displacement) operator $e^{-ipl/\hbar}$ (where p is the momentum operator, and l is the displacement distance) to the ground state. (See also Gottfried 1966, 262–64.)

19. Let

$$J_{\pm} = \hbar a_{\pm}^\dagger a_{\mp}, \qquad J_z = \frac{\hbar}{2}\left(a_+^\dagger a_+ - a_-^\dagger a_-\right), \qquad N = a_+^\dagger a_+ + a_-^\dagger a_-$$

where $a_{\pm}$ and $a_{\pm}^\dagger$ are the annihilation and creation operators of two *independent* simple harmonic oscillator satisfying the usual simple harmonic oscillator commutation relations. Prove

$$[J_z, J_{\pm}] = \pm\hbar J_{\pm}, \qquad [\mathbf{J}^2, J_z] = 0, \qquad \mathbf{J}^2 = \left(\frac{\hbar^2}{2}\right)N\left[\left(\frac{N}{2}\right)+1\right].$$

20. Consider a particle of mass m subject to a one-dimensional potential of the following form:

$$V = \begin{cases} \dfrac{1}{2}kx^2 & \text{for } x > 0 \\ \infty & \text{for } x < 0. \end{cases}$$

a. What is the ground-state energy?

b. What is the expectation value $\langle x^2\rangle$ for the ground state?

21. A particle in one dimension is trapped between two rigid walls:

$$V(x) = \begin{cases} 0, & \text{for } 0 < x < L \\ \infty, & \text{for } x < 0, \quad x > L. \end{cases}$$

At $t = 0$ it is known to be exactly at $x = L/2$ with certainty. What are the *relative* probabilities for the particle to be found in various energy eigenstates? Write down the wave function for $t \geq 0$. (You need not worry about absolute normalization, convergence, and other mathematical subtleties.)

22. Consider a particle in one dimension bound to a fixed center by a δ-function potential of the form

$$V(x) = -v_0\delta(x), \quad (v_0 \text{ real and positive}).$$

Find the wave function and the binding energy of the ground state. Are there excited bound states?

23. A particle of mass m in one dimension is bound to a fixed center by an attractive δ-function potential:

$$V(x) = -\lambda\delta(x), \quad (\lambda > 0).$$

At $t = 0$, the potential is suddenly switched off (that is, $V = 0$ for $t > 0$). Find the wave function for $t > 0$. (Be quantitative! But you need not attempt to evaluate an integral that may appear.)

24. A particle in one dimension $(-\infty < x < \infty)$ is subjected to a constant force derivable from

$$V = \lambda x, \quad (\lambda > 0).$$

a. Is the energy spectrum continuous or discrete? Write down an approximate expression for the energy eigenfunction specified by E. Also sketch it crudely.

b. Discuss briefly what changes are needed if V is replaced by

$$V = \lambda|x|.$$

25. Consider an electron confined to the *interior* of a hollow cylindrical shell whose axis coincides with the z-axis. The wave function is required to vanish on the inner and outer walls, $\rho = \rho_a$ and ρ_b, and also at the top and bottom, $z = 0$ and L.

a. Find the energy eigenfunctions. (Do not bother with normalization.) Show that the energy eigenvalues are given by

$$E_{lmn} = \left(\frac{\hbar^2}{2m_e}\right)\left[k_{mn}^2 + \left(\frac{l\pi}{L}\right)^2\right] \quad (l = 1,2,3,\ldots, \ m = 0,1,2,\ldots),$$

where k_{mn} is the nth root of the transcendental equation

$$J_m(k_{mn}\rho_b)N_m(k_{mn}\rho_a) - N_m(k_{mn}\rho_b)J_m(k_{mn}\rho_a) = 0.$$

b. Repeat the same problem when there is a uniform magnetic field $\mathbf{B} = B\hat{z}$ for $0 < \rho < \rho_a$. Note that the energy eigenvalues are influenced by the magnetic field even though the electron never "touches" the magnetic field. .

c. Compare, in particular, the ground state of the $B = 0$ problem with that of the $B \neq 0$ problem. Show that if we require the ground-state energy to be unchanged in the presence of B, we obtain "flux quantization"

$$\pi \rho_a^2 B = \frac{2\pi N \hbar c}{e}, \quad (N = 0, \pm 1, \pm 2, \dots).$$

26. Consider a particle moving in one dimension under the influence of a potential $V(x)$. Suppose its wave function can be written as $\exp[iS(x, t)/\hbar]$. Prove that $S(x, t)$ satisfies the classical Hamilton-Jacobi equation to the extent that $\hbar$ can be regarded as small in some sense. Show how one may obtain the correct wave function for a plane wave by starting with the solution of the classical Hamilton-Jacobi equation with $V(x)$ set equal to zero. Why do we get the exact wave function in this particular case?

27. Using spherical coordinates, obtain an expression for $\mathbf{j}$ for the ground and excited states of the hydrogen atom. Show, in particular, that for $m_l \neq 0$ states, there is a circulating flux in the sense that $\mathbf{j}$ is in the direction of increasing or decreasing ϕ, depending on whether m_l is positive or negative.

28. Derive (2.5.16) and obtain the three-dimensional generalization of (2.5.16).

29. Define the partition function as

$$Z = \int d^3x' K(\mathbf{x}', t; \mathbf{x}', 0)|_{\beta = it/\hbar},$$

as in (2.5.20)–(2.5.22). Show that the ground-state energy is obtained by taking

$$-\frac{1}{Z} \frac{\partial Z}{\partial \beta}, \quad (\beta \to \infty).$$

Illustrate this for a particle in a one-dimensional box.

30. The propagator in momentum space analogous to (2.5.26) is given by $\langle \mathbf{p}'', t | \mathbf{p}', t_0 \rangle$. Derive an explicit expression for $\langle \mathbf{p}'', t | \mathbf{p}', t_0 \rangle$ for the free-particle case.

31. a. Write down an expression for the classical action for a simple harmonic oscillator for a finite time interval.

    b. Construct $\langle x_n, t_n | x_{n-1}, t_{n-1} \rangle$ for a simple harmonic oscillator using Feynman's prescription for $t_n - t_{n-1} = \Delta t$ small. Keeping only terms up to order $(\Delta t)^2$, show that it is in complete agreement with the $t - t_0 \to 0$ limit of the propagator given by (2.5.26).

32. State the Schwinger action principle (see Finkelstein 1973, 155). Obtain the solution for $\langle x_2 t_2 | x_1 t_1 \rangle$ by integrating the Schwinger principle and compare it with the corresponding Feynman expression for $\langle x_2 t_2 | x_1 t_1 \rangle$. Describe the classical limits of these two expressions.

33. Show that the wave-mechanics approach to the gravity-induced problem discussed in Section 2.6 also leads to phase-difference expression (2.6.17).
34. a. Verify (2.6.25) and (2.6.27).
    b. Verify continuity equation (2.6.30) with $\mathbf{j}$ given by (2.6.31).
35. Consider the Hamiltonian of a spinless particle of charge e. In the presence of a static magnetic field, the interaction terms can be generated by

$$\mathbf{p}_{operator} \rightarrow \mathbf{p}_{operator} - \frac{e\mathbf{A}}{c},$$

where $\mathbf{A}$ is the appropriate vector potential. Suppose, for simplicity, that the magnetic field $\mathbf{B}$ is uniform in the positive z-direction. Prove that the above prescription indeed leads to the correct expression for the interaction of the orbital magnetic moment $(e/2mc)\mathbf{L}$ with the magnetic field $\mathbf{B}$. Show that there is also an extra term proportional to $B^2(x^2 + y^2)$, and comment briefly on its physical significance.
36. An electron moves in the presence of a uniform magnetic field in the z-direction ($\mathbf{B} = B\hat{z}$).
    a. Evaluate

$$[\Pi_x, \Pi_y],$$

where

$$\Pi_x \equiv p_x - \frac{eA_x}{c}, \qquad \Pi_y \equiv p_y - \frac{eA_y}{c}.$$

    b. By comparing the Hamiltonian and the commutation relation obtained in (a) with those of the one-dimensional oscillator problem, show how we can immediately write the energy eigenvalues as

$$E_{k,n} = \frac{\hbar^2 k^2}{2m} + \left(\frac{|eB|\hbar}{mc}\right)\left(n + \frac{1}{2}\right),$$

where $\hbar k$ is the continuous eigenvalue of the p_z operator and n is a nonnegative integer including zero.
37. Consider the neutron interferometer.

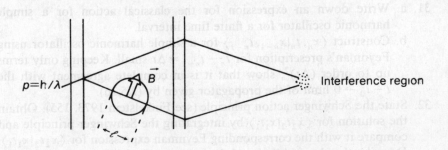

Prove that the difference in the magnetic fields that produce two successive maxima in the counting rates is given by

$$\Delta B = \frac{4\pi\hbar c}{|e|g_n \lambda l},$$

where g_n ($=-1.91$) is the neutron magnetic moment in units of $-e\hbar/2m_n c$. [If you had solved this problem in 1967, you could have published it in *Physical Review Letters*!]

CHAPTER 3

Theory of Angular Momentum

This chapter is concerned with a systematic treatment of angular momentum and related topics. The importance of angular momentum in modern
physics can hardly be overemphasized. A thorough understanding of angular momentum is essential in molecular, atomic, and nuclear spectroscopy;
angular-momentum considerations play an important role in scattering and
collision problems as well as in bound-state problems. Furthermore, angular-momentum concepts have important generalizations—isospin in nuclear
physics, SU(3), SU(2)⊗U(1) in particle physics, and so forth.

3.1. ROTATIONS AND ANGULAR MOMENTUM COMMUTATION RELATIONS

Finite Versus Infinitesimal Rotations

We recall from elementary physics that rotations about the same axis
commute, whereas rotations about different axes do not. For instance, a 30°
rotation about the z-axis followed by a 60° rotation about the same z-axis is
obviously equivalent to a 60° rotation followed by a 30° rotation, both
about the same axis. However, let us consider a 90° rotation about the
z-axis, denoted by $R_z(\pi/2)$, followed by a 90° rotation about the x-axis,
denoted by $R_x(\pi/2)$; compare this with a 90° rotation about the x-axis

followed by a 90° rotation about the z-axis. The net results are different, as we can see from Figure 3.1.

Our first basic task is to work out quantitatively the manner in which rotations about different axes *fail* to commute. To this end, we first recall how to represent rotations in three dimensions by 3×3 real, orthogonal matrices. Consider a vector $\mathbf{V}$ with components V_x, V_y, and V_z. When we rotate, the three components become some other set of numbers, V_x', V_y', and V_z'. The old and new components are related via a 3×3 orthogonal matrix R:

$$\begin{pmatrix} V_x' \\ V_y' \\ V_z' \end{pmatrix} = \begin{pmatrix} & & \\ & R & \\ & & \end{pmatrix} \begin{pmatrix} V_x \\ V_y \\ V_z \end{pmatrix}, \tag{3.1.1a}$$

$$RR^T = R^T R = 1, \tag{3.1.1b}$$

where the superscript T stands for a transpose of a matrix. It is a property of orthogonal matrices that

$$\sqrt{V_x^2 + V_y^2 + V_z^2} = \sqrt{V_x'^2 + V_y'^2 + V_z'^2} \tag{3.1.2}$$

is automatically satisfied.

FIGURE 3.1. Example to illustrate the noncommutativity of finite rotations.

To be definite, we consider a rotation about the z-axis by angle ϕ. The convention we follow throughout this book is that a rotation operation affects a physical system itself, as in Figure 3.1, while the coordinate axes remain *unchanged*. The angle ϕ is taken to be positive when the rotation in question is counterclockwise in the xy-plane, as viewed from the positive z-side. If we associate a right-handed screw with such a rotation, a positive ϕ rotation around the z-axis means that the screw is advancing in the positive z-direction. With this convention, we easily verify that

$$R_z(\phi) = \begin{pmatrix} \cos\phi & -\sin\phi & 0 \\ \sin\phi & \cos\phi & 0 \\ 0 & 0 & 1 \end{pmatrix}. \tag{3.1.3}$$

Had we adopted a different convention, in which a physical system remained fixed but the coordinate axes rotated, this same matrix with a positive ϕ would have represented a *clockwise* rotation of the x- and y-axes, when viewed from the positive z-side. It is obviously important not to mix the two conventions! Some authors distinguish the two approaches by using "active rotations" for physical systems rotated and "passive rotations" for the coordinate axes rotated.

We are particularly interested in an infinitesimal form of R_z:

$$R_z(\varepsilon) = \begin{pmatrix} 1 - \dfrac{\varepsilon^2}{2} & -\varepsilon & 0 \\ \varepsilon & 1 - \dfrac{\varepsilon^2}{2} & 0 \\ 0 & 0 & 1 \end{pmatrix}, \tag{3.1.4}$$

where terms of order ε^3 and higher are ignored. Likewise, we have

$$R_x(\varepsilon) = \begin{pmatrix} 1 & 0 & 0 \\ 0 & 1 - \dfrac{\varepsilon^2}{2} & -\varepsilon \\ 0 & \varepsilon & 1 - \dfrac{\varepsilon^2}{2} \end{pmatrix} \tag{3.1.5a}$$

and

$$R_y(\varepsilon) = \begin{pmatrix} 1 - \dfrac{\varepsilon^2}{2} & 0 & \varepsilon \\ 0 & 1 & 0 \\ -\varepsilon & 0 & 1 - \dfrac{\varepsilon^2}{2} \end{pmatrix}, \tag{3.1.5b}$$

which may be read from (3.1.4) by cyclic permutations of x, y, z —that is, $x \to y, y \to z, z \to x$. Compare now the effect of a y-axis rotation followed by an x-axis rotation with that of an x-axis rotation followed by a y-axis rotation. Elementary matrix manipulations lead to

$$R_x(\varepsilon)R_y(\varepsilon) = \begin{pmatrix} 1 - \dfrac{\varepsilon^2}{2} & 0 & \varepsilon \\ \varepsilon^2 & 1 - \dfrac{\varepsilon^2}{2} & -\varepsilon \\ -\varepsilon & \varepsilon & 1 - \varepsilon^2 \end{pmatrix} \qquad (3.1.6a)$$

and

$$R_y(\varepsilon)R_x(\varepsilon) = \begin{pmatrix} 1 - \dfrac{\varepsilon^2}{2} & \varepsilon^2 & \varepsilon \\ 0 & 1 - \dfrac{\varepsilon^2}{2} & -\varepsilon \\ -\varepsilon & \varepsilon & 1 - \varepsilon^2 \end{pmatrix} \qquad (3.1.6b)$$

From (3.1.6a) and (3.1.6b) we have the first important result: Infinitesimal rotations about different axes do commute if terms of order ε^2 and higher are ignored.* The second and even more important result concerns the manner in which rotations about different axes *fail* to commute when terms of order ε^2 are kept:

$$R_x(\varepsilon)R_y(\varepsilon) - R_y(\varepsilon)R_x(\varepsilon) = \begin{pmatrix} 0 & -\varepsilon^2 & 0 \\ \varepsilon^2 & 0 & 0 \\ 0 & 0 & 0 \end{pmatrix}$$

$$= R_z(\varepsilon^2) - 1, \qquad (3.1.7)$$

where all terms of order higher than ε^2 have been ignored throughout this derivation. We also have

$$1 = R_{any}(0) \qquad (3.1.8)$$

where *any* stands for any rotation axis. Thus the final result can be written as

$$R_x(\varepsilon)R_y(\varepsilon) - R_y(\varepsilon)R_x(\varepsilon) = R\ (\varepsilon^2) - R_{any}(0) \qquad (3.1.9)$$

This is an example of the commutation relations between rotation operations about different axes, which we will use later in deducing the angular-momentum commutation relations in quantum mechanics.

---

*Actually there is a familiar example of this in elementary mechanics. The angular velocity vector ω that characterizes an infinitesimal change in rotation angle during an infinitesimal time interval follows the usual rule of vector addition including commutativity of vector addition. However, we cannot ascribe a vectorial property to a *finite* angular change.

Infinitesimal Rotations in Quantum Mechanics

So far we have not used quantum-mechanical concepts. The matrix R is just a 3×3 orthogonal matrix acting on a vector $\mathbf{V}$ written in column matrix form. We must now understand how to characterize rotations in quantum mechanics.

Because rotations affect physical systems, the state ket corresponding to a rotated system is expected to look different from the state ket corresponding to the original unrotated system. Given a rotation operation R, characterized by a 3×3 orthogonal matrix R, we associate an operator $\mathscr{D}(R)$ in the appropriate ket space such that

$$|\alpha\rangle_R = \mathscr{D}(R)|\alpha\rangle, \qquad (3.1.10)$$

where $|\alpha\rangle_R$ and $|\alpha\rangle$ stand for the kets of the rotated and original system, respectively.* Note that the 3×3 orthogonal matrix R acts on a column matrix made up of the three components of a classical vector, while the operator $\mathscr{D}(R)$ acts on state vectors in ket space. The matrix representation of $\mathscr{D}(R)$, which we will study in great detail in the subsequent sections, depends on the dimensionality N of the particular ket space in question. For $N = 2$, appropriate for describing a spin $\frac{1}{2}$ system with no other degrees of freedom, $\mathscr{D}(R)$ is represented by a 2×2 matrix; for a spin 1 system, the appropriate representation is a 3×3 unitary matrix, and so on.

To construct the rotation operator $\mathscr{D}(R)$, it is again fruitful to examine first its properties under an infinitesimal rotation. We can almost guess how we must proceed by analogy. In both translations and time evolution, which we studied in Sections 1.6 and 2.1, respectively, the appropriate infinitesimal operators could be written as

$$U_\varepsilon = 1 - iG\varepsilon \qquad (3.1.11)$$

with a Hermitian operator G. Specifically,

$$G \to \frac{p_x}{\hbar}, \qquad \varepsilon \to dx' \qquad (3.1.12)$$

for an infinitesimal translation by a displacement dx' in the x-direction, and

$$G \to \frac{H}{\hbar}, \qquad \varepsilon \to dt \qquad (3.1.13)$$

for an infinitesimal time evolution with time displacement dt. We know from classical mechanics that angular momentum is the generator of rotation in much the same way as momentum and Hamiltonian are the generators of translation and time evolution, respectively. We therefore *define* the angular momentum operator J_k in such a way that the operator for an infinitesimal rotation around the kth axis by angle $d\phi$ can be

---

*The symbol $\mathscr{D}$ stems from the German word *Drehung*, meaning *rotation*.

obtained by letting

$$G \rightarrow \frac{J_k}{\hbar}, \qquad \varepsilon \rightarrow d\phi \qquad\qquad (3.1.14)$$

in (3.1.11). With J_k taken to be Hermitian, the infinitesimal rotation operator is guaranteed to be unitary and reduces to the identity operator in the limit $d\phi \rightarrow 0$. More generally, we have

$$\mathscr{D}(\hat{\mathbf{n}}, d\phi) = 1 - i\left(\frac{\mathbf{J} \cdot \hat{\mathbf{n}}}{\hbar}\right) d\phi \qquad\qquad (3.1.15)$$

for a rotation about the direction characterized by a unit vector $\hat{\mathbf{n}}$ by an infinitesimal angle $d\phi$.

We stress that in this book we do not define the angular-momentum operator to be $\mathbf{x} \times \mathbf{p}$. This is important because spin angular momentum, to which our general formalism also applies, has nothing to do with x_i and p_j. Put in another way, in classical mechanics one can prove that the angular momentum defined to be $\mathbf{x} \times \mathbf{p}$ is the generator of a rotation; in contrast, in quantum mechanics we *define* $\mathbf{J}$ so that the operator for an infinitesimal rotation takes form (3.1.15).

A finite rotation can be obtained by compounding successively infinitesimal rotations about the same axis. For instance, if we are interested in a finite rotation about the z-axis by angle ϕ, we consider

$$\begin{aligned}
\mathscr{D}_z(\phi) &= \lim_{N \rightarrow \infty} \left[1 - i\left(\frac{J_z}{\hbar}\right)\left(\frac{\phi}{N}\right)\right]^N \\
&= \exp\left(\frac{-iJ_z\phi}{\hbar}\right) \\
&= 1 - \frac{iJ_z\phi}{\hbar} - \frac{J_z^2\phi^2}{2\hbar^2} + \cdots. \qquad (3.1.16)
\end{aligned}$$

In order to obtain the angular-momentum commutation relations, we need one more concept. As we remarked earlier, for every rotation R represented by a 3×3 orthogonal matrix R there exists a rotation operator $\mathscr{D}(R)$ in the appropriate ket space. We further postulate that $\mathscr{D}(R)$ has the same group properties as R:

Identity: $\qquad\qquad R \cdot 1 = R \Rightarrow \mathscr{D}(R) \cdot 1 = \mathscr{D}(R)$ $\qquad$ (3.1.17a)

Closure: $\qquad\qquad R_1 R_2 = R_3 \Rightarrow \mathscr{D}(R_1)\mathscr{D}(R_2) = \mathscr{D}(R_3)$ $\qquad$ (3.1.17b)

Inverses: $\qquad\qquad RR^{-1} = 1 \Rightarrow \mathscr{D}(R)\mathscr{D}^{-1}(R) = 1$ $\qquad$ (3.1.17c)

$$R^{-1}R = 1 \Rightarrow \mathscr{D}^{-1}(R)\mathscr{D}(R) = 1$$

Associativity: $\quad R_1(R_2 R_3) = (R_1 R_2)R_3 = R_1 R_2 R_3$ $\qquad$ (3.1.17d)

$$\Rightarrow \mathscr{D}(R_1)[\mathscr{D}(R_2)\mathscr{D}(R_3)]$$

$$= [\mathscr{D}(R_1)\mathscr{D}(R_2)]\mathscr{D}(R_3)$$

$$= \mathscr{D}(R_1)\mathscr{D}(R_2)\mathscr{D}(R_3).$$

Let us now return to the fundamental commutation relations for rotation operations (3.1.9) written in terms of the R matrices. Its rotation operator analogue would read

$$\left(1 - \frac{iJ_x\varepsilon}{\hbar} - \frac{J_x^2\varepsilon^2}{2\hbar^2}\right)\left(1 - \frac{iJ_y\varepsilon}{\hbar} - \frac{J_y^2\varepsilon^2}{2\hbar^2}\right)$$

$$- \left(1 - \frac{iJ_y\varepsilon}{\hbar} - \frac{J_y^2\varepsilon^2}{2\hbar^2}\right)\left(1 - \frac{iJ_x\varepsilon}{\hbar} - \frac{J_x^2\varepsilon^2}{2\hbar^2}\right) = 1 - \frac{iJ_z\varepsilon^2}{\hbar} - 1. \quad (3.1.18)$$

Terms of order ε automatically drop out. Equating terms of order ε^2 on both sides of (3.1.18), we obtain

$$[J_x, J_y] = i\hbar J_z. \quad (3.1.19)$$

Repeating this kind of argument with rotations about other axes, we obtain

$$[J_i, J_j] = i\hbar\varepsilon_{ijk}J_k, \quad (3.1.20)$$

known as the **fundamental commutation relations of angular momentum**.

In general, when the generators of infinitesimal transformations do not commute, the corresponding group of operations is said to be **non-Abelian**. Because of (3.1.20), the rotation group in three dimensions is non-Abelian. In contrast, the translation group in three dimensions is Abelian because p_i and p_j commute even with $i \neq j$.

We emphasize that in obtaining the commutation relations (3.1.20) we have used the following two concepts:

1. J_k is the generator of rotation about the kth axis.
2. Rotations about different axes fail to commute.

It is no exaggeration to say that commutation relations (3.1.20) summarize in a compact manner *all* the basic properties of rotations in three dimensions.

3.2. SPIN $\frac{1}{2}$ SYSTEMS AND FINITE ROTATIONS

Rotation Operator for Spin $\frac{1}{2}$

The lowest number, N, of dimensions in which the angular-momentum commutation relations (3.1.20) are realized, is $N = 2$. The reader has already checked in Problem 8 of Chapter 1 that the operators defined by

$$S_x = \left(\frac{\hbar}{2}\right)\{(|+\rangle\langle-|)+(|-\rangle\langle+|)\},$$

$$S_y = \left(\frac{i\hbar}{2}\right)\{-(|+\rangle\langle-|)+(|-\rangle\langle+|)\}, \quad (3.2.1)$$

$$S_z = \left(\frac{\hbar}{2}\right)\{(|+\rangle\langle+|)-(|-\rangle\langle-|)\}$$

satisfy commutation relations (3.1.20) with J_k replaced by S_k. It is not a priori obvious that nature takes advantage of the lowest dimensional realization of (3.1.20), but numerous experiments—from atomic spectroscopy to nuclear magnetic resonance—suffice to convince us that this is in fact the case.

Consider a rotation by a finite angle ϕ about the z-axis. If the ket of a spin $\frac{1}{2}$ system before rotation is given by $|\alpha\rangle$, the ket after rotation is given by

$$|\alpha\rangle_R = \mathscr{D}_z(\phi)|\alpha\rangle \tag{3.2.2}$$

with

$$\mathscr{D}_z(\phi) = \exp\left(\frac{-iS_z\phi}{\hbar}\right). \tag{3.2.3}$$

To see that this operator really rotates the physical system, let us look at its effect on $\langle S_x\rangle$. Under rotation this expectation value changes as follows:

$$\langle S_x\rangle \rightarrow {}_R\langle\alpha|S_x|\alpha\rangle_R = \langle\alpha|\mathscr{D}_z^\dagger(\phi)S_x\mathscr{D}_z(\phi)|\alpha\rangle. \tag{3.2.4}$$

We must therefore compute

$$\exp\left(\frac{iS_z\phi}{\hbar}\right)S_x\exp\left(\frac{-iS_z\phi}{\hbar}\right). \tag{3.2.5}$$

For pedagogical reasons we evaluate this in two different ways.

Derivation 1: Here we use the specific form of S_x given by (3.2.1). We then obtain for (3.2.5)

$$\left(\frac{\hbar}{2}\right)\exp\left(\frac{iS_z\phi}{\hbar}\right)\{(|+\rangle\langle-|)+(|-\rangle\langle+|)\}\exp\left(\frac{-iS_z\phi}{\hbar}\right)$$

$$= \left(\frac{\hbar}{2}\right)\left(e^{i\phi/2}|+\rangle\langle-|e^{i\phi/2}+e^{-i\phi/2}|-\rangle\langle+|e^{-i\phi/2}\right)$$

$$= \frac{\hbar}{2}\left[\{(|+\rangle\langle-|)+(|-\rangle\langle+|)\}\cos\phi+i\{(|+\rangle\langle-|)-(|-\rangle\langle+|)\}\sin\phi\right]$$

$$= S_x\cos\phi - S_y\sin\phi. \tag{3.2.6}$$

Derivation 2: Alternatively we may use formula (2.3.47) to evaluate (3.2.5):

$$\exp\left(\frac{iS_z\phi}{\hbar}\right)S_x\exp\left(\frac{-iS_z\phi}{\hbar}\right) = S_x + \left(\frac{i\phi}{\hbar}\right)\underbrace{[S_z,S_x]}_{i\hbar S_y}$$

$$+ \left(\frac{1}{2!}\right)\left(\frac{i\phi}{\hbar}\right)^2\underbrace{[S_z,[S_z,S_x]]}_{\underbrace{i\hbar S_y}_{\hbar^2 S_x}} + \left(\frac{1}{3!}\right)\left(\frac{i\phi}{\hbar}\right)^3\underbrace{[S_z,[S_z,[S_z,S_x]]]}_{\underbrace{\hbar^2 S_x}_{\underbrace{ih^3 S_y}}} + \cdots$$

$$= S_x\left[1 - \frac{\phi^2}{2!} + \cdots\right] - S_y\left[\phi - \frac{\phi^3}{3!} + \cdots\right]$$

$$= S_x\cos\phi - S_y\sin\phi. \tag{3.2.7}$$

Notice that in derivation 2 we used only the commutation relations for S_i, so this method can be generalized to rotations of systems with angular momentum higher than $\frac{1}{2}$.

For spin $\frac{1}{2}$, both methods give

$$\langle S_x \rangle \rightarrow {}_R\langle \alpha | S_x | \alpha \rangle_R = \langle S_x \rangle \cos \phi - \langle S_y \rangle \sin \phi, \qquad (3.2.8)$$

where the expectation value without subscripts is understood to be taken with respect to the (old) unrotated system. Similarly,

$$\langle S_y \rangle \rightarrow \langle S_y \rangle \cos \phi + \langle S_x \rangle \sin \phi. \qquad (3.2.9)$$

As for the expectation value of S_z, there is no change because S_z commutes with $\mathscr{D}_z(\phi)$:

$$\langle S_z \rangle \rightarrow \langle S_z \rangle. \qquad (3.2.10)$$

Relations (3.2.8), (3.2.9), and (3.2.10) are quite reasonable. They show that rotation operator (3.2.3), when applied to the state ket, does rotate the expectation value of **S** around the z-axis by angle ϕ. In other words, the expectation value of the spin operator behaves as though it were a classical vector under rotation:

$$\langle S_k \rangle \rightarrow \sum_l R_{kl} \langle S_l \rangle, \qquad (3.2.11)$$

where R_{kl} are the elements of the 3×3 orthogonal matrix R that specifies the rotation in question. It should be clear from our derivation 2 that this property is not restricted to the spin operator of spin $\frac{1}{2}$ systems. In general, we have

$$\langle J_k \rangle \rightarrow \sum_l R_{kl} \langle J_l \rangle \qquad (3.2.12)$$

under rotation, where J_k are the generators of rotations satisfying the angular-momentum commutation relations (3.1.20). Later we will show that relations of this kind can be further generalized to any vector operator.

So far everything has been as expected. But now, be prepared for a surprise! We examine the effect of rotation operator (3.2.3) on a general ket,

$$|\alpha\rangle = |+\rangle\langle + |\alpha\rangle + |-\rangle\langle - |\alpha\rangle, \qquad (3.2.13)$$

a little more closely. We see that

$$\exp\left(\frac{-iS_z\phi}{\hbar}\right)|\alpha\rangle = e^{-i\phi/2}|+\rangle\langle + |\alpha\rangle + e^{i\phi/2}|-\rangle\langle - |\alpha\rangle. \quad (3.2.14)$$

The appearance of the half-angle $\phi/2$ here has an extremely interesting consequence.

Let us consider a rotation by 2π. We then have

$$|\alpha\rangle_{R_z(2\pi)} \rightarrow -|\alpha\rangle. \qquad (3.2.15)$$

So the ket for the 360° rotated state differs from the original ket by a minus sign. We would need a 720° ($\phi = 4\pi$) rotation to get back to the same ket with a *plus* sign. Notice that this minus sign disappears for the expectation value of **S** because **S** is sandwiched by $|\alpha\rangle$ and $\langle\alpha|$, both of which change sign. Will this minus sign ever be observable? We will give the answer to this interesting question after we discuss spin precession once again.

Spin Precession Revisited

We now treat the problem of spin precession, already discussed in Section 2.1, from a new point of view. We recall that the basic Hamiltonian of the problem is given by

$$H = -\left(\frac{e}{m_e c}\right)\mathbf{S}\cdot\mathbf{B} = \omega S_z, \tag{3.2.16}$$

where

$$\omega \equiv \frac{|e|B}{m_e c}. \tag{3.2.17}$$

The time-evolution operator based on this Hamiltonian is given by

$$\mathcal{U}(t,0) = \exp\left(\frac{-iHt}{\hbar}\right) = \exp\left(\frac{-iS_z\omega t}{\hbar}\right). \tag{3.2.18}$$

Comparing this equation with (3.2.3), we see that the time-evolution operator here is precisely the same as the rotation operator in (3.2.3) with ϕ set equal to ωt. In this manner we see immediately why this Hamiltonian causes spin precession. Paraphrasing (3.2.8), (3.2.9), and (3.2.10), we obtain

$$\langle S_x\rangle_t = \langle S_x\rangle_{t=0}\cos\omega t - \langle S_y\rangle_{t=0}\sin\omega t, \tag{3.2.19a}$$

$$\langle S_y\rangle_t = \langle S_y\rangle_{t=0}\cos\omega t + \langle S_x\rangle_{t=0}\sin\omega t, \tag{3.2.19b}$$

$$\langle S_z\rangle_t = \langle S_z\rangle_{t=0}. \tag{3.2.19c}$$

After $t = 2\pi/\omega$, the spin returns to its original direction.

This set of equations can be used to discuss the spin precession of a **muon**, an electronlike particle which, however, is 210 times as heavy. The muon magnetic moment can be determined from other experiments—for example, the hyperfine splitting in muonium, a bound state of a positive muon and an electron—to be $e\hbar/2m_\mu c$, just as expected from Dirac's relativistic theory of spin $\frac{1}{2}$ particles. (We will here neglect very small corrections that arise from quantum field theory effects). Knowing the magnetic moment we can predict the angular frequency of precession. So (3.2.19) can be and, in fact, has been checked experimentally. In practice, as the external magnetic field causes spin precession, the spin direction is analyzed by taking advantage of the fact that electrons from muon decay tend to be emitted preferentially in the direction opposite to the muon spin.

Let us now look at the time evolution of the state ket itself. Assuming that the initial $(t = 0)$ ket is given by (3.2.13), we obtain after time t

$$|\alpha, t_0 = 0; t\rangle = e^{-i\omega t/2}|+\rangle\langle+|\alpha\rangle + e^{+i\omega t/2}|-\rangle\langle-|\alpha\rangle. \quad (3.2.20)$$

Expression (3.2.20) acquires a minus sign at $t = 2\pi/\omega$, and we must wait until $t = 4\pi/\omega$ to get back to the original state ket with the same sign. To sum up, the period for the state ket is *twice* as long as the period for spin precession

$$\tau_{\text{precession}} = \frac{2\pi}{\omega}, \quad (3.2.21a)$$

$$\tau_{\text{state ket}} = \frac{4\pi}{\omega}. \quad (3.2.21b)$$

Neutron Interferometry Experiment to Study 2π Rotations

We now describe an experiment performed to detect the minus sign in (3.2.15). Quite clearly, if every state ket in the universe is multiplied by a minus sign, there will be no observable effect. The only way to detect the predicted minus sign is to make a comparison between an unrotated state and a rotated state. As in gravity-induced quantum interference, discussed in Section 2.6, we rely on the art of neutron interferometry to verify this extraordinary prediction of quantum mechanics.

A nearly monoenergetic beam of thermal neutrons is split into two parts—path A and path B; see Figure 3.2. Path A always goes through a magnetic-field-free region; in contrast, path B enters a small region where a static magnetic field is present. As a result, the neutron state ket going via path B suffers a phase change $e^{\mp i\omega T/2}$, where T is the time spent in the $\mathbf{B} \neq 0$ region and ω is the spin-precession frequency

$$\omega = \frac{g_n eB}{m_p c}, \quad (g_n \simeq -1.91) \quad (3.2.22)$$

for the neutron with a magnetic moment of $g_n e\hbar/2m_p c$, as we can see if we

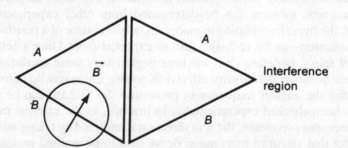

FIGURE 3.2. Experiment to study the predicted minus sign under a 2π rotation.

compare this with (3.2.17), which is appropriate for the electron with magnetic moment $eh/2m_ec$. When path A and path B meet again in the interference region of Figure 3.2, the amplitude of the neutron arriving via path B is

$$c_2 = c_2(B=0)e^{\mp i\omega T/2}, \tag{3.2.23}$$

while the amplitude of the neutron arriving via path A is c_1, independent of **B**. So the intensity observable in the interference region must exhibit a sinusoidal variation

$$\cos\left(\frac{\mp \omega T}{2} + \delta\right), \tag{3.2.24}$$

where δ is the phase difference between c_1 and c_2 $(B=0)$. In practice, T, the time spent in the $B \neq 0$ region, is fixed but the precession frequency ω is varied by changing the strength of the magnetic field. The intensity in the interference region as a function of B is predicted to have a sinusoidal variation. If we call ΔB the difference in B needed to produce successive maxima, we can easily show that

$$\Delta B = \frac{4\pi hc}{eg_n \lambda l}, \tag{3.2.25}$$

where l is the path length.

In deriving this formula we used the fact that a 4π rotation is needed for the state ket to return to the original ket with the same sign, as required by our formalism. If, on the other hand, our description of spin $\frac{1}{2}$ systems were incorrect and the ket were to return to its original ket with the same sign under a 2π rotation, the predicted value for ΔB would be just one-half of (3.2.25).

Two different groups have conclusively demonstrated experimentally that prediction (3.2.25) is correct to an accuracy of a fraction of a percent.[*] This is another triumph of quantum mechanics. The nontrivial prediction (3.2.15) has been experimentally established in a direct manner.

Pauli Two-Component Formalism

Manipulations with the state kets of spin $\frac{1}{2}$ systems can be conveniently carried out using the two-component spinor formalism introduced by W. Pauli in 1926. In Section 1.3 we learned how a ket (bra) can be represented by a column (row) matrix; all we have to do is arrange the expansion coefficients in terms of a certain specified set of base kets into a

---

[*] H. Rauch et al., *Phys. Lett.* **54A**, 425 (1975); S. A. Werner et al., *Phys. Rev. Lett.* **35** (1975), 1053.

column (row) matrix. In the spin $\frac{1}{2}$ case we have

$$|+\rangle \doteq \begin{pmatrix} 1 \\ 0 \end{pmatrix} \equiv \chi_+ \qquad |-\rangle \doteq \begin{pmatrix} 0 \\ 1 \end{pmatrix} \equiv \chi_-$$

$$\langle +| \doteq (1,0) = \chi_+^\dagger \qquad \langle -| \doteq (0,1) = \chi_-^\dagger \tag{3.2.26}$$

for the base kets and bras and

$$|\alpha\rangle = |+\rangle\langle +|\alpha\rangle + |-\rangle\langle -|\alpha\rangle \doteq \begin{pmatrix} \langle +|\alpha\rangle \\ \langle -|\alpha\rangle \end{pmatrix} \tag{3.2.27a}$$

and

$$\langle \alpha| = \langle \alpha|+\rangle\langle +| + \langle \alpha|-\rangle\langle -| \doteq (\langle \alpha|+\rangle, \langle \alpha|-\rangle) \tag{3.2.27b}$$

for an arbitrary state ket and the corresponding state bra. Column matrix (3.2.27a) is referred to as a **two-component spinor** and is written as

$$\chi = \begin{pmatrix} \langle +|\alpha\rangle \\ \langle -|\alpha\rangle \end{pmatrix} \equiv \begin{pmatrix} c_+ \\ c_- \end{pmatrix}$$

$$= c_+ \chi_+ + c_- \chi_-, \tag{3.2.28}$$

where c_+ and c_- are, in general, complex numbers. For $\chi^\dagger$ we have

$$\chi^\dagger = (\langle \alpha|+\rangle, \langle \alpha|-\rangle) = (c_+^*, c_-^*). \tag{3.2.29}$$

The matrix elements $\langle \pm |S_k|+\rangle$ and $\langle \pm |S_k|-\rangle$, apart from $\hbar/2$, are to be set equal to those of 2×2 matrices σ_k, known as the **Pauli matrices**. We identify

$$\langle \pm |S_k|+\rangle \equiv \left(\frac{\hbar}{2}\right)(\sigma_k)_{\pm,+}, \qquad \langle \pm |S_k|-\rangle \equiv \left(\frac{\hbar}{2}\right)(\sigma_k)_{\pm,-}. \tag{3.2.30}$$

We can now write the expectation value $\langle S_k \rangle$ in terms of χ and σ_k:

$$\langle S_k \rangle = \langle \alpha|S_k|\alpha\rangle = \sum_{a'=+,-} \sum_{a''=+,-} \langle \alpha|a'\rangle\langle a'|S_k|a''\rangle\langle a''|\alpha\rangle$$

$$= \left(\frac{\hbar}{2}\right)\chi^\dagger \sigma_k \chi, \tag{3.2.31}$$

where the usual rule of matrix multiplication is used in the last line. Explicitly, we see from (3.2.1) together with (3.2.30) that

$$\sigma_1 = \begin{pmatrix} 0 & 1 \\ 1 & 0 \end{pmatrix}, \qquad \sigma_2 = \begin{pmatrix} 0 & -i \\ i & 0 \end{pmatrix}, \qquad \sigma_3 = \begin{pmatrix} 1 & 0 \\ 0 & -1 \end{pmatrix} \tag{3.2.32}$$

where the subscripts 1, 2, and 3 refer to x, y, and z, respectively.

We record some properties of the Pauli matrices. First,

$$\sigma_i^2 = 1 \tag{3.2.33a}$$

$$\sigma_i \sigma_j + \sigma_j \sigma_i = 0, \quad \text{for } i \neq j, \tag{3.2.33b}$$

where the right-hand side of (3.2.33a) is to be understood as the 2×2

identity matrix. These two relations are, of course, equivalent to the anticommutation relations

$$\{\sigma_i, \sigma_j\} = 2\delta_{ij}. \qquad (3.2.34)$$

We also have the commutation relations

$$[\sigma_i, \sigma_j] = 2i\varepsilon_{ijk}\sigma_k, \qquad (3.2.35)$$

which we see to be the explicit 2×2 matrix realizations of the angular-momentum commutation relations (3.1.20). Combining (3.2.34) and (3.2.35), we can obtain

$$\sigma_1\sigma_2 = -\sigma_2\sigma_1 = i\sigma_3\ldots. \qquad (3.2.36)$$

Notice also that

$$\sigma_i^\dagger = \sigma_i, \qquad (3.2.37a)$$

$$\det(\sigma_i) = -1, \qquad (3.2.37b)$$

$$\text{Tr}(\sigma_i) = 0. \qquad (3.2.37c)$$

We now consider $\boldsymbol{\sigma} \cdot \mathbf{a}$, where $\mathbf{a}$ is a vector in three dimensions. This is actually to be understood as a 2×2 matrix. Thus

$$\boldsymbol{\sigma} \cdot \mathbf{a} \equiv \sum_k a_k \sigma_k$$

$$= \begin{pmatrix} +a_3 & a_1 - ia_2 \\ a_1 + ia_2 & -a_3 \end{pmatrix}. \qquad (3.2.38)$$

There is also a very important identity,

$$(\boldsymbol{\sigma} \cdot \mathbf{a})(\boldsymbol{\sigma} \cdot \mathbf{b}) = \mathbf{a} \cdot \mathbf{b} + i\boldsymbol{\sigma} \cdot (\mathbf{a} \times \mathbf{b}). \qquad (3.2.39)$$

To prove this all we need are the anticommutation and commutation relations, (3.2.34) and (3.2.35), respectively:

$$\sum_j \sigma_j a_j \sum_k \sigma_k b_k = \sum_j \sum_k \left(\frac{1}{2}\{\sigma_j, \sigma_k\} + \frac{1}{2}[\sigma_j, \sigma_k] \right) a_j b_k$$

$$= \sum_j \sum_k \left(\delta_{jk} + i\varepsilon_{jkl}\sigma_l \right) a_j b_k$$

$$= \mathbf{a} \cdot \mathbf{b} + i\boldsymbol{\sigma} \cdot (\mathbf{a} \times \mathbf{b}). \qquad (3.2.40)$$

If the components of $\mathbf{a}$ are real, we have

$$(\boldsymbol{\sigma} \cdot \mathbf{a})^2 = |\mathbf{a}|^2, \qquad (3.2.41)$$

where $|\mathbf{a}|$ is the magnitude of the vector $\mathbf{a}$.

Rotations in the Two-Component Formalism

Let us now study the 2×2 matrix representation of the rotation operator $\mathscr{D}(\hat{\mathbf{n}}, \phi)$. We have

$$\exp\left(\frac{-i\mathbf{S} \cdot \hat{\mathbf{n}}\phi}{\hbar} \right) \doteq \exp\left(\frac{-i\boldsymbol{\sigma} \cdot \hat{\mathbf{n}}\phi}{2} \right). \qquad (3.2.42)$$

Using

$$(\boldsymbol{\sigma}\cdot\hat{\mathbf{n}})^n = \begin{cases} 1 & \text{for } n \text{ even,} \\ \boldsymbol{\sigma}\cdot\hat{\mathbf{n}} & \text{for } n \text{ odd,} \end{cases} \tag{3.2.43}$$

which follows from (3.2.41), we can write

$$\exp\left(\frac{-i\boldsymbol{\sigma}\cdot\hat{\mathbf{n}}\phi}{2}\right) = \left[1 - \frac{(\boldsymbol{\sigma}\cdot\hat{\mathbf{n}})^2}{2!}\left(\frac{\phi}{2}\right)^2 + \frac{(\boldsymbol{\sigma}\cdot\hat{\mathbf{n}})^4}{4!}\left(\frac{\phi}{2}\right)^4 - \cdots\right]$$

$$- i\left[(\boldsymbol{\sigma}\cdot\hat{\mathbf{n}})\frac{\phi}{2} - \frac{(\boldsymbol{\sigma}\cdot\hat{\mathbf{n}})^3}{3!}\left(\frac{\phi}{2}\right)^3 + \cdots\right]$$

$$= 1\cos\left(\frac{\phi}{2}\right) - i\boldsymbol{\sigma}\cdot\hat{\mathbf{n}}\sin\left(\frac{\phi}{2}\right). \tag{3.2.44}$$

Explicitly, in 2×2 form we have

$$\exp\left(\frac{-i\boldsymbol{\sigma}\cdot\hat{\mathbf{n}}\phi}{2}\right) = \begin{pmatrix} \cos\left(\frac{\phi}{2}\right) - in_z\sin\left(\frac{\phi}{2}\right) & (-in_x - n_y)\sin\left(\frac{\phi}{2}\right) \\ (-in_x + n_y)\sin\left(\frac{\phi}{2}\right) & \cos\left(\frac{\phi}{2}\right) + in_z\sin\left(\frac{\phi}{2}\right) \end{pmatrix}$$

$$\tag{3.2.45}$$

Just as the operator $\exp(-i\mathbf{S}\cdot\hat{\mathbf{n}}\phi/\hbar)$ acts on a state ket $|\alpha\rangle$, the 2×2 matrix $\exp(-i\boldsymbol{\sigma}\cdot\hat{\mathbf{n}}\phi/2)$ acts on a two-component spinor χ. Under rotations we change χ as follows:

$$\chi \to \exp\left(\frac{-i\boldsymbol{\sigma}\cdot\hat{\mathbf{n}}\phi}{2}\right)\chi. \tag{3.2.46}$$

On the other hand, the σ_k's themselves are to remain *unchanged* under rotations. So strictly speaking, despite its appearance, $\boldsymbol{\sigma}$ is not to be regarded as a vector; rather, it is $\chi^\dagger\boldsymbol{\sigma}\chi$ which obeys the transformation property of a vector:

$$\chi^\dagger\sigma_k\chi \to \sum_l R_{kl}\chi^\dagger\sigma_l\chi. \tag{3.2.47}$$

An explicit proof of this may be given using

$$\exp\left(\frac{i\sigma_3\phi}{2}\right)\sigma_1\exp\left(\frac{-i\sigma_3\phi}{2}\right) = \sigma_1\cos\phi - \sigma_2\sin\phi \tag{3.2.48}$$

and so on, which is the 2×2 matrix analogue of (3.2.6).

In discussing a 2π rotation using the ket formalism, we have seen that a spin $\frac{1}{2}$ ket $|\alpha\rangle$ goes into $-|\alpha\rangle$. The 2×2 analogue of this statement is

$$\exp\left(\frac{-i\boldsymbol{\sigma}\cdot\hat{\mathbf{n}}\phi}{2}\right)\Bigg|_{\phi=2\pi} = -1, \quad \text{for any } \hat{\mathbf{n}}, \tag{3.2.49}$$

which is evident from (3.2.44).

As an instructive application of rotation matrix (3.2.45), let us see how we can construct an eigenspinor of $\boldsymbol{\sigma}\cdot\hat{\mathbf{n}}$ with eigenvalue $+1$, where $\hat{\mathbf{n}}$ is a unit vector in some specified direction. Our object is to construct χ satisfying

$$\boldsymbol{\sigma}\cdot\hat{\mathbf{n}}\chi = \chi. \tag{3.2.50}$$

In other words, we look for the two-component column matrix representation of $|\mathbf{S}\cdot\hat{\mathbf{n}}; +\rangle$ defined by

$$\mathbf{S}\cdot\hat{\mathbf{n}}|\mathbf{S}\cdot\hat{\mathbf{n}}; +\rangle = \left(\frac{\hbar}{2}\right)|\mathbf{S}\cdot\hat{\mathbf{n}}; +\rangle. \tag{3.2.51}$$

Actually this can be solved as a straightforward eigenvalue problem (see Problem 9 in Chapter 1), but here we present an alternative method based on rotation matrix (3.2.45).

Let the polar and the azimuthal angles that characterize $\hat{\mathbf{n}}$ be β and α, respectively. We start with $\begin{pmatrix} 1 \\ 0 \end{pmatrix}$, the two-component spinor that represents the spin-up state. Given this, we first rotate about the y-axis by angle β; we subsequently rotate by angle α about the z-axis. We see that the desired

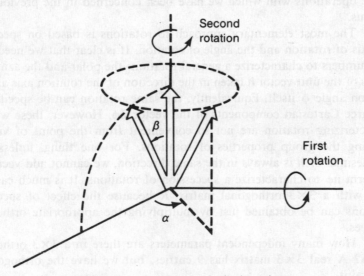

FIGURE 3.3. Construction of $\boldsymbol{\sigma}\cdot\hat{\mathbf{n}}$ eigenspinor.

spin state is then obtained; see Figure 3.3. In the Pauli spinor language this sequence of operations is equivalent to applying $\exp(-i\sigma_2\beta/2)$ to $\begin{pmatrix} 1 \\ 0 \end{pmatrix}$ followed by an application of $\exp(-i\sigma_3\alpha/2)$. The net result is

$$
\chi = \left[\cos\left(\frac{\alpha}{2}\right) - i\sigma_3\sin\left(\frac{\alpha}{2}\right)\right]\left[\cos\left(\frac{\beta}{2}\right) - i\sigma_2\sin\left(\frac{\beta}{2}\right)\right]\begin{pmatrix} 1 \\ 0 \end{pmatrix}
$$

$$
= \begin{pmatrix} \cos\left(\dfrac{\alpha}{2}\right) - i\sin\left(\dfrac{\alpha}{2}\right) & 0 \\ 0 & \cos\left(\dfrac{\alpha}{2}\right) + i\sin\left(\dfrac{\alpha}{2}\right) \end{pmatrix} \begin{pmatrix} \cos\left(\dfrac{\beta}{2}\right) & -\sin\left(\dfrac{\beta}{2}\right) \\ \sin\left(\dfrac{\beta}{2}\right) & \cos\left(\dfrac{\beta}{2}\right) \end{pmatrix} \begin{pmatrix} 1 \\ 0 \end{pmatrix}
$$

$$
= \begin{pmatrix} \cos\left(\dfrac{\beta}{2}\right) e^{-i\alpha/2} \\ \sin\left(\dfrac{\beta}{2}\right) e^{i\alpha/2} \end{pmatrix}, \tag{3.2.52}
$$

in complete agreement with Problem 9 of Chapter 1 if we realize that a phase common to both the upper and lower components is devoid of physical significance.

3.3. SO(3), SU(2), AND EULER ROTATIONS

Orthogonal Group

We will now study a little more systematically the group properties of the operations with which we have been concerned in the previous two sections.

The most elementary approach to rotations is based on specifying the axis of rotation and the angle of rotation. It is clear that we need three real numbers to characterize a general rotation: the polar and the azimuthal angles of the unit vector $\hat{n}$ taken in the direction of the rotation axis and the rotation angle ϕ itself. Equivalently, the same rotation can be specified by the three Cartesian components of the vector $\hat{n}\phi$. However, these ways of characterizing rotation are not so convenient from the point of view of studying the group properties of rotations. For one thing, unless ϕ is infinitesimal or $\hat{n}$ is always in the same direction, we cannot add vectors of the form $\hat{n}\phi$ to characterize a succession of rotations. It is much easier to work with a 3×3 orthogonal matrix R because the effect of successive rotations can be obtained just by multiplying the appropriate orthogonal matrices.

How many independent parameters are there in a 3×3 orthogonal matrix? A real 3×3 matrix has 9 entries, but we have the orthogonality constraint

$$
RR^T = 1. \tag{3.3.1}
$$

which corresponds to 6 independent equations because the product RR^T. being the same as $R^T R$, is a symmetrical matrix with 6 independent entries. As a result, there are 3 (that is, $9-6$) independent numbers in R, the same number previously obtained by a more elementary method.

The set of all multiplication operations with orthogonal matrices forms a group. By this we mean that the following four requirements are satisfied:

1. The product of any two orthogonal matrices is another orthogonal matrix, which is satisfied because

$$(R_1 R_2)(R_1 R_2)^T = R_1 R_2 R_2^T R_1^T = 1. \tag{3.3.2}$$

2. The associative law holds:

$$R_1(R_2 R_3) = (R_1 R_2)R_3. \tag{3.3.3}$$

3. The identity matrix 1—physically corresponding to no rotation —defined by

$$R1 = 1R = R \tag{3.3.4}$$

is a member of the class of all orthogonal matrices.

4. The inverse matrix R^{-1}—physically corresponding to rotation in the opposite sense—defined by

$$RR^{-1} = R^{-1}R = 1 \tag{3.3.5}$$

is also a member.

This group has the name SO(3), where S stands for special, O stands for orthogonal, 3 for three dimensions. Note only rotational operations are considered here, hence we have SO(3) rather than O(3) (which can include the inversion operation of Chapter 4 later).

Unitary unimodular group

In the previous section we learned yet another way to characterize an arbitrary rotation—that is, to look at the 2×2 matrix (3.2.45) that acts on the two-component spinor χ. Clearly, (3.2.45) is unitary. As a result, for the c_+ and c_-, defined in (3.2.28),

$$|c_+|^2 + |c_-|^2 = 1 \tag{3.3.6}$$

is left invariant. Furthermore, matrix (3.2.45) is unimodular; that is, its determinant is 1, as will be shown explicitly below.

We can write the most general unitary unimodular matrix as

$$U(a, b) = \begin{pmatrix} a & b \\ -b^* & a^* \end{pmatrix}, \tag{3.3.7}$$

where a and b are *complex* numbers satisfying the unimodular condition

$$|a|^2 + |b|^2 = 1. \tag{3.3.8}$$

We can easily establish the unitary property of (3.3.7) as follows:

$$U(a,b)^\dagger U(a,b) = \begin{pmatrix} a^* & -b \\ b^* & a \end{pmatrix}\begin{pmatrix} a & b \\ -b^* & a^* \end{pmatrix} = 1, \qquad (3.3.9)$$

where we have used (3.3.8). Notice that the number of independent real parameters in (3.3.7) is again three.

We can readily see that the 2×2 matrix (3.2.45) that characterizes a rotation of a spin $\frac{1}{2}$ system can be written as $U(a,b)$. Comparing (3.2.45) with (3.3.7), we identify

$$\operatorname{Re}(a) = \cos\left(\frac{\phi}{2}\right), \qquad \operatorname{Im}(a) = -n_z\sin\left(\frac{\phi}{2}\right),$$

$$\operatorname{Re}(b) = -n_y\sin\left(\frac{\phi}{2}\right), \qquad \operatorname{Im}(b) = -n_x\sin\left(\frac{\phi}{2}\right), \qquad (3.3.10)$$

from which the unimodular property of (3.3.8) is immediate. Conversely, it is clear that the most general unitary unimodular matrix of form (3.3.7) can be interpreted as representing a rotation.

The two complex numbers a and b are known as **Cayley-Klein parameters**. Historically the connection between a unitary unimodular matrix and a rotation was known long before the birth of quantum mechanics. In fact, the Cayley-Klein parameters were used to characterize complicated motions of gyroscopes in rigid-body kinematics.

Without appealing to the interpretations of unitary unimodular matrices in terms of rotations, we can directly check the group properties of multiplication operations with unitary unimodular matrices. Note in particular that

$$U(a_1, b_1)U(a_2, b_2) = U(a_1a_2 - b_1b_2^*, a_1b_2 + a_2^*b_1), \qquad (3.3.11)$$

where the unimodular condition for the product matrix is

$$|a_1a_2 - b_1b_2^*|^2 + |a_1b_2 + a_2^*b_1|^2 = 1. \qquad (3.3.12)$$

For the inverse of U we have

$$U^{-1}(a,b) = U(a^*, -b). \qquad (3.3.13)$$

This group is known as SU(2), where S stands for special, U for unitary, and 2 for dimensionality 2. In contrast, the group defined by multiplication operations with general 2×2 unitary matrices (not necessarily constrained to be unimodular) is known as U(2). The most general unitary matrix in two dimensions has four independent parameters and can be written as $e^{i\gamma}$ (with γ real) times a unitary unimodular matrix:

$$U = e^{i\gamma}\begin{pmatrix} a & b \\ -b^* & a^* \end{pmatrix}, \qquad |a|^2 + |b|^2 = 1, \qquad \gamma^* = \gamma. \qquad (3.3.14)$$

SU(2) is called a **subgroup** of U(2).

Because we can characterize rotations using both the SO(3) language and the SU(2) language, we may be tempted to conclude that the *groups* SO(3) and SU(2) are isomorphic—that is, that there is a one-to-one correspondence between an element of SO(3) and an element of SU(2). This inference is not correct. Consider a rotation by 2π and another one by 4π. In the SO(3) language, the matrices representing a 2π rotation and a 4π rotation are both 3×3 identity matrices; however, in the SU(2) language the corresponding matrices are -1 times the 2×2 identity matrix and the identity matrix itself, respectively. More generally, $U(a,b)$ and $U(-a,-b)$ both correspond to a *single* 3×3 matrix in the SO(3) language. The correspondence therefore is two-to-one; for a given R, the corresponding U is double-valued. One can say, however, that the two groups are *locally* isomorphic.

Euler Rotations

From classical mechanics the reader may be familiar with the fact that an arbitrary rotation of a rigid body can be accomplished in three steps, known as **Euler rotations**. The Euler rotation language, specified by three Euler angles, provides yet another way to characterize the most general rotation in three dimensions.

The three steps of Euler rotations are as follows. First, rotate the rigid body counterclockwise (as seen from the positive z-side) about the z-axis by angle α. Imagine now that there is a body y-axis embedded, so to speak, in the rigid body such that before the z-axis rotation is carried out, the body y-axis coincides with the usual y-axis, referred to as the **space-fixed y-axis**. Obviously, after the rotation about the z-axis, the body y-axis no longer coincides with the space-fixed y-axis; let us call the former the y'-axis. To see how all this may appear for a thin disk, refer to Figure 3.4a. We now perform a second rotation, this time about the y'-axis by angle β. As a result, the body z-axis no longer points in the space-fixed z-axis direction. We call the body-fixed z-axis after the second rotation the z'-axis; see Figure 3.4b. The third and final rotation is about the z'-axis by angle γ. The body y-axis now becomes the y''-axis of Figure 3.4c. In terms of 3×3 orthogonal matrices the product of the three operations can be written as

$$R(\alpha, \beta, \gamma) \equiv R_{z'}(\gamma) R_{y'}(\beta) R_z(\alpha). \qquad (3.3.15)$$

A cautionary remark is in order here. Most textbooks in classical mechanics prefer to perform the second rotation (the middle rotation) about the body x-axis rather than about the body y-axis (see, for example, Goldstein 1980). This convention is to be avoided in quantum mechanics for a reason that will become apparent in a moment.

In (3.3.15) there appear $R_{y'}$ and $R_{z'}$, which are matrices for rotations about body axes. This approach to Euler rotations is rather inconvenient in

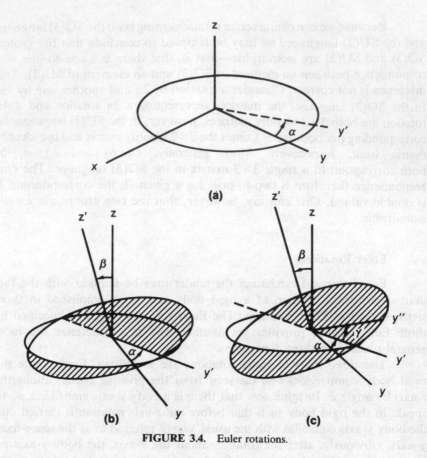

FIGURE 3.4. Euler rotations.

quantum mechanics because we earlier obtained simple expressions for the space-fixed (unprimed) axis components of the **S** operator, but not for the body-axis components. It is therefore desirable to express the body-axis rotations we considered in terms of space-fixed axis rotations. Fortunately there is a very simple relation, namely,

$$R_{y'}(\beta) = R_z(\alpha) R_y(\beta) R_z^{-1}(\alpha). \qquad (3.3.16)$$

The meaning of the right-hand side is as follows. First, bring the body y-axis of Figure 3.4a (that is, the y'-axis) back to the original fixed-space y-direction by rotating *clockwise* (as seen from the positive z-side) about the z-axis by angle α; then rotate about the y-axis by angle β. Finally, return the body y-axis to the direction of the y'-axis by rotating about the fixed-space z-axis (*not* about the z'-axis!) by angle α. Equation (3.3.16) tells us that the net effect of these rotations is a single rotation about the y'-axis by angle β.

To prove this assertion, let us look more closely at the effect of both sides of (3.3.16) on the circular disc of Figure 3.4a. Clearly, the orientation of the body y-axis is unchanged in both cases, namely, in the y'-direction. Furthermore, the orientation of the final body z-axis is the same whether we apply $R_{y'}(\beta)$ or $R_z(\alpha)R_y(\beta)R_z^{-1}(\alpha)$. In both cases the final body z-axis makes a polar angle β with the fixed z-axis (the same as the initial z-axis), and its azimuthal angle, as measured in the fixed-coordinate system, is just α. In other words, the final body z-axis is the same as the z'-axis of Figure 3.4b. Similarly, we can prove

$$R_{z'}(\gamma) = R_{y'}(\beta)R_z(\gamma)R_{y'}^{-1}(\beta). \tag{3.3.17}$$

Using (3.3.16) and (3.3.17), we can now rewrite (3.3.15). We obtain

$$R_{z'}(\gamma)R_{y'}(\beta)R_z(\alpha) = R_{y'}(\beta)R_z(\gamma)R_{y'}^{-1}(\beta)R_{y'}(\beta)R_z(\alpha)$$

$$= R_z(\alpha)R_y(\beta)R_z^{-1}(\alpha)R_z(\gamma)R_z(\alpha)$$

$$= R_z(\alpha)R_y(\beta)R_z(\gamma), \tag{3.3.18}$$

where in the final step we used the fact that $R_z(\gamma)$ and $R_z(\alpha)$ commute. To summarize,

$$R(\alpha,\beta,\gamma) = R_z(\alpha)R_y(\beta)R_z(\gamma), \tag{3.3.19}$$

where all three matrices on the right-hand side refer to *fixed*-axis rotations.

Now let us apply this set of operations to spin $\frac{1}{2}$ systems in quantum mechanics. Corresponding to the product of orthogonal matrices in (3.3.19) there exists a product of rotation operators in the ket space of the spin $\frac{1}{2}$ system under consideration:

$$\mathscr{D}(\alpha,\beta,\gamma) = \mathscr{D}_z(\alpha)\mathscr{D}_y(\beta)\mathscr{D}_z(\gamma). \tag{3.3.20}$$

The 2×2 matrix representation of this product is

$$\exp\left(\frac{-i\sigma_3\alpha}{2}\right)\exp\left(\frac{-i\sigma_2\beta}{2}\right)\exp\left(\frac{-i\sigma_3\gamma}{2}\right)$$

$$= \begin{pmatrix} e^{-i\alpha/2} & 0 \\ 0 & e^{i\alpha/2} \end{pmatrix}\begin{pmatrix} \cos(\beta/2) & -\sin(\beta/2) \\ \sin(\beta/2) & \cos(\beta/2) \end{pmatrix}\begin{pmatrix} e^{-i\gamma/2} & 0 \\ 0 & e^{i\gamma/2} \end{pmatrix}$$

$$= \begin{pmatrix} e^{-i(\alpha+\gamma)/2}\cos(\beta/2) & -e^{-i(\alpha-\gamma)/2}\sin(\beta/2) \\ e^{i(\alpha-\gamma)/2}\sin(\beta/2) & e^{i(\alpha+\gamma)/2}\cos(\beta/2) \end{pmatrix}, \tag{3.3.21}$$

where (3.2.44) was used. This matrix is clearly of the unitary unimodular form. Conversely, the most general 2×2 unitary unimodular matrix can be written in this Euler angle form.

Notice that the matrix elements of the second (middle) rotation $\exp(-i\sigma_y\phi/2)$ are purely real. This would not have been the case had we chosen to rotate about the x-axis rather than the y-axis, as done in most textbooks in classical mechanics. In quantum mechanics it pays to stick to our convention because we prefer the matrix elements of the second rotation, which is the only rotation matrix containing off-diagonal elements, to be purely real.*

The 2×2 matrix in (3.3.21) is called the $j = \frac{1}{2}$ irreducible representation of the rotation operator $\mathscr{D}(\alpha, \beta, \gamma)$. Its matrix elements are denoted by $\mathscr{D}_{m'm}^{(1/2)}(\alpha, \beta, \gamma)$. In terms of the angular-momentum operators we have

$$\mathscr{D}_{m'm}^{(1/2)}(\alpha, \beta, \gamma) = \left\langle j = \frac{1}{2}, m' \middle| \exp\left(\frac{-iJ_z\alpha}{\hbar}\right)\right.$$

$$\left. \times \exp\left(\frac{-iJ_y\beta}{\hbar}\right)\exp\left(\frac{-iJ_z\gamma}{\hbar}\right) \middle| j = \frac{1}{2}, m \right\rangle. \quad (3.3.22)$$

In Section 3.5 we will extensively study higher j-analogues of (3.3.21).

3.4. DENSITY OPERATORS AND PURE VERSUS MIXED ENSEMBLES

Polarized Versus Unpolarized Beams

The formalism of quantum mechanics developed so far makes statistical predictions on an *ensemble*, that is, a collection, of identically prepared physical systems. More precisely, in such an ensemble all members are supposed to be characterized by the same state ket $|\alpha\rangle$. A good example of this is a beam of silver atoms coming out of an SG filtering apparatus. Every atom in the beam has its spin pointing in the same direction, namely, the direction determined by the inhomogeneity of the magnetic field of the filtering apparatus. We have not yet discussed how to describe quantum mechanically an ensemble of physical systems for which some, say 60%, are characterized by $|\alpha\rangle$, and the remaining 40% are characterized by some other ket $|\beta\rangle$.

To illustrate vividly the incompleteness of the formalism developed so far, let us consider silver atoms coming directly out of a hot oven, yet to be subjected to a filtering apparatus of the Stern-Gerlach type. On symmetry grounds we expect that such atoms have *random* spin orientations; in other words, there should be no preferred direction associated with such an ensemble of atoms. According to the formalism developed so far, the most general state ket of a spin $\frac{1}{2}$ system is given by

$$|\alpha\rangle = c_+|+\rangle + c_-|-\rangle. \quad (3.4.1)$$

---

*This, of course, depends on our convention that the matrix elements of S_y (or, more generally, J_y) are taken to be purely imaginary.

Is this equation capable of describing a collection of atoms with random spin orientations? The answer is clearly no; (3.4.1) characterizes a state ket whose spin is pointing in *some definite direction*, namely, in the direction of $\hat{n}$, whose polar and azimuthal angles, β and α, respectively, are obtained by solving

$$\frac{c_+}{c_-} = \frac{\cos(\beta/2)}{e^{i\alpha}\sin(\beta/2)}; \qquad (3.4.2)$$

see (3.2.52).

To cope with a situation of this kind we introduce the concept of **fractional population**, or probability weight. An ensemble of silver atoms with completely random spin orientation can be viewed as a collection of silver atoms in which 50% of the members of the ensemble are characterized by $|+\rangle$ and the remaining 50% by $|-\rangle$. We specify such an ensemble by assigning

$$w_+ = 0.5, \qquad w_- = 0.5, \qquad (3.4.3)$$

where w_+ and w_- are the fractional population for spin-up and -down, respectively. Because there is no preferred direction for such a beam, it is reasonable to expect that this *same* ensemble can be regarded equally well as a 50-50 mixture of $|S_x; +\rangle$ and $|S_x; -\rangle$. The mathematical formalism needed to accomplish this will appear shortly.

It is very important to note that we are simply introducing here two *real* numbers w_+ and w_-. There is no information on the relative phase between the spin-up and the spin-down ket. Quite often we refer to such a situation as an **incoherent mixture** of spin-up and spin-down states. What we are doing here is to be clearly distinguished from what we did with a coherent linear superposition, for example,

$$\left(\frac{1}{\sqrt{2}}\right)|+\rangle + \left(\frac{1}{\sqrt{2}}\right)|-\rangle, \qquad (3.4.4)$$

where the phase relation between $|+\rangle$ and $|-\rangle$ contains vital information on the spin orientation in the xy-plane, in this case in the positive x-direction. In general, we should not confuse w_+ and w_- with $|c_+|^2$ and $|c_-|^2$. The probability concept associated with w_+ and w_- is much closer to that encountered in classical probability theory. The situation encountered in dealing with silver atoms directly from the hot oven may be compared with that of a graduating class in which 50% of the graduating seniors are male, the remaining 50% female. When we pick a student at random, the probability that the particular student is male (or female) is 0.5. Whoever heard of a student referred to as a coherent linear superposition of male and female with a particular phase relation?

The beam of silver atoms coming directly out of the oven is an example of a **completely random ensemble**; the beam is said to be **un-**

polarized because there is no preferred direction for spin orientation. In contrast, the beam that has gone through a selective Stern-Gerlach–type measurement is an example of a **pure ensemble**; the beam is said to be **polarized** because all members of the ensemble are characterized by a single common ket that describes a state with spin pointing in some definite direction. To appreciate the difference between a completely random ensemble and a pure ensemble, let us consider a rotatable SG apparatus where we can vary the direction of the inhomogeneous **B** just by rotating the apparatus. When a completely unpolarized beam directly out of the oven is subjected to such an apparatus, we *always* obtain two emerging beams of *equal* intensity *no matter what the orientation of the apparatus may be*. In contrast, if a polarized beam is subjected to such an apparatus, the relative intensities of the two emerging beams vary as the apparatus is rotated. For some *particular* orientation the ratio of the intensities actually becomes one to zero. In fact, the formalism we developed in Chapter 1 tells us that the relative intensities are simply $\cos^2(\beta/2)$ and $\sin^2(\beta/2)$, where β is the angle between the spin direction of the atoms and the direction of the inhomogeneous magnetic field in the SG apparatus.

A complete random ensemble and a pure ensemble can be regarded as the extremes of what is known as a **mixed ensemble**. In a mixed ensemble a certain fraction—for example, 70%—of the members are characterized by a state ket $|\alpha\rangle$, the remaining 30% by $|\beta\rangle$. In such a case the beam is said to be **partially polarized**. Here $|\alpha\rangle$ and $|\beta\rangle$ need not even be orthogonal; we can, for example, have 70% with spin in the positive x-direction and 30% with spin in the negative z-direction.*

Ensemble Averages and Density Operator

We now present the density operator formalism, pioneered by J. von Neumann in 1927, that quantitatively describes physical situations with mixed as well as pure ensembles. Our general discussion here is not restricted to spin $\frac{1}{2}$ systems, but for illustrative purposes we return repeatedly to spin $\frac{1}{2}$ systems.

A pure ensemble by definition is a collection of physical systems such that every member is characterized by the same ket $|\alpha\rangle$. In contrast, in a mixed ensemble, a fraction of the members with relative population w_1 are characterized by $|\alpha^{(1)}\rangle$, some other fraction with relative population w_2, by $|\alpha^{(2)}\rangle$, and so on. Roughly speaking, a mixed ensemble can be viewed as a mixture of pure ensembles, just as the name suggests. The fractional

---

*In the literature what we call pure and mixed ensembles are often referred to as pure and mixed states. In this book, however, we use *state* to mean a physical system described by a definite state ket $|\alpha\rangle$.

populations are constrained to satisfy the normalization condition

$$\sum_i w_i = 1. \tag{3.4.5}$$

As we mentioned previously, $|\alpha^{(1)}\rangle$ and $|\alpha^{(2)}\rangle$ need not be orthogonal. Furthermore, the number of terms in the i sum of (3.4.5) need not coincide with the dimensionality N of the ket space; it can easily exceed N. For example, for spin $\frac{1}{2}$ systems with $N = 2$, we may consider 40% with spin in the positive z-direction, 30% with spin in the positive x-direction, and the remaining 30% with spin in the negative y-direction.

Suppose we make a measurement on a mixed ensemble of some observable A. We may ask what is the average measured value of A when a large number of measurements are carried out. The answer is given by the **ensemble average** of A, which is defined by

$$[A] \equiv \sum_i w_i \langle \alpha^{(i)}|A|\alpha^{(i)}\rangle$$

$$= \sum_i \sum_{a'} w_i |\langle a'|\alpha^{(i)}\rangle|^2 a', \tag{3.4.6}$$

where $|a'\rangle$ is an eigenket of A. Recall that $\langle \alpha^{(i)}|A|\alpha^{(i)}\rangle$ is the usual quantum mechanical expectation value of A taken with respect to state $|\alpha^{(i)}\rangle$. Equation (3.4.6) tells us that these expectation values must further be weighted by the corresponding fractional populations w_i. Notice how probabilistic concepts enter twice; first in $|\langle a'|\alpha^{(i)}\rangle|^2$ for the quantum-mechanical probability for state $|\alpha^{(i)}\rangle$ to be found in an A eigenstate $|a'\rangle$; second, in the probability factor w_i for finding in the ensemble a quantum-mechanical state characterized by $|\alpha^{(i)}\rangle$.*

We can now rewrite ensemble average (3.4.6) using a more general basis, $\{|b'\rangle\}$:

$$[A] = \sum_i w_i \sum_{b'} \sum_{b''} \langle \alpha^{(i)}|b'\rangle \langle b'|A|b''\rangle \langle b''|\alpha^{(i)}\rangle$$

$$= \sum_{b'} \sum_{b''} \left(\sum_i w_i \langle b''|\alpha^{(i)}\rangle \langle \alpha^{(i)}|b'\rangle \right) \langle b'|A|b''\rangle. \tag{3.4.7}$$

The number of terms in the sum of the b' (b'') is just the dimensionality of the ket space, while the number of terms in the sum of the i depends on how the mixed ensemble is viewed as a mixture of pure ensembles. Notice that in this form the basic property of the ensemble which does not depend on the particular observable A is factored out. This motivates us to define the **density operator** ρ as follows:

$$\rho \equiv \sum_i w_i |\alpha^{(i)}\rangle \langle \alpha^{(i)}|. \tag{3.4.8}$$

---

*Quite often in the literature the ensemble average is also called the *expectation value*. However, in this book, the term expectation value is reserved for the average measured value when measurements are carried on a pure ensemble.

The elements of the corresponding **density matrix** have the following form:

$$\langle b''|\rho|b'\rangle = \sum_i w_i \langle b''|\alpha^{(i)}\rangle\langle\alpha^{(i)}|b'\rangle. \qquad (3.4.9)$$

The density operator contains all the physically significant information we can possibly obtain about the ensemble in question. Returning to (3.4.7), we see that the ensemble average can be written as

$$[A] = \sum_{b'}\sum_{b''}\langle b''|\rho|b'\rangle\langle b'|A|b''\rangle$$

$$= \text{tr}(\rho A). \qquad (3.4.10)$$

Because the trace is independent of representations, $\text{tr}(\rho A)$ can be evaluated using any convenient basis. As a result, (3.4.10) is an extremely powerful relation.

There are two properties of the density operator worth recording. First, the density operator is Hermitian, as is evident from (3.4.8). Second, the density operator satisfies the normalization condition

$$\text{tr}(\rho) = \sum_i\sum_{b'} w_i \langle b'|\alpha^{(i)}\rangle\langle\alpha^{(i)}|b'\rangle$$

$$= \sum_i w_i \langle\alpha^{(i)}|\alpha^{(i)}\rangle$$

$$= 1. \qquad (3.4.11)$$

Because of the Hermiticity and the normalization condition, for spin $\frac{1}{2}$ systems with dimensionality 2 the density operator, or the corresponding density matrix, is characterized by three independent real parameters. Four real numbers characterize a 2×2 Hermitian matrix. However, only three are independent because of the normalization condition. The three numbers needed are $[S_x]$, $[S_y]$, and $[S_z]$; the reader may verify that knowledge of these three ensemble averages is sufficient to reconstruct the density operator. The manner in which a mixed ensemble is formed can be rather involved. We may mix pure ensembles characterized by all kinds of $|\alpha^{(i)}\rangle$'s with appropriate w_i's; yet for spin $\frac{1}{2}$ systems three real numbers completely characterize the ensemble in question. This strongly suggests that a mixed ensemble can be decomposed into pure ensembles in many different ways. A problem to illustrate this point appears at the end of this chapter.

A pure ensemble is specified by $w_i = 1$ for some $|\alpha^{(i)}\rangle$—with $i = n$, for instance—and $w_i = 0$ for all other conceivable state kets, so the corresponding density operator is written as

$$\rho = |\alpha^{(n)}\rangle\langle\alpha^{(n)}| \qquad (3.4.12)$$

with no summation. Clearly, the density operator for a pure ensemble is idempotent, that is,

$$\rho^2 = \rho \qquad (3.4.13)$$

or, equivalently,

$$\rho(\rho - 1) = 0. \tag{3.4.14}$$

Thus, for a pure ensemble only, we have

$$\text{tr}(\rho^2) = 1. \tag{3.4.15}$$

in addition to (3.4.11). The eigenvalues of the density operator for a pure ensemble are zero or one, as can be seen by inserting a complete set of base kets that diagonalize the Hermitian operator ρ between ρ and $(\rho - 1)$ of (3.4.14). When diagonalized, the density matrix for a pure ensemble must therefore look like

(diagonal form)

$$\tag{3.4.16}$$

It can be shown that $\text{tr}(\rho^2)$ is maximal when the ensemble is pure; for a mixed ensemble $\text{tr}(\rho^2)$ is a positive number less than one.

Given a density operator, let us see how we can construct the corresponding density matrix in some specified basis. To this end we first recall that

$$|\alpha\rangle\langle\alpha| = \sum_{b'}\sum_{b''}|b'\rangle\langle b'|\alpha\rangle\langle\alpha|b''\rangle\langle b''|. \tag{3.4.17}$$

this shows that we can form the square matrix corresponding to $|\alpha^{(i)}\rangle\langle\alpha^{(i)}|$ by combining, in the sense of outer product, the column matrix formed by $\langle b'|\alpha^{(i)}\rangle$ with the row matrix formed by $\langle\alpha^{(i)}|b''\rangle$, which, of course, is equal to $\langle b''|\alpha^{(i)}\rangle^*$. The final step is to sum such square matrices with weighting factors w_i, as indicated in (3.4.8). The final form agrees with (3.4.9), as expected.

It is instructive to study several examples, all referring to spin $\frac{1}{2}$ systems.

Example 1. A completely polarized beam with $S_z +$.

$$\rho = |+\rangle\langle+| \doteq \begin{pmatrix} 1 \\ 0 \end{pmatrix}(1,0)$$

$$= \begin{pmatrix} 1 & 0 \\ 0 & 0 \end{pmatrix}. \tag{3.4.18}$$

Example 2. A completely polarized beam with $S_x \pm$.

$$\rho = |S_x; \pm\rangle\langle S_x; \pm| = \left(\frac{1}{\sqrt{2}}\right)(|+\rangle \pm |-\rangle)\left(\frac{1}{\sqrt{2}}\right)(\langle+| \pm \langle-|)$$

$$\doteq \begin{pmatrix} \dfrac{1}{2} & \pm\dfrac{1}{2} \\ \pm\dfrac{1}{2} & \dfrac{1}{2} \end{pmatrix}. \tag{3.4.19}$$

The ensembles of Examples 1 and 2 are both pure.

Example 3. An unpolarized beam. This can be regarded as an incoherent mixture of a spin-up ensemble and a spin-down ensemble with equal weights (50% each):

$$\rho = (\tfrac{1}{2})|+\rangle\langle+| + (\tfrac{1}{2})|-\rangle\langle-|$$

$$\doteq \begin{pmatrix} \tfrac{1}{2} & 0 \\ 0 & \tfrac{1}{2} \end{pmatrix}, \tag{3.4.20}$$

which is just the identity matrix divided by 2. As we remarked earlier, the same ensemble can also be regarded as an incoherent mixture of an $S_x +$ ensemble and an $S_x -$ ensemble with equal weights. It is gratifying that our formalism automatically satisfies the expectation

$$\begin{pmatrix} \tfrac{1}{2} & 0 \\ 0 & \tfrac{1}{2} \end{pmatrix} = \tfrac{1}{2}\begin{pmatrix} \tfrac{1}{2} & \tfrac{1}{2} \\ \tfrac{1}{2} & \tfrac{1}{2} \end{pmatrix} + \tfrac{1}{2}\begin{pmatrix} \tfrac{1}{2} & -\tfrac{1}{2} \\ -\tfrac{1}{2} & \tfrac{1}{2} \end{pmatrix}, \tag{3.4.21}$$

where we see from Example 2 that the two terms on the right-hand side are the density matrices for pure ensemble with $S_x +$ and $S_x -$. Because ρ in this case is just the identity operator divided by 2 (the dimensionality), we have

$$\text{tr}(\rho S_x) = \text{tr}(\rho S_y) = \text{tr}(\rho S_z) = 0, \tag{3.4.22}$$

where we used the fact that S_k is traceless. Thus for the ensemble average of **S** we have

$$[\mathbf{S}] = 0. \tag{3.4.23}$$

This is reasonable because there should be no preferred spin direction in a completely random ensemble of spin $\tfrac{1}{2}$ systems.

Example 4. As an example of a partially polarized beam, let us consider a 75-25 mixture of two pure ensembles, one with $S_z +$ and the other with $S_x +$:

$$w(S_z +) = 0.75, \qquad w(S_x +) = 0.25. \tag{3.4.24}$$

The corresponding ρ can be represented by

$$\rho \doteq \tfrac{3}{4}\begin{pmatrix} 1 & 0 \\ 0 & 0 \end{pmatrix} + \tfrac{1}{4}\begin{pmatrix} \tfrac{1}{2} & \tfrac{1}{2} \\ \tfrac{1}{2} & \tfrac{1}{2} \end{pmatrix}$$

$$= \begin{pmatrix} \tfrac{7}{8} & \tfrac{1}{8} \\ \tfrac{1}{8} & \tfrac{1}{8} \end{pmatrix}, \tag{3.4.25}$$

from which follows

$$[S_x] = \frac{\hbar}{8}, \qquad [S_y] = 0, \qquad [S_z] = \frac{3\hbar}{8}. \tag{3.4.26}$$

We leave as an exercise for the reader the task of showing that this ensemble can be decomposed in ways other than (3.4.24).

Time Evolution of Ensembles

How does the density operator ρ change as a function of time? Let us suppose that at some time t_0 the density operator is given by

$$\rho(t_0) = \sum_i w_i |\alpha^{(i)}\rangle \langle \alpha^{(i)}|. \tag{3.4.27}$$

If the ensemble is to be left undisturbed, we cannot change the fractional population w_i. So the change in ρ is governed solely by the time evolution of state ket $|\alpha^{(i)}\rangle$:

$$|\alpha^{(i)}\rangle \quad \text{at} \quad t_0 \to |\alpha^{(i)}, t_0; t\rangle. \tag{3.4.28}$$

From the fact that $|\alpha^{(i)}, t_0; t\rangle$ satisfies the Schrödinger equation we obtain

$$i\hbar \frac{\partial \rho}{\partial t} = \sum_i w_i \big(H |\alpha^{(i)}, t_0; t\rangle \langle \alpha^{(i)}, t_0; t| - |\alpha^{(i)}, t_0; t\rangle \langle \alpha^{(i)}, t_0; t| H \big)$$

$$= -[\rho, H]. \tag{3.4.29}$$

This looks like the Heisenberg equation of motion except that the sign is wrong! This is not disturbing because ρ is not a dynamic observable in the Heisenberg picture. On the contrary, ρ is built up of Schrödinger-picture state kets and state bras which evolve in time according to the Schrödinger equation.

It is amusing that (3.4.29) can be regarded as the quantum-mechanical analogue of Liouville's theorem in classical statistical mechanics,

$$\frac{\partial \rho_{\text{classical}}}{\partial t} = -[\rho_{\text{classical}}, H]_{\text{classical}}, \tag{3.4.30}$$

where $\rho_{\text{classical}}$ stands for the density of representative points in phase space.* Thus the name *density operator* for the ρ appearing in (3.4.29) is

---

*Remember, a pure classical state is one represented by a single moving point in phase space $(q_1, \ldots, q_f, p_1, \ldots, p_f)$ at each instant of time. A classical statistical state, on the other hand, is described by our nonnegative density function $\rho_{\text{classical}}(q_1, \ldots, q_f, p_1, \ldots, p_f, t)$ such that the probability that a system is found in the interval $dq_1, \ldots, dp_f$ at time t is $\rho_{\text{classical}} \, dq_1, \ldots, dp_f$.

indeed appropriate. The classical analogue of (3.4.10) for the ensemble average of some observable A is given by

$$A_{\text{average}} = \frac{\int \rho_{\text{classical}} A(q, p) \, d\Gamma_{q,p}}{\int \rho_{\text{classical}} \, d\Gamma_{q,p}}, \qquad (3.4.31)$$

where $d\Gamma_{q,p}$ stands for a volume element in phase space.

Continuum Generalizations

So far we have considered density operators in ket space where the base kets are labeled by the discrete-eigenvalues of some observable. The concept of density matrix can be generalized to cases where the base kets used are labeled by continuous eigenvalues. In particular, let us consider the ket space spanned by the position eigenkets $|x'\rangle$. The analogue of (3.4.10) is given by

$$[A] = \int d^3x' \int d^3x'' \langle x''|\rho|x'\rangle \langle x'|A|x''\rangle. \qquad (3.4.32)$$

The density matrix here is actually a function of x' and x'', namely,

$$\langle x''|\rho|x'\rangle = \langle x''|\left(\sum_i w_i |\dot{\alpha}^{(i)}\rangle \langle \alpha^{(i)}| \right)|x'\rangle$$

$$= \sum_i w_i \psi_i(x'') \psi_i^*(x'), \qquad (3.4.33)$$

where ψ_i is the wave function corresponding to the state ket $|\alpha^{(i)}\rangle$. Notice that the diagonal element (that is, $x' = x''$) of this is just the weighted sum of the probability densities. Once again, the term *density matrix* is indeed appropriate.

In continuum cases, too, it is important to keep in mind that the same mixed ensemble can be decomposed in different ways into pure ensembles. For instance, it is possible to regard a "realistic" beam of particles either as a mixture of plane-wave states (monoenergetic free-particle states) or as a mixture of wave-packet states.

Quantum Statistical Mechanics

We conclude this section with a brief discussion on the connection between the density operator formalism and statistical mechanics. Let us first record some properties of completely random and of pure ensembles.

The density matrix of a completely random ensemble looks like

$$\rho \doteq \frac{1}{N} \begin{pmatrix} 1 & & & & & & \\ & 1 & & & & \text{\huge 0} & \\ & & 1 & & & & \\ & & & \ddots & & & \\ & & & & 1 & & \\ & & & & & 1 & \\ \text{\huge 0} & & & & & & 1 \end{pmatrix} \qquad (3.4.34)$$

in any representation [compare Example 3 with (3.4.20)]. This follows from the fact that all states corresponding to the base kets with respect to which the density matrix is written are equally populated. In contrast, in the basis where ρ is diagonalized, we have (3.4.16) for the matrix representation of the density operator for a pure ensemble. The two diagonal matrices (3.4.34) and (3.4.16), both satisfying the normalization requirement (3.4.11), cannot look more different. It would be desirable if we could somehow construct a quantity that characterizes this dramatic difference.

Thus we define a quantity called σ by

$$\sigma = -\text{tr}(\rho \ln \rho). \qquad (3.4.35)$$

The logarithm of the operator ρ may appear rather formidable, but the meaning of (3.4.35) is quite unambiguous if we use the basis in which ρ is diagonal:

$$\sigma = -\sum_k \rho_{kk}^{(\text{diag})} \ln \rho_{kk}^{(\text{diag})}. \qquad (3.4.36)$$

Because each element $\rho_{kk}^{(\text{diag})}$ is a real number between 0 and 1, σ is necessarily positive semidefinite. For a completely random ensemble (3.4.34), we have

$$\sigma = -\sum_{k=1}^{N} \frac{1}{N} \ln \left(\frac{1}{N} \right) = \ln N. \qquad (3.4.37)$$

In contrast, for a pure ensemble (3.4.16) we have

$$\sigma = 0 \qquad (3.4.38)$$

where we have used

$$\rho_{kk}^{(\text{diag})} = 0 \quad or \quad \ln \rho_{kk}^{(\text{diag})} = 0 \qquad (3.4.39)$$

for each term in (3.4.36).

We now argue that physically σ can be regarded as a quantitative measure of disorder. A pure ensemble is an ensemble with a maximum amount of order because all members are characterized by the same quantum-mechanical state ket; it may be likened to marching soldiers in a well-regimented army. According to (3.4.38), σ vanishes for such an ensemble. On the other extreme, a completely random ensemble, in which all quantum-mechanical states are equally likely, may be likened to drunken soldiers wandering around in random directions. According to (3.4.37), σ is large; indeed, we will show later that $\ln N$ is the maximum possible value for σ subject to the normalization condition

$$\sum_k \rho_{kk} = 1. \tag{3.4.40}$$

In thermodynamics we learn that a quantity called **entropy** measures disorder. It turns out that our σ is related to the entropy per constituent member, denoted by S, of the ensemble via

$$S = k\sigma, \tag{3.4.41}$$

where k is a universal constant identifiable with the Boltzmann constant. In fact, (3.4.41) may be taken as the *definition* of entropy in quantum statistical mechanics.

We now show how the density operator ρ can be obtained for an ensemble in thermal equilibrium. The basic assumption we make is that nature tends to maximize σ subject to the constraint that the ensemble average of the Hamiltonian has a certain prescribed value. To justify this assumption would involve us in a delicate discussion of how equilibrium is established as a result of interactions with the environment, which is beyond the scope of this book. In any case, once thermal equilibrium is established, we expect

$$\frac{\partial \rho}{\partial t} = 0. \tag{3.4.42}$$

Because of (3.4.29), this means that ρ and H can be simultaneously diagonalized. So the kets used in writing (3.4.36) may be taken to be energy eigenkets. With this choice ρ_{kk} stands for the fractional population for an energy eigenstate with energy eigenvalue E_k.

Let us maximize σ by requiring that

$$\delta\sigma = 0. \tag{3.4.43}$$

However, we must take into account the constraint that the ensemble average of H has a certain prescribed value. In the language of statistical mechanics, $[H]$ is identified with the internal energy per constituent denoted by U:

$$[H] = \mathrm{tr}(\rho H) = U. \tag{3.4.44}$$

In addition, we should not forget the normalization constraint (3.4.40). So our basic task is to require (3.4.43) subject to the constraints

$$\delta[H] = \sum_k \delta\rho_{kk} E_k = 0 \tag{3.4.45a}$$

and

$$\delta(\text{tr}\,\rho) = \sum_k \delta\rho_{kk} = 0. \qquad (3.4.45b)$$

We can most readily accomplish this by using Lagrange multipliers. We obtain

$$\sum_k \delta\rho_{kk}\big[(\ln\rho_{kk}+1)+\beta E_k+\gamma\big] = 0, \qquad (3.4.46)$$

which for an arbitrary variation is possibly only if

$$\rho_{kk} = \exp(-\beta E_k - \gamma - 1). \qquad (3.4.47)$$

The constant γ can be eliminated using the normalization condition (3.4.40), and our final result is

$$\rho_{kk} = \frac{\exp(-\beta E_k)}{\displaystyle\sum_l^N \exp(-\beta E_l)}, \qquad (3.4.48)$$

which directly gives the fractional population for an energy eigenstate with eigenvalue E_k. It is to be understood throughout that the sum is over distinct energy eigenstates; if there is degeneracy we must sum over states with the same energy eigenvalue.

The density matrix element (3.4.48) is appropriate for what is known in statistical mechanics as a **canonical ensemble**. Had we attempted to maximize σ without the internal-energy constraint (3.4.45a), we would have obtained instead

$$\rho_{kk} = \frac{1}{N}, \qquad \text{(independent of } k\text{)}, \qquad (3.4.49)$$

which is the density matrix element appropriate for a completely random ensemble. Comparing (3.4.48) with (3.4.49), we infer that a completely random ensemble can be regarded as the $\beta \to 0$ limit (physically the high-temperature limit) of a canonical ensemble.

We recognize the denominator of (3.4.48) as the partition function

$$Z = \sum_k^N \exp(-\beta E_k) \qquad (3.4.50)$$

in statistical mechanics. It can also be written as

$$Z = \text{tr}(e^{-\beta H}). \qquad (3.4.51)$$

Knowing ρ_{kk} given in the energy basis, we can write the density operator as

$$\rho = \frac{e^{-\beta H}}{Z}. \qquad (3.4.52)$$

This is the most basic equation from which everything follows. We can immediately evaluate the ensemble average of any observable A:

$$[A] = \frac{\text{tr}(e^{-\beta H}A)}{Z}$$

$$= \frac{\left[\sum_{k}^{N}\langle A\rangle_k \exp(-\beta E_k)\right]}{\sum_{k}^{N}\exp(-\beta E_k)}. \tag{3.4.53}$$

In particular, for the internal energy per constituent we obtain

$$U = \frac{\left[\sum_{k}^{N}E_k\exp(-\beta E_k)\right]}{\sum_{k}^{N}\exp(-\beta E_k)}$$

$$= -\frac{\partial}{\partial \beta}(\ln Z), \tag{3.4.54}$$

a formula well known to every student of statistical mechanics.

The parameter β is related to the temperature T as follows:

$$\beta = \frac{1}{kT} \tag{3.4.55}$$

where k is the Boltzmann constant. It is instructive to convince ourselves of this identification by comparing the ensemble average $[H]$ of simple harmonic oscillators with the kT expected for the internal energy in the classical limit, which is left as an exercise. We have already commented that in the high-temperature limit, a canonical ensemble becomes a completely random ensemble in which all energy eigenstates are equally populated. In the opposite low-temperature limit ($\beta \to \infty$), (3.4.48) tells us that a canonical ensemble becomes a pure ensemble where only the ground state is populated.

As a simple illustrative example, consider a canonical ensemble made up of spin $\frac{1}{2}$ systems, each with a magnetic moment $e\hbar/2m_e c$ subjected to a uniform magnetic field in the z-direction. The Hamiltonian relevant to this problem has already been given [see (3.2.16)]. Because H and S_z commute, the density matrix for this canonical ensemble is diagonal in the S_z basis. Thus

$$\rho \doteq \frac{\begin{pmatrix} e^{-\beta\hbar\omega/2} & 0 \\ 0 & e^{\beta\hbar\omega/2} \end{pmatrix}}{Z}, \tag{3.4.56}$$

where the partition function is just

$$Z = e^{-\beta\hbar\omega/2} + e^{\beta\hbar\omega/2}. \tag{3.4.57}$$

From this we compute

$$[S_x] = [S_y] = 0, \quad [S_z] = -\left(\frac{\hbar}{2}\right) \tanh\left(\frac{\beta\hbar\omega}{2}\right). \tag{3.4.58}$$

The ensemble average of the magnetic moment component is just $e/m_e c$ times $[S_z]$. The paramagnetic susceptibility χ may be computed from

$$\left(\frac{e}{m_e c}\right)[S_z] = \chi B. \tag{3.4.59}$$

In this way we arrive at Brillouin's formula for χ:

$$\chi = \left(\frac{|e|\hbar}{2m_e cB}\right) \tanh\left(\frac{\beta\hbar\omega}{2}\right). \tag{3.4.60}$$

3.5. EIGENVALUES AND EIGENSTATES OF ANGULAR MOMENTUM

Up to now our discussion of angular momentum has been confined exclusively to spin $\frac{1}{2}$ systems with dimensionality $N = 2$. In this and subsequent sections we study more-general angular momentum states. To this end we first work out the eigenvalues and eigenkets of $\mathbf{J}^2$ and J_z and derive the expressions for matrix elements of angular momentum operators, first obtained in a 1926 paper by M. Born, W. Heisenberg, and P. Jordan.

Commutation Relations and the Ladder Operators

Everything we will do follows from the angular-momentum commutation relations (3.1.20), where we may recall that J_i is defined as the generator of infinitesimal rotation. The first important property we derive from the basic commutation relations is the existence of a new operator $\mathbf{J}^2$, defined by

$$\mathbf{J}^2 \equiv J_x J_x + J_y J_y + J_z J_z, \tag{3.5.1}$$

that commutes with every one of J_k:

$$[\mathbf{J}^2, J_k] = 0, \quad (k = 1, 2, 3). \tag{3.5.2}$$

To prove this let us look at the $k = 3$ case:

$$\begin{aligned}
\left[J_x J_x + J_y J_y + J_z J_z, J_z\right] &= J_x[J_x, J_z] + [J_x, J_z]J_x + J_y[J_y, J_z] + [J_y, J_z]J_y \\
&= J_x(-i\hbar J_y) + (-i\hbar J_y)J_x + J_y(i\hbar J_x) + (i\hbar J_x)J_y \\
&= 0.
\end{aligned} \tag{3.5.3}$$

The proofs for the cases where $k = 1$ and 2 follow by cyclic permutation $(1 \rightarrow 2 \rightarrow 3 \rightarrow 1)$ of the indices. Because J_x, J_y, and J_z do not commute with each other, we can choose only one of them to be the observable to be diagonalized simultaneously with J^2. By convention we choose J_z for this purpose.

We now look for the simultaneous eigenkets of $\mathbf{J}^2$ and J_z. We denote the eigenvalues of $\mathbf{J}^2$ and J_z by a and b, respectively:

$$J^2|a, b\rangle = a|a, b\rangle \qquad (3.5.4a)$$

$$J_z|a, b\rangle = b|a, b\rangle. \qquad (3.5.4b)$$

To determine the allowed values for a and b, it is convenient to work with the non-Hermitian operators

$$J_\pm \equiv J_x \pm iJ_y, \qquad (3.5.5)$$

called the **ladder operators**, rather than with J_x and J_y. They satisfy the commutation relations

$$[J_+, J_-] = 2\hbar J_z \qquad (3.5.6a)$$

and

$$[J_z, J_\pm] = \pm \hbar J_\pm, \qquad (3.5.6b)$$

which can easily be obtained from (3.1.20). Note also that

$$[\mathbf{J}^2, J_\pm] = 0, \qquad (3.5.7)$$

which is an obvious consequence of (3.5.2).

What is the physical meaning of $J_\pm$? To answer this we examine how J_z acts on $J_\pm|a, b\rangle$:

$$J_z(J_\pm|a, b\rangle) = ([J_z, J_\pm] + J_\pm J_z)|a, b\rangle$$

$$= (b \pm \hbar)(J_\pm|a, b\rangle) \qquad (3.5.8)$$

where we have used (3.5.6b). In other words, if we apply $J_+(J_-)$ to a J_z eigenket, the resulting ket is still a J_z eigenket except that its eigenvalue is now increased (decreased) by one unit of $\hbar$. So now we see why $J_\pm$, which step one step up (down) on the "ladder" of J_z eigenvalues, are known as the ladder operators.

We now digress to recall that the commutation relations in (3.5.6b) are reminiscent of some commutation relations we encountered in the earlier chapters. In discussing the translation operator $\mathcal{T}(\mathbf{l})$ we had

$$[x_i, \mathcal{T}(\mathbf{l})] = l_i \mathcal{T}(\mathbf{l}); \qquad (3.5.9)$$

also, in discussing the simple harmonic oscillator we had

$$[N, a^\dagger] = a^\dagger, \qquad [N, a] = -a. \qquad (3.5.10)$$

We see that both (3.5.9) and (3.5.10) have a structure similar to (3.5.6b). The physical interpretation of the translation operator is that it changes the eigenvalue of the position operator x by l in much the same way as the ladder operator J_+ changes the eigenvalue of J_z by one unit of $\hbar$. Likewise, the oscillator creation operator $a^\dagger$ increases the eigenvalue of the number operator N by unity.

Even though $J_\pm$ changes the eigenvalue of J_z by one unit of h, it does not change the eigenvalue of $\mathbf{J}^2$:

$$\mathbf{J}^2(J_\pm|a,b\rangle) = J_\pm \mathbf{J}^2|a,b\rangle$$
$$= a(J_\pm|a,b\rangle), \qquad (3.5.11)$$

where we have used (3.5.7). To summarize, $J_\pm|a,b\rangle$ are simultaneous eigenkets of $\mathbf{J}^2$ and J_z with eigenvalues a and $b \pm \hbar$. We may write

$$J_\pm|a,b\rangle = c_\pm|a,b\pm\hbar\rangle, \qquad (3.5.12)$$

where the proportionality constant $c_\pm$ will be determined later from the normalization requirement of the angular-momentum eigenkets.

Eigenvalues of $\mathbf{J}^2$ and J_z

We now have the machinery needed to construct angular-momentum eigenkets and to study their eigenvalue spectrum. Suppose we apply J_+ successively, say n times, to a simultaneous eigenket of $\mathbf{J}^2$ and J_z. We then obtain another eigenket of $\mathbf{J}^2$ and J_z with the J_z eigenvalue increased by $n\hbar$, while its $\mathbf{J}^2$ eigenvalue is unchanged. However, this process cannot go on indefinitely. It turns out that there exists an upper limit to b (the J_z eigenvalue) for a given a (the $\mathbf{J}^2$ eigenvalue):

$$a \geq b^2. \qquad (3.5.13)$$

To prove this assertion we first note that

$$\mathbf{J}^2 - J_z^2 = \tfrac{1}{2}(J_+J_- + J_-J_+)$$
$$= \tfrac{1}{2}(J_+J_+^\dagger + J_+^\dagger J_+). \qquad (3.5.14)$$

Now $J_+J_+^\dagger$ and $J_+^\dagger J_+$ must have nonnegative expectation values because

$$J_+^\dagger|a,b\rangle \overset{\text{DC}}{\leftrightarrow} \langle a,b|J_+, \qquad J_+|a,b\rangle \overset{\text{DC}}{\leftrightarrow} \langle a,b|J_+^\dagger; \qquad (3.5.15)$$

thus

$$\langle a,b|(\mathbf{J}^2 - J_z^2)|a,b\rangle \geq 0, \qquad (3.5.16)$$

which, in turn, implies (3.5.13). It therefore follows that there must be a b_{max} such that

$$J_+|a,b_{max}\rangle = 0. \qquad (3.5.17)$$

Stated another way, the eigenvalue of b cannot be increased beyond b_{max}. Now (3.5.17) also implies

$$J_-J_+|a,b_{max}\rangle = 0. \qquad (3.5.18)$$

But

$$J_- J_+ = J_x^2 + J_y^2 - i(J_y J_x - J_x J_y)$$
$$= \mathbf{J}^2 - J_z^2 - \hbar J_z. \tag{3.5.19}$$

So

$$(\mathbf{J}^2 - J_z^2 - \hbar J_z)|a, b_{max}\rangle = 0. \tag{3.5.20}$$

Because $|a, b_{max}\rangle$ itself is not a null ket, this relationship is possible only if

$$a - b_{max}^2 - b_{max}\hbar = 0 \tag{3.5.21}$$

or

$$a = b_{max}(b_{max} + \hbar). \tag{3.5.22}$$

In a similar manner we argue from (3.5.13) that there must also exist a b_{min} such that

$$J_-|a, b_{min}\rangle = 0. \tag{3.5.23}$$

By writing $J_+ J_-$ as

$$J_+ J_- = \mathbf{J}^2 - J_z^2 + \hbar J_z \tag{3.5.24}$$

in analogy with (3.5.19), we conclude that

$$a = b_{min}(b_{min} - \hbar). \tag{3.5.25}$$

By comparing (3.5.22) with (3.5.25) we infer that

$$b_{max} = -b_{min}, \tag{3.5.26}$$

with b_{max} positive, and that the allowed values of b lie within

$$-b_{max} \le b \le b_{max}. \tag{3.5.27}$$

Clearly, we must be able to reach $|a, b_{max}\rangle$ by applying J_+ successively to $|a, b_{min}\rangle$ a finite number of times. We must therefore have

$$b_{max} = b_{min} + n\hbar, \tag{3.5.28}$$

where n is some integer. As a result, we get

$$b_{max} = \frac{n\hbar}{2}. \tag{3.5.29}$$

It is more conventional to work with j, defined to be $b_{max}/\hbar$, instead of with b_{max} so that

$$j = \frac{n}{2}. \tag{3.5.30}$$

The maximum value of the J_z eigenvalue is $j\hbar$, where j is either an integer or a half-integer. Equation (3.5.22) implies that the eigenvalue of $\mathbf{J}^2$ is given by

$$a = \hbar^2 j(j+1). \tag{3.5.31}$$

Let us also define m so that

$$b \equiv m\hbar. \tag{3.5.32}$$

If j is an integer, all m values are integers; if j is a half-integer, all m values are half-integers. The allowed m-values for a given j are

$$m = \underbrace{-j, -j+1, \ldots, j-1, j}_{2j+1 \text{ states}}. \tag{3.5.33}$$

Instead of $|a, b\rangle$ it is more convenient to denote a simultaneous eigenket of $\mathbf{J}^2$ and J_z by $|j, m\rangle$. The basic eigenvalue equations now read

$$\mathbf{J}^2|j, m\rangle = j(j+1)\hbar^2|j, m\rangle \tag{3.5.34a}$$

and

$$J_z|j, m\rangle = m\hbar|j, m\rangle, \tag{3.5.34b}$$

with j either an integer or a half-integer and m given by (3.5.33). It is very important to recall here that we have used only the commutation relations (3.1.20) to obtain these results. The quantization of angular momentum, manifested in (3.5.34), is a direct consequence of the angular-momentum commutation relations, which, in turn, follow from the properties of rotations together with the definition of J_k as the generator of rotation.

Matrix Elements of Angular-Momentum Operators

Let us work out the matrix elements of the various angular-momentum operators. Assuming $|j, m\rangle$ to be normalized, we obviously have from (3.5.34)

$$\langle j', m'|\mathbf{J}^2|j, m\rangle = j(j+1)\hbar^2\delta_{j'j}\delta_{m'm} \tag{3.5.35a}$$

and

$$\langle j', m'|J_z|j, m\rangle = m\hbar\delta_{j'j}\delta_{m'm}. \tag{3.5.35b}$$

To obtain the matrix elements of $J_\pm$, we first consider

$$\langle j, m|J_+^\dagger J_+|j, m\rangle = \langle j, m|(\mathbf{J}^2 - J_z^2 - \hbar J_z)|j, m\rangle$$
$$= \hbar^2[j(j+1) - m^2 - m]. \tag{3.5.36}$$

Now $J_+|j, m\rangle$ must be the same as $|j, m+1\rangle$ (normalized) up to a multiplicative constant [see (3.5.12)]. Thus

$$J_+|j, m\rangle = c_{jm}^+|j, m+1\rangle. \tag{3.5.37}$$

Comparison with (3.5.36) leads to

$$|c_{jm}^+|^2 = \hbar^2[j(j+1) - m(m+1)]$$
$$= \hbar^2(j-m)(j+m+1). \tag{3.5.38}$$

So we have determined c_{jm}^+ up to an arbitrary phase factor. It is customary to choose c_{jm}^+ to be real and positive by convention. So

$$J_+|j,m\rangle = \sqrt{(j-m)(j+m+1)}\,\hbar|j,m+1\rangle. \tag{3.5.39}$$

Similarly, we can derive

$$J_-|j,m\rangle = \sqrt{(j+m)(j-m+1)}\,\hbar|j,m-1\rangle. \tag{3.5.40}$$

Finally, we determine the matrix elements of $J_\pm$ to be

$$\langle j',m'|J_\pm|j,m\rangle = \sqrt{(j\mp m)(j\pm m+1)}\,\hbar\delta_{j'j}\delta_{m',m\pm 1}. \tag{3.5.41}$$

Representations of the Rotation Operator

Having obtained the matrix elements of J_z and $J_\pm$, we are now in a position to study the matrix elements of the rotation operator $\mathscr{D}(R)$. If a rotation R is specified by $\hat{\mathbf{n}}$ and ϕ, we can define its matrix elements by

$$\mathscr{D}_{m'm}^{(j)}(R) = \langle j,m'|\exp\left(\frac{-i\mathbf{J}\cdot\hat{\mathbf{n}}\phi}{\hbar}\right)|j,m\rangle. \tag{3.5.42}$$

These matrix elements are sometimes called **Wigner functions** after E. P. Wigner, who made pioneering contributions to the group-theoretical properties of rotations in quantum mechanics. Notice here that the same j-value appears in the ket and bra of (3.5.42); we need not consider matrix elements of $\mathscr{D}(R)$ between states with different j-values because they all vanish trivially. This is because $\mathscr{D}(R)|j,m\rangle$ is still an eigenket of $\mathbf{J}^2$ with the same eigenvalue $j(j+1)\hbar^2$:

$$\mathbf{J}^2\mathscr{D}(R)|j,m\rangle = \mathscr{D}(R)\mathbf{J}^2|j,m\rangle$$

$$= j(j+1)\hbar^2[\mathscr{D}(R)|j,m\rangle], \tag{3.5.43}$$

which follows directly from the fact that $\mathbf{J}^2$ commutes with J_k (hence with any function of J_k). Simply stated, rotations cannot change the j-value, which is an eminently sensible result.

Often in the literature the $(2j+1)\times(2j+1)$ matrix formed by $\mathscr{D}_{m'm}^{(j)}(R)$ is referred to as the $(2j+1)$-*dimensional irreducible representation* of the rotation operator $\mathscr{D}(R)$. This means that the matrix which corresponds to an arbitrary rotation operator in ket space *not* necessarily characterized by a single j-value can, with a suitable choice of basis, be brought to block-diagonal form:

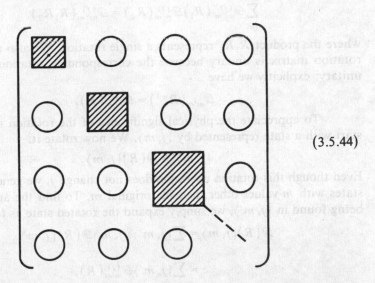

$$(3.5.44)$$

where each shaded square is a $(2j+1) \times (2j+1)$ square matrix formed by $\mathcal{D}^{(j)}_{m'm}$ with some definite value of j. Furthermore, each square matrix itself cannot be broken into smaller blocks

$$(3.5.45)$$

with any choice of basis.

The rotation matrices characterized by definite j form a group. First, the identity is a member because the rotation matrix corresponding to no rotation ($\phi = 0$) is the $(2j+1) \times (2j+1)$ identity matrix. Second, the inverse is also a member; we simply reverse the rotation angle ($\phi \to -\phi$) without changing the rotation axis $\hat{n}$. Third, the product of any two members is also a member; explicitly we have

$$\sum_{m'} \mathscr{D}_{m''m'}^{(j)}(R_1)\mathscr{D}_{m'm}^{(j)}(R_2) = \mathscr{D}_{m''m}^{(j)}(R_1 R_2), \tag{3.5.46}$$

where the product $R_1 R_2$ represents a single rotation. We also note that the rotation matrix is unitary because the corresponding rotation operator is unitary; explicitly we have

$$\mathscr{D}_{m'm}(R^{-1}) = \mathscr{D}_{mm'}^{*}(R). \tag{3.5.47}$$

To appreciate the physical significance of the rotation matrix let us start with a state represented by $|j, m\rangle$. We now rotate it:

$$|j, m\rangle \rightarrow \mathscr{D}(R)|j, m\rangle. \tag{3.5.48}$$

Even though this rotation operation does not change j, we generally obtain states with m-values other than the original m. To find the amplitude for being found in $|j, m'\rangle$, we simply expand the rotated state as follows:

$$\mathscr{D}(R)|j, m\rangle = \sum_{m'} |j, m'\rangle\langle j, m'|\mathscr{D}(R)|j, m\rangle$$

$$= \sum_{m'} |j, m'\rangle\mathscr{D}_{m'm}^{(j)}(R), \tag{3.5.49}$$

where, in using the completeness relation, we took advantage of the fact that $\mathscr{D}(R)$ connects only states with the same j. So the matrix element $\mathscr{D}_{m'm}^{(j)}(R)$ is simply the amplitude for the rotated state to be found in $|j, m'\rangle$ when the original unrotated state is given by $|j, m\rangle$.

In Section 3.3 we saw how Euler angles may be used to characterize the most general rotation. We now consider the matrix realization of (3.3.20) for an arbitrary j (not necessarily $\frac{1}{2}$):

$$\mathscr{D}_{m'm}^{(j)}(\alpha, \beta, \gamma) = \langle j, m'|\exp\left(\frac{-iJ_z\alpha}{\hbar}\right)\exp\left(\frac{-iJ_y\beta}{\hbar}\right)\exp\left(\frac{-iJ_z\gamma}{\hbar}\right)|j, m\rangle$$

$$= e^{-i(m'\alpha + m\gamma)}\langle j, m'|\exp\left(\frac{-iJ_y\beta}{\hbar}\right)|j, m\rangle. \tag{3.5.50}$$

Notice that the only nontrivial part is the middle rotation about the y-axis, which mixes different m-values. It is convenient to define a new matrix $d^{(j)}(\beta)$ as

$$d_{m'm}^{(j)}(\beta) \equiv \langle j, m'|\exp\left(\frac{-iJ_y\beta}{\hbar}\right)|j, m\rangle. \tag{3.5.51}$$

Finally, let us turn to some examples. The $j = \frac{1}{2}$ case has already been worked out in Section 3.3. See the middle matrix of (3.3.21),

$$d^{(1/2)} = \begin{pmatrix} \cos\left(\dfrac{\beta}{2}\right) & -\sin\left(\dfrac{\beta}{2}\right) \\ \sin\left(\dfrac{\beta}{2}\right) & \cos\left(\dfrac{\beta}{2}\right) \end{pmatrix} \tag{3.5.52}$$

The next simplest case is $j = 1$, which we consider in some detail. Clearly, we must first obtain the 3×3 matrix representation of J_y. Because

$$J_y = \frac{(J_+ - J_-)}{2i} \qquad (3.5.53)$$

from the defining equation (3.5.5) for $J_\pm$, we can use (3.5.41) to obtain

$$J_y^{(j=1)} = \left(\frac{\hbar}{2}\right) \begin{pmatrix} 0 & -\sqrt{2}\,i & 0 \\ \sqrt{2}\,i & 0 & -\sqrt{2}\,i \\ 0 & \sqrt{2}\,i & 0 \end{pmatrix} \begin{matrix} m'=1 \\ m'=0. \\ m'=-1 \end{matrix} \qquad (3.5.54)$$

with the column labels $m = 1$, $m = 0$, $m = -1$.

Our next task is to work out the Taylor expansion of $\exp(-iJ_y\beta/\hbar)$. Unlike the case $j = \frac{1}{2}$, $[J_y^{(j=1)}]^2$ is *independent* of 1 and $J_y^{(j=1)}$. However, it is easy to work out

$$\left(\frac{J_y^{(j=1)}}{\hbar}\right)^3 = \frac{J_y^{(j=1)}}{\hbar}. \qquad (3.5.55)$$

Consequently, for $j = 1$ *only*, it is legitimate to replace

$$\exp\left(\frac{-iJ_y\beta}{\hbar}\right) \rightarrow 1 - \left(\frac{J_y}{\hbar}\right)^2 (1 - \cos\beta) - i\left(\frac{J_y}{\hbar}\right)\sin\beta, \qquad (3.5.56)$$

as the reader may verify in detail. Explicitly we have

$$d^{(1)}(\beta) = \begin{pmatrix} \left(\frac{1}{2}\right)(1+\cos\beta) & -\left(\frac{1}{\sqrt{2}}\right)\sin\beta & \left(\frac{1}{2}\right)(1-\cos\beta) \\ \left(\frac{1}{\sqrt{2}}\right)\sin\beta & \cos\beta & -\left(\frac{1}{\sqrt{2}}\right)\sin\beta \\ \left(\frac{1}{2}\right)(1-\cos\beta) & \left(\frac{1}{\sqrt{2}}\right)\sin\beta & \left(\frac{1}{2}\right)(1+\cos\beta) \end{pmatrix}.$$

$$(3.5.57)$$

Clearly, this method becomes time-consuming for large j. In Section 3.8 we will learn a much easier method for obtaining $d_{mm'}^{(j)}(\beta)$ for *any j*.

3.6. ORBITAL ANGULAR MOMENTUM

We introduced the concept of angular momentum by defining it to be the generator of an infinitesimal rotation. There is another way to approach the subject of angular momentum when spin-angular momentum is zero or can be ignored. The angular momentum **J** for a single particle is then the same as orbital angular momentum, which is defined as

$$\mathbf{L} = \mathbf{x} \times \mathbf{p}. \qquad (3.6.1)$$

In this section we explore the connection between the two approaches.

Orbital Angular Momentum as Rotation Generator

We first note that the orbital angular-momentum operator defined as (3.6.1) satisfies the angular-momentum commutation relations

$$[L_i, L_j] = i\varepsilon_{ijk}\hbar L_k \qquad (3.6.2)$$

by virtue of the commutation relations among the components of $\mathbf{x}$ and $\mathbf{p}$. This can easily be proved as follows:

$$
\begin{aligned}
[L_x, L_y] &= [yp_z - zp_y, zp_x - xp_z] \\
&= [yp_z, zp_x] + [zp_y, xp_z] \\
&= yp_x[p_z, z] + p_y x[z, p_z] \\
&= i\hbar(xp_y - yp_x) \\
&= i\hbar L_z \\
&\vdots
\end{aligned}
\qquad (3.6.3)
$$

Next we let

$$1 - i\left(\frac{\delta\phi}{\hbar}\right)L_z = 1 - i\left(\frac{\delta\phi}{\hbar}\right)(xp_y - yp_x) \qquad (3.6.4)$$

act on an arbitrary position eigenket $|x', y', z'\rangle$ to examine whether it can be interpreted as the infinitesimal rotation operator about the z-axis by angle $\delta\phi$. Using the fact that momentum is the generator of translation, we obtain [see (1.6.32)]

$$
\begin{aligned}
\left[1 - i\left(\frac{\delta\phi}{\hbar}\right)L_z\right]|x', y', z'\rangle &= \left[1 - i\left(\frac{p_y}{\hbar}\right)(\delta\phi x') + i\left(\frac{p_x}{\hbar}\right)(\delta\phi y')\right]|x', y', z'\rangle \\
&= |x' - y'\delta\phi, y' + x'\delta\phi, z'\rangle.
\end{aligned}
\qquad (3.6.5)
$$

This is precisely what we expect if L_z generates an infinitesimal rotation about the z-axis. So we have demonstrated that if $\mathbf{p}$ generates translation, then $\mathbf{L}$ generates rotation.

Suppose the wave function for an arbitrary physical state of a spinless particle is given by $\langle x', y', z'|\alpha\rangle$. After an infinitesimal rotation about the z-axis is performed, the wave function for the rotated state is

$$\langle x', y', z'|\left[1 - i\left(\frac{\delta\phi}{\hbar}\right)L_z\right]|\alpha\rangle = \langle x' + y'\delta\phi, y' - x'\delta\phi, z'|\alpha\rangle. \qquad (3.6.6)$$

It is actually more transparent to change the coordinate basis

$$\langle x', y', z'|\alpha\rangle \to \langle r, \theta, \phi|\alpha\rangle. \qquad (3.6.7)$$

For the rotated state we have, according to (3.6.6),

$$
\begin{aligned}
\langle r, \theta, \phi|\left[1 - i\left(\frac{\delta\phi}{\hbar}\right)L_z\right]|\alpha\rangle &= \langle r, \theta, \phi - \delta\phi|\alpha\rangle \\
&= \langle r, \theta, \phi|\alpha\rangle - \delta\phi\frac{\partial}{\partial\phi}\langle r, \theta, \phi|\alpha\rangle. \qquad (3.6.8)
\end{aligned}
$$

Because $\langle r, \theta, \phi |$ is an arbitrary position eigenket, we can identify

$$\langle \mathbf{x}'|L_z|\alpha \rangle - - i\hbar \frac{\partial}{\partial \phi} \langle \mathbf{x}'|\alpha \rangle, \tag{3.6.9}$$

which is a well-known result from wave mechanics. Even though this relation can also be obtained just as easily using the position representation of the momentum operator, the derivation given here emphasizes the role of L_z as the generator of rotation.

We next consider a rotation about the x-axis by angle $\delta \phi_x$. In analogy with (3.6.6) we have

$$\langle x', y', z'| \left[1 - i \left(\frac{\delta \phi_x}{\hbar} \right) L_x \right] |\alpha \rangle = \langle x', y' + z'\delta \phi_x, z' - y'\delta \phi_x |\alpha \rangle.$$

$$\tag{3.6.10}$$

By expressing x', y', and z' in spherical coordinates, we can show that

$$\langle \mathbf{x}'|L_x|\alpha \rangle = - i\hbar \left(- \sin\phi \frac{\partial}{\partial \theta} - \cot\theta \cos\phi \frac{\partial}{\partial \phi} \right) \langle \mathbf{x}'|\alpha \rangle. \tag{3.6.11}$$

Likewise,

$$\langle \mathbf{x}'|L_y|\alpha \rangle = - i\hbar \left(\cos\phi \frac{\partial}{\partial \theta} - \cot\theta \sin\phi \frac{\partial}{\partial \phi} \right) \langle \mathbf{x}'|\alpha \rangle. \tag{3.6.12}$$

Using (3.6.11) and (3.6.12), for the ladder operator $L_\pm$ defined as in (3.5.5), we have

$$\langle \mathbf{x}'|L_\pm|\alpha \rangle = - i\hbar e^{\pm i\phi} \left(\pm i \frac{\partial}{\partial \theta} - \cot\theta \frac{\partial}{\partial \phi} \right) \langle \mathbf{x}'|\alpha \rangle. \tag{3.6.13}$$

Finally, it is possible to write $\langle \mathbf{x}'|\mathbf{L}^2|\alpha \rangle$ using

$$\mathbf{L}^2 = L_z^2 + (\tfrac{1}{2})(L_+ L_- + L_- L_+), \tag{3.6.14}$$

(3.6.9), and (3.6.13), as follows:

$$\langle \mathbf{x}'|\mathbf{L}^2|\alpha \rangle = - \hbar^2 \left[\frac{1}{\sin^2\theta} \frac{\partial^2}{\partial \phi^2} + \frac{1}{\sin\theta} \frac{\partial}{\partial \theta} \left(\sin\theta \frac{\partial}{\partial \theta} \right) \right] \langle \mathbf{x}'|\alpha \rangle. \tag{3.6.15}$$

Apart from $1/r^2$, we recognize the differential operator that appears here to be just the angular part of the Laplacian in spherical coordinates.

It is instructive to establish this connection between the $\mathbf{L}^2$ operator and the angular part of the Laplacian in another way by looking directly at the kinetic-energy operator. We first record an important operator identity,

$$\mathbf{L}^2 = \mathbf{x}^2\mathbf{p}^2 - (\mathbf{x}\cdot\mathbf{p})^2 + i\hbar\mathbf{x}\cdot\mathbf{p}, \tag{3.6.16}$$

where $\mathbf{x}^2$ is understood to be the operator $\mathbf{x}\cdot\mathbf{x}$, just as $\mathbf{p}^2$ stands for the operator $\mathbf{p} \cdot \mathbf{p}$. The proof of this is straightforward:

$$
\begin{aligned}
\mathbf{L}^2 &= \sum_{ijlmk} \varepsilon_{ijk} x_i p_j \varepsilon_{lmk} x_l p_m \\
&= \sum_{ijlm} (\delta_{il}\delta_{jm} - \delta_{im}\delta_{jl}) x_i p_j x_l p_m \\
&= \sum_{ijlm} \left[\delta_{il}\delta_{jm} x_i (x_l p_j - i\hbar\delta_{jl}) p_m - \delta_{im}\delta_{jl} x_i p_j (p_m x_l + i\hbar\delta_{lm}) \right] \\
&= \mathbf{x}^2 \mathbf{p}^2 - i\hbar \mathbf{x} \cdot \mathbf{p} - \sum_{ijlm} \delta_{im}\delta_{jl} \left[x_i p_m (x_l p_j - i\hbar\delta_{jl}) + i\hbar\delta_{lm} x_i p_j \right] \\
&= \mathbf{x}^2 \mathbf{p}^2 - (\mathbf{x} \cdot \mathbf{p})^2 + i\hbar \mathbf{x} \cdot \mathbf{p}.
\end{aligned}
\tag{3.6.17}
$$

Before taking the preceding expression between $\langle \mathbf{x}'|$ and $|\alpha\rangle$, first note that

$$
\begin{aligned}
\langle \mathbf{x}'|\mathbf{x} \cdot \mathbf{p}|\alpha \rangle &= \mathbf{x}' \cdot (-i\hbar\nabla' \langle \mathbf{x}'|\alpha\rangle) \\
&= -i\hbar r \frac{\partial}{\partial r} \langle \mathbf{x}'|\alpha\rangle.
\end{aligned}
\tag{3.6.18}
$$

Likewise,

$$
\begin{aligned}
\langle \mathbf{x}'|(\mathbf{x} \cdot \mathbf{p})^2|\alpha \rangle &= -\hbar^2 r \frac{\partial}{\partial r} \left(r \frac{\partial}{\partial r} \langle \mathbf{x}'|\alpha\rangle \right) \\
&= -\hbar^2 \left(r^2 \frac{\partial^2}{\partial r^2} \langle \mathbf{x}'|\alpha\rangle + r \frac{\partial}{\partial r} \langle \mathbf{x}'|\alpha\rangle \right).
\end{aligned}
\tag{3.6.19}
$$

Thus

$$
\langle \mathbf{x}'|\mathbf{L}^2|\alpha \rangle = r^2 \langle \mathbf{x}'|\mathbf{p}^2|\alpha\rangle + \hbar^2 \left(r^2 \frac{\partial^2}{\partial r^2} \langle \mathbf{x}'|\alpha\rangle + 2r \frac{\partial}{\partial r} \langle \mathbf{x}'|\alpha\rangle \right).
\tag{3.6.20}
$$

In terms of the kinetic energy $\mathbf{p}^2/2m$, we have

$$
\begin{aligned}
\frac{1}{2m} \langle \mathbf{x}'|\mathbf{p}^2|\alpha \rangle &= -\left(\frac{\hbar^2}{2m} \right) \nabla'^2 \langle \mathbf{x}'|\alpha\rangle \\
&= -\left(\frac{\hbar^2}{2m} \right) \left(\frac{\partial^2}{\partial r^2} \langle \mathbf{x}'|\alpha\rangle + \frac{2}{r} \frac{\partial}{\partial r} \langle \mathbf{x}'|\alpha\rangle - \frac{1}{\hbar^2 r^2} \langle \mathbf{x}'|\mathbf{L}^2|\alpha\rangle \right).
\end{aligned}
\tag{3.6.21}
$$

The first two terms in the last line are just the radial part of the Laplacian acting on $\langle \mathbf{x}'|\alpha\rangle$. The last term must then be the angular part of the Laplacian acting on $\langle \mathbf{x}'|\alpha\rangle$, in complete agreement with (3.6.15).

Spherical Harmonics

Consider a spinless particle subjected to a spherical symmetrical potential. The wave equation is known to be separable in spherical coordinates and the energy eigenfunctions can be written as

$$\langle \mathbf{x}'|n,l,m \rangle = R_{nl}(r)Y_l^m(\theta,\phi), \qquad (3.6.22)$$

where the position vector $\mathbf{x}'$ is specified by the spherical coordinates r, θ, and ϕ, and n stands for some quantum number other than l and m, for example, the radial quantum number for bound-state problems or the energy for a free-particle spherical wave. As will be made clearer in Section 3.10, this form can be regarded as a direct consequence of the rotational invariance of the problem. When the Hamiltonian is spherically symmetrical, H commutes with L_z and $\mathbf{L}^2$, and the energy eigenkets are expected to be eigenkets of $\mathbf{L}^2$ and L_z also. Because L_k with $k = 1,2,3$ satisfy the angular-momentum commutation relations, the eigenvalues of $\mathbf{L}^2$ and L_z are expected to be $l(l+1)\hbar^2$, and $m\hbar = [-l\hbar,(-l+1)\hbar,\ldots,(l-1)\hbar, l\hbar]$.

Because the angular dependence is common to all problems with spherical symmetry, we can isolate it and consider

$$\langle \hat{\mathbf{n}}|l,m \rangle = Y_l^m(\theta,\phi) = Y_l^m(\hat{\mathbf{n}}), \qquad (3.6.23)$$

where we have defined a **direction eigenket** $|\hat{\mathbf{n}}\rangle$. From this point of view, $Y_l^m(\theta,\phi)$ is the amplitude for a state characterized by l, m to be found in the direction $\hat{\mathbf{n}}$ specified by θ and ϕ.

Suppose we have relations involving orbital angular-momentum eigenkets. We can immediately write the corresponding relations involving the spherical harmonics. For example, take the eigenvalue equation

$$L_z|l,m \rangle = m\hbar|l,m \rangle. \qquad (3.6.24)$$

Multiplying $\langle \hat{\mathbf{n}}|$ on the left and using (3.6.9), we obtain

$$-i\hbar \frac{\partial}{\partial \phi}\langle \hat{\mathbf{n}}|l,m \rangle = m\hbar \langle \hat{\mathbf{n}}|l,m \rangle. \qquad (3.6.25)$$

We recognize this equation to be

$$-i\hbar \frac{\partial}{\partial \phi}Y_l^m(\theta,\phi) = m\hbar Y_l^m(\theta,\phi), \qquad (3.6.26)$$

which implies that the ϕ-dependence $Y_l^m(\theta,\phi)$ must behave like $e^{im\phi}$. Likewise, corresponding to

$$\mathbf{L}^2|l,m \rangle = l(l+1)\hbar^2|l,m \rangle, \qquad (3.6.27)$$

we have [see (3.6.15)]

$$\left[\frac{1}{\sin\theta} \frac{\partial}{\partial \theta}\left(\sin\theta \frac{\partial}{\partial \theta}\right) + \frac{1}{\sin^2\theta} \frac{\partial^2}{\partial \phi^2} + l(l+1)\right]Y_l^m = 0, \qquad (3.6.28)$$

which is simply the partial differential equation satisfied by Y_l^m itself. The orthogonality relation

$$\langle l',m'|l,m \rangle = \delta_{ll'}\delta_{mm'} \qquad (3.6.29)$$

leads to

$$\int_0^{2\pi} d\phi \int_{-1}^1 d(\cos\theta) Y_{l'}^{m'*}(\theta,\phi) Y_l^m(\theta,\phi) = \delta_{ll'}\delta_{mm'}, \qquad (3.6.30)$$

where we have used the completeness relation for the direction eigenkets,

$$\int d\Omega_{\hat{n}} |\hat{n}\rangle\langle\hat{n}| = 1. \qquad (3.6.31)$$

To obtain the Y_l^m themselves, we may start with the $m = l$ case. We have

$$L_+ |l, l\rangle = 0, \qquad (3.6.32)$$

which, because of (3.6.13), leads to

$$-i\hbar e^{i\phi}\left[i\frac{\partial}{\partial\theta} - \cot\theta\frac{\partial}{\partial\phi}\right]\langle\hat{n}|l, l\rangle = 0. \qquad (3.6.33)$$

Remembering that the ϕ-dependence must behave like $e^{il\phi}$, we can easily show that this partial differential equation is satisfied by

$$\langle\hat{n}|l, l\rangle = Y_l^l(\theta,\phi) = c_l e^{il\phi}\sin^l\theta, \qquad (3.6.34)$$

where c_l is the normalization constant determined from (3.6.30) to be*

$$c_l = \left[\frac{(-1)^l}{2^l l!}\right]\sqrt{\frac{[(2l+1)(2l)!]}{4\pi}} \qquad (3.6.35)$$

Starting with (3.6.34) we can use

$$\langle\hat{n}|l, m-1\rangle = \frac{\langle\hat{n}|L_-|l, m\rangle}{\sqrt{(l+m)(l-m+1)}\,\hbar}$$

$$= \frac{1}{\sqrt{(l+m)(l-m+1)}} e^{-i\phi}\left(-\frac{\partial}{\partial\theta} + i\cot\theta\frac{\partial}{\partial\phi}\right)\langle\hat{n}|l, m\rangle$$

$$\qquad (3.6.36)$$

successively to obtain all Y_l^m with l fixed. Because this is done in many textbooks on elementary quantum mechanics, we will not work out the details here. The result for $m \geq 0$ is

$$Y_l^m(\theta,\phi) = \frac{(-1)^l}{2^l l!}\sqrt{\frac{(2l+1)}{4\pi}\frac{(l+m)!}{(l-m)!}} e^{im\phi}\frac{1}{\sin^m\theta}\frac{d^{l-m}}{d(\cos\theta)^{l-m}}(\sin\theta)^{2l}, \qquad (3.6.37)$$

---

*Normalization condition (3.6.30), of course, does not determine the phase of c_l. The factor $(-1)^l$ is inserted so that when we use the L_- operator successively to reach the state $m = 0$, we obtain Y_l^0 with the same sign as the Legendre polynomial $P_l(\cos\theta)$ whose phase is fixed by $P_l(1) = 1$ [see (3.6.39)].

and we define Y_l^{-m} by

$$Y_l^{-m}(\theta,\phi) = (-1)^m [Y_l^m(\theta,\phi)]^*. \qquad (3.6.38)$$

Regardless of whether m is positive or negative, the θ-dependent part of $Y_l^m(\theta,\phi)$ is $[\sin\theta]^{|m|}$ times a polynomial in $\cos\theta$ with a highest power of $l - |m|$. For $m = 0$, we obtain

$$Y_l^0(\theta,\phi) = \sqrt{\frac{2l+1}{4\pi}} P_l(\cos\theta). \qquad (3.6.39)$$

From the point of view of the angular-momentum commutation relations alone, it might not appear obvious why l cannot be a half-integer. It turns out that several arguments can be advanced against half-integer l-values. First, for half-integer l, and hence for half-integer m, the wave function would acquire a minus sign,

$$e^{im(2\pi)} = -1, \qquad (3.6.40)$$

under a 2π rotation. As a result, the wave function would not be single-valued; we pointed out in Section 2.4 that the wave function must be single-valued because of the requirement that the expansion of a state ket in terms of position eigenkets be unique. We can prove that if $\mathbf{L}$, defined to be $\mathbf{x} \times \mathbf{p}$, is to be identified as the generator of rotation, then the wave function must acquire a plus sign under a 2π rotation. This follows from the fact that the wave function for a 2π-rotated state is the original wave function itself with no sign change:

$$\langle \mathbf{x}' | \exp\left(\frac{-iL_z 2\pi}{\hbar}\right) | \alpha \rangle = \langle x'\cos 2\pi + y'\sin 2\pi, y'\cos 2\pi - x'\sin 2\pi, z' | \alpha \rangle$$

$$= \langle \mathbf{x}' | \alpha \rangle, \qquad (3.6.41)$$

where we have used the finite-angle version of (3.6.6). Next, let us suppose $Y_l^m(\theta,\phi)$ with a half-integer l were possible. To be specific, we choose the simplest case, $l = m = \frac{1}{2}$. According to (3.6.34) we would have

$$Y_{1/2}^{1/2}(\theta,\phi) = c_{1/2} e^{i\phi/2} \sqrt{\sin\theta}. \qquad (3.6.42)$$

From the property of L_- [see (3.6.36)] we would then obtain

$$Y_{1/2}^{-1/2}(\theta,\phi) = e^{-i\phi}\left(-\frac{\partial}{\partial\theta} + i\cot\theta \frac{\partial}{\partial\phi}\right)\left(c_{1/2}e^{i\phi/2}\sqrt{\sin\theta}\right)$$

$$= -c_{1/2}e^{-i\phi/2}\cot\theta\sqrt{\sin\theta}. \qquad (3.6.43)$$

This expression is not permissible because it is singular at $\theta = 0, \pi$. What is worse, from the partial differential equation

$$\left\langle \hat{\mathbf{n}} \Big| L_- \Big| \frac{1}{2}, -\frac{1}{2} \right\rangle = -i\hbar e^{-i\phi}\left(-i\frac{\partial}{\partial\theta} - \cot\theta \frac{\partial}{\partial\phi}\right)\left\langle \hat{\mathbf{n}} \Big| \frac{1}{2}, -\frac{1}{2} \right\rangle$$

$$= 0 \qquad (3.6.44)$$

we directly obtain

$$Y_{1/2}^{-1/2} = c_{1/2}' e^{-i\phi/2}\sqrt{\sin\theta}, \tag{3.6.45}$$

in sharp contradiction with (3.6.43). Finally, we know from the Sturm-Liouville theory of differential equations that the solutions of (3.6.28) with l integer form a complete set. An arbitrary function of θ and ϕ can be expanded in terms of Y_l^m with integer l and m only. For all these reasons it is futile to contemplate orbital angular momentum with half-integer l-values.

Spherical Harmonics as Rotation Matrices

We conclude this section on orbital angular momentum by discussing the spherical harmonics from the point of view of the rotation matrices introduced in the last section. We can readily establish the desired connection between the two approaches by constructing the most general direction eigenket $|\hat{\mathbf{n}}\rangle$ by applying appropriate rotation operators to $|\hat{\mathbf{z}}\rangle$, the direction eigenket in the positive z-direction. We wish to find $\mathcal{D}(R)$ such that

$$|\hat{\mathbf{n}}\rangle = \mathcal{D}(R)|\hat{\mathbf{z}}\rangle. \tag{3.6.46}$$

We can rely on the technique used in constructing the eigenspinor of $\boldsymbol{\sigma}\cdot\hat{\mathbf{n}}$ in Section 3.2. We first rotate about the y-axis by angle θ, then around the z-axis by angle ϕ; see Figure 3.3 with $\beta \to \theta$, $\alpha \to \phi$. In the notation of Euler angles we have

$$\mathcal{D}(R) = \mathcal{D}(\alpha = \phi, \beta = \theta, \gamma = 0). \tag{3.6.47}$$

Writing (3.6.46) as

$$|\hat{\mathbf{n}}\rangle = \sum_l \sum_m \mathcal{D}(R)|l,m\rangle\langle l,m|\hat{\mathbf{z}}\rangle, \tag{3.6.48}$$

we see that $|\hat{\mathbf{n}}\rangle$, when expanded in terms of $|l,m\rangle$, contains all possible l-values. However, when this equation is multiplied by $\langle l,m'|$ on the left, only one term in the l-sum contributes, namely,

$$\langle l,m'|\hat{\mathbf{n}}\rangle = \sum_m \mathcal{D}_{m'm}^{(l)}(\alpha = \phi, \beta = \theta, \gamma = 0)\langle l,m|\hat{\mathbf{z}}\rangle. \tag{3.6.49}$$

Now $\langle l,m|\hat{\mathbf{z}}\rangle$ is just a number; in fact, it is precisely $Y_l^{m*}(\theta,\phi)$ evaluated at $\theta = 0$ with ϕ undetermined. At $\theta = 0$, Y_l^m is known to vanish for $m \neq 0$, which can also be seen directly from the fact that $|\hat{\mathbf{z}}\rangle$ is an eigenket of L_z (which equals $xp_y - yp_x$) with eigenvalue zero. So we can write

$$\langle l,m|\hat{\mathbf{z}}\rangle = Y_l^{m*}(\theta = 0, \phi \text{ undetermined})\delta_{m0}$$

$$= \sqrt{\frac{(2l+1)}{4\pi}}\, P_l(\cos\theta)\bigg|_{\cos\theta = 1}\delta_{m0}$$

$$= \sqrt{\frac{(2l+1)}{4\pi}}\,\delta_{m0}. \tag{3.6.50}$$

Returning to (3.6.49), we have

$$Y_l^{m'*}(\theta,\phi) = \sqrt{\frac{(2l+1)}{4\pi}} \, \mathcal{D}_{m'0}^{(l)}(\alpha = \phi, \beta = \theta, \gamma = 0) \qquad (3.6.51)$$

or

$$\mathcal{D}_{m0}^{(l)}(\alpha,\beta,\gamma=0) = \sqrt{\frac{4\pi}{(2l+1)}} \, Y_l^{m*}(\theta,\phi)\Bigg|_{\theta=\beta,\,\phi=\alpha} \qquad (3.6.52)$$

Notice the $m = 0$ case, which is of particular importance:

$$d_{00}^{(l)}(\beta)\big|_{\beta=\theta} = P_l(\cos\theta). \qquad (3.6.53)$$

3.7. ADDITION OF ANGULAR MOMENTA

Angular-momentum addition has important applications in all areas of modern physics—from atomic spectroscopy to nuclear and particle collisions. Furthermore, a study of angular-momentum addition provides an excellent opportunity to illustrate the concept of change of basis, which we discussed extensively in Chapter 1.

Simple Examples of Angular-Momentum Addition

Before studying a formal theory of angular-momentum addition, it is worth looking at two simple examples with which the reader may be familiar: (1) how to add orbital angular momentum and spin-angular momentum and (2) how to add the spin-angular momenta of two spin $\frac{1}{2}$ particles.

Previously we studied both spin $\frac{1}{2}$ systems with all quantum-mechanical degrees of freedom other than spin—such as position and momentum —ignored and quantum-mechanical particles with the space degrees of freedom (such as position or momentum) taken into account but the internal degrees of freedom (such as spin) ignored. A realistic description of a particle with spin must of course take into account both the space degree of freedom and the internal degrees of freedom. The base ket for a spin $\frac{1}{2}$ particle may be visualized to be in the direct-product space of the infinite-dimensional ket space spanned by the position eigenkets $\{|\mathbf{x}'\rangle\}$ and the two-dimensional spin space spanned by $|+\rangle$ and $|-\rangle$. Explicitly, we have for the base ket

$$|\mathbf{x}', \pm\rangle = |\mathbf{x}'\rangle \otimes |\pm\rangle, \qquad (3.7.1)$$

where any operator in the space spanned by $\{|\mathbf{x}'\rangle\}$ commutes with any operator in the two-dimensional space spanned by $|\pm\rangle$.

The rotation operator still takes the form $\exp(-i\mathbf{J}\cdot\hat{\mathbf{n}}\phi/\hbar)$ but $\mathbf{J}$, the generator of rotations, is now made up of two parts, namely,

$$\mathbf{J} = \mathbf{L} + \mathbf{S}. \qquad (3.7.2)$$

It is actually more obvious to write (3.7.2) as

$$\mathbf{J} = \mathbf{L}\otimes 1 + 1\otimes \mathbf{S}, \qquad (3.7.3)$$

where the 1 in $\mathbf{L}\otimes 1$ stands for the identity operator in the spin space, while the 1 in $1\otimes\mathbf{S}$ stands for the identity operator in the infinite-dimensional ket space spanned by the position eigenkets. Because $\mathbf{L}$ and $\mathbf{S}$ commute, we can write

$$\mathcal{D}(R) = \mathcal{D}^{(\text{orb})}(R)\otimes\mathcal{D}^{(\text{spin})}(R)$$

$$= \exp\left(\frac{-i\mathbf{L}\cdot\hat{\mathbf{n}}\phi}{\hbar}\right)\otimes\exp\left(\frac{-i\mathbf{S}\cdot\hat{\mathbf{n}}\phi}{\hbar}\right). \qquad (3.7.4)$$

The wave function for a particle with spin is written as

$$\langle \mathbf{x}', \pm|\alpha\rangle = \psi_{\pm}(\mathbf{x}'). \qquad (3.7.5)$$

The two components $\psi_{\pm}$ are often arranged in column matrix form as follows:

$$\begin{pmatrix} \psi_{+}(\mathbf{x}') \\ \psi_{-}(\mathbf{x}') \end{pmatrix}, \qquad (3.7.6)$$

where $|\psi_{\pm}(\mathbf{x}')|^2$ stands for the probability density for the particle to be found at $\mathbf{x}'$ with spin up and down, respectively. Instead of $|\mathbf{x}'\rangle$ as the base kets for the space part, we may use $|n, l, m\rangle$, which are eigenkets of $\mathbf{L}^2$ and L_z with eigenvalues $\hbar^2 l(l+1)$ and $m_l\hbar$, respectively. For the spin part, $|\pm\rangle$ are eigenkets of $\mathbf{S}^2$ and S_z with eigenvalues $3\hbar^2/4$ and $\pm\hbar/2$, respectively. However, as we will show later, we can also use base kets which are eigenkets of $\mathbf{J}^2$, J_z, $\mathbf{L}^2$, and $\mathbf{S}^2$. In other words, we can expand a state ket of a particle with spin in terms of simultaneous eigenkets of $\mathbf{L}^2$, $\mathbf{S}^2$, L_z, and S_z or in terms of simultaneous eigenkets of $\mathbf{J}^2$, J_z, $\mathbf{L}^2$, and $\mathbf{S}^2$. We will study in detail how the two descriptions are related.

As a second example, we study two spin $\frac{1}{2}$ particles—say two electrons—with the orbital degree of freedom suppressed. The total spin operator is usually written as

$$\mathbf{S} = \mathbf{S}_1 + \mathbf{S}_2, \qquad (3.7.7)$$

but again it is to be understood as

$$\mathbf{S}_1\otimes 1 + 1\otimes\mathbf{S}_2, \qquad (3.7.8)$$

where the 1 in the first (second) term stands for the identity operator in the spin space of electron 2 (1). We, of course, have

$$\left[S_{1x}, S_{2y}\right] = 0 \qquad (3.7.9)$$

and so forth. Within the space of electron 1(2) we have the usual commutation relations

$$\left[S_{1x}, S_{1y}\right] = i\hbar S_{1z}, \left[S_{2x}, S_{2y}\right] = i\hbar S_{2z}, \dots. \qquad (3.7.10)$$

As a direct consequence of (3.7.9) and (3.7.10), we have

$$\left[S_x, S_y\right] = i\hbar S_z \qquad (3.7.11)$$

and so on for the *total* spin operator.

The eigenvalues of the various spin operators are denoted as follows:

$$\mathbf{S}^2 = (\mathbf{S}_1 + \mathbf{S}_2)^2 : s(s+1)\hbar^2$$

$$S_z = S_{1z} + S_{2z} : m\hbar$$

$$S_{1z} : m_1\hbar \qquad (3.7.12)$$

$$S_{2z} : m_2\hbar$$

Again, we can expand the ket corresponding to an arbitrary spin state of two electrons in terms of either the eigenkets of $\mathbf{S}^2$ and S_z or the eigenkets of S_{1z} and S_{2z}. The two possibilities are as follows:

1. The $\{m_1, m_2\}$ representation based on the eigenkets of S_{1z} and S_{2z}:

$$|++\rangle, |+-\rangle, |-+\rangle, \quad \text{and} \quad |--\rangle, \qquad (3.7.13)$$

where $|+-\rangle$ stands for $m_1 = \frac{1}{2}$, $m_2 = -\frac{1}{2}$, and so forth.

2. The $\{s, m\}$ representation (or the triplet-singlet representation) based on the eigenkets of $\mathbf{S}^2$ and S_z:

$$|s = 1, m = \pm 1, 0\rangle, |s = 0, m = 0\rangle, \qquad (3.7.14)$$

where $s = 1$ ($s = 0$) is referred to as spin triplet (spin singlet).

Notice that in each set there are four base kets. The relationship between the two sets of base kets is as follows:

$$|s = 1, m = 1\rangle = |++\rangle, \qquad (3.7.15a)$$

$$|s = 1, m = 0\rangle = \left(\frac{1}{\sqrt{2}}\right)(|+-\rangle + |-+\rangle), \qquad (3.7.15b)$$

$$|s = 1, m = -1\rangle = |--\rangle, \qquad (3.7.15c)$$

$$|s = 0, m = 0\rangle = \left(\frac{1}{\sqrt{2}}\right)(|+-\rangle - |-+\rangle). \qquad (3.7.15d)$$

The right-hand side of (3.7.15a) tells us that we have both electrons with spin up; this situation can correspond only to $s = 1$, $m = 1$. We can obtain (3.7.15b) from (3.7.15a) by applying the ladder operator

$$S_- \equiv S_{1-} + S_{2-}$$

$$= \left(S_{1x} - iS_{1y}\right) + \left(S_{2x} - iS_{2y}\right) \qquad (3.7.16)$$

to both sides of (3.7.15a). In doing so we must remember that an electron 1 operator like S_{1-} affects just the first entry of $|++\rangle$, and so on. We can write

$$S_-|s=1, m=1\rangle = (S_{1-} + S_{2-})|++\rangle \qquad (3.7.17)$$

as

$$\sqrt{(1+1)(1-1+1)}\,|s=1, m=0\rangle = \sqrt{(\tfrac{1}{2}+\tfrac{1}{2})(\tfrac{1}{2}-\tfrac{1}{2}+1)}\ \times|-+\rangle$$
$$+ \sqrt{(\tfrac{1}{2}+\tfrac{1}{2})(\tfrac{1}{2}-\tfrac{1}{2}+1)}\,|+-\rangle,$$

$$(3.7.18)$$

which immediately leads to (3.7.15b). Likewise, we can obtain $|s=1$, $m=-1\rangle$ by applying (3.7.16) once again to (3.7.15b). Finally, we can obtain (3.7.15d) by requiring it to be orthogonal to the other three kets, in particular to (3.7.15b).

The coefficients that appear on the right-hand side of (3.7.15) are the simplest example of **Clebsch-Gordan coefficients** to be discussed further at a later time. They are simply the elements of the transformation matrix that connects the $\{m_1, m_2\}$ basis to the $\{s, m\}$ basis. It is instructive to derive these coefficients in another way. Suppose we write the 4×4 matrix corresponding to

$$\mathbf{S}^2 = \mathbf{S}_1^2 + \mathbf{S}_2^2 + 2\mathbf{S}_1\cdot\mathbf{S}_2$$
$$= \mathbf{S}_1^2 + \mathbf{S}_2^2 + 2S_{1z}S_{2z} + S_{1+}S_{2-} + S_{1-}S_{2+} \qquad (3.7.19)$$

using the (m_1, m_2) basis. The square matrix is obviously not diagonal because an operator like S_{1+} connects $|-+\rangle$ with $|++\rangle$. The unitary matrix that diagonalizes this matrix carries the $|m_1, m_2\rangle$ base kets into the $|s, m\rangle$ base kets. The elements of this unitary matrix are precisely the Clebsch-Gordan coefficients for this problem. The reader is encouraged to work out all this in detail.

Formal Theory of Angular-Momentum Addition

Having gained some physical insight by considering simple examples, we are now in a position to study more systematically the formal theory of angular-momentum addition. Consider two angular-momentum operators $\mathbf{J}_1$ and $\mathbf{J}_2$ in different subspaces. The components of $\mathbf{J}_1(\mathbf{J}_2)$ satisfy the usual angular-momentum commutation relations:

$$[J_{1i}, J_{1j}] = i\hbar\varepsilon_{ijk}J_{1k} \qquad (3.7.20a)$$

and

$$[J_{2i}, J_{2j}] = i\hbar\varepsilon_{ijk}J_{2k}. \qquad (3.7.20b)$$

However, we have

$$[J_{1k}, J_{2l}] = 0 \tag{3.7.21}$$

between any pair of operators from different subspaces.

The infinitesimal rotation operator that affects both subspace 1 and subspace 2 is written as

$$\left(1 - \frac{i\mathbf{J}_1 \cdot \hat{\mathbf{n}}\delta\phi}{\hbar}\right) \otimes \left(1 - \frac{i\mathbf{J}_2 \cdot \hat{\mathbf{n}}\delta\phi}{\hbar}\right) = 1 - \frac{i(\mathbf{J}_1 \otimes 1 + 1 \otimes \mathbf{J}_2) \cdot \hat{\mathbf{n}}\delta\phi}{\hbar}. \tag{3.7.22}$$

We define the total angular momentum by

$$\mathbf{J} \equiv \mathbf{J}_1 \otimes 1 + 1 \otimes \mathbf{J}_2, \tag{3.7.23}$$

which is more commonly written as

$$\mathbf{J} = \mathbf{J}_1 + \mathbf{J}_2. \tag{3.7.24}$$

The finite-angle version of (3.7.22) is

$$\mathscr{D}_1(R) \otimes \mathscr{D}_2(R) = \exp\left(\frac{-i\mathbf{J}_1 \cdot \hat{\mathbf{n}}\phi}{\hbar}\right) \otimes \exp\left(\frac{-i\mathbf{J}_2 \cdot \hat{\mathbf{n}}\phi}{\hbar}\right). \tag{3.7.25}$$

Notice the appearance of the same axis of rotation and the same angle of rotation.

It is very important to note that the total $\mathbf{J}$ satisfies the angular-momentum commutation relations

$$[J_i, J_j] = i\hbar\varepsilon_{ijk}J_k \tag{3.7.26}$$

as a direct consequence of (3.7.20) and (3.7.21). In other words, $\mathbf{J}$ is an angular momentum in the sense of Section 3.1. Physically this is reasonable because $\mathbf{J}$ is the generator for the *entire* system. Everything we learned in Section 3.5—for example, the eigenvalue spectrum of $\mathbf{J}^2$ and J_z and the matrix elements of the ladder operators—also holds for the total $\mathbf{J}$.

As for the choice of base kets we have two options.

Option A: Simultaneous eigenkets of $\mathbf{J}_1^2$, $\mathbf{J}_2^2$, J_{1z}, and J_{2z}, denoted by $|j_1 j_2; m_1 m_2\rangle$. Obviously the four operators commute with each other. The defining equations are

$$\mathbf{J}_1^2 |j_1 j_2; m_1 m_2\rangle = j_1(j_1 + 1)\hbar^2 |j_1 j_2; m_1 m_2\rangle, \tag{3.7.27a}$$

$$J_{1z} |j_1 j_2; m_1 m_2\rangle = m_1 \hbar |j_1 j_2; m_1 m_2\rangle, \tag{3.7.27b}$$

$$\mathbf{J}_2^2 |j_1 j_2; m_1 m_2\rangle = j_2(j_2 + 1)\hbar^2 |j_1 j_2; m_1 m_2\rangle, \tag{3.7.27c}$$

$$J_{2z} |j_1 j_2; m_1 m_2\rangle = m_2 \hbar |j_1 j_2; m_1 m_2\rangle. \tag{3.7.27d}$$

Option B: Simultaneous eigenkets of $\mathbf{J}^2$, $\mathbf{J}_1^2$, $\mathbf{J}_2^2$, and J_z. First, note that this set of operators mutually commute. In particular, we have

$$[\mathbf{J}^2, \mathbf{J}_1^2] = 0, \tag{3.7.28}$$

which can readily be seen by writing $\mathbf{J}^2$ as

$$\mathbf{J}^2 = \mathbf{J}_1^2 + \mathbf{J}_2^2 + 2J_{1z}J_{2z} + J_{1+}J_{2-} + J_{1-}J_{2+}. \qquad (3.7.29)$$

We use $|j_1, j_2; jm\rangle$ to denote the base kets of option B:

$$\mathbf{J}_1^2|j_1j_2; jm\rangle = j_1(j_1+1)\hbar^2|j_1j_2; jm\rangle, \qquad (3.7.30a)$$

$$\mathbf{J}_2^2|j_1j_2; jm\rangle = j_2(j_2+1)\hbar^2|j_1j_2; jm\rangle, \qquad (3.7.30b)$$

$$\mathbf{J}^2|j_1j_2; jm\rangle = j(j+1)\hbar^2|j_1j_2; jm\rangle, \qquad (3.7.30c)$$

$$J_z|j_1j_2; jm\rangle = m\hbar|j_1j_2; jm\rangle. \qquad (3.7.30d)$$

Quite often j_1, j_2 are understood, and the base kets are written simply as $|j, m\rangle$.

It is very important to note that even though

$$[\mathbf{J}^2, J_z] = 0, \qquad (3.7.31)$$

we have

$$[\mathbf{J}^2, J_{1z}] \neq 0, \qquad [\mathbf{J}^2, J_{2z}] \neq 0, \qquad (3.7.32)$$

as the reader may easily verify using (3.7.29). This means that we cannot add $\mathbf{J}^2$ to the set of operators of option A. Likewise, we cannot add J_{1z} and/or J_{2z} to the set of operators of option B. We have two possible sets of base kets corresponding to the two maximal sets of mutually compatible observables we have constructed.

Let us consider the unitary transformation in the sense of Section 1.5 that connects the two bases:

$$|j_1j_2; jm\rangle = \sum_{m_1}\sum_{m_2}|j_1j_2; m_1m_2\rangle\langle j_1j_2; m_1m_2|j_1j_2; jm\rangle, \qquad (3.7.33)$$

where we have used

$$\sum_{m_1}\sum_{m_2}|j_1j_2; m_1m_2\rangle\langle j_1j_2; m_1m_2| = 1 \qquad (3.7.34)$$

and where the right-hand side is the identity operator in the ket space of given j_1 and j_2. The elements of this transformation matrix $\langle j_1j_2; m_1m_2|j_1j_2; jm\rangle$ are Clebsch-Gordan coefficients.

There are many important properties of Clebsch-Gordan coefficients that we are now ready to study. First, the coefficients vanish unless

$$m = m_1 + m_2. \qquad (3.7.35)$$

To prove this, first note that

$$(J_z - J_{1z} - J_{2z})|j_1j_2; jm\rangle = 0. \qquad (3.7.36)$$

Multiplying $\langle j_1j_2; m_1m_2|$ on the left, we obtain

$$(m - m_1 - m_2)\langle j_1j_2; m_1m_2|j_1j_2; jm\rangle = 0, \qquad (3.7.37)$$

which proves our assertion. Admire the power of the Dirac notation! It really pays to write the Clebsch-Gordan coefficients in Dirac's bracket form, as we have done.

Second, the coefficients vanish unless

$$|j_1 - j_2| \le j \le j_1 + j_2. \tag{3.7.38}$$

This property may appear obvious from the vector model of angular-momentum addition, where we visualize $\mathbf{J}$ to be the vectorial sum of $\mathbf{J}_1$ and $\mathbf{J}_2$. However, it is worth checking this point by showing that if (3.7.38) holds, then the dimensionality of the space spanned by $\{|j_1 j_2; m_1 m_2\rangle\}$ is the same as that of the space spanned by $\{|j_1 j_2; jm\rangle\}$. For the (m_1, m_2) way of counting we obtain

$$N = (2j_1 + 1)(2j_2 + 1) \tag{3.7.39}$$

because for given j_1 there are $2j_1 + 1$ possible values of m_1; a similar statement is true for the other angular momentum j_2. As for the (j, m) way of counting, we note that for each j, there are $2j + 1$ states, and according to (3.7.38), j itself runs from $j_1 - j_2$ to $j_1 + j_2$, where we have assumed, without loss of generality, that $j_1 \ge j_2$. We therefore obtain

$$
\begin{aligned}
N &= \sum_{j=j_1-j_2}^{j_1+j_2} (2j+1) \\
&= \tfrac{1}{2}\big[\{2(j_1 - j_2)+1\} + \{2(j_1 + j_2)+1\}\big](2j_2 + 1) \\
&= (2j_1 + 1)(2j_2 + 1). \tag{3.7.40}
\end{aligned}
$$

Because both ways of counting give the same N-value, we see that (3.7.38) is quite consistent.*

The Clebsch-Gordan coefficients form a unitary matrix. Furthermore, the matrix elements are taken to be real by convention. An immediate consequence of this is that the inverse coefficient $\langle j_1 j_2; jm|j_1 j_2; m_1 m_2\rangle$ is the same as $\langle j_1 j_2; m_1 m_2|j_1 j_2; jm\rangle$ itself. A real unitary matrix is orthogonal, so we have the orthogonality condition

$$\sum_j \sum_m \langle j_1 j_2; m_1 m_2|j_1 j_2; jm\rangle\langle j_1 j_2; m_1' m_2'|j_1 j_2; jm\rangle = \delta_{m_1 m_1'}\delta_{m_2 m_2'},$$

$$\tag{3.7.41}$$

which is obvious from the orthonormality of $\{|j_1 j_2; m_1 m_2\rangle\}$ together with the reality of the Clebsch-Gordan coefficients. Likewise, we also have

$$\sum_{m_1}\sum_{m_2} \langle j_1 j_2; m_1 m_2|j_1 j_2; jm\rangle\langle j_1 j_2; m_1 m_2|j_1 j_2; j'm'\rangle = \delta_{jj'}\delta_{mm'}.$$

$$\tag{3.7.42}$$

---

*A complete proof of (3.7.38) is given in Gottfried 1966, 215, and also in Appendix B of this book.

As a special case of this we may set $j' = j$, $m' = m = m_1 + m_2$. We then obtain

$$\sum_{m_1} \sum_{m_2} |\langle j_1 j_2; m_1 m_2 | j_1 j_2; jm \rangle|^2 = 1, \qquad (3.7.43)$$

which is just the normalization condition for $|j_1 j_2; jm\rangle$.

Some authors use somewhat different notations for the Clebsch-Gordan coefficients. Instead of $\langle j_1 j_2; m_1 m_2 | j_1 j_2; jm \rangle$ we sometimes see $\langle j_1 m_1 j_2 m_2 | j_1 j_2 jm \rangle$, $C(j_1 j_2 j; m_1 m_2 m)$, $C_{j_1 j_2}(jm; m_1 m_2)$, and so on. They can also be written in terms of **Wigner's 3-j symbol**, which is occasionally found in the literature:

$$\langle j_1 j_2; m_1 m_2 | j_1 j_2; jm \rangle = (-1)^{j_1 - j_2 + m} \sqrt{2j + 1} \begin{pmatrix} j_1 & j_2 & j \\ m_1 & m_2 & -m \end{pmatrix}.$$

$$(3.7.44)$$

Recursion Relations for the Clebsch-Gordan Coefficients*

With j_1, j_2, and j fixed, the coefficients with different m_1 and m_2 are related to each other by **recursion relations**. We start with

$$J_\pm |j_1 j_2; jm \rangle = (J_{1\pm} + J_{2\pm}) \sum_{m_1} \sum_{m_2} |j_1 j_2; m_1 m_2 \rangle \langle j_1 j_2; m_1 m_2 | j_1 j_2; jm \rangle.$$

$$(3.7.45)$$

Using (3.5.39) and (3.5.40) we obtain (with $m_1 \to m_1'$, $m_2 \to m_2'$)

$$\sqrt{(j \mp m)(j \pm m + 1)} \, |j_1 j_2; j, m \pm 1 \rangle$$
$$= \sum_{m_1'} \sum_{m_2'} \left(\sqrt{(j_1 \mp m_1')(j_1 \pm m_1' + 1)} \, |j_1 j_2; m_1' \pm 1, m_2' \rangle \right.$$
$$\left. + \sqrt{(j_2 \mp m_2')(j_2 \pm m_2' + 1)} \, |j_1 j_2; m_1', m_2' \pm 1 \rangle \right)$$
$$\times \langle j_1 j_2; m_1' m_2' | j_1 j_2; jm \rangle. \qquad (3.7.46)$$

Our next step is to multiply by $\langle j_1 j_2; m_1 m_2 |$ on the left and use orthonormality, which means that nonvanishing contributions from the right-hand side are possible only with

$$m_1 = m_1' \pm 1, \qquad m_2 = m_2' \qquad (3.7.47)$$

for the first term and

$$m_1 = m_1', \qquad m_2 = m_2' \pm 1 \qquad (3.7.48)$$

---

*More-detailed discussion of Clebsch-Gordan and Racah coefficients, recoupling, and the like is given in A. R. Edmonds 1960, for instance.

for the second term. In this manner we obtain the desired recursion relations:

$$\sqrt{(j \mp m)(j \pm m + 1)} \langle j_1 j_2; m_1 m_2 | j_1 j_2; j, m \pm 1 \rangle$$
$$= \sqrt{(j_1 \mp m_1 + 1)(j_1 \pm m_1)} \langle j_1 j_2; m_1 \mp 1, m_2 | j_1 j_2; jm \rangle$$
$$+ \sqrt{(j_2 \mp m_2 + 1)(j_2 \pm m_2)} \langle j_1 j_2; m_1, m_2 \mp 1 | j_1 j_2; jm \rangle.$$
(3.7.49)

It is important to note that because the $J_{\pm}$ operators have shifted the m-values, the nonvanishing condition (3.7.35) for the Clebsch-Gordan coefficients has now become [when applied to (3.7.49)]

$$m_1 + m_2 = m \pm 1.$$
(3.7.50)

We can appreciate the significance of the recursion relations by looking at (3.7.49) in an $m_1 m_2$-plane. The J_+ recursion relation (upper sign) tells us that the coefficient at (m_1, m_2) is related to the coefficients at $(m_1 - 1, m_2)$ and $(m_1, m_2 - 1)$, as shown in Figure 3.5a. Likewise, the J_- recursion relation (lower sign) relates the three coefficients whose m_1, m_2 values are given in Figure 3.5b.

Recursion relations (3.7.49), together with normalization condition (3.7.43), almost uniquely determine all Clebsch-Gordan coefficients. (We say "almost uniquely" because certain sign conventions have yet to be specified.) Our strategy is as follows. We go back to the $m_1 m_2$-plane, again for fixed j_1, j_2, and j, and plot the boundary of the allowed region determined by

$$|m_1| \leq j_1, \qquad |m_2| \leq j_2, \qquad -j \leq m_1 + m_2 \leq j;$$
(3.7.51)

see Figure 3.6a. We may start with the upper right-hand corner, denoted by A. Because we work near A at the start, a more detailed "map" is in order;

(a) J_+ relation   **(b)** J_- relation

FIGURE 3.5. $m_1 m_2$-plane showing the Clebsch-Gordan coefficients related by the recursion relations (3.7.49).

see Figure 3.6b. We apply the J_- recursion relation (3.7.49) (lower sign), with $(m_1, m_2 + 1)$ corresponding to A. Observe now that the recursion relation connects A with only B because the site corresponding to $(m_1 + 1, m_2)$ is forbidden by $m_1 \le j_1$. As a result, we can obtain the Clebsch-Gordan coefficient of B in terms of the coefficient of A. Next, we form a J_+ triangle made up of A, B, and D. This enables us to obtain the coefficient of D once the coefficient of A is specified. We can continue in this fashion: Knowing B and D, we can get to E; knowing B and E we can get to C, and so on. With enough patience we can obtain the Clebsch-Gordan coefficient of every site in terms of the coefficient of starting site, A. For overall normalization we use (3.7.43). The final overall sign is fixed by convention. (See the following example.)

As an important practical example we consider the problem of adding the orbital and spin-angular momenta of a single spin $\frac{1}{2}$ particle. We have

$$j_1 = l \ \text{(integer)}, \qquad m_1 = m_l,$$
$$j_2 = s = \tfrac{1}{2}, \qquad m_2 = m_s = \pm \tfrac{1}{2}. \qquad (3.7.52)$$

The allowed values of j are given by

$$j = l \pm \tfrac{1}{2}, \quad l > 0; \qquad j = \tfrac{1}{2}, \quad l = 0 \qquad (3.7.53)$$

So for each l there are two possible j-values; for example, for $l = 1$ (p state) we get, in spectroscopic notation, $p_{3/2}$ and $p_{1/2}$, where the subscript refers to j. The $m_1 m_2$-plane, or better the $m_l m_s$-plane, of this problem is particularly simple. The allowed sites form only two rows: the upper row for $m_s = \frac{1}{2}$ and the lower row for $m_s = -\frac{1}{2}$; see Figure 3.7. Specifically, we work out

(a)   (b)

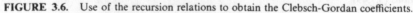

FIGURE 3.6. Use of the recursion relations to obtain the Clebsch-Gordan coefficients.

FIGURE 3.7. Recursion relations used to obtain the Clebsch-Gordan coefficients for $j_1 = l$ and $j_2 = s = \frac{1}{2}$.

the case $j = l + \frac{1}{2}$. Because m_s cannot exceed $\frac{1}{2}$, we can use the J_- recursion in such a way that we always stay in the upper row ($m_2 = m_s = \frac{1}{2}$), while the m_l-value changes by one unit each time we consider a new J_- triangle. Suppressing $j_1 = l$, $j_2 = \frac{1}{2}$ in writing the Clebsch-Gordan coefficients, we obtain from (3.7.49) (lower sign)

$$\sqrt{\left(l + \tfrac{1}{2} + m + 1\right)\left(l + \tfrac{1}{2} - m\right)}\, \left\langle m - \tfrac{1}{2}, \tfrac{1}{2} \middle| l + \tfrac{1}{2}, m \right\rangle$$
$$= \sqrt{\left(l + m + \tfrac{1}{2}\right)\left(l - m + \tfrac{1}{2}\right)}\, \left\langle m + \tfrac{1}{2}, \tfrac{1}{2} \middle| l + \tfrac{1}{2}, m + 1 \right\rangle, \quad (3.7.54)$$

where we have used

$$m_1 = m_l = m - \tfrac{1}{2}, \qquad m_2 = m_s = \tfrac{1}{2}. \quad (3.7.55)$$

In this way we can move horizontally by one unit:

$$\left\langle m - \tfrac{1}{2}, \tfrac{1}{2} \middle| l + \tfrac{1}{2}, m \right\rangle = \sqrt{\frac{l + m + \tfrac{1}{2}}{l + m + \tfrac{3}{2}}}\, \left\langle m + \tfrac{1}{2}, \tfrac{1}{2} \middle| l + \tfrac{1}{2}, m + 1 \right\rangle. \quad (3.7.56)$$

We can in turn express $\left\langle m + \tfrac{1}{2}, \tfrac{1}{2} \middle| l + \tfrac{1}{2}, m + 1 \right\rangle$ in terms of $\left\langle m + \tfrac{3}{2}, \tfrac{1}{2} \middle| l + \tfrac{1}{2}, m + 2 \right\rangle$, and so forth. Clearly, this procedure can be continued until m_l reaches l, the maximum possible value:

$$\left\langle m - \tfrac{1}{2}, \tfrac{1}{2} \middle| l + \tfrac{1}{2}, m \right\rangle = \sqrt{\frac{l + m + \tfrac{1}{2}}{l + m + \tfrac{3}{2}}} \sqrt{\frac{l + m + \tfrac{3}{2}}{l + m + \tfrac{5}{2}}} \left\langle m + \tfrac{3}{2}, \tfrac{1}{2} \middle| l + \tfrac{1}{2}, m + 2 \right\rangle$$

$$= \sqrt{\frac{l + m + \tfrac{1}{2}}{l + m + \tfrac{3}{2}}} \sqrt{\frac{l + m + \tfrac{3}{2}}{l + m + \tfrac{5}{2}}} \sqrt{\frac{l + m + \tfrac{5}{2}}{l + m + \tfrac{7}{2}}}$$

$$\times \left\langle m + \tfrac{5}{2}, \tfrac{1}{2} \middle| l + \tfrac{1}{2}, m + 3 \right\rangle$$

$$\vdots$$

$$= \sqrt{\frac{l + m + \tfrac{1}{2}}{2l + 1}}\, \left\langle l, \tfrac{1}{2} \middle| l + \tfrac{1}{2}, l + \tfrac{1}{2} \right\rangle. \quad (3.7.57)$$

Consider the angular-momentum configuration in which m_l and m_s are both maximal, that is, l and $\frac{1}{2}$, respectively. The total $m = m_l + m_s$ is $l + \frac{1}{2}$, which is possible only for $j = l + \frac{1}{2}$ and not for $j = l - \frac{1}{2}$. So $|m_l = l$, $m_s = \frac{1}{2}\rangle$ must be equal to $|j = l + \frac{1}{2}, \ m = l + \frac{1}{2}\rangle$ up to a phase factor. We take this phase factor to be real and positive by convention. With this choice we have

$$\langle l, \tfrac{1}{2} | l + \tfrac{1}{2}, l + \tfrac{1}{2}\rangle = 1. \tag{3.7.58}$$

Returning to (3.7.57), we finally obtain

$$\left\langle m - \frac{1}{2}, \frac{1}{2} \middle| l + \frac{1}{2}, m \right\rangle = \sqrt{\frac{l + m + \frac{1}{2}}{2l + 1}}. \tag{3.7.59}$$

But this is only about one-fourth of the story. We must still determine the value of the question marks that appear in the following:

$$\left| j = l + \frac{1}{2}, m \right\rangle = \sqrt{\frac{l + m + \frac{1}{2}}{2l + 1}} \left| m_l = m - \frac{1}{2}, m_s = \frac{1}{2} \right\rangle$$
$$+ ? \left| m_l = m + \frac{1}{2}, m_s = -\frac{1}{2} \right\rangle, \tag{3.7.60}$$

$$\left| j = l - \frac{1}{2}, m \right\rangle = ? \left| m_l = m - \frac{1}{2}, m_s = \frac{1}{2} \right\rangle + ? \left| m_l = m + \frac{1}{2}, m_s = -\frac{1}{2} \right\rangle.$$

We note that the transformation matrix with fixed m from the (m_l, m_s) basis to the (j, m) basis is, because of orthogonality, expected to have the form

$$\begin{pmatrix} \cos\alpha & \sin\alpha \\ -\sin\alpha & \cos\alpha \end{pmatrix}. \tag{3.7.61}$$

Comparison with (3.7.60) shows that $\cos\alpha$ is (3.7.59) itself; so we can readily determine $\sin\alpha$ up to a sign ambiguity:

$$\sin^2\alpha = 1 - \frac{(l + m + \frac{1}{2})}{(2l + 1)} = \frac{(l - m + \frac{1}{2})}{(2l + 1)}. \tag{3.7.62}$$

We claim that $\langle m_l = m + \frac{1}{2}, m_s = -\frac{1}{2} | j = l + \frac{1}{2}, m \rangle$ must be positive because all $j = l + \frac{1}{2}$ states are reachable by applying the J_- operator successively to $|j = l + \frac{1}{2}, m = l + \frac{1}{2}\rangle$, and the matrix elements of J_- are always positive by convention. So the 2×2 transformation matrix (3.7.61) can be only

$$\begin{pmatrix} \sqrt{\dfrac{l + m + \frac{1}{2}}{2l + 1}} & \sqrt{\dfrac{l - m + \frac{1}{2}}{2l + 1}} \\[3mm] -\sqrt{\dfrac{l - m + \frac{1}{2}}{2l + 1}} & \sqrt{\dfrac{l + m + \frac{1}{2}}{2l + 1}} \end{pmatrix}. \tag{3.7.63}$$

We define **spin-angular functions** in two-component form as follows:

$$\mathscr{Y}_l^{j=l\pm 1/2, m} = \pm \sqrt{\frac{l \pm m + \frac{1}{2}}{2l+1}} \, Y_l^{m-1/2}(\theta, \phi)\chi_+$$

$$+ \sqrt{\frac{l \mp m + \frac{1}{2}}{2l+1}} \, Y_l^{m+1/2}(\theta, \phi)\chi_-$$

$$= \frac{1}{\sqrt{2l+1}} \begin{pmatrix} \pm\sqrt{l \pm m + \frac{1}{2}} \, Y_l^{m-1/2}(\theta, \phi) \\ \sqrt{l \mp m + \frac{1}{2}} \, Y_l^{m+1/2}(\theta, \phi) \end{pmatrix}. \quad (3.7.64)$$

They are, by construction, simultaneous eigenfunctions of $\mathbf{L}^2$, $\mathbf{S}^2$, $\mathbf{J}^2$, and J_z. They are also eigenfunctions of $\mathbf{L}\cdot\mathbf{S}$ but $\mathbf{L}\cdot\mathbf{S}$, being just

$$\mathbf{L}\cdot\mathbf{S} = (\tfrac{1}{2})(\mathbf{J}^2 - \mathbf{L}^2 - \mathbf{S}^2), \quad (3.7.65)$$

is not independent. Indeed, its eigenvalue can easily be computed as follows:

$$\left(\frac{\hbar^2}{2}\right)\left[j(j+1) - l(l+1) - \frac{3}{4}\right] = \begin{cases} \dfrac{l\hbar^2}{2} & \text{for } j = l+\tfrac{1}{2}, \\[2mm] -\dfrac{(l+1)\hbar^2}{2} & \text{for } j = l-\tfrac{1}{2}. \end{cases}$$

$$(3.7.66)$$

Clebsch-Gordan Coefficients and Rotation Matrices

Angular-momentum addition may be discussed from the point of view of rotation matrices. Consider the rotation operator $\mathscr{D}^{(j_1)}(R)$ in the ket space spanned by the angular-momentum eigenkets with eigenvalue j_1. Likewise, consider $\mathscr{D}^{(j_2)}(R)$. The product $\mathscr{D}^{(j_1)} \otimes \mathscr{D}^{(j_2)}$ is reducible in the sense that after suitable choice of base kets, its matrix representation can take the following form:

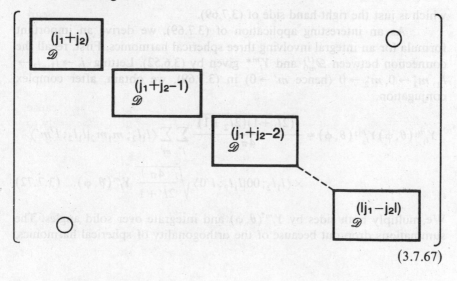

$$(3.7.67)$$

In the notation of group theory this is written as

$$\mathscr{D}^{(j_1)} \otimes \mathscr{D}^{(j_2)} = \mathscr{D}^{(j_1+j_2)} \oplus \mathscr{D}^{(j_1+j_2-1)} \oplus \cdots \oplus \mathscr{D}^{(|j_1-j_2|)}. \quad (3.7.68)$$

In terms of the elements of rotation matrices, we have an important expansion known as the **Clebsch-Gordan series**:

$$\mathscr{D}_{m_1m_1'}^{(j_1)}(R)\mathscr{D}_{m_2m_2'}^{(j_2)}(R) = \sum_j \sum_m \sum_{m'} \langle j_1j_2; m_1m_2|j_1j_2; jm\rangle$$

$$\times \langle j_1j_2; m_1'm_2'|j_1j_2; jm'\rangle \mathscr{D}_{mm'}^{(j)}(R), \quad (3.7.69)$$

where the j-sum runs from $|j_1 - j_2|$ to $j_1 + j_2$. The proof of this equation follows. First, note that the left-hand side of (3.7.69) is the same as

$$\langle j_1j_2; m_1m_2|\mathscr{D}(R)|j_1j_2; m_1'm_2'\rangle = \langle j_1m_1|\mathscr{D}(R)|j_1m_1'\rangle \langle j_2m_2|\mathscr{D}(R)|j_2m_2'\rangle$$

$$= \mathscr{D}_{m_1m_1'}^{(j_1)}(R)\mathscr{D}_{m_2m_2'}^{(j_2)}(R). \quad (3.7.70)$$

But the same matrix element is also computable by inserting a complete set of states in the (j, m) basis. Thus

$$\langle j_1j_2; m_1m_2|\mathscr{D}(R)|j_1j_2; m_1'm_2'\rangle$$

$$= \sum_j \sum_m \sum_{j'} \sum_{m'} \langle j_1j_2; m_1m_2|j_1j_2; jm\rangle\langle j_1j_2; jm|\mathscr{D}(R)|j_1j_2; j'm'\rangle$$

$$\times \langle j_1j_2; j'm'|j_1j_2; m_1'm_2'\rangle$$

$$= \sum_j \sum_m \sum_{j'} \sum_{m'} \langle j_1j_2; m_1m_2|j_1j_2; jm\rangle\mathscr{D}_{mm'}^{(j)}(R)\delta_{jj'}$$

$$\times \langle j_1j_2; m_1'm_2'|j_1j_2; j'm'\rangle, \quad (3.7.71)$$

which is just the right-hand side of (3.7.69).

As an interesting application of (3.7.69), we derive an important formula for an integral involving three spherical harmonics. First, recall the connection between $\mathscr{D}_{m0}^{(l)}$ and Y_l^{m*} given by (3.6.52). Letting $j_1 \to l_1$, $j_2 \to l_2$, $m_1' \to 0$, $m_2' \to 0$ (hence $m' \to 0$) in (3.7.69), we obtain, after complex conjugation,

$$Y_{l_1}^{m_1}(\theta,\phi)Y_{l_2}^{m_2}(\theta,\phi) = \frac{\sqrt{(2l_1+1)(2l_2+1)}}{4\pi} \sum_{l'} \sum_{m'} \langle l_1l_2; m_1m_2|l_1l_2; l'm'\rangle$$

$$\times \langle l_1l_2; 00|l_1l_2; l'0\rangle \sqrt{\frac{4\pi}{2l'+1}} \, Y_{l'}^{m'}(\theta,\phi). \quad (3.7.72)$$

We multiply both sides by $Y_l^{m*}(\theta,\phi)$ and integrate over solid angles. The summations drop out because of the orthogonality of spherical harmonics, and we are left with

$$\int d\Omega \, Y_l^{m*}(\theta,\phi) Y_{l_1}^{m_1}(\theta,\phi) Y_{l_2}^{m_2}(\theta,\phi)$$

$$= \sqrt{\frac{(2l_1+1)(2l_2+1)}{4\pi(2l+1)}} \, \langle l_1 l_2; 00 | l_1 l_2; l0 \rangle \langle l_1 l_2; m_1 m_2 | l_1 l_2; lm \rangle.$$

$$(3.7.73)$$

The square root factor times the first Clebsch-Gordan coefficient is independent of orientations; that is, of m_1 and m_2. The second Clebsch-Gordan coefficient is the one appropriate for adding l_1 and l_2 to obtain total l. Equation (3.7.73) turns out to be a special case of the Wigner-Eckart theorem to be derived in Section 3.10. This formula is extremely useful in evaluating multipole matrix elements in atomic and nuclear spectroscopy.

3.8. SCHWINGER'S OSCILLATOR MODEL OF ANGULAR MOMENTUM

Angular Momentum and Uncoupled Oscillators

There exists a very interesting connection between the algebra of angular momentum and the algebra of two independent (that is, uncoupled) oscillators, which was worked out in J. Schwinger's notes [see *Quantum Theory of Angular Momentum*, edited by L. C. Biedenharn and H. Van Dam, Academic Press (1965), p. 229]. Let us consider two simple harmonic oscillators, which we call the *plus type* and the *minus type*. We have the annihilation and creation operators, denoted by a_+ and $a_+^\dagger$ for the plus-type oscillator; likewise, we have a_- and $a_-^\dagger$ for the minus-type oscillators. We also define the number operators N_+ and N_- as follows:

$$N_+ \equiv a_+^\dagger a_+, \qquad N_- \equiv a_-^\dagger a_-. \qquad (3.8.1)$$

We assume that the usual commutation relations among a, $a^\dagger$, and N hold for oscillators of the same type (see Section 2.3).

$$[a_+, a_+^\dagger] = 1, \qquad [a_-, a_-^\dagger] = 1, \qquad (3.8.2a)$$

$$[N_+, a_+] = -a_+, \qquad [N_-, a_-] = -a_-, \qquad (3.8.2b)$$

$$[N_+, a_+^\dagger] = a_+^\dagger, \qquad [N_-, a_-^\dagger] = a_-^\dagger. \qquad (3.8.2c)$$

However, we assume that any pair of operators between different oscillators commute:

$$[a_+, a_-^\dagger] = [a_-, a_+^\dagger] = 0 \qquad (3.8.3)$$

and so forth. So it is in this sense that we say the two oscillators are uncoupled.

Because N_+ and N_- commute by virtue of (3.8.3), we can build up simultaneous eigenkets of N_+ and N_- with eigenvalues n_+ and n_-, respectively. So we have the following eigenvalue equations for $N_\pm$:

$$N_+|n_+,n_-\rangle = n_+|n_+,n_-\rangle, \qquad N_-|n_+,n_-\rangle = n_-|n_+,n_-\rangle. \quad (3.8.4)$$

In complete analogy with (2.3.16) and (2.3.17), the creation and annihilation operators, $a_\pm^\dagger$ and $a_\pm$, act on $|n_+,n_-\rangle$ as follows:

$$a_+^\dagger|n_+,n_-\rangle = \sqrt{n_++1}\,|n_++1,n_-\rangle, \qquad a_-^\dagger|n_+,n_-\rangle = \sqrt{n_-+1}\,|n_+,n_-+1\rangle,$$
$$(3.8.5a)$$

$$a_+|n_+,n_-\rangle = \sqrt{n_+}\,|n_+-1,n_-\rangle, \qquad a_-|n_+,n_-\rangle = \sqrt{n_-}\,|n_+,n_--1\rangle.$$
$$(3.8.5b)$$

We can obtain the most general eigenkets of N_+ and N_- by applying $a_+^\dagger$ and $a_-^\dagger$ successively to the **vacuum ket** defined by

$$a_+|0,0\rangle = 0, \qquad a_-|0,0\rangle = 0. \quad (3.8.6)$$

In this way we obtain

$$|n_+,n_-\rangle = \frac{\left(a_+^\dagger\right)^{n_+}\left(a_-^\dagger\right)^{n_-}}{\sqrt{n_+!}\,\sqrt{n_-!}}|0,0\rangle. \quad (3.8.7)$$

Next, we *define*

$$J_+ \equiv \hbar a_+^\dagger a_-, \qquad J_- \equiv \hbar a_-^\dagger a_+, \quad (3.8.8a)$$

and

$$J_z \equiv \left(\frac{\hbar}{2}\right)\left(a_+^\dagger a_+ - a_-^\dagger a_-\right) = \left(\frac{\hbar}{2}\right)\left(N_+ - N_-\right). \quad (3.8.8b)$$

We can readily prove that these operators satisfy the angular-momentum commutation relations of the usual form

$$[J_z, J_\pm] = \pm\hbar J_\pm, \quad (3.8.9a)$$
$$[J_+, J_-] = 2\hbar J_z. \quad (3.8.9b)$$

For example, we prove (3.8.9b) as follows:

$$\hbar^2[a_+^\dagger a_-, a_-^\dagger a_+] = \hbar^2 a_+^\dagger a_- a_-^\dagger a_+ - \hbar^2 a_-^\dagger a_+ a_+^\dagger a_-$$
$$= \hbar^2 a_+^\dagger\,(a_-^\dagger a_- + 1)a_+ - \hbar^2 a_-^\dagger\,(a_+^\dagger a_+ + 1)a_-$$
$$= \hbar^2(a_+^\dagger a_+ - a_-^\dagger a_-) = 2\hbar J_z. \quad (3.8.10)$$

Defining the *total N* to be

$$N \equiv N_+ + N_- = a_+^\dagger a_+ + a_-^\dagger a_-, \quad (3.8.11)$$

we can also prove

$$\mathbf{J}^2 \equiv J_z^2 + \left(\frac{1}{2}\right)(J_+ J_- + J_- J_+)$$

$$= \left(\frac{\hbar^2}{2}\right) N \left(\frac{N}{2} + 1\right), \qquad (3.8.12)$$

which is left as an exercise.

What are the physical interpretations of all this? We associate spin up ($m = \frac{1}{2}$) with one quantum unit of the plus-type oscillator and spin down ($m = -\frac{1}{2}$) with one quantum unit of the minus-type oscillator. If you like, you may imagine one spin $\frac{1}{2}$ "particle" with spin up (down) with each quantum unit of the plus- (minus-) type oscillator. The eigenvalues n_+ and n_- are just the number of spins up and spins down, respectively. The meaning of J_+ is that it destroys one unit of spin down with the z-component of spin-angular momentum $-\hbar/2$ and creates one unit of spin up with the z-component of spin-angular momentum $+\hbar/2$; the z-component of angular momentum is therefore increased by $\hbar$. Likewise J_- destroys one unit of spin up and creates one unit of spin down; the z-component of angular momentum is therefore decreased by $\hbar$. As for the J_z operator, it simply counts $\hbar/2$ times the difference of n_+ and n_-, just the z-component of the total angular momentum. With (3.8.5) at our disposal we can easily examine how $J_\pm$ and J_z act on $|n_+, n_-\rangle$ as follows:

$$J_+ |n_+, n_-\rangle = \hbar a_+^\dagger a_- |n_+, n_-\rangle = \sqrt{n_-(n_+ + 1)}\, \hbar |n_+ + 1, n_- - 1\rangle,$$

$$(3.8.13a)$$

$$J_- |n_+, n_-\rangle = \hbar a_-^\dagger a_+ |n_+, n_-\rangle = \sqrt{n_+(n_- + 1)}\, \hbar |n_+ - 1, n_- + 1\rangle,$$

$$(3.8.13b)$$

$$J_z |n_+, n_-\rangle = \left(\frac{\hbar}{2}\right)(N_+ - N_-)|n_+, n_-\rangle = \left(\frac{1}{2}\right)(n_+ - n_-)\hbar |n_+, n_-\rangle.$$

$$(3.8.13c)$$

Notice that in all these operations, the sum $n_+ + n_-$, which corresponds to the total number of spin $\frac{1}{2}$ particles remains unchanged.

Observe now that (3.8.13a), (3.8.13b), and (3.8.13c) reduce to the familiar expressions for the $J_\pm$ and J_z operators we derived in Section 3.5, provided we substitute

$$n_+ \to j + m, \qquad n_- \to j - m. \qquad (3.8.14)$$

The square root factors in (3.8.13a) and (3.8.13b) change to

$$\sqrt{n_-(n_+ + 1)} \to \sqrt{(j - m)(j + m + 1)},$$

$$\sqrt{n_+(n_- + 1)} \to \sqrt{(j + m)(j - m + 1)}, \qquad (3.8.15)$$

which are exactly the square root factors appearing in (3.5.39) and (3.5.41).

Notice also that the eigenvalue of the $\mathbf{J}^2$ operator defined by (3.8.12) changes as follows:

$$\left(\frac{\hbar^2}{2}\right)(n_+ + n_-)\left[\frac{(n_+ + n_-)}{2} + 1\right] \to \hbar^2 j(j+1). \qquad (3.8.16)$$

All this may not be too surprising because we have already proved that $J_\pm$ and $\mathbf{J}^2$ operators we constructed out of the oscillator operators satisfy the usual angular-momentum commutation relations. But it is instructive to see in an explicit manner the connection between the oscillator matrix elements and angular-momentum matrix elements. In any case, it is now natural to use

$$j \equiv \frac{(n_+ + n_-)}{2}, \qquad m \equiv \frac{(n_+ - n_-)}{2} \qquad (3.8.17)$$

in place of n_+ and n_- to characterize simultaneous eigenkets of $\mathbf{J}^2$ and J_z. According to (3.8.13a) the action of J_+ changes n_+ into $n_+ + 1$, n_- into $n_- - 1$, which means that j is unchanged and m goes into $m + 1$. Likewise, we see that the J_- operator that changes n_+ into $n_+ - 1$; n_- into $n_- + 1$ lowers m by one unit without changing j. We can now write as (3.8.7) for the most general N_+, N_- eigenket

$$|j, m\rangle = \frac{\left(a_+^\dagger\right)^{j+m}\left(a_-^\dagger\right)^{j-m}}{\sqrt{(j+m)!(j-m)!}}|0\rangle, \qquad (3.8.18)$$

where we have used $|0\rangle$ for the vacuum ket, earlier denoted by $|0,0\rangle$.

A special case of (3.8.18) is of interest. Let us set $m = j$, which physically means that the eigenvalue of J_z is as large as possible for a given j. We have

$$|j, j\rangle = \frac{\left(a_+^\dagger\right)^{2j}}{\sqrt{(2j)!}}|0\rangle. \qquad (3.8.19)$$

We can imagine this state to be built up of $2j$ spin $\frac{1}{2}$ particles with their spins all pointing in the positive z-direction.

In general, we note that a complicated object of high j can be visualized as being made up of primitive spin $\frac{1}{2}$ particles, $j + m$ of them with spin up and the remaining $j - m$ of them with spin down. This picture is extremely convenient even though we obviously cannot always regard an object of angular momentum j literally as a composite system of spin $\frac{1}{2}$ particles. All we are saying is that, *as far as the transformation properties under rotations are concerned*, we can visualize any object of angular momentum j as a composite system of $2j$ spin $\frac{1}{2}$ particles formed in the manner indicated by (3.8.18).

From the point of view of angular-momentum addition developed in the previous section, we can add the spins of $2j$ spin $\frac{1}{2}$ particles to obtain states with angular momentum $j, j-1, j-2, \ldots$. As a simple example, we can add the spin-angular momenta of two spin $\frac{1}{2}$ particles to obtain a total angular momentum of zero as well as one. In Schwinger's oscillator scheme, however, we obtain only states with angular momentum j when we start with $2j$ spin $\frac{1}{2}$ particles. In the language of permutation symmetry to be developed in Chapter 6, only totally symmetrical states are constructed by this method. The primitive spin $\frac{1}{2}$ particles appearing here are actually *bosons*! This method is quite adequate if our purpose is to examine the properties under rotations of states characterized by j and m without asking how such states are built up initially.

The reader who is familiar with isospin in nuclear and particle physics may note that what we are doing here provides a new insight into the isospin (or isotopic spin) formalism. The operator J_+ that destroys one unit of the minus type and creates one unit of the plus type is completely analogous to the isospin ladder operator T_+ (sometimes denoted by I_+) that annihilates a neutron (isospin down) and creates a proton (isospin up), thus raising the z-component of isospin by one unit. In contrast, J_z is analogous to T_z, which simply counts the difference between the number of protons and neutrons in nuclei.

Explicit Formula for Rotation Matrices

Schwinger's scheme can be used to derive, in a very simple way, a closed formula for rotation matrices, first obtained by E. P. Wigner using a similar (but not identical) method. We apply the rotation operator $\mathscr{D}(R)$ to $|j, m\rangle$, written as (3.8.18). In the Euler angle notation the only nontrivial rotation is the second one about the y-axis, so we direct our attention to

$$\mathscr{D}(R) = \mathscr{D}(\alpha, \beta, \gamma)|_{\alpha=\gamma=0} = \exp\left(\frac{-iJ_y\beta}{\hbar}\right). \tag{3.8.20}$$

We have

$$\mathscr{D}(R)|j, m\rangle = \frac{\left[\mathscr{D}(R)a_+^\dagger \mathscr{D}^{-1}(R)\right]^{j+m}\left[\mathscr{D}(R)a_-^\dagger \mathscr{D}^{-1}(R)\right]^{j-m}}{\sqrt{(j+m)!(j-m)!}}\mathscr{D}(R)|0\rangle. \tag{3.8.21}$$

Now, $\mathscr{D}(R)$ acting on $|0\rangle$ just reproduces $|0\rangle$ because, by virtue of (3.8.6), only the leading term, 1, in the expansion of exponential (3.8.20) contributes. So

$$\mathscr{D}(R)a_\pm^\dagger \mathscr{D}^{-1}(R) = \exp\left(\frac{-iJ_y\beta}{\hbar}\right)a_\pm^\dagger \exp\left(\frac{iJ_y\beta}{\hbar}\right). \tag{3.8.22}$$

Thus we may use formula (2.3.47). Letting

$$G \rightarrow \frac{-J_y}{\hbar}, \qquad \lambda \rightarrow \beta \tag{3.8.23}$$

in (2.3.47), we realize that we must look at various commutators, namely,

$$\left[\frac{-J_y}{\hbar}, a_+^\dagger\right] = \left(\frac{1}{2i}\right)[a_-^\dagger a_+, a_+^\dagger] = \left(\frac{1}{2i}\right)a_-^\dagger,$$

$$\left[\frac{-J_y}{\hbar}, \left[\frac{-J_y}{\hbar}, a_+^\dagger\right]\right] = \left[\frac{-J_y}{\hbar}, \frac{a_-^\dagger}{2i}\right] = \left(\frac{1}{4}\right)a_+^\dagger \tag{3.8.24}$$

and so forth. Clearly, we always obtain either $a_+^\dagger$ or $a_-^\dagger$. Collecting terms, we get

$$\mathcal{D}(R)a_+^\dagger \mathcal{D}^{-1}(R) = a_+^\dagger \cos\left(\frac{\beta}{2}\right) + a_-^\dagger \sin\left(\frac{\beta}{2}\right). \tag{3.8.25}$$

Likewise,

$$\mathcal{D}(R)a_-^\dagger \mathcal{D}^{-1}(R) = a_-^\dagger \cos\left(\frac{\beta}{2}\right) - a_+^\dagger \sin\left(\frac{\beta}{2}\right). \tag{3.8.26}$$

Actually this result is not surprising. After all, the basic spin-up state is supposed to transform as

$$a_+^\dagger |0\rangle \rightarrow \cos\left(\frac{\beta}{2}\right)a_+^\dagger |0\rangle + \sin\left(\frac{\beta}{2}\right)a_-^\dagger |0\rangle \tag{3.8.27}$$

under a rotation about the y-axis. Substituting (3.8.25) and (3.8.26) into (3.8.21) and recalling the binomial theorem

$$(x+y)^N = \sum_k \frac{N! x^{N-k} y^k}{(N-k)! k!}, \tag{3.8.28}$$

we obtain

$$\mathcal{D}(\alpha=0, \beta, \gamma=0|j,m\rangle = \sum_k \sum_l \frac{(j+m)!(j-m)!}{(j+m-k)! k!(j-m-l)! l!}$$

$$\times \frac{\left[a_+^\dagger \cos(\beta/2)\right]^{j+m-k}\left[a_-^\dagger \sin(\beta/2)\right]^k}{\sqrt{(j+m)!(j-m)!}}$$

$$\times [-a_+^\dagger \sin(\beta/2)]^{j-m-l}[a_-^\dagger \cos(\beta/2)]^l |0\rangle. \tag{3.8.29}$$

We may compare (3.8.29) with

$$\mathcal{D}(\alpha=0, \beta, \gamma=0)|j,m\rangle = \sum_{m'} |j,m'\rangle d_{m'm}^{(j)}(\beta)$$

$$= \sum_{m'} d_{m'm}^{(j)}(\beta) \frac{\left(a_+^\dagger\right)^{j+m'}\left(a_-^\dagger\right)^{j-m'}}{\sqrt{(j+m')!(j-m')!}} |0\rangle. \tag{3.8.30}$$

We can obtain an explicit form for $d_{m'm}^{(j)}(\beta)$ by equating the coefficients of powers of $a_+^\dagger$ in (3.8.29) and (3.8.30). Specifically, we want to compare $a_+^\dagger$ raised to $j + m'$ in (3.8.30) with $a_+^\dagger$ raised to $2j - k - l$, so we identify

$$l = j - k - m'. \tag{3.8.31}$$

We are seeking $d_{m'm}(\beta)$ with m' fixed. The k-sum and the l-sum in (3.8.29) are not independent of each other; we eliminate l in favor of k by taking advantage of (3.8.31). As for the powers of $a_-^\dagger$, we note that $a_-^\dagger$ raised to $j - m'$ in (3.8.30) automatically matches with $a_-^\dagger$ raised to $k + l$ in (3.8.29) when (3.8.31) is imposed. The last step is to identify the exponents of $\cos(\beta/2)$, $\sin(\beta/2)$, and (-1), which are, respectively,

$$j + m - k + l = 2j - 2k + m - m', \tag{3.8.32a}$$

$$k + j - m - l = 2k - m + m', \tag{3.8.32b}$$

$$j - m - l = k - m + m', \tag{3.8.32c}$$

where we have used (3.8.31) to eliminate l. In this way we obtain **Wigner's formula** for $d_{m'm}^{(j)}(\beta)$:

$$d_{m'm}^{(j)}(\beta) = \sum_k (-1)^{k-m+m'} \frac{\sqrt{(j+m)!(j-m)!(j+m')!(j-m')!}}{(j+m-k)!k!(j-k-m')!(k-m+m')!}$$

$$\times \left(\cos\frac{\beta}{2}\right)^{2j-2k+m-m'} \left(\sin\frac{\beta}{2}\right)^{2k-m+m'}, \tag{3.8.33}$$

where we take the sum over k whenever none of the arguments of factorials in the denominator are negative.

3.9. SPIN CORRELATION MEASUREMENTS AND BELL'S INEQUALITY

Correlations in Spin-Singlet States

The simplest example of angular-momentum addition we encountered in Section 3.7 was concerned with a composite system made up of spin $\frac{1}{2}$ particles. In this section we use such a system to illustrate one of the most astonishing consequences of quantum mechanics.

Consider a two-electron system in a spin-singlet state, that is, with a total spin of zero. We have already seen that the state ket can be written as [see (3.7.15d)]

$$|\text{spin singlet}\rangle = \left(\frac{1}{\sqrt{2}}\right)(|\hat{z}+;\hat{z}-\rangle - |\hat{z}-;\hat{z}+\rangle), \tag{3.9.1}$$

where we have explicitly indicated the quantization direction. Recall that

$|\hat{z}+;\hat{z}-\rangle$ means that electron 1 is in the spin-up state and electron 2 is in the spin-down state. The same is true for $|\hat{z}-;\hat{z}+\rangle$.

Suppose we make a measurement on the spin component of one of the electrons. Clearly, there is a 50-50 chance of getting either up or down because the composite system may be in $|\hat{z}+;\hat{z}-\rangle$ or $|\hat{z}-;\hat{z}+\rangle$ with equal probabilities. But if one of the components is shown to be in the spin-up state, the other is necessarily in the spin-down state, and vice versa. When the spin component of electron 1 is shown to be up, the measurement apparatus has selected the first term, $|\hat{z}+;\hat{z}-\rangle$ of (3.9.1); a subsequent measurement of the spin component of electron 2 must ascertain that the state ket of the composite system is given by $|\hat{z}+;\hat{z}-\rangle$.

It is remarkable that this kind of correlation can persist even if the two particles are well separated and have ceased to interact provided that as they fly apart, there is no change in their spin states. This is certainly the case for a $J=0$ system disintegrating spontaneously into two spin $\frac{1}{2}$ particles with no relative orbital angular momentum, because angular-momentum conservation must hold in the disintegration process. An example of this would be a rare decay of the η meson (mass 549 MeV$/c^2$) into a muon pair

$$\eta \to \mu^+ + \mu^- \tag{3.9.2}$$

which, unfortunately, has a branching ratio of only approximately 6×10^{-6}. More realistically, in proton-proton scattering at low kinetic energies, the Pauli principle to be discussed in Chapter 6 forces the interacting protons to be in $^1S_0$ (orbital angular momentum 0, spin-singlet state), and the spin states of the scattered protons must be correlated in the manner indicated by (3.9.1) even after they get separated by a *macroscopic distance*.

To be more pictorial we consider a system of two spin $\frac{1}{2}$ particles moving in opposite directions, as in Figure 3.8. Observer A specializes in measuring S_z of particle 1 (flying to the right), while observer B specializes in measuring S_z of particle 2 (flying to the left). To be specific, let us assume that observer A finds S_z to be positive for particle 1. Then he or she can predict, even before B performs any measurement, the outcome of B's measurement with certainty: B must find S_z to be negative for particle 2. On the other hand, if A makes no measurement, B has a 50-50 chance of getting S_z+ or S_z-.

This by itself might not be so peculiar. One may say, "It is just like an urn known to contain one black ball and one white ball. When we blindly pick one of them, there is a 50-50 chance of getting black or white. But if the first ball we pick is black, then we can predict with certainty that the second ball will be white."

It turns out that this analogy is too simple. The actual quantum-mechanical situation is far more sophisticated than that! This is because observers may choose to measure S_x in place of S_z. The *same* pair of

FIGURE 3.8.   Spin correlation in a spin-singlet state.

"quantum-mechanical balls" can be analyzed either in terms of black and white *or* in terms of blue and red!

Recall now that for a single spin $\frac{1}{2}$ system the S_x eigenkets and S_z eigenkets are related as follows:

$$|\hat{x}\pm\rangle = \left(\frac{1}{\sqrt{2}}\right)(|\hat{z}+\rangle \pm |\hat{z}-\rangle), \qquad |\hat{z}\pm\rangle = \left(\frac{1}{\sqrt{2}}\right)(|\hat{x}+\rangle \pm |\hat{x}-\rangle).$$

$$(3.9.3)$$

Returning now to our composite system, we can rewrite spin-singlet ket (3.9.1) by choosing the x-direction as the axis of quantization:

$$|\text{spin singlet}\rangle = \left(\frac{1}{\sqrt{2}}\right)(|\hat{x}-;\hat{x}+\rangle - |\hat{x}+;\hat{x}-\rangle). \qquad (3.9.4)$$

Apart from the overall sign, which in any case is a matter of convention, we could have guessed this form directly from (3.9.1) because spin-singlet states have no preferred direction in space. Let us now suppose that observer A can choose to measure S_z or S_x of particle 1 by changing the orientation of his or her spin analyzer, while observer B always specializes in measuring S_x of particle 2. If A determines S_z of particle 1 to be positive, B clearly has a 50-50 chance for getting S_x+ or S_x-; even though S_z of particle 2 is known to be negative with certainty, its S_x is completely undetermined. On the other hand, let us suppose that A also chooses to measure S_x; if observer A determines S_x of particle 1 to be positive, then without fail, observer B will measure S_x of particle 2 to be negative. Finally, if A chooses to make no measurement, B, of course, will have a 50-50 chance of getting S_x+ or S_x-. To sum up:

1. If A measures S_z and B measures S_x, there is a completely random correlation between the two measurements.
2. If A measures S_x and B measures S_x, there is a 100% (opposite sign) correlation between the two measurements.
3. If A makes no measurement, B's measurements show random results.

Table 3.1 shows all possible results of such measurements when B and A are allowed to choose to measure S_x or S_z.

TABLE 3.1. Spin-correlation Measurements

Spin component measured by A	A's result	Spin component measured by B	B's result
z	+	z	−
z	−	x	+
x	−	z	−
x	−	z	+
z	+	x	−
x	+	x	−
z	+	x	+
x	−	x	+
z	−	z	+
z	−	x	−
x	+	z	+
x	+	z	−

These considerations show that the outcome of B's measurement appears to depend on what kind of measurement A decides to perform: an S_x measurement, an S_z measurement, or no measurement. Notice again that A and B can be miles apart with no possibility of communications or mutual interactions. Observer A can decide how to orient his or her spin-analyzer apparatus long after the two particles have separated. It is as though particle 2 "knows" which spin component of particle 1 is being measured.

The orthodox quantum-mechanical interpretation of this situation is as follows. A measurement is a selection (or filtration) process. When S_z of particle 1 is measured to be positive, then component $|\hat{z}+;\hat{z}-\rangle$ is selected. A subsequent measurement of the other particle's S_z merely ascertains that the system is still in $|\hat{z}+;\hat{z}-\rangle$. We must accept that a measurement on what appears to be a part of the system is to be regarded as a measurement on the whole system.

Einstein's Locality Principle and Bell's Inequality

Many physicists have felt uncomfortable with the preceding orthodox interpretation of spin-correlation measurements. Their feelings are typified in the following frequently quoted remarks by A. Einstein, which we call **Einstein's locality principle**: "But on one supposition we should, in my opinion, absolutely hold fast: The real factual situation of the system S_2 is independent of what is done with the system S_1, which is spatially separated from the former." Because this problem was first discussed in a

1935 paper of A. Einstein, B. Podolsky, and N. Rosen, it is sometimes known as the Einstein-Podolsky-Rosen paradox.*

Some have argued that the difficulties encountered here are inherent in the probabilistic interpretations of quantum mechanics and that the dynamic behavior at the microscopic level appears probabilistic only because some yet unknown parameters—so-called hidden variables—have not been specified. It is not our purpose here to discuss various alternatives to quantum mechanics based on hidden-variable or other considerations. Rather, let us ask, Do such theories make predictions different from those of quantum mechanics? Until 1964, it could be thought that the alternative theories could be concocted in such a way that they would give no predictions, other than the usual quantum-mechanical predictions, that could be verified experimentally. The whole debate would have belonged to the realm of metaphysics rather than physics. It was then pointed out by J. S. Bell that the alternative theories based on Einstein's locality principle actually predict a *testable inequality relation* among the observables of spin-correlation experiments that *disagrees* with the predictions of quantum mechanics.

We derive Bell's inequality within the framework of a simple model, conceived by E. P. Wigner, that incorporates the essential features of the various alternative theories. Proponents of this model agree that it is impossible to determine S_x and S_z simultaneously. However, when we have a large number of spin $\frac{1}{2}$ particles, we assign a certain fraction of them to have the following property:

If S_z is measured, we obtain a plus sign with certainty.

If S_x is measured, we obtain a minus sign with certainty.

A particle satisfying this property is said to belong to type $(\hat{z}+, \hat{x}-)$. Notice that we are not asserting that we can simultaneously measure S_z and S_x to be $+$ and $-$, respectively. When we measure S_z, we do not measure S_x, and vice versa. We are assigning definite values of spin components *in more than one direction* with the understanding that only one or the other of the components can actually be measured. Even though this approach is fundamentally different from that of quantum mechanics, the quantum-mechanical predictions for S_z and S_x measurements performed on the spin-up $(S_z +)$ state are reproduced provided there are as many particles belonging to type $(\hat{z}+, \hat{x}+)$ as to type $(\hat{z}+, \hat{x}-)$.

Let us now examine how this model can account for the results of spin-correlation measurements made on composite spin-singlet systems.

---

*To be historically accurate, the original Einstein-Podolsky-Rosen paper dealt with measurements of x and p. The use of composite spin $\frac{1}{2}$ systems to illustrate the Einstein-Podolsky-Rosen paradox started with D. Bohm.

Clearly, for a particular pair, there must be a perfect matching between particle 1 and particle 2 to ensure zero total angular momentum: If particle 1 is of type $(\hat{z}+,\hat{x}-)$, then particle 2 must belong to type $(\hat{z}-,\hat{x}+)$, and so forth. The results of correlation measurements, such as in Table 3.1, can be reproduced if particle 1 and particle 2 are matched as follows:

particle 1   particle 2

$$(\hat{z}+,\hat{x}-) \leftrightarrow (\hat{z}-,\hat{x}+), \tag{3.9.5a}$$

$$(\hat{z}+,\hat{x}+) \leftrightarrow (\hat{z}-,\hat{x}-), \tag{3.9.5b}$$

$$(\hat{z}-,\hat{x}+) \leftrightarrow (\hat{z}+,\hat{x}-), \tag{3.9.5c}$$

$$(\hat{z}-,\hat{x}-) \leftrightarrow (\hat{z}+,\hat{x}+) \tag{3.9.5d}$$

with equal populations, that is, 25% each. A very important assumption is implied here. Suppose a particular pair belongs to type (3.9.5a) and observer A decides to measure S_z of particle 1; then he or she necessarily obtains a plus sign regardless of whether B decides to measure S_z or S_x. It is in this sense that Einstein's locality principle is incorporated in this model: A's result is predetermined independently of B's choice as to what to measure.

In the examples considered so far, this model has been successful in reproducing the predictions of quantum mechanics. We now consider more-complicated situations where the model leads to predictions different from the usual quantum-mechanical predictions. This time we start with three unit vectors $\hat{a}$, $\hat{b}$, and $\hat{c}$, which are, in general, not mutually orthogonal. We imagine that one of the particles belongs to some definite type, say $(\hat{a}-,\hat{b}+,\hat{c}+)$, which means that if $\mathbf{S}\cdot\hat{a}$ is measured, we obtain a minus sign with certainty; if $\mathbf{S}\cdot\hat{b}$ is measured, we obtain a plus sign with certainty; if $\mathbf{S}\cdot\hat{c}$ is measured, we obtain a plus with certainty. Again there must be a perfect matching in the sense that the other particle necessarily belongs to type $(\hat{a}+,\hat{b}-,\hat{c}-)$ to ensure zero total angular momentum. In any given event, the particle pair in question must be a member of one of the eight types shown in Table 3.2. These eight possibilities are mutually exclusive and disjoint. The population of each type is indicated in the first column.

Let us suppose that observer A finds $\mathbf{S}_1\cdot\hat{a}$ to be plus and observer B finds $\mathbf{S}_2\cdot\hat{b}$ to be plus also. It is clear from Table 3.2 that the pair belong to either type 3 or type 4, so the number of particle pairs for which this situation is realized is $N_3 + N_4$. Because N_i is positive semidefinite, we must have inequality relations like

$$N_3 + N_4 \le (N_2 + N_4) + (N_3 + N_7). \tag{3.9.6}$$

Let $P(\hat{a}+;\hat{b}+)$ be the probability that, in a random selection, observer A measures $\mathbf{S}_1\cdot\hat{a}$ to be $+$ and observer B measures $\mathbf{S}_2\cdot\hat{b}$ to be $+$, and so on.

TABLE 3.2. Spin-component Matching in the Alternative Theories

Population	Particle 1	Particle 2
N_1	$(\hat{\mathbf{a}}+,\hat{\mathbf{b}}+,\hat{\mathbf{c}}+)$	$(\hat{\mathbf{a}}-,\hat{\mathbf{b}}-,\hat{\mathbf{c}}-)$
N_2	$(\hat{\mathbf{a}}+,\hat{\mathbf{b}}+,\hat{\mathbf{c}}-)$	$(\hat{\mathbf{a}}-,\hat{\mathbf{b}}-,\hat{\mathbf{c}}+)$
N_3	$(\hat{\mathbf{a}}+,\hat{\mathbf{b}}-,\hat{\mathbf{c}}+)$	$(\hat{\mathbf{a}}-,\hat{\mathbf{b}}+,\hat{\mathbf{c}}-)$
N_4	$(\hat{\mathbf{a}}+,\hat{\mathbf{b}}-,\hat{\mathbf{c}}-)$	$(\hat{\mathbf{a}}-,\hat{\mathbf{b}}+,\hat{\mathbf{c}}+)$
N_5	$(\hat{\mathbf{a}}-,\hat{\mathbf{b}}+,\hat{\mathbf{c}}+)$	$(\hat{\mathbf{a}}+,\hat{\mathbf{b}}-,\hat{\mathbf{c}}-)$
N_6	$(\hat{\mathbf{a}}-,\hat{\mathbf{b}}+,\hat{\mathbf{c}}-)$	$(\hat{\mathbf{a}}+,\hat{\mathbf{b}}-,\hat{\mathbf{c}}+)$
N_7	$(\hat{\mathbf{a}}-,\hat{\mathbf{b}}-,\hat{\mathbf{c}}+)$	$(\hat{\mathbf{a}}+,\hat{\mathbf{b}}+,\hat{\mathbf{c}}-)$
N_8	$(\hat{\mathbf{a}}-,\hat{\mathbf{b}}-,\hat{\mathbf{c}}-)$	$(\hat{\mathbf{a}}+,\hat{\mathbf{b}}+,\hat{\mathbf{c}}+)$

Clearly, we have

$$P(\hat{\mathbf{a}}+ ;\hat{\mathbf{b}}+) = \frac{(N_3 + N_4)}{\Sigma_i^8 N_i}. \qquad (3.9.7)$$

In a similar manner, we obtain

$$P(\hat{\mathbf{a}}+ ;\hat{\mathbf{c}}+) = \frac{(N_2 + N_4)}{\Sigma_i^8 N_i} \quad \text{and} \quad P(\hat{\mathbf{c}}+ ;\hat{\mathbf{b}}+) = \frac{(N_3 + N_7)}{\Sigma_i^8 N_i}. \qquad (3.9.8)$$

The positivity condition (3.9.6) now becomes

$$P(\hat{\mathbf{a}}+ ;\hat{\mathbf{b}}+) \le P(\hat{\mathbf{a}}+ ;\hat{\mathbf{c}}+) + P(\hat{\mathbf{c}}+ ;\hat{\mathbf{b}}+). \qquad (3.9.9)$$

This is **Bell's inequality**, which follows from Einstein's locality principle.

Quantum Mechanics and Bell's Inequality

We now return to the world of quantum mechanics. In quantum mechanics we do not talk about a certain fraction of particle pairs, say $N_3/\Sigma_i^8 N_i$, belonging to type 3. Instead, we characterize all spin-singlet systems by the same ket (3.9.1); in the language of Section 3.4 we are concerned here with a pure ensemble. Using this ket and the rules of quantum mechanics we have developed, we can unambiguously calculate each of the three terms in inequality (3.9.9).

We first evaluate $P(\hat{\mathbf{a}}+ ;\hat{\mathbf{b}}+)$. Suppose observer A finds $\mathbf{S}_1\cdot\hat{\mathbf{a}}$ to be positive; because of the 100% (opposite sign) correlation we discussed earlier, B's measurement of $\mathbf{S}_2\cdot\hat{\mathbf{a}}$ will yield a minus sign with certainty. But to calculate $P(\hat{\mathbf{a}}+ ;\hat{\mathbf{b}}+)$ we must consider a new quantization axis $\hat{\mathbf{b}}$ that makes an angle θ_{ab} with $\hat{\mathbf{a}}$; see Figure 3.9. According to the formalism of Section 3.2, the probability that the $\mathbf{S}_2\cdot\hat{\mathbf{b}}$ measurement yields $+$ when particle 2 is known to be in an eigenket of $\mathbf{S}_2\cdot\hat{\mathbf{a}}$ with negative eigenvalue is

FIGURE 3.9. Evaluation of $P(\hat{\mathbf{a}}+;\hat{\mathbf{b}}+)$.

given by

$$\cos^2\left[\frac{(\pi - \theta_{ab})}{2}\right] = \sin^2\left(\frac{\theta_{ab}}{2}\right). \tag{3.9.10}$$

As a result, we obtain

$$P(\hat{\mathbf{a}}+;\hat{\mathbf{b}}+) = \left(\frac{1}{2}\right)\sin^2\left(\frac{\theta_{ab}}{2}\right), \tag{3.9.11}$$

where the factor $\frac{1}{2}$ arises from the probability of initially obtaining $\mathbf{S}_1 \cdot \hat{\mathbf{a}}$ with $+$. Using (3.9.11) and its generalization to the other two terms of (3.9.9), we can write Bell's inequality as

$$\sin^2\left(\frac{\theta_{ab}}{2}\right) \leq \sin^2\left(\frac{\theta_{ac}}{2}\right) + \sin^2\left(\frac{\theta_{cb}}{2}\right). \tag{3.9.12}$$

We now show that inequality (3.9.12) is not always possible from a geometric point of view. For simplicity let us choose $\hat{\mathbf{a}}$, $\hat{\mathbf{b}}$, and $\hat{\mathbf{c}}$ to lie in a plane, and let $\hat{\mathbf{c}}$ bisect the two directions defined by $\hat{\mathbf{a}}$ and $\hat{\mathbf{b}}$:

$$\theta_{ab} = 2\theta, \qquad \theta_{ac} = \theta_{cb} = \theta. \tag{3.9.13}$$

Inequality (3.9.12) is then violated for

$$0 < \theta < \frac{\pi}{2}. \tag{3.9.14}$$

For example, take $\theta = \pi/4$; we then obtain

$$0.500 \leq 0.292 \quad ?? \tag{3.9.15}$$

So the quantum-mechanical predictions are not compatible with Bell's inequality. There is a real observable—in the sense of being experimentally verifiable—difference between quantum mechanics and the alternative theories satisfying Einstein's locality principle.

Several experiments have been performed to test Bell's inequality. In one of the experiments spin correlations between the final protons in low-energy proton-proton scattering were measured. In all other experiments photon-polarization correlations between a pair of photons in a cascade transition of an excited atom $(Ca, Hg, \ldots)$,

$$(J = 0) \xrightarrow{\gamma} (J = 1) \xrightarrow{\gamma} (J = 0), \qquad (3.9.16)$$

or in the decay of a positronium (an $e^+ e^-$ bound state in $^1S_0$) were measured; studying photon-polarization correlations should be just as good in view of the analogy developed in Section 1.1: *

$$
\begin{aligned}
S_z + & \rightarrow \hat{\varepsilon} \quad \text{in } x\text{-direction,} \\
S_z - & \rightarrow \hat{\varepsilon} \quad \text{in } y\text{-direction,} \\
S_x + & \rightarrow \hat{\varepsilon} \quad \text{in } 45^\circ \text{ diagonal direction,} \\
S_x - & \rightarrow \hat{\varepsilon} \quad \text{in } 135^\circ \text{ diagonal direction.}
\end{aligned}
\qquad (3.9.17)
$$

The results of all recent precision experiments have conclusively established that Bell's inequality was violated, in one case by more than nine standard deviations. Furthermore, in all these experiments the inequality relation was violated in such a way that the quantum-mechanical predictions were fulfilled within error limits. In this controversy, quantum mechanics has triumphed with flying colors.

The fact that the quantum-mechanical predictions have been verified does not mean that the whole subject is now a triviality. Despite the experimental verdict we may still feel psychologically uncomfortable about many aspects of measurements of this kind. Consider in particular the following point: Right after observer A performs a measurement on particle 1, how does particle 2—which may, in principle, be many light years away from particle 1—get to "know" how to orient its spin so that the remarkable correlations apparent in Table 3.1 are realized? In one of the experiments to test Bell's inequality (performed by A. Aspect and collaborators) the analyzer settings were changed so rapidly that A's decision as to what to measure could not be made until it was too late for any kind of influence, traveling slower than light, to reach B.

We conclude this section by showing that despite these peculiarities we cannot use spin-correlation measurements to transmit any useful information between two macroscopically separated points. In particular, superluminal (faster than light) communications are impossible.

Suppose A and B both agree in advance to measure S_z; then, without asking A, B knows precisely what A is getting. But this does not mean that

*It should be kept in mind here that by working with photons we are going outside the realm of nonrelativistic quantum mechanics, which is the subject of this book.

A and B are communicating; B just observes a random sequence of positive and negative signs. There is obviously no useful information contained in it. B verifies the remarkable correlations predicted by quantum mechanics only after he or she gets together with A and compares the notes (or computer sheets).

It might be thought that A and B can communicate if one of them suddenly changes the orientation of his or her analyzing apparatus. Let us suppose that A agrees initially to measure S_z, and B, S_x. The results of A's measurements are completely uncorrelated with the results of B's measurements, so there is no information transferred. But then, suppose A suddenly breaks his or her promise and without telling B starts measuring S_x. There are now complete correlations between A's results and B's results. However, B has no way of inferring that A has changed the orientation of his or her analyzer. B continues to see just a random sequence of $+$'s and $-$'s by looking at his or her own notebook *only*. So again there is no information transferred.

3.10. TENSOR OPERATORS

Vector Operator

We have been using notations such as **x**, **p**, **S**, and **L**, but as yet we have not systematically discussed their rotational properties. They are vector operators, but what are their properties under rotations? In this section we give a precise quantum-mechanical definition of vector operators based on their commutation relations with the angular-momentum operator. We then generalize to tensor operators with more-complicated transformation properties and derive an important theorem on the matrix elements of vector and tensor operators.

We all know that a **vector** in classical physics is a quantity with three components that transforms by definition like $V_i \rightarrow \Sigma_j R_{ij} V_j$ under a rotation. It is reasonable to demand that the expectation value of a vector operator V in quantum mechanics be transformed like a classical vector under rotation. Specifically, as the state ket is changed under rotation according to

$$|\alpha\rangle \rightarrow \mathscr{D}(R)|\alpha\rangle, \qquad (3.10.1)$$

the expectation value of **V** is assumed to change as follows:

$$\langle\alpha|V_i|\alpha\rangle \rightarrow \langle\alpha|\mathscr{D}^\dagger(R)V_i\mathscr{D}(R)|\alpha\rangle = \sum_j R_{ij}\langle\alpha|V_j|\alpha\rangle. \qquad (3.10.2)$$

This must be true for an arbitrary ket $|\alpha\rangle$. Therefore,

$$\mathscr{D}^\dagger(R)V_i\mathscr{D}(R) = \sum_j R_{ij}V_j \qquad (3.10.3)$$

must hold as an **operator equation**, where R_{ij} is the 3×3 matrix that corresponds to rotation R.

Let us now consider a specific case, an infinitesimal rotation. When the rotation is infinitesimal, we have

$$\mathcal{D}(R) = 1 - \frac{i\varepsilon \mathbf{J} \cdot \hat{\mathbf{n}}}{\hbar}. \tag{3.10.4}$$

We can now write (3.10.3) as

$$V_i + \frac{\varepsilon}{i\hbar}[V_i, \mathbf{J} \cdot \hat{\mathbf{n}}] = \sum_j R_{ij}(\hat{\mathbf{n}}; \varepsilon) V_j. \tag{3.10.5}$$

In particular, for $\hat{\mathbf{n}}$ along the z-axis, we have

$$R(\hat{\mathbf{z}}; \varepsilon) = \begin{pmatrix} 1 & -\varepsilon & 0 \\ \varepsilon & 1 & 0 \\ 0 & 0 & 1 \end{pmatrix}, \tag{3.10.6}$$

so

$$i = 1: \quad V_x + \frac{\varepsilon}{i\hbar}[V_x, J_z] = V_x - \varepsilon V_y \tag{3.10.7a}$$

$$i = 2: \quad V_y + \frac{\varepsilon}{i\hbar}[V_y, J_z] = \varepsilon V_x + V_y \tag{3.10.7b}$$

$$i = 3: \quad V_z + \frac{\varepsilon}{i\hbar}[V_z, J_z] = V_z. \tag{3.10.7c}$$

This means that **V** must satisfy the commutation relations

$$[V_i, J_j] = i\varepsilon_{ijk}\hbar V_k. \tag{3.10.8}$$

Clearly, the behavior of **V** under a *finite* rotation is completely determined by the preceding commutation relations; we just apply the by-now familiar formula (2.3.47) to

$$\exp\left(\frac{iJ_j\phi}{\hbar}\right) V_i \exp\left(\frac{-iJ_j\phi}{\hbar}\right). \tag{3.10.9}$$

We simply need to calculate

$$[J_j,[J_j,[\cdots[J_j,V_i]\cdots]]]. \tag{3.10.10}$$

Multiple commutators keep on giving back to us V_i or V_k ($k \neq i, j$) as in spin case (3.2.7).

We can use (3.10.8) as the *defining* property of a vector operator. Notice that the angular-momentum commutation relations are a special case of (3.10.8) in which we let $V_i \rightarrow J_i, V_k \rightarrow J_k$. Other special cases are $[y, L_z] = i\hbar x$, $[x, L_z] = -i\hbar y$, $[p_x, L_z] = -i\hbar p_y$, $[p_y, L_z] = i\hbar p_x$; these can be proved explicitly.

Cartesian Tensors Versus Irreducible Tensors

In classical physics it is customary to define a tensor $T_{ijk\ldots}$ by generalizing $V_i \to \sum_j R_{ij} V_j$ as follows:

$$T_{ijk\ldots} \to \sum_{i'} \sum_{j'} \sum_{k'} \cdots R_{ii'} R_{jj'} \ldots T_{i'j'k'\ldots} \qquad (3.10.11)$$

under a rotation specified by the 3×3 orthogonal matrix R. The number of indices is called the **rank** of a tensor. Such a tensor is known as a **Cartesian tensor**.

The simplest example of a Cartesian tensor of rank 2 is a **dyadic** formed out of two vectors **U** and **V**. One simply takes a Cartesian component of **U** and a Cartesian component of **V** and puts them together:

$$T_{ij} \equiv U_i V_j. \qquad (3.10.12)$$

Notice that we have nine components altogether. They obviously transform like (3.10.11) under rotation.

The trouble with a Cartesian tensor like (3.10.12) is that it is reducible—that is, it can be decomposed into objects that transform differently under rotations. Specifically, for the dyadic in (3.10.12) we have

$$U_i V_j = \frac{\mathbf{U} \cdot \mathbf{V}}{3} \delta_{ij} + \frac{(U_i V_j - U_j V_i)}{2} + \left(\frac{U_i V_j + U_j V_i}{2} - \frac{\mathbf{U} \cdot \mathbf{V}}{3} \delta_{ij} \right).$$

$$(3.10.13)$$

The first term on the right-hand side, $\mathbf{U} \cdot \mathbf{V}$, is a scalar product invariant under rotation. The second is an antisymmetric tensor which can be written as vector product $\varepsilon_{ijk} (\mathbf{U} \times \mathbf{V})_k$. There are altogether 3 independent components. The last is a 3×3 symmetric traceless tensor with 5 ($= 6 - 1$, where 1 comes from the traceless condition) independent components. The number of independent components checks:

$$3 \times 3 = 1 + 3 + 5. \qquad (3.10.14)$$

We note that the numbers appearing on the right-hand side of (3.10.14) are precisely the multiplicities of objects with angular momentum $l = 0$, $l = 1$, and $l = 2$, respectively. This suggests that the dyadic has been decomposed into tensors that can transform like spherical harmonics with $l = 0$, 1, and 2. In fact, (3.10.13) is the simplest nontrivial example to illustrate the reduction of a Cartesian tensor into irreducible **spherical tensors**.

Before presenting the precise definition of a spherical tensor, we first give an example of a spherical tensor of rank k. Suppose we take a spherical harmonic $Y_l^m(\theta, \phi)$. We have already seen that it can be written as $Y_l^m(\hat{\mathbf{n}})$, where the orientation of $\hat{\mathbf{n}}$ is characterized by θ and ϕ. We now replace $\hat{\mathbf{n}}$ by some vector **V**. The result is that we have a spherical tensor of rank k (in place of l) with magnetic quantum number q (in place of m), namely,

$$T_q^{(k)} = Y_{l=k}^{m=q}(\mathbf{V}). \qquad (3.10.15)$$

Specifically, in the case $k = 1$ we take spherical harmonics with $l = 1$ and replace $(z/r) = (\hat{\mathbf{n}})_z$ by V_z, and so on.

$$Y_1^0 = \sqrt{\frac{3}{4\pi}} \cos\theta = \sqrt{\frac{3}{4\pi}} \frac{z}{r} \to T_0^{(1)} = \sqrt{\frac{3}{4\pi}} V_z,$$

$$Y_1^{\pm 1} = \mp\sqrt{\frac{3}{4\pi}} \frac{x \pm iy}{\sqrt{2}\, r} \to T_{\pm 1}^{(1)} = \sqrt{\frac{3}{4\pi}} \left(\mp \frac{V_x \pm iV_y}{\sqrt{2}} \right). \qquad (3.10.16)$$

Obviously this can be generalized for higher k, for example,

$$Y_2^{\pm 2} = \sqrt{\frac{15}{32\pi}} \frac{(x \pm iy)^2}{r^2} \to T_{\pm 2}^{(2)} = \sqrt{\frac{15}{32\pi}} \left(V_x \pm iV_y \right)^2. \qquad (3.10.17)$$

$T_q^{(k)}$ are irreducible, just as Y_l^m are. For this reason, working with spherical tensors is more satisfactory than working with Cartesian tensors.

To see the transformation of spherical tensors constructed in this manner, let us first review how Y_l^m transform under rotations. First, we have for the direction eigenket;

$$|\hat{\mathbf{n}}\rangle \to \mathscr{D}(R)|\hat{\mathbf{n}}\rangle \equiv |\hat{\mathbf{n}}'\rangle, \qquad (3.10.18)$$

which defines the rotated eigenket $|\hat{\mathbf{n}}'\rangle$. We wish to examine how $Y_l^m(\hat{\mathbf{n}}') = \langle \hat{\mathbf{n}}'|l, m\rangle$ would look in terms of $Y_l^m(\hat{\mathbf{n}})$. We can easily see this by starting with

$$\mathscr{D}(R^{-1})|l, m\rangle = \sum_{m'} |l, m'\rangle \mathscr{D}_{m'm}^{(l)}(R^{-1}) \qquad (3.10.19)$$

and contracting with $\langle \hat{\mathbf{n}}|$ on the left, using (3.10.18):

$$Y_l^m(\hat{\mathbf{n}}') = \sum_{m'} Y_l^{m'}(\hat{\mathbf{n}}) \mathscr{D}_{m'm}^{(l)}(R^{-1}). \qquad (3.10.20)$$

If there is an operator that acts like $Y_l^m(\mathbf{V})$, it is then reasonable to expect

$$\mathscr{D}^\dagger(R) Y_l^m(\mathbf{V}) \mathscr{D}(R) = \sum_{m'} Y_l^{m'}(\mathbf{V}) \mathscr{D}_{mm'}^{(l)*}(R), \qquad (3.10.21)$$

where we have used the unitarity of the rotation operator to rewrite $\mathscr{D}_{m'm}^{(l)}(R^{-1})$.

All this work is just to motivate the definition of a spherical tensor. We now consider spherical tensors in quantum mechanics. Motivated by (3.10.21) we define a spherical tensor operator of rank k with $(2k + 1)$ components as

$$\mathscr{D}^\dagger(R) T_q^{(k)} \mathscr{D}(R) = \sum_{q'=-k}^{k} \mathscr{D}_{qq'}^{(k)*}(R) T_{q'}^{(k)} \qquad (3.10.22a)$$

or, equivalently,

$$\mathscr{D}(R)T_q^{(k)}\mathscr{D}^\dagger(R) = \sum_{q'=-k}^{k} \mathscr{D}_{q'q}^{(k)}(R)T_{q'}^{(k)}. \tag{3.10.22b}$$

This definition holds regardless of whether $T_q^{(k)}$ can be written as $Y_{l=k}^{m=q}(\mathbf{V})$; for example, $(U_x + iU_y)(V_x + iV_y)$ is the $q = +2$ component of a spherical tensor of rank 2 even though, unlike $(V_x + iV_y)^2$, it cannot be written as $Y_k^q(\mathbf{V})$.

A more convenient definition of a spherical tensor is obtained by considering the infinitesimal form of (3.10.22b), namely,

$$\left(1 + \frac{i\mathbf{J}\cdot\hat{\mathbf{n}}\varepsilon}{\hbar}\right)T_q^{(k)}\left(1 - \frac{i\mathbf{J}\cdot\hat{\mathbf{n}}\varepsilon}{\hbar}\right) = \sum_{q'=-k}^{k} T_{q'}^{(k)}\langle kq'|\left(1 + \frac{i\mathbf{J}\cdot\hat{\mathbf{n}}\varepsilon}{\hbar}\right)|kq\rangle$$

$$\tag{3.10.23}$$

or

$$[\mathbf{J}\cdot\hat{\mathbf{n}}, T_q^{(k)}] = \sum_{q'} T_{q'}^{(k)}\langle kq'|\mathbf{J}\cdot\hat{\mathbf{n}}|kq\rangle. \tag{3.10.24}$$

By taking $\hat{\mathbf{n}}$ in the $\hat{\mathbf{z}}$- and in the $(\hat{\mathbf{x}} \pm i\hat{\mathbf{y}})$ directions and using the nonvanishing matrix elements of J_z and $J_\pm$ [see (3.5.35b) and (3.5.41)], we obtain

$$\left[J_z, T_q^{(k)}\right] = \hbar q T_q^{(k)} \tag{3.10.25a}$$

and

$$\left[J_\pm, T_q^{(k)}\right] = \hbar\sqrt{(k \mp q)(k \pm q + 1)}\, T_{q\pm1}^{(k)}. \tag{3.10.25b}$$

These commutation relations can be considered as a definition of spherical tensors in place of (3.10.22).

Product of Tensors

We have seen how to form a scalar, vector (or antisymmetric tensor), and a traceless symmetric tensor out of two vectors using the Cartesian tensor language. Of course, spherical tensor language can also be used (Baym 1969, Chapter 17), for example,

$$T_0^{(0)} = \frac{-\mathbf{U}\cdot\mathbf{V}}{3} = \frac{(U_{+1}V_{-1} + U_{-1}V_{+1} - U_0V_0)}{3},$$

$$T_q^{(1)} = \frac{(\mathbf{U}\times\mathbf{V})_q}{i\sqrt{2}},$$

$$T_{\pm2}^{(2)} = U_{\pm1}V_{\pm1}, \tag{3.10.26}$$

$$T_{\pm1}^{(2)} = \frac{U_{\pm1}V_0 + U_0V_{\pm1}}{\sqrt{2}},$$

$$T_0^{(2)} = \frac{U_{+1}V_{-1} + 2U_0V_0 + U_{-1}V_{+1}}{\sqrt{6}},$$

where $U_q(V_q)$ is the qth component of a spherical tensor of rank 1, corresponding to vector $\mathbf{U}(\mathbf{V})$. The preceding transformation properties can be checked by comparing with Y_l^m and remembering that $U_{+1} = -(U_x + iU_y)/\sqrt{2}$, $U_{-1} = (U_x - iU_y)/\sqrt{2}$, $U_0 = U_z$. A similar check can be made for $V_{\pm 1,0}$. For instance,

$$Y_2^0 = \sqrt{\frac{5}{16\pi}} \frac{3z^2 - r^2}{r^2},$$

where $3z^2 - r^2$ can be written as

$$2z^2 + 2\left[-\frac{(x + iy)}{\sqrt{2}} \frac{(x - iy)}{\sqrt{2}}\right];$$

hence, Y_2^0 is just a special case of $T_0^{(2)}$ for $\mathbf{U} = \mathbf{V} = \mathbf{r}$.

A more systematic way of forming tensor products goes as follows. We start by stating a theorem:

Theorem. Let $X_{q_1}^{(k_1)}$ and $Z_{q_2}^{(k_2)}$ be irreducible spherical tensors of rank k_1 and k_2, respectively. Then

$$T_q^{(k)} = \sum_{q_1} \sum_{q_2} \langle k_1 k_2; q_1 q_2 | k_1 k_2; kq \rangle X_{q_1}^{(k_1)} Z_{q_2}^{(k_2)} \qquad (3.10.27)$$

is a spherical (irreducible) tensor of rank k.

Proof. We must show that under rotation $T_q^{(k)}$ must transform according to (3.10.22)

$$\mathscr{D}^\dagger(R) T_q^{(k)} \mathscr{D}(R) = \sum_{q_1} \sum_{q_2} \langle k_1 k_2; q_1 q_2 | k_1 k_2; kq \rangle$$

$$\times \mathscr{D}^\dagger(R) X_{q_1}^{(k_1)} \mathscr{D}(R) \mathscr{D}^\dagger(R) Z_{q_2}^{(k_2)} \mathscr{D}(R)$$

$$= \sum_{q_1} \sum_{q_2} \sum_{q_1'} \sum_{q_2'} \langle k_1 k_2; q_1 q_2 | k_1 k_2; kq \rangle$$

$$\times X_{q_1'}^{(k_1)} \mathscr{D}_{q_1' q_1}^{(k_1)}(R^{-1}) Z_{q_2'}^{(k_2)} \mathscr{D}_{q_2' q_2}^{(k_2)}(R^{-1})$$

$$= \sum_{k''} \sum_{q_1} \sum_{q_2} \sum_{q_1'} \sum_{q_2'} \sum_{q''} \sum_{q'} \langle k_1 k_2; q_1 q_2 | k_1 k_2; kq \rangle$$

$$\times \langle k_1 k_2; q_1' q_2' | k_1, k_2; k''q' \rangle$$

$$\times \langle k_1 k_2; q_1 q_2 | k_1 k_2; k''q'' \rangle \mathscr{D}_{q'q''}^{(k'')}(R^{-1}) X_{q_1'}^{(k_1)} Z_{q_2'}^{(k_2)},$$

where we have used the Clebsch-Gordan series formula (3.7.69). The preceding expression becomes

$$= \sum_{k''} \sum_{q_1'} \sum_{q_2'} \sum_{q''} \sum_{q'} \delta_{kk''} \delta_{qq''} \langle k_1 k_2; q_1' q_2' | k_1 k_2; k''q' \rangle \mathscr{D}_{q'q''}^{(k'')}(R^{-1}) X_{q_1'}^{(k_1)} Z_{q_2'}^{(k_2)},$$

where we have used the orthogonality of Clebsch-Gordan coefficients (3.7.42). Finally, this expression reduces to

$$= \sum_{q'} \left(\sum_{q_1'} \sum_{q_2'} \langle k_1 k_2; q_1' q_2' | k_1 k_2; kq' \rangle X_{q_1'}^{(k_1)} Z_{q_2'}^{(k_2)} \right) \mathscr{D}_{q'q}^{(k)}(R^{-1})$$

$$= \sum_{q'} T_{q'}^{(k)} \mathscr{D}_{q'q}^{(k)}(R^{-1}) = \sum_{q'} \mathscr{D}_{qq'}^{(k)*}(R) T_{q'}^{(k)} \qquad \qquad \square$$

The foregoing shows how we can construct tensor operators of higher or lower ranks by multiplying two tensor operators. Furthermore, the manner in which we construct tensor products out of two tensors is completely analogous to the manner in which we construct an angular-momentum eigenstate by adding two angular momentums; exactly the same Clebsch-Gordan coefficients appear if we let $k_{1,2} \to j_{1,2}, q_{1,2} \to m_{1,2}$.

Matrix Elements of Tensor Operators; the Wigner-Eckart Theorem

In considering the interactions of an electromagnetic field with atoms and nuclei, it is often necessary to evaluate matrix elements of tensor operators with respect to angular-momentum eigenstates. Examples of this will be given in Chapter 5. In general, it is a formidable dynamic task to calculate such matrix elements. However, there are certain properties of these matrix elements that follow purely from kinematic or geometric considerations, which we now discuss.

First, there is a very simple m-selection rule:

m-selection Rule

$$\langle \alpha', j'm' | T_q^{(k)} | \alpha, jm \rangle = 0, \quad \text{unless } m' = q + m. \qquad (3.10.28)$$

Proof. Using (3.10.25a), we have

$$\langle \alpha', j'm' | \left(\left[J_z, T_q^{(k)} \right] - \hbar q T_q^{(k)} \right) | \alpha, jm \rangle = \left[(m' - m)\hbar - \hbar q \right]$$

$$\times \langle \alpha', j'm' | T_q^{(k)} | \alpha, jm \rangle = 0;$$

hence,

$$\langle \alpha', j'm' | T_q^{(k)} | \alpha, jm \rangle = 0 \quad \text{unless } m' = q + m. \qquad \square$$

Another way to see this is to note that transformation property of $T_q^{(k)} | \alpha, jm \rangle$ under rotation, namely,

$$\mathscr{D} T_q^{(k)} | \alpha, jm \rangle = \mathscr{D} T_q^{(k)} \mathscr{D}^\dagger \mathscr{D} | \alpha, jm \rangle. \qquad (3.10.29)$$

If we now let $\mathscr{D}$ stand for a rotation operator around the z-axis, we get [see

(3.10.22b) and (3.1.16)]

$$\mathscr{D}(\hat{z}, \phi) T_q^{(k)} |\alpha, jm\rangle = e^{-iq\phi} e^{-im\phi} T_q^{(k)} |\alpha, jm\rangle, \qquad (3.10.30)$$

which is orthogonal to $|\alpha', j'm'\rangle$ unless $q + m = m'$.

We are going to prove one of the most important theorems in quantum mechanics, the **Wigner-Eckart theorem.**

The Wigner-Eckart Theorem. The matrix elements of tensor operators with respect to angular-momentum eigenstates satisfy

$$\langle \alpha', j'm' | T_q^{(k)} | \alpha, jm \rangle = \langle jk; mq | jk; j'm' \rangle \frac{\langle \alpha'j' \| T^{(k)} \| \alpha j \rangle}{\sqrt{2j+1}},$$

$$(3.10.31)$$

where the **double-bar matrix element** *is independent of m and m', and q.*

Before we present a proof of this theorem, let us look at its significance. First, we see that the matrix element is written as the product of two factors. The first factor is a Clebsch-Gordan coefficient for adding j and k to get j'. It depends only on the geometry, that is, the way the system is oriented with respect to the z-axis. There is no reference whatsoever to the particular nature of the tensor operator. The second factor does depend on the dynamics, for instance, α may stand for the radial quantum number and its evaluation may involve, for example, evaluation of radial integrals. On the other hand, it is completely independent of the magnetic quantum numbers m, m', and q, which specify the orientation of the physical system. To evaluate $\langle \alpha', j'm' | T_q^{(k)} | \alpha, jm \rangle$ with various combinations of m, m', and q' it is sufficient to know just one of them; all others can be related geometrically because they are proportional to Clebsch-Gordan coefficients, which are known. The common proportionality factor is $\langle \alpha'j' \| T^{(k)} \| \alpha j \rangle$, which makes no reference whatsoever to the geometric features.

The selection rules for the tensor operator matrix element can be immediately read off from the selection rules for adding angular momentum. Indeed, from the requirement that the Clebsch-Gordan coefficient be nonvanishing, we immediately obtain the m-selection rule (3.10.28) derived before and also the triangular relation

$$|j - k| \le j' \le j + k. \qquad (3.10.32)$$

Now we prove the theorem.

Proof. Using (3.10.25b) we have

$$\langle \alpha', j'm' | [J_{\pm}, T_q^{(k)}] | \alpha, jm \rangle = \hbar \sqrt{(k \mp q)(k \pm q + 1)} \langle \alpha', j'm' | T_{q \pm 1}^{(k)} | \alpha, jm \rangle,$$

$$(3.10.33)$$

or using (3.5.39) and (3.5.40) we have

$$\sqrt{(j' \pm m')(j' \mp m'+1)} \langle \alpha', j', m' \mp 1 | T_q^{(k)} | \alpha, jm \rangle$$

$$= \sqrt{(j \mp m)(j \pm m+1)} \langle \alpha', j'm' | T_q^{(k)} | \alpha, j, m \pm 1 \rangle$$

$$+ \sqrt{(k \mp q)(k \pm q+1)} \langle \alpha', j'm' | T_{q \pm 1}^{(k)} | \alpha, jm \rangle. \qquad (3.10.34)$$

Compare this with the recursion relation for the Clebsch-Gordan coefficient (3.7.49). Note the striking similarity if we substitute $j' \to j$, $m' \to m$, $j \to j_1$, $m \to m_1$, $k \to j_2$, and $q \to m_2$. Both recursion relations are of the form $\sum_j a_{ij} x_j = 0$, that is, first-order linear homogeneous equations with the same coefficients a_{ij}. Whenever we have

$$\sum_j a_{ij} x_j = 0, \qquad \sum_j a_{ij} y_j = 0, \qquad (3.10.35)$$

we cannot solve for the x_j (or y_j) individually but we can solve for the ratios; so

$$\frac{x_j}{x_k} = \frac{y_j}{y_k} \quad \text{or} \quad x_j = cy_j, \qquad (3.10.36)$$

where c is a universal proportionality factor. Noting that $\langle j_1 j_2; m_1, m_2 \pm 1 | j_1 j_2; jm \rangle$ in the Clebsch-Gordan recursion relation (3.7.49) corresponds to $\langle \alpha', j'm' | T_{q \pm 1}^{(k)} | \alpha, jm \rangle$, we see that

$$\langle \alpha', j'm' | T_{q \pm 1}^{(k)} | \alpha, jm \rangle = \text{(universal proportionality constant independent of}$$

$$m, q, \text{ and } m') \langle jk; m q \pm 1 | jk; j'm' \rangle, \qquad (3.10.37)$$

which proves the theorem.   □

Let us now look at two simple examples of the Wigner-Eckart theorem.

Example 1. Tensor of rank 0, that is, scalar $T_0^{(0)} = S$. The matrix element of a scalar operator satisfies

$$\langle \alpha', j'm' | S | \alpha, jm \rangle = \delta_{jj'} \delta_{mm'} \frac{\langle \alpha'j' \| S \| \alpha j \rangle}{\sqrt{2j+1}} \qquad (3.10.38)$$

because S acting on $|\alpha, jm \rangle$ is like adding an angular momentum of zero. Thus the scalar operator cannot change j, m values.

Example 2. Vector operator which in the spherical tensor language is a rank 1 tensor. The spherical component of $\mathbf{V}$ can be written as $V_{q= \pm 1,0}$, so we have the selection rule

$$\Delta m \equiv m' - m = \pm 1, 0 \qquad \Delta j \equiv j' - j = \begin{cases} \pm 1 \\ 0. \end{cases} \qquad (3.10.39)$$

In addition, the $0 \rightarrow 0$ transition is forbidden. This selection rule is of fundamental importance in the theory of radiation; it is the dipole selection rule obtained in the long-wavelength limit of emitted photons.*

For $j = j'$ the Wigner-Eckart theorem—when applied to the vector operator—takes a particularly simple form, often known as the **projection theorem** for obvious reasons.

The Projection Theorem

$$\langle \alpha', jm'|V_q|\alpha, jm \rangle = \frac{\langle \alpha', jm|\mathbf{J} \cdot \mathbf{V}|\alpha, jm \rangle}{\hbar^2 j(j+1)} \langle jm'|J_q|jm \rangle, \quad (3.10.40)$$

where analogous to our discussion after (3.10.26) we choose

$$J_{\pm 1} = \mp \frac{1}{\sqrt{2}}(J_x \pm iJ_y) = \mp \frac{1}{\sqrt{2}} J_{\pm}, \qquad J_0 = J_z. \quad (3.10.41)$$

Proof. Noting (3.10.26) we have

$$\langle \alpha', jm|\mathbf{J} \cdot \mathbf{V}|\alpha, jm \rangle = \langle \alpha', jm|(J_0 V_0 - J_{+1}V_{-1} - J_{-1}V_{+1})|\alpha, jm \rangle$$

$$= m\hbar \langle \alpha', jm|V_0|\alpha, jm \rangle + \frac{\hbar}{\sqrt{2}}\sqrt{(j+m)(j-m+1)}$$

$$\times \langle \alpha', j\, m-1|V_{-1}|\alpha, jm \rangle$$

$$- \frac{\hbar}{\sqrt{2}}\sqrt{(j-m)(j+m+1)}\langle \alpha', j\, m+1|V_{+1}|\alpha, jm \rangle$$

$$= c_{jm}\langle \alpha'j\|\mathbf{V}\|\alpha j \rangle \quad (3.10.42)$$

by the Wigner-Eckart theorem (3.10.31), where c_{jm} is independent of α, α', and $\mathbf{V}$, and the matrix elements of $V_{0, \pm 1}$ are all proportional to the double-bar matrix element (sometimes also called the **reduced matrix element**). Furthermore, c_{jm} is independent of m because $\mathbf{J} \cdot \mathbf{V}$ is a scalar operator, so we may as well write it as c_j. Because c_j does not depend on $\mathbf{V}$, (3.10.42) holds even if we let $\mathbf{V} \rightarrow \mathbf{J}$ and $\alpha' \rightarrow \alpha$, that is,

$$\langle \alpha, jm|\mathbf{J}^2|\alpha, jm \rangle = c_j\langle \alpha j\|\mathbf{J}\|\alpha j \rangle. \quad (3.10.43)$$

Returning to the Wigner-Eckart theorem applied to V_q and J_q, we have

$$\frac{\langle \alpha', jm'|V_q|\alpha, jm \rangle}{\langle \alpha, jm'|J_q|\alpha, jm \rangle} = \frac{\langle \alpha'j\|\mathbf{V}\|\alpha j \rangle}{\langle \alpha j\|\mathbf{J}\|\alpha j \rangle}. \quad (3.10.44)$$

---

*Additional parity selection rules are discussed in Chapter 4, Section 2. They lead to these $E1$ dipole selection rules.

But the right-hand side of (3.10.44) is the same as $\langle \alpha', jm|\mathbf{J} \cdot \mathbf{V}|\alpha, jm \rangle$ $/\langle \alpha, jm|\mathbf{J}^2|\alpha, jm \rangle$ by (3.10.42) and (3.10.43). Moreover, the left-hand side of (3.10.43) is just $j(j+1)\hbar^2$. So

$$\langle \alpha', jm'|V_q|\alpha, jm \rangle = \frac{\langle \alpha', jm|\mathbf{J} \cdot \mathbf{V}|\alpha, jm \rangle}{\hbar^2 j(j+1)} \langle jm'|J_q|jm \rangle, \quad (3.10.45)$$

which proves the projection theorem. $\square$

We will give applications of the theorem in subsequent sections.

PROBLEMS

1. Find the eigenvalues and eigenvectors of $\sigma_y = \begin{pmatrix} 0 & -i \\ i & 0 \end{pmatrix}$. Suppose an electron is in the spin state $\begin{pmatrix} \alpha \\ \beta \end{pmatrix}$. If s_y is measured, what is the probability of the result $\hbar/2$?

2. Consider the 2×2 matrix defined by

$$U = \frac{a_0 + i\boldsymbol{\sigma} \cdot \mathbf{a}}{a_0 - i\boldsymbol{\sigma} \cdot \mathbf{a}},$$

   where a_0 is a real number and $\mathbf{a}$ is a three-dimensional vector with real components.

   a. Prove that U is unitary and unimodular.

   b. In general, a 2×2 unitary unimodular matrix represents a rotation in three dimensions. Find the axis and angle of rotation appropriate for U in terms of a_0, a_1, a_2, and a_3.

3. The spin-dependent Hamiltonian of an electron-positron system in the presence of a uniform magnetic field in the z-direction can be written as

$$H = A\mathbf{S}^{(e^-)} \cdot \mathbf{S}^{(e^+)} + \left(\frac{eB}{mc}\right)\left(S_z^{(e^-)} - S_z^{(e^+)}\right).$$

   Suppose the spin function of the system is given by $\chi_+^{(e^-)}\chi_-^{(e^+)}$.

   a. Is this an eigenfunction of H in the limit $A \to 0$, $eB/mc \neq 0$? If it is, what is the energy eigenvalue? If it is not, what is the expectation value of H?

   b. Same problem when $eB/mc \to 0$, $A \neq 0$.

4. Consider a *spin* 1 particle. Evaluate the matrix elements of

$$S_z(S_z + \hbar)(S_z - \hbar) \quad \text{and} \quad S_x(S_x + \hbar)(S_x - \hbar).$$

5. Let the Hamiltonian of a rigid body be

$$H = \frac{1}{2}\left(\frac{K_1^2}{I_1} + \frac{K_2^2}{I_2} + \frac{K_3^2}{I_3}\right),$$

   where $\mathbf{K}$ is the angular momentum in the body frame. From this expression obtain the Heisenberg equation of motion for **K** and then find Euler's equation of motion in the correspondence limit.

6. Let $U = e^{iG_3\alpha}e^{iG_2\beta}e^{iG_3\gamma}$, where (α, β, γ) are the Eulerian angles. In order that U represent a rotation (α, β, γ), what are the commutation rules satisfied by the G_k? Relate **G** to the angular momentum operators.

7. What is the meaning of the following equation:

$$U^{-1}A_kU = \sum R_{kl}A_l,$$

where the three components of **A** are matrices? From this equation show that matrix elements $\langle m|A_k|n\rangle$ transform like vectors.

8. Consider a sequence of Euler rotations represented by

$$\mathcal{D}^{(1/2)}(\alpha, \beta, \gamma) = \exp\left(\frac{-i\sigma_3\alpha}{2}\right)\exp\left(\frac{-i\sigma_2\beta}{2}\right)\exp\left(\frac{-i\sigma_3\gamma}{2}\right)$$

$$= \begin{pmatrix} e^{-i(\alpha+\gamma)/2}\cos\dfrac{\beta}{2} & -e^{-i(\alpha-\gamma)/2}\sin\dfrac{\beta}{2} \\ e^{i(\alpha-\gamma)/2}\sin\dfrac{\beta}{2} & e^{i(\alpha+\gamma)/2}\cos\dfrac{\beta}{2} \end{pmatrix}.$$

Because of the group properties of rotations, we expect that this sequence of operations is equivalent to a *single* rotation about some axis by an angle θ. Find θ.

9. a. Consider a pure ensemble of identically prepared spin $\frac{1}{2}$ systems. Suppose the expectation values $\langle S_x \rangle$ and $\langle S_z \rangle$ and the sign of $\langle S_y \rangle$ are known. Show how we may determine the state vector. Why is it unnecessary to know the magnitude of $\langle S_y \rangle$?

   b. Consider a mixed ensemble of spin $\frac{1}{2}$ systems. Suppose the ensemble averages $[S_x]$, $[S_y]$, and $[S_z]$ are all known. Show how we may construct the 2×2 density matrix that characterizes the ensemble.

10. a. Prove that the time evolution of the density operator ρ (in the Schrödinger picture) is given by

$$\rho(t) = \mathscr{U}(t, t_0)\rho(t_0)\mathscr{U}^\dagger(t, t_0).$$

   b. Suppose we have a pure ensemble at $t = 0$. Prove that it cannot evolve into a mixed ensemble as long as the time evolution is governed by the Schrödinger equation.

11. Consider an ensemble of spin 1 systems. The density matrix is now a 3×3 matrix. How many independent (real) parameters are needed to characterize the density matrix? What must we know in addition to $[S_x]$, $[S_y]$, and $[S_z]$ to characterize the ensemble completely?

12. An angular-momentum eigenstate $|j, m = m_{\max} = j\rangle$ is rotated by an infinitesimal angle ε about the y-axis. Without using the explicit form of the $d^{(j)}_{m'm}$ function, obtain an expression for the probability for the new rotated state to be found in the original state up to terms of order ε^2.

13. Show that the 3×3 matrices G_i $(i = 1, 2, 3)$ whose elements are given by

$$(G_i)_{jk} = -i\hbar\varepsilon_{ijk},$$

where j and k are the row and column indices, satisfy the angular momentum commutation relations. What is the physical (or geometric) significance of the transformation matrix that connects G_i to the more usual 3×3 representations of the angular-momentum operator J_i with J_3 taken to be diagonal? Relate your result to

$$\mathbf{V} \rightarrow \mathbf{V} + \hat{\mathbf{n}}\delta\phi \times \mathbf{V}$$

under infinitesimal rotations. (*Note*: This problem may be helpful in understanding the photon spin.)

14. a. Let $\mathbf{J}$ be angular momentum. It may stand for orbital $\mathbf{L}$, spin $\mathbf{S}$, or $\mathbf{J}_{\text{total}}$.) Using the fact that $J_x, J_y, J_z (J_\pm \equiv J_x \pm iJ_y)$ satisfy the usual angular-momentum commutation relations, prove

$$\mathbf{J}^2 = J_z^2 + J_+ J_- - \hbar J_z.$$

b. Using (a) (or otherwise), derive the "famous" expression for the coefficient c_- that appears in

$$J_- \psi_{jm} = c_- \psi_{j, m-1}.$$

15. The wave function of a particle subjected to a spherically symmetrical potential $V(r)$ is given by

$$\psi(\mathbf{x}) = (x + y + 3z)f(r).$$

a. Is ψ an eigenfunction of $\mathbf{L}^2$? If so, what is the l-value? If not, what are the possible values of l we may obtain when $\mathbf{L}^2$ is measured?

b. What are the probabilities for the particle to be found in various m_l states?

c. Suppose it is known somehow that $\psi(\mathbf{x})$ is an energy eigenfunction with eigenvalue E. Indicate how we may find $V(r)$.

16. A particle in a spherically symmetrical potential is known to be in an eigenstate of $\mathbf{L}^2$ and L_z with eigenvalues $\hbar^2 l(l+1)$ and $m\hbar$, respectively. Prove that the expectation values between $|lm\rangle$ states satisfy

$$\langle L_x \rangle = \langle L_y \rangle = 0, \qquad \langle L_x^2 \rangle = \langle L_y^2 \rangle = \frac{[l(l+1)\hbar^2 - m^2\hbar^2]}{2}.$$

Interpret this result semiclassically.

17. Suppose a half-integer l-value, say $\frac{1}{2}$, were allowed for orbital angular momentum. From

$$L_+ Y_{1/2, 1/2}(\theta, \phi) = 0,$$

we may deduce, as usual,

$$Y_{1/2, 1/2}(\theta, \phi) \propto e^{i\phi/2}\sqrt{\sin\theta}.$$

Now try to construct $Y_{1/2,\,-1/2}(\theta,\phi)$; by (a) applying L_- to $Y_{1/2,1/2}(\theta,\phi)$; and (b) using $L_-Y_{1/2,\,-1/2}(\theta,\phi)=0$. Show that the two procedures lead to contradictory results. (This gives an argument against half-integer l-values for orbital angular momentum.)

18. Consider an orbital angular-momentum eigenstate $|l=2, m=0\rangle$. Suppose this state is rotated by an angle β about the y-axis. Find the probability for the new state to be found in $m=0$, ± 1, and ± 2. (The spherical harmonics for $l=0$, 1, and 2 given in Appendix A may be useful.)

19. What is the physical significance of the operators

$$K_+ \equiv a_+^\dagger a_-^\dagger \quad \text{and} \quad K_- \equiv a_+ a_-$$

in Schwinger's scheme for angular momentum? Give the nonvanishing matrix elements of K_+.

20. We are to add angular momenta $j_1=1$ and $j_2=1$ to form $j=2$, 1, and 0 states. Using either the ladder operator method or the recursion relation, express all (nine) $\{j,m\}$ eigenkets in terms of $|j_1 j_2; m_1 m_2\rangle$. Write your answer as

$$|j=1, m=1\rangle = \frac{1}{\sqrt{2}}|+,0\rangle - \frac{1}{\sqrt{2}}|0,+\rangle, \ldots,$$

where $+$ and 0 stand for $m_{1,2}=1,0$, respectively.

21. a. Evaluate

$$\sum_{m=-j}^{j} |d_{mm'}^{(j)}(\beta)|^2 m$$

for *any* j (integer or half-integer); then check your answer for $j=\tfrac{1}{2}$.

b. Prove, for any j,

$$\sum_{m=-j}^{j} m^2 |d_{m'm}^{(j)}(\beta)|^2 = \tfrac{1}{2}j(j+1)\sin^2\beta + m'^2\tfrac{1}{2}(3\cos^2\beta - 1).$$

[*Hint*: This can be proved in many ways. You may, for instance, examine the rotational properties of J_z^2 using the spherical (irreducible) tensor language.]

22. a. Consider a system with $j=1$. Explicitly write

$$\langle j=1, m'|J_y|j=1, m\rangle$$

in 3×3 matrix form.

b. Show that for $j=1$ only, it is legitimate to replace $e^{-iJ_y\beta/\hbar}$ by

$$1 - i\left(\frac{J_y}{\hbar}\right)\sin\beta - \left(\frac{J_y}{\hbar}\right)^2(1-\cos\beta).$$

c. Using (b), prove

$$d^{(j=1)}(\beta) =$$

$$
\begin{pmatrix}
\left(\dfrac{1}{2}\right)(1+\cos\beta) & -\left(\dfrac{1}{\sqrt{2}}\right)\sin\beta & \left(\dfrac{1}{2}\right)(1-\cos\beta) \\[2mm]
\left(\dfrac{1}{\sqrt{2}}\right)\sin\beta & \cos\beta & -\left(\dfrac{1}{\sqrt{2}}\right)\sin\beta \\[2mm]
\left(\dfrac{1}{2}\right)(1-\cos\beta) & \left(\dfrac{1}{\sqrt{2}}\right)\sin\beta & \left(\dfrac{1}{2}\right)(1+\cos\beta)
\end{pmatrix}
$$

23. Express the matrix element $\langle \alpha_2\beta_2\gamma_2 | J_3^2 | \alpha_1\beta_1\gamma_1\rangle$ in terms of a series in

$$\mathscr{D}_{mn}^{j}(\alpha\beta\gamma) = \langle \alpha\beta\gamma | jmn\rangle.$$

24. Consider a system made up of two spin $\frac{1}{2}$ particles. Observer A specializes in measuring the spin components of one of the particles (s_{1z}, s_{1x} and so on), while observer B measures the spin components of the other particle. Suppose the system is known to be in a spin-singlet state, that is, $S_{\text{total}} = 0$.

   a. What is the probability for observer A to obtain $s_{1z} = \hbar/2$ when observer B makes no measurement? Same problem for $s_{1x} = \hbar/2$.

   b. Observer B determines the spin of particle 2 to be in the $s_{2z} = \hbar/2$ state with certainty. What can we then conclude about the outcome of observer A's measurement if (i) A measures s_{1z} and (ii) A measures s_{1x}? Justify your answer.

25. Consider a spherical tensor of rank 1 (that is, a vector)

$$V_{\pm1}^{(1)} = \mp\frac{V_x \pm iV_y}{\sqrt{2}}, \qquad V_0^{(1)} = V_z.$$

Using the expression for $d^{(j=1)}$ given in Problem 22, evaluate

$$\sum_{q'} d_{qq'}^{(1)}(\beta) V_{q'}^{(1)}$$

and show that your results are just what you expect from the transformation properties of $V_{x,y,z}$ under rotations about the y-axis.

26. a. Construct a spherical tensor of rank 1 out of two different vectors $\mathbf{U} = (U_x, U_y, U_z)$ and $\mathbf{V} = (V_x, V_y, V_z)$. Explicitly write $T_{\pm1,0}^{(1)}$ in terms of $U_{x,y,z}$ and $V_{x,y,z}$.

   b. Construct a spherical tensor of rank 2 out of two different vectors $\mathbf{U}$ and $\mathbf{V}$. Write down explicitly $T_{\pm2,\pm1,0}^{(2)}$ in terms of $U_{x,y,z}$ and $V_{x,y,z}$.

27. Consider a spinless particle bound to a fixed center by a central force potential.

a. Relate, as much as possible, the matrix elements

$$\langle n', l', m' | \mp \frac{1}{\sqrt{2}}(x \pm iy) | n, l, m \rangle \quad \text{and} \quad \langle n', l', m' | z | n, l, m \rangle$$

using *only* the Wigner-Eckart theorem. Make sure to state under what conditions the matrix elements are nonvanishing.

b. Do the same problem using wave functions $\psi(\mathbf{x}) = R_{nl}(r) Y_l^m(\theta, \phi)$.

28. a. Write xy, xz, and $(x^2 - y^2)$ as components of a spherical (irreducible) tensor of rank 2.

b. The expectation value

$$Q \equiv e \langle \alpha, j, m = j | (3z^2 - r^2) | \alpha, j, m = j \rangle$$

is known as the *quadrupole moment*. Evaluate

$$e \langle \alpha, j, m' | (x^2 - y^2) | \alpha, j, m = j \rangle,$$

(where $m' = j, j-1, j-2, \ldots$) in terms of Q and appropriate Clebsch-Gordan coefficients.

29. A spin $\frac{3}{2}$ nucleus situated at the origin is subjected to an external inhomogeneous electric field. The basic electric quadrupole interaction may by taken to be

$$H_{\text{int}} = \frac{eQ}{2s(s-1)\hbar^2} \left[\left(\frac{\partial^2 \phi}{\partial x^2} \right)_0 S_x^2 + \left(\frac{\partial^2 \phi}{\partial y^2} \right)_0 S_y^2 + \left(\frac{\partial^2 \phi}{\partial z^2} \right)_0 S_z^2 \right],$$

where ϕ is the electrostatic potential satisfying Laplace's equation and the coordinate axes are so chosen that

$$\left(\frac{\partial^2 \phi}{\partial x \partial y} \right)_0 = \left(\frac{\partial^2 \phi}{\partial y \partial z} \right)_0 = \left(\frac{\partial^2 \phi}{\partial x \partial z} \right)_0 = 0.$$

Show that the interaction energy can be written as

$$A(3S_z^2 - \mathbf{S}^2) + B(S_+^2 + S_-^2),$$

and express A and B in terms of $(\partial^2 \phi / \partial x^2)_0$ and so on. Determine the energy eigenkets (in terms of $|m\rangle$, where $m = \pm \frac{3}{2}, \pm \frac{1}{2}$) and the corresponding energy eigenvalues. Is there any degeneracy?

CHAPTER 4

Symmetry in Quantum Mechanics

Having studied the theory of rotation in detail, we are in a position to discuss, in more general terms, the connection between symmetries, degeneracies, and conservation laws. We have deliberately postponed this very important topic until now so that we can discuss it using the rotation symmetry of Chapter 3 as an example.

4.1. SYMMETRIES, CONSERVATION LAWS, AND DEGENERACIES

Symmetries in Classical Physics

We begin with an elementary review of the concepts of symmetry and conservation law in classical physics. In the Lagrangian formulation of quantum mechanics, we start with the Lagrangian L, which is a function of a generalized coordinate q_i and the corresponding generalized velocity $\dot{q}_i$. If L is unchanged under displacement,

$$q_i \to q_i + \delta q_i, \tag{4.1.1}$$

then we must have

$$\frac{\partial L}{\partial q_i} = 0. \tag{4.1.2}$$

It then follows, by virtue of the Lagrange equation, $d/dt \, (\partial L/\partial \dot{q}_i) - \partial L/\partial q_i = 0$, that

$$\frac{dp_i}{dt} = 0, \qquad (4.1.3)$$

where the canonical momentum is defined as

$$p_i = \frac{\partial L}{\partial \dot{q}_i}. \qquad (4.1.4)$$

So if L is unchanged under displacement (4.1.1), then we have a conserved quantity, the canonical momentum conjugate to q_i.

Likewise, in the Hamiltonian formulation based on H regarded as a function of q_i and p_i, we have

$$\frac{dp_i}{dt} = 0 \qquad (4.1.5)$$

whenever

$$\frac{\partial H}{\partial q_i} = 0. \qquad (4.1.6)$$

So if the Hamiltonian does not explicitly depend on q_i, which is another way of saying H has a symmetry under $q_i \rightarrow q_i + \delta q_i$, we have a conserved quantity.

Symmetry in Quantum Mechanics

In quantum mechanics we have learned to associate a **unitary operator**, say $\mathscr{S}$, with an operation like translation or rotation. It has become customary to call $\mathscr{S}$ a **symmetry operator** regardless of whether the physical system itself possesses the symmetry corresponding to $\mathscr{S}$. Further, we have learned that for symmetry operations that differ infinitesimally from the identity transformation, we can write

$$\mathscr{S} = 1 - \frac{i\varepsilon}{\hbar} G, \qquad (4.1.7)$$

where G is the Hermitian generator of the symmetry operator in question. Let us now suppose that H is invariant under $\mathscr{S}$. We then have

$$\mathscr{S}^{\dagger} H \mathscr{S} = H. \qquad (4.1.8)$$

But this is equivalent to

$$[G, H] = 0. \qquad (4.1.9)$$

By virtue of the Heisenberg equation of motion, we have

$$\frac{dG}{dt} = 0; \qquad (4.1.10)$$

hence, G is a constant of the motion. For instance, if H is invariant under translation, then momentum is a constant of the motion; if H is invariant under rotation, then angular momentum is a constant of the motion.

It is instructive to look at the connection between (4.1.9) and conservation of G from the point of view of an eigenket of G when G commutes with H. Suppose at t_0 the system is in an eigenstate of G. Then the ket at a later time obtained by applying the time-evolution operator

$$|g', t_0; t\rangle = U(t, t_0)|g'\rangle \qquad (4.1.11)$$

is also an eigenket of G with the same eigenvalue g'. In other words, once a ket is a G eigenket, it is always a G eigenket with the same eigenvalue. The proof of this is extremely simple once we realize that (4.1.9) and (4.1.10) also imply that G commutes with the time-evolution operator, namely,

$$G[U(t, t_0)|g'\rangle] = U(t, t_0)G|g'\rangle = g'[U(t, t_0)|g'\rangle]. \qquad (4.1.12)$$

Degeneracies

Let us now turn to the concept of degeneracies. Even though degeneracies may be discussed at the level of classical mechanics—for instance in discussing closed (nonprecessing) orbits in the Kepler problem (Goldstein 1980)—this concept plays a far more important role in quantum mechanics. Let us suppose that

$$[H, \mathcal{S}] = 0 \qquad (4.1.13)$$

for some symmetry operator and $|n\rangle$ is an energy eigenket with eigenvalue E_n. Then $\mathcal{S}|n\rangle$ is also an energy eigenket with the same energy, because

$$H(\mathcal{S}|n\rangle) = \mathcal{S}H|n\rangle = E_n(\mathcal{S}|n\rangle). \qquad (4.1.14)$$

Suppose $|n\rangle$ and $\mathcal{S}|n\rangle$ represent different states. Then these are two states with the same energy, that is, they are degenerate. Quite often $\mathcal{S}$ is characterized by continuous parameters, say λ, in which case all states of the form $\mathcal{S}(\lambda)|n\rangle$ have the same energy.

We now consider rotation specifically. Suppose the Hamiltonian is rotationally invariant, so

$$[\mathcal{D}(R), H] = 0, \qquad (4.1.15)$$

which necessarily implies that

$$[\mathbf{J}, H] = 0, \qquad [\mathbf{J}^2, H] = 0. \qquad (4.1.16)$$

We can then form simultaneous eigenkets of H, $\mathbf{J}^2$, and J_z, denoted by $|n; j, m\rangle$. The argument just given implies that all states of the form

$$\mathcal{D}(R)|n; j, m\rangle \qquad (4.1.17)$$

have the same energy. We saw in Chapter 3 that under rotation different

m-values get mixed up. In general, $\mathcal{D}(R)|n; j, m\rangle$ is a linear combination of $2j + 1$ independent states. Explicitly,

$$\mathcal{D}(R)|n; j,m\rangle = \sum_{m'} |n; j,m'\rangle \mathcal{D}^{(j)}_{m'm}(R), \qquad (4.1.18)$$

and by changing the continuous parameter that characterizes the rotation operator $\mathcal{D}(R)$, we can get different linear combinations of $|n; j, m'\rangle$. If all states of form $\mathcal{D}(R)|n; j, m\rangle$ with arbitrary $\mathcal{D}(R)$ are to have the same energy, it is then essential that each of $|n; j, m\rangle$ with different m must have the same energy. So the degeneracy here is $(2j + 1)$-fold, just equal to the number of possible m-values. This point is also evident from the fact that all states obtained by successively applying $J_{\pm}$, which commutes with H, to $|n; jm\rangle$ have the same energy.

As an application, consider an atomic electron whose potential is written as $V(r) + V_{LS}(r)\mathbf{L}\cdot\mathbf{S}$. Because r and $\mathbf{L}\cdot\mathbf{S}$ are both rotationally invariant, we expect a $(2j + 1)$-fold degeneracy for each atomic level. On the other hand, suppose there is an external electric or magnetic field, say in the z-direction. The rotational symmetry is now manifestly broken; as a result, the $(2j + 1)$-fold degeneracy is no longer expected and states characterized by different m-values no longer have the same energy. We will examine how this splitting arises in Chapter 5.

4.2. DISCRETE SYMMETRIES, PARITY, OR SPACE INVERSION

So far we have considered continuous symmetry operators—that is, operations that can be obtained by applying successively infinitesimal symmetry operations. All symmetry operations useful in quantum mechanics are not necessarily of this form. In this chapter we consider three symmetry operations that can be considered to be discrete, as opposed to continuous —parity, lattice translation, and time reversal.

The first operation we consider is **parity**, or space inversion. The parity operation, as applied to transformation on the coordinate system, changes a right-handed (RH) system into a left-handed (LH) system, as shown in Figure 4.1. However, in this book we consider a transformation on state kets rather than on the coordinate system. Given $|\alpha\rangle$, we consider a space-inverted state, assumed to be obtained by applying a unitary operator π known as the **parity operator**, as follows:

$$|\alpha\rangle \rightarrow \pi|\alpha\rangle. \qquad (4.2.1)$$

We require the expectation value of $\mathbf{x}$ taken with respect to the space-inverted state to be opposite in sign.

$$\langle \alpha|\pi^{\dagger}\mathbf{x}\pi|\alpha\rangle = -\langle \alpha|\mathbf{x}|\alpha\rangle, \qquad (4.2.2)$$

FIGURE 4.1.   Right-handed (RH) and left-handed (LH) systems.

a very reasonable requirement. This is accomplished if

$$\pi^{\dagger}\mathbf{x}\pi = -\mathbf{x} \tag{4.2.3}$$

or

$$\mathbf{x}\pi = -\pi\mathbf{x}, \tag{4.2.4}$$

where we have used the fact that π is unitary. In other words, $\mathbf{x}$ and π must *anti*commute.

How does an eigenket of the position operator transform under parity? We claim that

$$\pi|\mathbf{x}'\rangle = e^{i\delta}|-\mathbf{x}'\rangle \tag{4.2.5}$$

where $e^{i\delta}$ is a phase factor (δ real). To prove this assertion let us note that

$$\mathbf{x}\pi|\mathbf{x}'\rangle = -\pi\mathbf{x}|\mathbf{x}'\rangle = (-\mathbf{x}')\pi|\mathbf{x}'\rangle. \tag{4.2.6}$$

This equation says that $\pi|\mathbf{x}'\rangle$ is an eigenket of $\mathbf{x}$ with eigenvalue $-\mathbf{x}'$, so it must be the same as a position eigenket $|-\mathbf{x}'\rangle$ up to a phase factor.

It is customary to take $e^{i\delta} = 1$ by convention. Substituting this in (4.2.5), we have $\pi^2|\mathbf{x}'\rangle = |\mathbf{x}'\rangle$; hence, $\pi^2 = 1$—that is, we come back to the same state by applying π twice. We easily see from (4.2.5) that π is now not only unitary but also Hermitian:

$$\pi^{-1} = \pi^{\dagger} = \pi. \tag{4.2.7}$$

Its eigenvalue can be only $+1$ or -1.

What about the momentum operator? The momentum $\mathbf{p}$ is like $m\,d\mathbf{x}/dt$, so it is natural to expect it to be odd under parity, like $\mathbf{x}$. A more satisfactory argument considers the momentum operator as the generator of translation. Since translation followed by parity is equivalent to parity followed by translation in the *opposite* direction, as can be seen from Figure

4.2, then

$$\pi \mathcal{T}(d\mathbf{x}') = \mathcal{T}(-d\mathbf{x}')\pi \qquad (4.2.8)$$

$$\pi\left(1 - \frac{i\mathbf{p}\cdot d\mathbf{x}'}{\hbar}\right)\pi^\dagger = 1 + \frac{i\mathbf{p}\cdot d\mathbf{x}'}{\hbar}, \qquad (4.2.9)$$

from which follows

$$\{\pi, \mathbf{p}\} = 0 \quad \text{or} \quad \pi^\dagger\mathbf{p}\pi = -\mathbf{p}. \qquad (4.2.10)$$

We can now discuss the behavior of $\mathbf{J}$ under parity. First, for orbital angular momentum we clearly have

$$[\pi, \mathbf{L}] = 0 \qquad (4.2.11)$$

because

$$\mathbf{L} = \mathbf{x} \times \mathbf{p}, \qquad (4.2.12)$$

and both $\mathbf{x}$ and $\mathbf{p}$ are odd under parity. However, to show that this property also holds for spin, it is best to use the fact that $\mathbf{J}$ is the generator of rotation. For 3×3 orthogonal matrices, we have

$$R^{(\text{parity})}R^{(\text{rotation})} = R^{(\text{rotation})}R^{(\text{parity})}, \qquad (4.2.13)$$

where explicitly

$$R^{(\text{parity})} = \begin{pmatrix} -1 & & 0 \\ & -1 & \\ 0 & & -1 \end{pmatrix}; \qquad (4.2.14)$$

that is, the parity and rotation operations commute. In quantum mechanics, it is natural to postulate the corresponding relation for the unitary operators, so

$$\pi \mathscr{D}(R) = \mathscr{D}(R)\pi, \qquad (4.2.15)$$

FIGURE 4.2. Translation followed by parity, and vice versa.

where $\mathscr{D}(R) = 1 - i\mathbf{J}\cdot\hat{\mathbf{n}}\varepsilon/\hbar$. From (4.2.15) it follows that

$$[\pi, \mathbf{J}] = 0 \quad \text{or} \quad \pi^\dagger \mathbf{J}\pi = \mathbf{J}. \tag{4.2.16}$$

This together with (4.2.11) means that the spin operator (given by $\mathbf{J} = \mathbf{L} + \mathbf{S}$) also transforms in the same way as $\mathbf{L}$.

Under rotations, $\mathbf{x}$ and $\mathbf{J}$ transform in the same way, so they are both vectors, or spherical tensors, of rank 1. However, $\mathbf{x}$ (or $\mathbf{p}$) is odd under parity [see (4.2.3) and (4.2.10)], while $\mathbf{J}$ is even under parity [see (4.2.16)]. Vectors that are odd under parity are called **polar vectors**, while vectors that are even under parity are called **axial vectors**, or **pseudovectors**.

Let us now consider operators like $\mathbf{S}\cdot\mathbf{x}$. Under rotations they transform like ordinary scalars, such as $\mathbf{S}\cdot\mathbf{L}$ or $\mathbf{x}\cdot\mathbf{p}$. Yet under space inversion we have

$$\pi^{-1}\mathbf{S}\cdot\mathbf{x}\pi = -\mathbf{S}\cdot\mathbf{x}, \tag{4.2.17}$$

while for ordinary scalars we have

$$\pi^{-1}\mathbf{L}\cdot\mathbf{S}\pi = \mathbf{L}\cdot\mathbf{S} \tag{4.2.18}$$

and so on. The operator $\mathbf{S}\cdot\mathbf{x}$ is an example of a **pseudoscalar**.

Wave Functions Under Parity

Let us now look at the parity property of wave functions. First, let ψ be the wave function of a spinless particle whose state ket is $|\alpha\rangle$:

$$\psi(\mathbf{x}') = \langle \mathbf{x}'|\alpha\rangle. \tag{4.2.19}$$

The wave function of the space-inverted state, represented by the state ket $\pi|\alpha\rangle$, is

$$\langle \mathbf{x}'|\pi|\alpha\rangle = \langle -\mathbf{x}'|\alpha\rangle = \psi(-\mathbf{x}'). \tag{4.2.20}$$

Suppose $|\alpha\rangle$ is an eigenket of parity. We have already seen that the eigenvalue of parity must be ± 1, so

$$\pi|\alpha\rangle = \pm|\alpha\rangle. \tag{4.2.21}$$

Let us look at its corresponding wave function,

$$\langle \mathbf{x}'|\pi|\alpha\rangle = \pm\langle \mathbf{x}'|\alpha\rangle. \tag{4.2.22}$$

But we also have

$$\langle \mathbf{x}'|\pi|\alpha\rangle = \langle -\mathbf{x}'|\alpha\rangle, \tag{4.2.23}$$

so the state $|\alpha\rangle$ is even or odd under parity depending on whether the corresponding wave function satisfies

$$\psi(-\mathbf{x}') = \pm\psi(\mathbf{x}')\begin{cases} \text{even parity,} \\ \text{odd parity.} \end{cases} \tag{4.2.24}$$

Not all wave functions of physical interest have definite parities in the sense of (4.2.24). Consider, for instance, the momentum eigenket. The momentum operator anticommutes with the parity operator, so the momentum eigenket is not expected to be a parity eigenket. Indeed, it is easy to see that the plane wave, which is the wave function for a momentum eigenket, does not satisfy (4.2.24).

An eigenket of orbital angular momentum is expected to be a parity eigenket because $\mathbf{L}$ and π commute [see (4.2.11)]. To see how an eigenket of $\mathbf{L}^2$ and L_z behaves under parity, let us examine the properties of its wave function under space inversion,

$$\langle \mathbf{x}'|\alpha, lm\rangle = R_\alpha(r)Y_l^m(\theta,\phi). \tag{4.2.25}$$

The transformation $\mathbf{x}' \to -\mathbf{x}'$ is accomplished by letting

$$r \to r$$

$$\theta \to \pi - \theta \qquad (\cos\theta \to -\cos\theta) \tag{4.2.26}$$

$$\phi \to \phi + \pi \qquad \left(e^{im\phi} \to (-1)^m e^{im\phi}\right).$$

Using the explicit form of

$$Y_l^m = (-1)^m \sqrt{\frac{(2l+1)(l-m)!}{4\pi(l+m)!}} \, P_l^m(\cos\theta)e^{im\phi} \tag{4.2.27}$$

for positive m, with (3.6.38), where

$$P_l^{|m|}(\cos\theta) = \frac{(-1)^{m+l}}{2^l l!}\frac{(l+|m|)!}{(l-|m|)!}\sin^{-|m|}\theta\left(\frac{d}{d(\cos\theta)}\right)^{l-|m|}\sin^{2l}\theta, \tag{4.2.28}$$

we can readily show that

$$Y_l^m \to (-1)^l Y_l^m \tag{4.2.29}$$

as θ and ϕ are changed, as in (4.2.26). Therefore, we can conclude that

$$\pi|\alpha, lm\rangle = (-1)^l|\alpha, lm\rangle. \tag{4.2.30}$$

It is actually not necessary to look at Y_l^m; an easier way to obtain the same result is to work with $m = 0$ and note that $L_\pm^r|l, m=0\rangle$ $(r = 0,1,\ldots,l)$ must have the same parity because π and $(L_\pm)^r$ commute.

Let us now look at the parity properties of energy eigenstates. We begin by stating a very important theorem.

Theorem. *Suppose*

$$[H, \pi] = 0 \tag{4.2.31}$$

and $|n\rangle$ is a nondegenerate eigenket of H with eigenvalue E_n:

$$H|n\rangle = E_n|n\rangle; \tag{4.2.32}$$

then $|n\rangle$ *is also a parity eigenket.*

Proof. We prove this theorem by first noting that

$$\tfrac{1}{2}(1 \pm \pi)|n\rangle \qquad\qquad\qquad (4.2.33)$$

is a parity eigenket with eigenvalues ± 1 (just use $\pi^2 = 1$). But this is also an energy eigenket with eigenvalue E_n. Furthermore, $|n\rangle$ and (4.2.33) must represent the same state, otherwise there would be two states with the same energy—a contradiction of our nondegenerate assumption. It therefore follows that $|n\rangle$, which is the same as (4.2.33) up to a multiplicative constant, must be a parity eigenket with parity ± 1.   □

As an example, let us look at the simple harmonic oscillator (SHO). The ground state $|0\rangle$ has even parity because its wave function, being Gaussian, is even under $x' \to -x'$. The first excited state,

$$|1\rangle = a^{\dagger}|0\rangle, \qquad\qquad\qquad (4.2.34)$$

must have an odd parity because $a^{\dagger}$ is linear in x and p, which are both odd [see (2.3.2)]. In general, the parity of the nth excited state of the simple harmonic operator is given by $(-1)^n$.

It is important to note that the nondegenerate assumption is essential here. For instance, consider the hydrogen atom in nonrelativistic quantum mechanics. As is well known, the energy eigenvalues depend only on the principal quantum number n (for example, $2p$ and $2s$ states are degenerate) —the Coulomb potential is obviously invariant under parity—yet an energy eigenket

$$c_p|2p\rangle + c_s|2s\rangle \qquad\qquad\qquad (4.2.35)$$

is obviously not a parity eigenket.

As another example, consider a momentum eigenket. Momentum anticommutes with parity, so—even though free-particle Hamiltonian H is invariant under parity—the momentum eigenket (though obviously an energy eigenket) is not a parity eigenket. Our theorem remains intact because we have here a degeneracy between $|\mathbf{p}'\rangle$ and $|-\mathbf{p}'\rangle$, which have the same energy. In fact, we can easily construct linear combinations $(1/\sqrt{2})(|\mathbf{p}'\rangle \pm |-\mathbf{p}'\rangle)$, which are parity eigenkets with eigenvalues ± 1. In terms of wave-function language, $e^{i\mathbf{p}' \cdot \mathbf{x}'/\hbar}$ does not have a definite parity, but $\cos \mathbf{p}' \cdot \mathbf{x}'/\hbar$ and $\sin \mathbf{p}' \cdot \mathbf{x}'/\hbar$ do.

Symmetrical Double-Well Potential

As an elementary but instructive example, we consider a symmetrical double-well potential; see Figure 4.3. The Hamiltonian is obviously invariant under parity. In fact, the two lowest lying states are as shown in

Symmetric |S>   Anti-symmetric |A>

FIGURE 4.3. The symmetrical double well with the two lowest lying states $|S\rangle$ (symmetrical) and $|A\rangle$ (antisymmetrical) shown.

Figure 4.3, we can see by working out the explicit solutions involving sine and cosine in classically allowed regions and sinh and cosh in the classically forbidden region. The solutions are matched where the potential is discontinuous; we call them the **symmetrical state** $|S\rangle$ and the **antisymmetrical state** $|A\rangle$. Of course, they are simultaneous eigenkets of H and π. Calculation also shows that

$$E_A > E_S, \tag{4.2.36}$$

which we can infer from Figure 4.3 by noting that the wave function of the antisymmetrical state has a greater curvature. The energy difference is very tiny if the middle barrier is high, a point which we will discuss later.

We can form

$$|R\rangle = \frac{1}{\sqrt{2}}(|S\rangle + |A\rangle) \tag{4.2.37a}$$

and

$$|L\rangle = \frac{1}{\sqrt{2}}(|S\rangle - |A\rangle). \tag{4.2.37b}$$

The wave functions of (4.2.37a) and (4.2.37b) are largely concentrated in the right-hand side and the left-hand side, respectively. They are obviously not parity eigenstates; in fact, under parity $|R\rangle$ and $|L\rangle$ are interchanged. Note that they are not energy eigenstates either. Indeed, they are classical examples of **nonstationary states**. To be precise, let us assume that the system is represented by $|R\rangle$ at $t = 0$. At a later time, we have

$$|R, t_0 = 0; t\rangle = \frac{1}{\sqrt{2}}\left(e^{-iE_s t/\hbar}|S\rangle + e^{-iE_A t/\hbar}|A\rangle\right)$$

$$= \frac{1}{\sqrt{2}}e^{-iE_s t/\hbar}\left(|S\rangle + e^{-i(E_A - E_S)t/\hbar}|A\rangle\right). \tag{4.2.38}$$

At time $t = T/2 \equiv 2\pi\hbar/2(E_A - E_S)$, the system is found in pure $|L\rangle$. At $t = T$, we are back to pure $|R\rangle$, and so forth. Thus, in general, we have an oscillation between $|R\rangle$ and $|L\rangle$ with angular frequency

$$\omega = \frac{(E_A - E_S)}{\hbar}. \tag{4.2.39}$$

This oscillatory behavior can also be considered from the viewpoint of tunneling in quantum mechanics. A particle initially confined to the right-hand side can tunnel through the classically forbidden region (the middle barrier) into the left-hand side, then back to the right-hand side, and so on. But now let the middle barrier become infinitely high; see Figure 4.4. The $|S\rangle$ and $|A\rangle$ states are now degenerate, so (4.2.37a) and (4.2.37b) are also energy eigenkets even though they are not parity eigenkets. Once the system is found in $|R\rangle$, it remains so forever (oscillation time between $|S\rangle$ and $|A\rangle$ is now ∞). Because the middle barrier is infinitely high, there is no possibility for tunneling. Thus when there is degeneracy, the physically realizable energy eigenkets need not be parity eigenkets. We have a ground state which is asymmetrical despite the fact that the Hamiltonian itself is symmetrical under space inversion, so with degeneracy the symmetry of H is not necessarily obeyed by energy eigenstates $|S\rangle$ and $|A\rangle$.

This is a very simple example of broken symmetry and degeneracy. Nature is full of situations analogous to this. Consider a ferromagnet. The basic Hamiltonian for iron atoms is rotationally invariant, but the ferromagnet clearly has a definite direction in space; hence, the (infinite) number of ground states is *not* rotationally invariant, since the spins are all aligned along some definite (but arbitrary) direction.

A textbook example of a system that illustrates the actual importance of the symmetrical double well is an ammonia molecule, NH_3; see Figure 4.5. We imagine that the three H atoms form the three corners of an equilateral triangle. The N atom can be up or down, where the directions up and down are defined because the molecule is rotating around the axis as

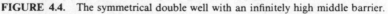

FIGURE 4.4.   The symmetrical double well with an infinitely high middle barrier.

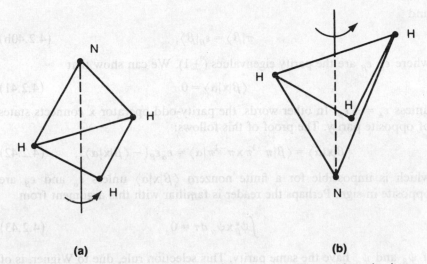

FIGURE 4.5. An ammonia molecule, NH_3, where the three H atoms form the three corners of an equilateral triangle.

shown in Figure 4.5. The up and down positions for the N atom are analogous to R and L of the double-well potential. The parity and energy eigenstates are *superpositions* of Figure 4.5a and Figure 4.5b in the sense of (4.2.37a) and (4.2.37b), respectively, and the energy difference between the simultaneous eigenstates of energy and parity correspond to an oscillation frequency of 24,000 MHz—a wavelength of about 1 cm, which is in the microwave region. In fact, NH_3 is of fundamental importance in maser physics.

There are naturally occurring organic molecules, such as sugar or amino acids, which are of the R-type (or L-type) only. Such molecules which have definite handedness are called **optical isomers**. In many cases the oscillation time is practically infinite—on the order of 10^4–10^6 years—so R-type molecules remain right-handed for all practical purposes. It is amusing that if we attempt to synthesize such organic molecules in the laboratory, we find equal mixtures of R and L. Why we have a preponderance of one type is nature's deepest mystery. Is it due to a genetic accident, like the spiral shell of a snail or the fact that our hearts are on the left-hand side?

Parity-Selection Rule

Suppose $|\alpha\rangle$ and $|\beta\rangle$ are parity eigenstates:

$$\pi|\alpha\rangle = \varepsilon_\alpha|\alpha\rangle \qquad (4.2.40a)$$

and

$$\pi|\beta\rangle = \varepsilon_\beta|\beta\rangle, \qquad (4.2.40b)$$

where ε_α, ε_β are the parity eigenvalues (± 1). We can show that

$$\langle\beta|\mathbf{x}|\alpha\rangle = 0 \qquad (4.2.41)$$

unless $\varepsilon_\alpha = -\varepsilon_\beta$. In other words, the parity-odd operator $\mathbf{x}$ connects states of opposite parity. The proof of this follows:

$$\langle\beta|\mathbf{x}|\alpha\rangle = \langle\beta|\pi^{-1}\pi\mathbf{x}\pi^{-1}\pi|\alpha\rangle = \varepsilon_\alpha\varepsilon_\beta(-\langle\beta|\mathbf{x}|\alpha\rangle), \qquad (4.2.42)$$

which is impossible for a finite nonzero $\langle\beta|\mathbf{x}|\alpha\rangle$ unless ε_α and ε_β are opposite in sign. Perhaps the reader is familiar with this argument from

$$\int\psi_\beta^*\mathbf{x}\psi_\alpha\,d\tau = 0 \qquad (4.2.43)$$

if ψ_β and ψ_α have the same parity. This selection rule, due to Wigner, is of importance in discussing radiative transitions between atomic states. As we will discuss in greater detail later, radiative transitions take place between states of opposite parity as a consequence of multipole expansion formalism. This rule was known phenomenologically from analysis of spectral lines, before the birth of quantum mechanics, as **Laporte's rule**. It was Wigner who showed that Laporte's rule is a consequence of the parity-selection rule.

If the basic Hamiltonian H is invariant under parity, nondegenerate energy eigenstates [as a corollary of (4.2.43)] cannot possess a permanent electric dipole moment:

$$\langle n|\mathbf{x}|n\rangle = 0. \qquad (4.2.44)$$

This follows trivially from (4.2.43), because with the nondegenerate assumption, energy eigenstates are also parity eigenstates [see (4.2.32) and (4.2.33)]. For a degenerate state, it is perfectly all right to have an electric dipole moment. We will see an example of this when we discuss the linear Stark effect in Chapter 5.

Our considerations can be generalized: Operators that are odd under parity, like $\mathbf{p}$ or $\mathbf{S}\cdot\mathbf{x}$, have nonvanishing matrix elements only between states of opposite parity. In contrast, operators that are even under parity connect states of the same parity.

Parity Nonconservation

The basic Hamiltonian responsible for the so-called weak interaction of elementary particles is not invariant under parity. In decay processes we can have final states which are superpositions of opposite parity states. Observable quantities like the angular distribution of decay products can depend on pseudoscalars such as $\langle S \rangle \cdot p$. It is remarkable that parity conservation was believed to be a sacred principle until 1956, when Lee and Yang speculated that parity is not conserved in weak interactions and proposed crucial experiments to test the validity of parity conservation. Subsequent experiments indeed showed that observable effects do depend on pseudoscalar quantities such as correlation between $\langle S \rangle$ and p. Because parity is not conserved in weak interactions, previously thought "pure" nuclear and atomic states are, in fact, parity mixtures. These subtle effects have also been found experimentally.

4.3. LATTICE TRANSLATION AS A DISCRETE SYMMETRY

We now consider another kind of discrete symmetry operation, namely, lattice translation. This subject has extremely important applications in solid-state physics.

Consider a periodic potential in one dimension, where $V(x \pm a) = V(x)$, as depicted in Figure 4.6. Realistically, we may consider the motion

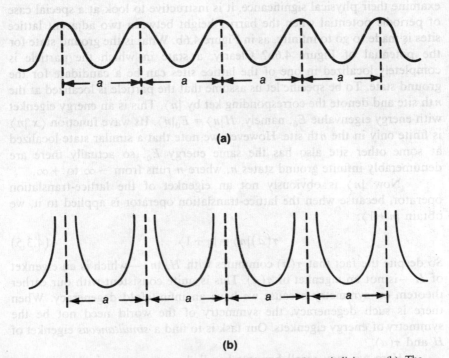

FIGURE 4.6. (a) Periodic potential in one dimension with periodicity a. (b) The periodic potential when the barrier height between two adjacent lattice sites becomes infinite.

of an electron in a chain of regularly spaced positive ions. In general, the Hamiltonian is not invariant under a translation represented by $\tau(l)$ with l arbitrary, where $\tau(l)$ has the property (see Section 1.6)

$$\tau^\dagger(l)x\tau(l) = x + l, \qquad \tau(l)|x'\rangle = |x'+l\rangle. \qquad (4.3.1)$$

However, when l coincides with the lattice spacing a, we do have

$$\tau^\dagger(a)V(x)\tau(a) = V(x+a) = V(x). \qquad (4.3.2)$$

Because the kinetic-energy part of the Hamiltonian H is invariant under the translation with any displacement, the entire Hamiltonian satisfies

$$\tau^\dagger(a)H\tau(a) = H. \qquad (4.3.3)$$

Because $\tau(a)$ is unitary, we have [from (4.3.3)]

$$[H, \tau(a)] = 0, \qquad (4.3.4)$$

so the Hamiltonian and $\tau(a)$ can be simultaneously diagonalized. Although $\tau(a)$ is unitary, it is not Hermitian, so we expect the eigenvalue to be a *complex* number of modulus 1.

Before we determine the eigenkets and eigenvalues of $\tau(a)$ and examine their physical significance, it is instructive to look at a special case of periodic potential when the barrier height between two adjacent lattice sites is made to go to infinity, as in Figure 4.6b. What is the ground state for the potential of Figure 4.6b? Clearly, a state in which the particle is completely localized in one of the lattice sites can be a candidate for the ground state. To be specific let us assume that the particle is localized at the nth site and denote the corresponding ket by $|n\rangle$. This is an energy eigenket with energy eigenvalue E_0, namely, $H|n\rangle = E_0|n\rangle$. Its wave function $\langle x'|n\rangle$ is finite only in the nth site. However, we note that a similar state localized at some other site also has the same energy E_0, so actually there are denumerably infinite ground states n, where n runs from $-\infty$ to $+\infty$.

Now $|n\rangle$ is obviously not an eigenket of the lattice-translation operator, because when the lattice-translation operator is applied to it, we obtain $|n+1\rangle$:

$$\tau(a)|n\rangle = |n+1\rangle. \qquad (4.3.5)$$

So despite the fact that $\tau(a)$ commutes with H, $|n\rangle$—which is an eigenket of H—is not an eigenket of $\tau(a)$. This is quite consistent with our earlier theorem on symmetry because we have an infinitefold degeneracy. When there is such degeneracy, the symmetry of the world need not be the symmetry of energy eigenkets. Our task is to find a *simultaneous* eigenket of H and $\tau(a)$.

Here we may recall how we handled a somewhat similar situation with the symmetrical double-well potential of the previous section. We noted that even though neither $|R\rangle$ nor $|L\rangle$ is an eigenket of π, we could easily form a symmetrical and an antisymmetrical combination of $|R\rangle$ and $|L\rangle$ that are parity eigenkets. The case is analogous here. Let us specifically form a linear combination

$$|\theta\rangle \equiv \sum_{n=-\infty}^{\infty} e^{in\theta}|n\rangle, \qquad (4.3.6)$$

where θ is a real parameter with $-\pi \leq \theta \leq \pi$. We assert that $|\theta\rangle$ is a simultaneous eigenket of H and $\tau(a)$. That it is an H eigenket is obvious because $|n\rangle$ is an energy eigenket with eigenvalue E_0, independent of n. To show that it is also an eigenket of the lattice translation operator we apply $\tau(a)$ as follows:

$$\tau(a)|\theta\rangle = \sum_{n=-\infty}^{\infty} e^{in\theta}|n+1\rangle = \sum_{n=-\infty}^{\infty} e^{i(n-1)\theta}|n\rangle$$
$$= e^{-i\theta}|\theta\rangle. \qquad (4.3.7)$$

Note that this simultaneous eigenket of H and $\tau(a)$ is parameterized by a continuous parameter θ. Furthermore, the energy eigenvalue E_0 is independent of θ.

Let us now return to the more realistic situation of Figure 4.6a, where the barrier between two adjacent lattice sites is not infinitely high. We can construct a localized ket $|n\rangle$ just as before with the property $\tau(a)|n\rangle = |n+1\rangle$. However, this time we expect that there is some leakage possible into neighboring lattice sites due to quantum-mechanical tunneling. In other words, the wave function $\langle x'|n\rangle$ has a tail extending to sites other than the nth site. The diagonal elements of H in the $\{|n\rangle\}$ basis are all equal because of translation invariance, that is,

$$\langle n|H|n\rangle = E_0, \qquad (4.3.8)$$

independent of n, as before. However we suspect that H is not completely diagonal in the $\{|n\rangle\}$ basis due to leakage. Now, suppose the barriers between adjacent sites are high (but not infinite). We then expect matrix elements of H between distant sites to be completely negligible. Let us assume that the only nondiagonal elements of importance connect immediate neighbors. That is,

$$\langle n'|H|n\rangle \neq 0 \quad \text{only if } n' = n \quad \text{or} \quad n' = n \pm 1. \qquad (4.3.9)$$

In solid-state physics this assumption is known as the **tight-binding approximation**. Let us define

$$\langle n \pm 1|H|n\rangle = -\Delta. \qquad (4.3.10)$$

Clearly, Δ is again independent of n due to translation invariance of the Hamiltonian. To the extent that $|n\rangle$ and $|n'\rangle$ are orthogonal when $n \neq n'$,

we obtain

$$H|n\rangle = E_0|n\rangle - \Delta|n+1\rangle - \Delta|n-1\rangle. \qquad (4.3.11)$$

Note that $|n\rangle$ is no longer an energy eigenket.

As we have done with the potential of Figure 4.6b, let us form a linear combination

$$|\theta\rangle = \sum_{n=-\infty}^{\infty} e^{in\theta}|n\rangle. \qquad (4.3.12)$$

Clearly, $|\theta\rangle$ is an eigenket of translation operator $\tau(a)$ because the steps in (4.3.7) still hold. A natural question is, is $|\theta\rangle$ an energy eigenket? To answer this question, we apply H:

$$H\sum e^{in\theta}|n\rangle = E_0\sum e^{in\theta}|n\rangle - \Delta\sum e^{in\theta}|n+1\rangle - \Delta\sum e^{in\theta}|n-1\rangle$$

$$= E_0\sum e^{in\theta}|n\rangle - \Delta\sum(e^{in\theta-i\theta} + e^{in\theta+i\theta})|n\rangle$$

$$= (E_0 - 2\Delta\cos\theta)\sum e^{in\theta}|n\rangle. \qquad (4.3.13)$$

The big difference between this and the previous situation is that the energy eigenvalue now depends on the continuous real parameter θ. The degeneracy is lifted as Δ becomes finite, and we have a continuous distribution of energy eigenvalues between $E_0 - 2\Delta$ and $E_0 + 2\Delta$. See Figure 4.7, where we visualize how the energy levels start forming a continuous energy band as Δ is increased from zero.

To see the physical meaning of the parameter θ let us study the wave function $\langle x'|\theta\rangle$. For the wave function of the lattice-translated state $\tau(a)|\theta\rangle$,

FIGURE 4.7. Energy levels forming a continuous energy band as Δ is increased from zero.

we obtain

$$\langle x'|\tau(a)|\theta\rangle = \langle x' - a|\theta\rangle \tag{4.3.14}$$

by letting $\tau(a)$ act on $\langle x'|$. But we can also let $\tau(a)$ operate on $|\theta\rangle$ and use (4.3.7). Thus

$$\langle x'|\tau(a)|\theta\rangle = e^{-i\theta}\langle x'|\theta\rangle, \tag{4.3.15}$$

so

$$\langle x' - a|\theta\rangle = \langle x'|\theta\rangle e^{-i\theta}. \tag{4.3.16}$$

We solve this equation by setting

$$\langle x'|\theta\rangle = e^{ikx'}u_k(x'), \tag{4.3.17}$$

with $\theta = ka$, where $u_k(x')$ is a periodic function with period a, as we can easily verify by explicit substitutions, namely,

$$e^{ik(x'-a)}u_k(x' - a) = e^{ikx'}u_k(x')e^{-ika}. \tag{4.3.18}$$

Thus we get the important condition known as **Bloch's theorem**: The wave function of $|\theta\rangle$, which is an eigenket of $\tau(a)$, can be written as a plane wave $e^{ikx'}$ times a periodic function with periodicity a. Notice that the only fact we used was that $|\theta\rangle$ is an eigenket of $\tau(a)$ with eigenvalue $e^{-i\theta}$ [see (4.3.7)]. In particular, the theorem holds even if the tight-binding approximation (4.3.9) breaks down.

We are now in a position to interpret our earlier result (4.3.13) for $|\theta\rangle$ given by (4.3.12). We know that the wave function is a plane wave characterized by the propagation wave vector k modulated by a periodic function $u_k(x')$ [see (4.3.17)]. As θ varies from $-\pi$ to π, the wave vector k varies from $-\pi/a$ to π/a. The energy eigenvalue E now depends on k as follows:

$$E(k) = E_0 - 2\Delta\cos ka. \tag{4.3.19}$$

Notice that this energy eigenvalue equation is independent of the detailed shape of the potential as long as the tight-binding approximation is valid. Note also that there is a cutoff in the wave vector k of the Bloch wave function (4.3.17) given by $|k| = \pi/a$. Equation (4.3.19) defines a dispersion curve, as shown in Figure 4.8. As a result of tunneling, the denumerably infinitefold degeneracy is now completely lifted, and the allowed energy values form a continuous band between $E_0 - 2\Delta$ and $E_0 + 2\Delta$, known as the **Brillouin zone**.

So far we have considered only one particle moving in a periodic potential. In a more realistic situation we must look at many electrons moving in such a potential. Actually the electrons satisfy the Pauli exclusion principle, as we will discuss more systematically in Chapter 6, and they start filling the band. In this way, the main qualitative features of metals,

FIGURE 4.8. Dispersion curve for $E(k)$ versus k in the Brillouin zone $|k| \leq \pi/a$.

semiconductors, and the like can be understood as a consequence of translation invariance supplemented by the exclusion principle.

The reader may have noted the similarity between the symmetrical double-well problem of Section 4.2 and the periodic potential of this section. Comparing Figures 4.3 and 4.6, we note that they can be regarded as opposite extremes (two versus infinite) of potentials with a finite number of troughs.

4.4. THE TIME-REVERSAL DISCRETE SYMMETRY

In this section we study another discrete symmetry operator, called **time reversal**. This is a difficult topic for the novice, partly because the term *time reversal* is a misnomer; it reminds us of science fiction. Actually what we do in this section can be more appropriately characterized by the term *reversal of motion*. Indeed, that is the terminology used by E. Wigner, who formulated time reversal in a very fundamental paper written in 1932.

For orientation purposes let us look at classical mechanics. Suppose there is a trajectory of a particle subject to a certain force field; see Figure 4.9. At $t = 0$, let the particle stop and reverse its motion: $\mathbf{p}|_{t=0} \to -\mathbf{p}|_{t=0}$. The particle traverses backward along the same trajectory. If you run the motion picture of trajectory (a) backward as in (b), you may have a hard time telling whether this is the correct sequence.

More formally, if $\mathbf{x}(t)$ is a solution to

$$m\ddot{\mathbf{x}} = -\nabla V(\mathbf{x}), \tag{4.4.1}$$

then $\mathbf{x}(-t)$ is also a possible solution in the same force field derivable from V. It is, of course, important to note that we do not have a dissipative force

(a)   **(b)**

FIGURE 4.9. (a) Classical trajectory which stops at $t = 0$ and (b) reverses its motion $\mathbf{p}|_{t=0} \to -\mathbf{p}|_{t=0}$.

here. A block sliding on a table decelerates (due to friction) and eventually stops. But have you ever seen a block on a table spontaneously start to move and accelerate?

With a magnetic field you may be able to tell the difference. Imagine that you are taking the motion picture of a spiraling electron trajectory in a magnetic field. You may be able to tell whether the motion picture is run forward or backward by comparing the sense of rotation with the magnetic pole labeling N and S. However, from a microscopic point of view, **B** is produced by moving charges via an electric current; if you could reverse the current that causes **B**, then the situation would be quite symmetrical. In terms of the picture shown in Figure 4.10, you may have figured out that N and S are mislabeled! Another more formal way of saying all this is that the Maxwell equations, for example,

$$\nabla \cdot \mathbf{E} = 4\pi\rho, \quad \nabla \times \mathbf{B} - \frac{1}{c}\frac{\partial \mathbf{E}}{\partial t} = \frac{4\pi \mathbf{j}}{c}, \quad \nabla \times \mathbf{E} = -\frac{1}{c}\frac{\partial \mathbf{B}}{\partial t}, \quad (4.4.2)$$

and the Lorentz force equation $\mathbf{F} = e[\mathbf{E} + (1/c)(\mathbf{v} \times \mathbf{B})]$ are invariant under $t \to -t$ provided we also let

$$\mathbf{E} \to \mathbf{E}, \quad \mathbf{B} \to -\mathbf{B}, \quad \rho \to \rho, \quad \mathbf{j} \to -\mathbf{j}, \quad \mathbf{v} \to -\mathbf{v}. \quad (4.4.3)$$

Let us now look at wave mechanics, where the basic equation of the Schrödinger wave equation is

$$ih\frac{\partial \psi}{\partial t} = \left(-\frac{\hbar^2}{2m}\nabla^2 + V \right)\psi. \quad (4.4.4)$$

Suppose $\psi(\mathbf{x}, t)$ is a solution. We can easily verify that $\psi(\mathbf{x}, -t)$ is not a solution, because of the appearance of the first-order time derivative. However, $\psi^*(\mathbf{x}, -t)$ is a solution, as you may verify by complex conjugation of (4.4.4). It is instructive to convince ourselves of this point for an

FIGURE 4.10.   Electron trajectory between the north and south poles of a magnet.

energy eigenstate, that is, by substituting

$$\psi(\mathbf{x}, t) = u_n(\mathbf{x})e^{-iE_n t/\hbar}, \qquad \psi^*(\mathbf{x}, -t) = u_n^*(\mathbf{x})e^{-iE_n t/\hbar} \qquad (4.4.5)$$

into the Schrödinger equation (4.4.4). Thus we conjecture that time reversal must have something to do with complex conjugation. If at $t = 0$ the wave function is given by

$$\psi = \langle \mathbf{x} | \alpha \rangle, \qquad (4.4.6)$$

then the wave function for the corresponding time-reversed state is given by $\langle \mathbf{x} | \alpha \rangle^*$. We will later show that this is indeed the case for the wave function of a spinless system. As an example, you may easily check this point for the wave function of a plane wave; see Problem 8 of this chapter.

Digression on Symmetry Operations

Before we begin a systematic treatment of the time-reversal operator, some general remarks on symmetry operations are in order. Consider a symmetry operation

$$|\alpha\rangle \to |\tilde{\alpha}\rangle, \qquad |\beta\rangle \to |\tilde{\beta}\rangle. \qquad (4.4.7)$$

One may argue that it is natural to require the inner product $\langle \beta | \alpha \rangle$ to be preserved, that is,

$$\langle \tilde{\beta} | \tilde{\alpha} \rangle = \langle \beta | \alpha \rangle. \qquad (4.4.8)$$

Indeed, for symmetry operations such as rotations, translations, and even parity, this is indeed the case. If $|\alpha\rangle$ is rotated and $|\beta\rangle$ is also rotated in the same manner, $\langle\beta|\alpha\rangle$ is unchanged. Formally this arises from the fact that, for the symmetry operations considered in the previous sections, the corresponding symmetry operator is unitary, so

$$\langle\beta|\alpha\rangle \rightarrow \langle\beta|U^\dagger U|\alpha\rangle = \langle\beta|\alpha\rangle. \qquad (4.4.9)$$

However, in discussing time reversal, we see that requirement (4.4.8) turns out to be too restrictive. Instead, we merely impose the weaker requirement that

$$|\langle\tilde{\beta}|\tilde{\alpha}\rangle| = |\langle\beta|\alpha\rangle|. \qquad (4.4.10)$$

Requirement (4.4.8) obviously satisfies (4.4.10). But this is not the only way;

$$\langle\tilde{\beta}|\tilde{\alpha}\rangle = \langle\beta|\alpha\rangle^* = \langle\alpha|\beta\rangle \qquad (4.4.11)$$

works equally well. We pursue the latter possibility in this section because from our earlier discussion based on the Schrödinger equation we inferred that time reversal has something to do with complex conjugation.

Definition. *The transformation*

$$|\alpha\rangle \rightarrow |\tilde{\alpha}\rangle = \theta|\alpha\rangle, \qquad |\beta\rangle \rightarrow |\tilde{\beta}\rangle = \theta|\beta\rangle \qquad (4.4.12)$$

*is said to be **antiunitary** if*

$$\langle\tilde{\beta}|\tilde{\alpha}\rangle = \langle\beta|\alpha\rangle^*, \qquad (4.4.13a)$$

$$\theta(c_1|\alpha\rangle + c_2|\beta\rangle) = c_1^*\theta|\alpha\rangle + c_2^*\theta|\beta\rangle. \qquad (4.4.13b)$$

In such a case the operator θ is an antiunitary operator. Relation (4.4.13b) alone defines an **antilinear** operator.

We now claim that an antiunitary operator can be written as

$$\theta = UK, \qquad (4.4.14)$$

where U is a unitary operator and K is the complex-conjugate operator that forms the complex conjugate of any coefficient that multiplies a ket (and stands on the right of K). Before checking (4.4.13) let us examine the property of the K operator. Suppose we have a ket multiplied by a complex number c. We then have

$$Kc|\alpha\rangle = c^*K|\alpha\rangle. \qquad (4.4.15)$$

One may further ask, What happens if $|\alpha\rangle$ is expanded in terms of base kets $\{|a'\rangle\}$? Under the action K we have

$$|\alpha\rangle = \sum_{a'}|a'\rangle\langle a'|\alpha\rangle \overset{K}{\rightarrow} |\tilde{\alpha}\rangle = \sum_{a'}\langle a'|\alpha\rangle^*K|a'\rangle$$

$$= \sum_{a'}\langle a'|\alpha\rangle^*|a'\rangle. \qquad (4.4.16)$$

Notice that K acting on the base ket does not change the base ket. The explicit representation of $|a'\rangle$ is

$$|a'\rangle = \begin{pmatrix} 0 \\ 0 \\ \vdots \\ 0 \\ 1 \\ 0 \\ \vdots \\ 0 \end{pmatrix}, \tag{4.4.17}$$

and there is nothing to be changed by K. The reader may wonder, for instance, whether the S_y eigenkets for a spin $\frac{1}{2}$ system change under K. The answer is that if the S_z eigenkets are used as base kets, we must change the S_y eigenkets because the S_y eigenkets (1.1.14) undergo under K

$$K\left(\frac{1}{\sqrt{2}}|+\rangle \pm \frac{i}{\sqrt{2}}|-\rangle\right) \rightarrow \frac{1}{\sqrt{2}}|+\rangle \mp \frac{i}{\sqrt{2}}|-\rangle. \tag{4.4.18}$$

On the other hand, if the S_y eigenkets themselves are used as the base kets, we do not change the S_y eigenkets under the action of K. Thus the effect of K changes with the basis. As a result, the form of U in (4.4.14) also depends on the particular representation (that is, the choice of base kets) used. Gottfried puts it aptly: "If the basis is changed, the work of U and K has to be reapportioned."

Returning to $\theta = UK$ and (4.4.13), let us first check property (4.4.13b). We have

$$\theta(c_1|\alpha\rangle + c_2|\beta\rangle) = UK(c_1|\alpha\rangle + c_2|\beta\rangle)$$

$$= c_1^* UK|\alpha\rangle + c_2^* UK|\beta\rangle$$

$$= c_1^* \theta|\alpha\rangle + c_2^* \theta|\beta\rangle, \tag{4.4.19}$$

so (4.4.13b) indeed holds. Before checking (4.4.13a), we assert that it is always safer to work with the action of θ on kets only. We can figure out how the bras change just by looking at the corresponding kets. In particular, it is not necessary to consider θ acting on bras from the right, nor is it necessary to define $\theta^\dagger$. We have

$$|\alpha\rangle \xrightarrow{\theta} |\tilde{\alpha}\rangle = \sum_{a'} \langle a'|\alpha\rangle^* UK|a'\rangle$$

$$= \sum_{a'} \langle a'|\alpha\rangle^* U|a'\rangle$$

$$= \sum_{a'} \langle \alpha|a'\rangle U|a'\rangle. \tag{4.4.20}$$

As for $|\beta\rangle$, we have

$$|\tilde{\beta}\rangle = \sum_{a'} \langle a'|\beta\rangle^* U|a'\rangle \overset{\text{DC}}{\leftrightarrow} \langle \tilde{\beta}| = \sum_{a'} \langle a'|\beta\rangle \langle a'|U^\dagger$$

$$\langle \tilde{\beta}|\tilde{\alpha}\rangle = \sum_{a''} \sum_{a'} \langle a''|\beta\rangle \langle a''|U^\dagger U|a'\rangle \langle \alpha|a'\rangle$$

$$= \sum_{a'} \langle \alpha|a'\rangle \langle a'|\beta\rangle = \langle \alpha|\beta\rangle$$

$$= \langle \beta|\alpha\rangle^*, \tag{4.4.21}$$

so this checks.

In order for (4.4.10) to be satisfied, it is of physical interest to consider just two types of transformation—unitary and antiunitary. Other possibilities are related to either of the preceding via trivial phase changes. The proof of this assertion is actually very difficult and will not be discussed further here (Gottfried 1966, 226–28).

Time-Reversal Operator

We are finally in a position to present a formal theory of time reversal. Let us denote the time-reversal operator by Θ, to be distinguished from θ, a general antiunitary operator. Consider

$$|\alpha\rangle \rightarrow \Theta|\alpha\rangle, \tag{4.4.22}$$

where $\Theta|\alpha\rangle$ is the time-reversed state. More appropriately, $\Theta|\alpha\rangle$ should be called the motion-reversed state. If $|\alpha\rangle$ is a momentum eigenstate $|\mathbf{p}'\rangle$, we expect $\Theta|\alpha\rangle$ to be $|-\mathbf{p}'\rangle$ up to a possible phase. Likewise, $\mathbf{J}$ is to be reversed under time reversal.

We now deduce the fundamental property of the time-reversal operator by looking at the time evolution of the time-reversed state. Consider a physical system represented by a ket $|\alpha\rangle$, say at $t = 0$. Then at a slightly later time $t = \delta t$, the system is found in

$$|\alpha, t_0 = 0; t = \delta t\rangle = \left(1 - \frac{iH}{\hbar}\delta t\right)|\alpha\rangle, \tag{4.4.23}$$

where H is the Hamiltonian that characterizes the time evolution. Instead of the preceding equation, suppose we first apply Θ, say at $t = 0$, and then let the system evolve under the influence of the Hamiltonian H. We then have at δt

$$\left(1 - \frac{iH\delta t}{\hbar}\right)\Theta|\alpha\rangle. \tag{4.4.24a}$$

If motion obeys symmetry under time reversal, we expect the preceding state ket to be the same as

$$\Theta|\alpha, t_0 = 0; t = -\delta t\rangle \tag{4.4.24b}$$

that is, first consider a state ket at *earlier* time $t = -\delta t$, and then reverse **p** and **J**; see Figure 4.11. Mathematically,

$$\left(1 - \frac{iH}{\hbar}\delta t\right)\Theta|\alpha\rangle = \Theta\left(1 - \frac{iH}{\hbar}(-\delta t)\right)|\alpha\rangle. \qquad (4.4.25)$$

If the preceding relation is to be true for any ket, we must have

$$-iH\Theta|\rangle = \Theta iH|\rangle, \qquad (4.4.26)$$

where the blank ket $|\rangle$ emphasizes that (4.4.26) is to be true for any ket.

We now argue that Θ *cannot* be unitary if the motion of time reversal is to make sense. Suppose Θ were unitary. It would then be legitimate to cancel the i's in (4.4.26), and we would have the operator equation

$$-H\Theta = \Theta H. \qquad (4.4.27)$$

Consider an energy eigenket $|n\rangle$ with energy eigenvalue E_n. The corresponding time-reversed state would be $\Theta|n\rangle$, and we would have, because of (4.4.27),

$$H\Theta|n\rangle = -\Theta H|n\rangle = (-E_n)\Theta|n\rangle. \qquad (4.4.28)$$

This equation says that $\Theta|n\rangle$ is an eigenket of the Hamiltonian with energy eigenvalues $-E_n$. But this is nonsensical even in the very elementary case of a free particle. We know that the energy spectrum of the free particle is positive semidefinite—from 0 to $+\infty$. There is no state lower than a

FIGURE 4.11.   Momentum before and after time reversal at time $t = 0$ and $t = \pm \delta t$.

particle at rest (momentum eigenstate with momentum eigenvalue zero); the energy spectrum ranging from $-\infty$ to 0 would be completely unacceptable. We can also see this by looking at the structure of the free-particle Hamiltonian. We expect $\mathbf{p}$ to change sign but not $\mathbf{p}^2$; yet (4.4.27) would imply that

$$\Theta^{-1}\frac{\mathbf{p}^2}{2m}\Theta = \frac{-\mathbf{p}^2}{2m}. \qquad (4.4.29)$$

All these arguments strongly suggest that if time reversal is to be a useful symmetry at all, we are not allowed to cancel the i's in (4.4.26); hence, Θ had better be antiunitary. In this case the right-hand side of (4.4.26) becomes

$$\Theta iH|\,\rangle = -i\Theta H|\,\rangle \qquad (4.4.30)$$

by antilinear property (4.4.13b). Now at last we can cancel the i's in (4.4.26) leading, finally, via (4.4.30) to

$$\Theta H = H\Theta. \qquad (4.4.31)$$

Equation (4.4.31) expresses the fundamental property of the Hamiltonian under time reversal. With this equation the difficulties mentioned earlier [see (4.4.27) to (4.4.29)] are absent, and we obtain physically sensible results. From now on we will always take Θ to be antiunitary.

We mentioned earlier that it is best to avoid an antiunitary operator acting on bras from the right. Nevertheless, we may use

$$\langle\beta|\Theta|\alpha\rangle, \qquad (4.4.32)$$

which is always to be understood as

$$(\langle\beta|)\cdot(\Theta|\alpha\rangle) \qquad (4.4.33)$$

and never as

$$(\langle\beta|\Theta)\cdot|\alpha\rangle. \qquad (4.4.34)$$

In fact, we do not even attempt to define $\langle\beta|\Theta$. This is one place where the Dirac bra-ket notation is a little confusing. After all, that notation was invented to handle linear operators, not antilinear operators.

With this cautionary remark, we are in a position to discuss the behavior of operators under time reversal. We continue to take the point of view that the Θ operator is to act on kets

$$|\tilde{\alpha}\rangle = \Theta|\alpha\rangle, \qquad |\tilde{\beta}\rangle = \Theta|\beta\rangle, \qquad (4.4.35)$$

yet it is often convenient to talk about operators—in particular, observables —which are odd or even under time reversal. We start with an important identity, namely,

$$\langle\beta|\otimes|\alpha\rangle = \langle\tilde{\alpha}|\Theta\otimes^\dagger\Theta^{-1}|\tilde{\beta}\rangle, \qquad (4.4.36)$$

where $\otimes$ is a linear operator. This identity follows solely from the antiunitary nature of Θ. To prove this let us define

$$|\gamma\rangle \equiv \otimes^\dagger |\beta\rangle. \qquad (4.4.37)$$

By dual correspondence we have

$$|\gamma\rangle \overset{DC}{\leftrightarrow} \langle\beta|\otimes = \langle\gamma|. \qquad (4.4.38)$$

Hence,

$$\begin{aligned}
\langle\beta|\otimes|\alpha\rangle = \langle\gamma|\alpha\rangle &= \langle\tilde{\alpha}|\tilde{\gamma}\rangle \\
&= \langle\tilde{\alpha}|\Theta\otimes^\dagger|\beta\rangle = \langle\tilde{\alpha}|\Theta\otimes^\dagger\Theta^{-1}\Theta|\beta\rangle \\
&= \langle\tilde{\alpha}|\Theta\otimes^\dagger\Theta^{-1}|\tilde{\beta}\rangle, \qquad (4.4.39)
\end{aligned}$$

which proves the identity. In particular, for *Hermitian* observables A we get

$$\langle\beta|A|\alpha\rangle = \langle\tilde{\alpha}|\Theta A\Theta^{-1}|\tilde{\beta}\rangle. \qquad (4.4.40)$$

We say that observables are even or odd under time reversal according to whether we have the upper or lower sign in

$$\Theta A\Theta^{-1} = \pm A. \qquad (4.4.41)$$

Note that this equation, together with (4.4.40), gives a phase restriction on the matrix elements of A taken with respect to time reversed states as follows:

$$\langle\beta|A|\alpha\rangle = \pm\langle\tilde{\beta}|A|\tilde{\alpha}\rangle^*. \qquad (4.4.42)$$

If $|\beta\rangle$ is identical to $|\alpha\rangle$, so that we are talking about expectation values, we have

$$\langle\alpha|A|\alpha\rangle = \pm\langle\tilde{\alpha}|A|\tilde{\alpha}\rangle, \qquad (4.4.43)$$

where $\langle\tilde{\alpha}|A|\tilde{\alpha}\rangle$ is the expectation value taken with respect to the time-reversed state.

As an example, let us look at the expectation value of $\mathbf{p}$. It is reasonable to expect that the expectation value of $\mathbf{p}$ taken with respect to the time-reversed state be of opposite sign. Thus

$$\langle\alpha|\mathbf{p}|\alpha\rangle = -\langle\tilde{\alpha}|\mathbf{p}|\tilde{\alpha}\rangle, \qquad (4.4.44)$$

so we take $\mathbf{p}$ to be an odd operator, namely,

$$\Theta\mathbf{p}\Theta^{-1} = -\mathbf{p}. \qquad (4.4.45)$$

This implies that

$$\begin{aligned}
\mathbf{p}\Theta|\mathbf{p}'\rangle &= -\Theta\mathbf{p}\Theta^{-1}\Theta|\mathbf{p}'\rangle \\
&= (-\mathbf{p}')\Theta|\mathbf{p}'\rangle. \qquad (4.4.46)
\end{aligned}$$

Equation (4.4.46) agrees with our earlier assertion that $\Theta|\mathbf{p}'\rangle$ is a momentum eigenket with eigenvalue $-\mathbf{p}'$. It can be identified with $|-\mathbf{p}'\rangle$ itself with a suitable choice of phase. Likewise, we obtain

$$\Theta x \Theta^{-1} = x$$

$$\Theta |x'\rangle = |x'\rangle \quad \text{(up to a phase)} \tag{4.4.47}$$

from the (eminently reasonable) requirement

$$\langle \alpha |x| \alpha \rangle = \langle \tilde{\alpha} |x| \tilde{\alpha} \rangle. \tag{4.4.48}$$

We can now check the invariance of the fundamental commutation relation

$$[x_i, p_j]|\rangle = i\hbar \delta_{ij}|\rangle, \tag{4.4.49}$$

where the blank ket $|\rangle$ stands for any ket. Applying Θ to both sides of (4.4.49), we have

$$\Theta [x_i, p_j] \Theta^{-1} \Theta |\rangle = \Theta i\hbar \delta_{ij}|\rangle, \tag{4.4.50}$$

which leads to, after passing Θ through $i\hbar$,

$$[x_i, (-p_j)]\Theta |\rangle = -i\hbar \delta_{ij} \Theta |\rangle. \tag{4.4.51}$$

Note that the fundamental commutation relation $[x_i, p_j] = i\hbar \delta_{ij}$ is preserved by virtue of the fact that Θ is antiunitary. This can be given as yet another reason for taking Θ to be antiunitary; otherwise, we will be forced to abandon either (4.4.45) or (4.4.47)! Similarly, to preserve

$$[J_i, J_j] = i\hbar \varepsilon_{ijk} J_k, \tag{4.4.52}$$

the angular-momentum operator must be odd under time reversal, that is,

$$\Theta J \Theta^{-1} = -J. \tag{4.4.53}$$

This is consistent for spinless system where J is just $x \times p$. Alternatively, we could have deduced this relation by noting that the rotational operator and the time-reversal operator commute (note the extra i!).

Wave Function

Suppose at some given time, say at $t = 0$, a spinless single-particle system is found in a state represented by $|\alpha\rangle$. Its wave function $\langle x'|\alpha\rangle$ appears as the expansion coefficient in the position representation

$$|\alpha\rangle = \int d^3x' |x'\rangle \langle x'|\alpha\rangle. \tag{4.4.54}$$

Applying the time-reversal operator

$$\Theta |\alpha\rangle = \int d^3x' \, \Theta |x'\rangle \langle x'|\alpha\rangle^*$$

$$= \int d^3x' |x'\rangle \langle x'|\alpha\rangle^*, \tag{4.4.55}$$

where we have chosen the phase convention so that $\Theta |x'\rangle$ is $|x'\rangle$ itself. We then recover the rule

$$\psi(\mathbf{x}') \rightarrow \psi^*(\mathbf{x}') \tag{4.4.56}$$

inferred earlier by looking at the Schrödinger wave equation [see (4.4.5)]. The angular part of the wave function is given by a spherical harmonic Y_l^m. With the usual phase convention we have

$$Y_l^m(\theta, \phi) \rightarrow Y_l^{m*}(\theta, \phi) = (-1)^m Y_l^{-m}(\theta, \phi). \tag{4.4.57}$$

Now $Y_l^m(\theta, \phi)$ is the wave function for $|l, m\rangle$ [see (3.6.23)]; therefore, from (4.4.56) we deduce

$$\Theta|l, m\rangle = (-1)^m |l, -m\rangle. \tag{4.4.58}$$

If we study the probability current density (2.4.16) for a wave function of type (3.6.22) going like $R(r)Y_l^m$, we shall conclude that for $m > 0$ the current flows in the counterclockwise direction, as seen from the positive z-axis. The wave function for the corresponding time-reversed state has its probability current flowing in the opposite direction because the sign of m is reversed. All this is very reasonable.

As a nontrivial consequence of time-reversal invariance, we state an important theorem on the reality of the energy eigenfunction of a spinless particle.

Theorem. Suppose the Hamiltonian is invariant under time reversal and the energy eigenket $|n\rangle$ is nondegenerate; then the corresponding energy eigenfunction is real (or, more generally, a real function times a phase factor independent of $\mathbf{x}$).

Proof. To prove this, first note that

$$H\Theta|n\rangle = \Theta H|n\rangle = E_n\Theta|n\rangle, \tag{4.4.59}$$

so $|n\rangle$ and $\Theta|n\rangle$ have the same energy. The nondegeneracy assumption prompts us to conclude that $|n\rangle$ and $\Theta|n\rangle$ must represent the *same* state; otherwise there would be two different states with the same energy E_n, an obvious contradiction! Let us recall that the wave functions for $|n\rangle$ and $\Theta|n\rangle$ are $\langle\mathbf{x}'|n\rangle$ and $\langle\mathbf{x}'|n\rangle^*$, respectively. They must be the same—that is,

$$\langle\mathbf{x}'|n\rangle = \langle\mathbf{x}'|n\rangle^* \tag{4.4.60}$$

for all practical purposes—or, more precisely, they can differ at most by a phase factor independent of $\mathbf{x}$.   □

Thus if we have, for instance, a nondegenerate bound state, its wave function is always real. On the other hand, in the hydrogen atom with $l \neq 0$, $m \neq 0$, the energy eigenfunction characterized by definite (n, l, m) quantum numbers is complex because Y_l^m is complex; this does not contradict the theorem because $|n, l, m\rangle$ and $|n, l, -m\rangle$ are degenerate. Similarly, the wave function of a plane wave $e^{i\mathbf{p}\cdot\mathbf{x}/\hbar}$ is complex, but it is degenerate with $e^{-i\mathbf{p}\cdot\mathbf{x}/\hbar}$.

We see that for a spinless system, the wave function for the time-reversed state, say at $t = 0$, is simply obtained by complex conjugation. In terms of ket $|\alpha\rangle$ written as in (4.4.16) or in (4.4.54), the Θ operator is the complex conjugate operator K itself because K and Θ have the same effect when acting on the base ket $|a'\rangle$ (or $|\mathbf{x}'\rangle$). We may note, however, that the situation is quite different when the ket $|\alpha\rangle$ is expanded in terms of the momentum eigenket because Θ must change $|\mathbf{p}'\rangle$ into $|-\mathbf{p}'\rangle$ as follows:

$$\Theta|\alpha\rangle = \int d^3p'|-\mathbf{p}'\rangle\langle\mathbf{p}'|\alpha\rangle^* = \int d^3p'|\mathbf{p}'\rangle\langle-\mathbf{p}'|\alpha\rangle^*. \quad (4.4.61)$$

It is apparent that the momentum-space wave function of the time-reversed state is not just the complex conjugate of the original momentum-space wave function; rather, we must identify $\phi^*(-\mathbf{p}')$ as the momentum-space wave function for the time-reversed state. This situation once again illustrates the basic point that the particular form of Θ depends on the particular representation used.

Time Reversal for a Spin $\frac{1}{2}$ System

The situation is even more interesting for a particle with spin—spin $\frac{1}{2}$, in particular. We recall from Section 3.2 that the eigenket of $\mathbf{S}\cdot\hat{\mathbf{n}}$ with eigenvalue $\hbar/2$ can be written as

$$|\hat{\mathbf{n}}; +\rangle = e^{-iS_z\alpha/\hbar}e^{-iS_y\beta/\hbar}|+\rangle, \quad (4.4.62)$$

where $\hat{\mathbf{n}}$ is characterized by the polar and azimuthal angles β and α, respectively. Noting (4.4.53) we have

$$\Theta|\hat{\mathbf{n}}; +\rangle = e^{-iS_z\alpha/\hbar}e^{-iS_y\beta/\hbar}\Theta|+\rangle = \eta|\hat{\mathbf{n}}; -\rangle. \quad (4.4.63)$$

On the other hand, we can easily verify that

$$|\hat{\mathbf{n}}; -\rangle = e^{-i\alpha S_z/\hbar}e^{-i(\pi+\beta)S_y/\hbar}|+\rangle. \quad (4.4.64)$$

In general, we saw earlier that the product UK is an antiunitary operator. Comparing (4.4.63) and (4.4.64) with Θ set equal to UK, and noting that K acting on the base ket $|+\rangle$ gives just $|+\rangle$, we see that

$$\Theta = \eta e^{-i\pi S_y/\hbar}K = -i\eta\left(\frac{2S_y}{\hbar}\right)K, \quad (4.4.65)$$

where η stands for an arbitrary phase (a complex number of modulus unity). Another way to be convinced of (4.4.65) is to verify that if $\chi(\hat{\mathbf{n}}; +)$ is the two-component eigenspinor corresponding to $|\mathbf{n}; +\rangle$ [in the sense that

$\boldsymbol{\sigma} \cdot \hat{\mathbf{n}} \chi(\hat{\mathbf{n}}; +) = \chi(\hat{\mathbf{n}}; +)]$, then

$$-i\sigma_y \chi^*(\hat{\mathbf{n}}; +) \tag{4.4.66}$$

(note the complex conjugation!) is the eigenspinor corresponding to $|\hat{\mathbf{n}}; -\rangle$, again up to an arbitrary phase, see Problem 7 of this chapter. The appearance of S_y or σ_y can be traced to the fact that we are using the representation in which S_z is diagonal and the nonvanishing matrix elements of S_y are purely imaginary.

Let us now note

$$e^{-i\pi S_y/\hbar}|+\rangle = +|-\rangle, \qquad e^{-i\pi S_y/\hbar}|-\rangle = -|+\rangle. \tag{4.4.67}$$

Using (4.4.67), we are in a position to work out the effect of Θ, written as (4.4.65), on the most general spin $\frac{1}{2}$ ket:

$$\Theta(c_+|+\rangle + c_-|-\rangle) = +\eta c_+^*|-\rangle - \eta c_-^*|+\rangle. \tag{4.4.68}$$

Let us apply Θ once again:

$$\begin{aligned}\Theta^2(c_+|+\rangle + c_-|-\rangle) &= -|\eta|^2 c_+|+\rangle - |\eta|^2 c_-|-\rangle \\ &= -(c_+|+\rangle + c_-|-\rangle)\end{aligned} \tag{4.4.69}$$

or

$$\Theta^2 = -1, \tag{4.4.70}$$

(where -1 is to be understood as -1 times the identity operator) for *any* spin orientation. This is an extraordinary result. It is crucial to note here that our conclusion is completely independent of the choice of phase; (4.4.70) holds no matter what phase convention we may use for η. In contrast, we may note that two successive applications of Θ to a spinless state give

$$\Theta^2 = +1 \tag{4.4.71}$$

as is evident from, say, (4.4.58).

More generally, we now prove

$$\Theta^2|j \text{ half-integer}\rangle = -|j \text{ half-integer}\rangle \tag{4.4.72a}$$

$$\Theta^2|j \text{ integer}\rangle = +|j \text{ integer}\rangle. \tag{4.4.72b}$$

Thus the eigenvalue of Θ^2 is given by $(-1)^{2j}$. We first note that (4.4.65) generalizes for arbitrary j to

$$\Theta = \eta e^{-i\pi J_y/\hbar} K. \tag{4.4.73}$$

For a ket $|\alpha\rangle$ expanded in terms of $|j, m\rangle$ base eigenkets, we have

$$\begin{aligned}\Theta\left(\Theta \sum |jm\rangle\langle jm|\alpha\rangle\right) &= \Theta\left(\eta \sum e^{-i\pi J_y/\hbar}|jm\rangle\langle jm|\alpha\rangle^*\right) \\ &= |\eta|^2 e^{-2i\pi J_y/\hbar} \sum |jm\rangle\langle jm|\alpha\rangle.\end{aligned} \tag{4.4.74}$$

But

$$e^{-2i\pi J_y/\hbar}|jm\rangle = (-1)^{2j}|jm\rangle, \qquad (4.4.75)$$

as is evident from the properties of angular-momentum eigenstates under rotation by 2π.

In (4.4.72b), $|j$ integer$\rangle$ may stand for the spin state

$$\frac{1}{\sqrt{2}}(|+-\rangle \pm |-+\rangle) \qquad (4.4.76)$$

of a two-electron system or the orbital state $|l, m\rangle$ of a spinless particle. It is important only that j is an integer. Likewise, $|j$ half-integer$\rangle$ may stand, for example, for a three-electron system in any configuration. Actually, for a system made up exclusively of electrons, any system with an odd (even) number of electrons—regardless of their spatial orientation (for example, relative orbital angular momentum)—is odd (even) under Θ^2; they need not even be $\mathbf{J}^2$ eigenstates!

We make a parenthetical remark on the phase convention. In our earlier discussion based on the position representation, we saw that with the usual convention for spherical harmonics it is natural to choose the arbitrary phase for $|l, m\rangle$ under time reversal so that

$$\Theta|l, m\rangle = (-1)^m|l, -m\rangle. \qquad (4.4.77)$$

Some authors find it attractive to generalize this to obtain

$$\Theta|j, m\rangle = (-1)^m|j, -m\rangle \quad (j \text{ an integer}) \qquad (4.4.78)$$

regardless of whether j refers to l or s (for an integer spin system). We may naturally ask, is this compatible with (4.4.72a) for a spin $\frac{1}{2}$ system when we visualize $|j, m\rangle$ as being built up of "primitive" spin $\frac{1}{2}$ objects according to Wigner and Schwinger. It is easy to see that (4.4.72a) is indeed consistent provided we choose η in (4.4.73) to be $+i$. In fact, in general, we can take

$$\Theta|j, m\rangle = i^{2m}|j, -m\rangle \qquad (4.4.79)$$

for any j—either a half-integer j or an integer j; see Problem 10 of this chapter. The reader should be warned, however, that this is not the only convention found in the literature. (See, for instance, Frauenfelder and Henley 1974.) For some physical applications, it is more convenient to use other choices; for instance, the phase convention that makes the $\mathbf{J}_\pm$ operator matrix elements simple is *not* the phase convention that makes the time-reversal operator properties simple. We emphasize once again that (4.4.70) is completely independent of phase convention.

Having worked out the behavior of angular-momentum eigenstates under time reversal, we are in a position to study once again the expectation values of a Hermitian operator. Recalling (4.4.43), we obtain under time reversal (canceling the i^{2m} factors)

$$\langle \alpha, j, m|A|\alpha, j, m\rangle = \pm\langle \alpha, j, -m|A|\alpha, j, -m\rangle. \qquad (4.4.80)$$

Now suppose A is a component of a spherical tensor $T_q^{(k)}$. Because of the Wigner-Eckart theorem, it is sufficient to examine just the matrix element of the $q = 0$ component. In general, $T^{(k)}$ (assumed to be Hermitian) is said to be even or odd under time reversal depending on how its $q = 0$ component satisfies the upper or lower sign in

$$\Theta T_{q=0}^{(k)} \Theta^{-1} = \pm T_{q=0}^{(k)}. \tag{4.4.81}$$

Equation (4.4.80) for $A = T_0^{(k)}$ becomes

$$\langle \alpha, j, m | T_0^{(k)} | \alpha, j, m \rangle = \pm \langle \alpha, j, -m | T_0^{(k)} | \alpha, j, -m \rangle. \tag{4.4.82}$$

Due to (3.6.46)–(3.6.49), we expect $|\alpha, j, -m\rangle = \mathscr{D}(0, \pi, 0)|\alpha, j, m\rangle$ up to a phase. We next use (3.10.22) for $T_0^{(k)}$, which leads to

$$\mathscr{D}^\dagger(0, \pi, 0) T_0^{(k)} \mathscr{D}(0, \pi, 0) = (-1)^k T_0^{(k)} + (q \neq 0 \text{ components}),$$

$$\tag{4.4.83}$$

where we have used $\mathscr{D}_{00}^{(k)}(0, \pi, 0) = P_k(\cos \pi) = (-1)^k$, and the $q \neq 0$ components give vanishing contributions when sandwiched between $\langle \alpha, j, m |$ and $|\alpha, j, m\rangle$. The net result is

$$\langle \alpha, j, m | T_0^{(k)} | \alpha, j, m \rangle = \pm (-1)^k \langle \alpha, j, m | T_0^{(k)} | \alpha, j, m \rangle. \tag{4.4.84}$$

As an example, taking $k = 1$, the expectation value $\langle \mathbf{x} \rangle$ taken with respect to eigenstates of j, m vanishes. We may argue that we already know $\langle \mathbf{x} \rangle = 0$ from parity inversion if the expectation value is taken with respect to parity eigenstates [see (4.2.41)]. But note that here $|\alpha, j, m\rangle$ need not be parity eigenkets! For example, the $|j, m\rangle$ for spin $\frac{1}{2}$ particles could be $c_s |s_{1/2}\rangle + c_p |p_{1/2}\rangle$.

Interactions with Electric and Magnetic Fields; Kramers Degeneracy

Consider charged particles in an external electric or magnetic field. If we have only a static electric field interacting with the electric charge, the interaction part of the Hamiltonian is just

$$V(\mathbf{x}) = e\phi(\mathbf{x}), \tag{4.4.85}$$

where $\phi(\mathbf{x})$ is the electrostatic potential. Because $\phi(\mathbf{x})$ is a real function of the time-reversal even operator $\mathbf{x}$, we have

$$[\Theta, H] = 0. \tag{4.4.86}$$

Unlike the parity case, (4.4.86) does not lead to an interesting conservation law. The reason is that

$$\Theta U(t, t_0) \neq U(t, t_0) \Theta \tag{4.4.87}$$

even if (4.4.86) holds, so our discussion following (4.1.9) of Section 4.1 breaks down. As a result, there is no such thing as the "conservation of time-reversal quantum number." As we already mentioned, requirement (4.4.86) does, however, lead to a nontrivial phase restriction—the reality of a nondegenerate wave function for a spinless system [see (4.4.59) and (4.4.60)].

Another far-reaching consequence of time-reversal invariance is the **Kramers degeneracy**. Suppose H and Θ commute, and let $|n\rangle$ and $\Theta|n\rangle$ be the energy eigenket and its time-reversed state, respectively. It is evident from (4.4.86) that $|n\rangle$ and $\Theta|n\rangle$ belong to the same energy eigenvalue $E_n(H\Theta|n\rangle = \Theta H|n\rangle = E_n\Theta|n\rangle)$. The question is, Does $|n\rangle$ represent the same state as $\Theta|n\rangle$? If it does, $|n\rangle$ and $\Theta|n\rangle$ can differ at most by a phase factor. Hence,

$$\Theta|n\rangle = e^{i\delta}|n\rangle. \tag{4.4.88}$$

Applying Θ again to (4.4.88), we have $\Theta^2|n\rangle = \Theta e^{i\delta}|n\rangle = e^{-i\delta}\Theta|n\rangle = e^{-i\delta}e^{i\delta}|n\rangle$; hence,

$$\Theta^2|n\rangle = +|n\rangle. \tag{4.4.89}$$

But this relation is impossible for half-integer j systems, for which Θ^2 is always -1, so we are led to conclude that $|n\rangle$ and $\Theta|n\rangle$, which have the same energy, must correspond to distinct states—that is, there must be a degeneracy. This means, for instance, that for a system composed of an odd number of electrons in an external electric field $\mathbf{E}$, each energy level must be at least twofold degenerate no matter how complicated $\mathbf{E}$ may be. Considerations along this line have interesting applications to electrons in crystals where odd-electron and even-electron systems exhibit very different behaviors. Historically, Kramers inferred degeneracy of this kind by looking at explicit solutions of the Schrödinger equation; subsequently, Wigner pointed out that Kramers degeneracy is a consequence of time-reversal invariance.

Let us now turn to interactions with an external magnetic field. The Hamiltonian H may then contain terms like

$$\mathbf{S}\cdot\mathbf{B}, \qquad \mathbf{p}\cdot\mathbf{A}+\mathbf{A}\cdot\mathbf{p}, \qquad (\mathbf{B}=\nabla\times\mathbf{A}), \tag{4.4.90}$$

where the magnetic field is to be regarded as external. The operators $\mathbf{S}$ and $\mathbf{p}$ are odd under time reversal; these interaction terms therefore do lead to

$$\Theta H \neq H\Theta. \tag{4.4.91}$$

As a trivial example, for a spin $\frac{1}{2}$ system the spin-up state $|+\rangle$ and its time-reversed state $|-\rangle$ no longer have the same energy in the presence of an external magnetic field. In general, Kramers degeneracy in a system containing an odd number of electrons can be lifted by applying an external magnetic field.

Notice that when we treat $\mathbf{B}$ as external, we do not change $\mathbf{B}$ under time reversal; this is because the atomic electron is viewed as a closed quantum-mechanical system to which we apply the time-reversal operator.

This should not be confused with our earlier remarks concerning the invariance of the Maxwell equations (4.4.2) and the Lorentz force equation under $t \rightarrow - t$ and (4.4.3). There we were to apply time reversal to the *whole world*, for example, even to the currents in the wire that produces the **B** field!

PROBLEMS

1. Calculate the *three lowest* energy levels, together with their degeneracies, for the following systems (assume equal mass *distinguishable* particles):
   a. Three noninteracting spin $\frac{1}{2}$ particles in a box of length L.
   b. Four noninteracting spin $\frac{1}{2}$ particles in a box of length L.
2. Let $\mathcal{T}_{\mathbf{d}}$ denote the translation operator (displacement vector **d**); $\mathcal{D}(\hat{\mathbf{n}}, \phi)$, the rotation operator ($\hat{\mathbf{n}}$ and ϕ are the axis and angle of rotation, respectively); and π the parity operator. Which, if any, of the following pairs commute? Why?
   a. $\mathcal{T}_{\mathbf{d}}$ and $\mathcal{T}_{\mathbf{d}'}$ (**d** and **d′** in different directions).
   b. $\mathcal{D}(\hat{\mathbf{n}}, \phi)$ and $\mathcal{D}(\hat{\mathbf{n}}', \phi')$ ($\hat{\mathbf{n}}$ and $\hat{\mathbf{n}}'$ in different directions).
   c. $\mathcal{T}_{\mathbf{d}}$ and π.
   d. $\mathcal{D}(\hat{\mathbf{n}}, \phi)$ and π.
3. A quantum-mechanical state Ψ is known to be a simultaneous eigenstate of two Hermitian operators A and B which *anticommute*,

$$AB + BA = 0.$$

   What can you say about the eigenvalues of A and B for state Ψ? Illustrate your point using the parity operator (which can be chosen to satisfy $\pi = \pi^{-1} = \pi^{\dagger}$) and the momentum operator.
4. A spin $\frac{1}{2}$ particle is bound to a fixed center by a spherically symmetrical potential.
   a. Write down the spin angular function $\mathcal{Y}_{l=0}^{j=1/2, \, m=1/2}$.
   b. Express $(\boldsymbol{\sigma} \cdot \mathbf{x}) \, \mathcal{Y}_{l=0}^{j=1/2, \, m=1/2}$ in terms of some other $\mathcal{Y}_{l}^{j, \, m}$.
   c. Show that your result in (b) is understandable in view of the transformation properties of the operator $\mathbf{S} \cdot \mathbf{x}$ under rotations and under space inversion (parity).
5. Because of weak (neutral-current) interactions there is a parity-violating potential between the atomic electron and the nucleus as follows:

$$V = \lambda \left[\delta^{(3)}(\mathbf{x}) \mathbf{S} \cdot \mathbf{p} + \mathbf{S} \cdot \mathbf{p} \delta^{(3)}(\mathbf{x}) \right],$$

   where **S** and **p** are the spin and momentum operators of the electron, and the nucleus is assumed to be situated at the origin. As a result, the ground state of an alkali atom, usually characterized by $|n, l, j, m\rangle$ actually contains very tiny contributions from other eigenstates as follows:

$$|n, l, j, m\rangle \rightarrow |n, l, j, m\rangle + \sum_{n'l'j'm'} C_{n'l'j'm'}|n', l', j', m'\rangle.$$

On the basis of symmetry considerations *alone*, what can you say about (n', l', j', m'), which give rise to nonvanishing contributions? Suppose the radial wave functions and the energy levels are all known. Indicate how you may calculate $C_{n'l'j'm'}$. Do we get further restrictions on (n', l', j', m')?

6. Consider a symmetric rectangular double-well potential:

$$V = \begin{cases} \infty & \text{for } |x| > a + b; \\ 0 & \text{for } a < |x| < a + b; \\ V_0 > 0 & \text{for } |x| < a. \end{cases}$$

Assuming that V_0 is very high compared to the quantized energies of low-lying states, obtain an approximate expression for the energy splitting between the two lowest-lying states.

7. a. Let $\psi(\mathbf{x}, t)$ be the wave function of a spinless particle corresponding to a plane wave in three dimensions. Show that $\psi^*(\mathbf{x}, -t)$ is the wave function for the plane wave with the momentum direction reversed.

   b. Let $\chi(\hat{\mathbf{n}})$ be the two-component eigenspinor of $\boldsymbol{\sigma} \cdot \hat{\mathbf{n}}$ with eigenvalue $+1$. *Using the explicit form of* $\chi(\hat{\mathbf{n}})$ (in terms of the polar and azimuthal angles β and γ that characterize $\hat{\mathbf{n}}$) verify that $-i\sigma_2\chi^*(\hat{\mathbf{n}})$ is the two-component eigenspinor with the spin direction reversed.

8. a. Assuming that the Hamiltonian is invariant under time reversal, prove that the wave function for a spinless nondegenerate system at any given instant of time can always be chosen to be real.

   b. The wave function for a plane-wave state at $t = 0$ is given by a complex function $e^{i\mathbf{p} \cdot \mathbf{x}/\hbar}$ Why does this not violate time-reversal invariance?

9. Let $\phi(\mathbf{p}')$ be the momentum-space wave function for state $|\alpha\rangle$, that is, $\phi(\mathbf{p}') = \langle \mathbf{p}'|\alpha\rangle$. Is the momentum-space wave function for the time-reversed state $\Theta|\alpha\rangle$ given by $\phi(\mathbf{p}')$, $\phi(-\mathbf{p}')$, $\phi^*(\mathbf{p}')$, or $\phi^*(-\mathbf{p}')$? Justify your answer.

10. a. What is the time-reversed state corresponding to $\mathcal{D}(R)|j, m\rangle$?

    b. Using the properties of time reversal and rotations, prove

$$\mathcal{D}^{(j)*}_{m'm}(R) = (-1)^{m-m'}\mathcal{D}^{(j)}_{-m',-m}(R).$$

    c. Prove $\Theta|j, m\rangle = i^{2m}|j, -m\rangle$.

11. Suppose a spinless particle is bound to a fixed center by a potential $V(\mathbf{x})$ so asymmetrical that no energy level is degenerate. Using time-

reversal invariance prove

$$\langle \mathbf{L} \rangle = 0$$

for any energy eigenstate. (This is known as **quenching** of orbital angular momentum.) If the wave function of such a nondegenerate eigenstate is expanded as

$$\sum_l \sum_m F_{lm}(r) Y_l^m(\theta, \phi),$$

what kind of phase restrictions do we obtain on $F_{lm}(r)$?

12. The Hamiltonian for a spin 1 system is given by

$$H = AS_z^2 + B\left(S_x^2 - S_y^2\right).$$

Solve this problem *exactly* to find the normalized energy eigenstates and eigenvalues. (A spin-dependent Hamiltonian of this kind actually appears in crystal physics.) Is this Hamiltonian invariant under time reversal? How do the normalized eigenstates you obtained transform under time reversal?

CHAPTER 5

Approximation Methods

Few problems in quantum mechanics—with either time-independent or time-dependent Hamiltonians—can be solved exactly. Inevitably we are forced to resort to some form of approximation methods. One may argue that with the advent of high-speed computers it is always possible to obtain the desired solution numerically to the requisite degree of accuracy; nevertheless, it remains important to understand the basic physics of the approximate solutions even before we embark on ambitious computer calculations. This chapter is devoted to a fairly systematic discussion of approximate solutions to bound-state problems.

5.1. TIME-INDEPENDENT PERTURBATION THEORY: NONDEGENERATE CASE

Statement of the Problem

The approximation method we consider here is time-independent perturbation theory—sometimes known as the Rayleigh-Schrödinger perturbation theory. We consider a time-independent Hamiltonian H such that it can be split into two parts, namely,

$$H = H_0 + V, \tag{5.1.1}$$

285

where the $V = 0$ problem is assumed to have been solved in the sense that both the exact energy eigenkets $|n^{(0)}\rangle$ and the exact energy eigenvalues $E_n^{(0)}$ are known:

$$H_0|n^{(0)}\rangle = E_n^{(0)}|n^{(0)}\rangle. \tag{5.1.2}$$

We are required to find approximate eigenkets and eigenvalues for the *full* Hamiltonian problem

$$(H_0 + V)|n\rangle = E_n|n\rangle, \tag{5.1.3}$$

where V is known as the **perturbation**; it is not, in general, the full-potential operator. For example, suppose we consider the hydrogen atom in an external electric or magnetic field. The unperturbed Hamiltonian H_0 is taken to be the kinetic energy $\mathbf{p}^2/2m$ *and* the Coulomb potential due to the presence of the proton nucleus $-e^2/r$. Only that part of the potential due to the interaction with the external $\mathbf{E}$ or $\mathbf{B}$ field is represented by the perturbation V.

Instead of (5.1.3) it is customary to solve

$$(H_0 + \lambda V)|n\rangle = E_n|n\rangle, \tag{5.1.4}$$

where λ is a continuous real parameter. This parameter is introduced to keep track of the number of times the perturbation enters. At the end of the calculation we may set $\lambda \to 1$ to get back to the full-strength case. In other words, we assume that the strength of the perturbation can be controlled. The parameter λ can be visualized to vary continuously from 0 to 1, the $\lambda = 0$ case corresponding to the unperturbed problem and $\lambda = 1$ corresponding to the full-strength problem of (5.1.3). In physical situations where this approximation method is applicable, we expect to see a smooth transition of $|n^0\rangle$ into $|n\rangle$ and $E_n^{(0)}$ into E_n as λ is "dialed" from 0 to 1.

The method rests on the expansion of the energy eigenvalues and energy eigenkets in power of λ. This means that we implicitly assume the analyticity of the energy eigenvalues and eigenkets in a complex λ-plane around $\lambda = 0$. Of course, if our method is to be of practical interest, good approximations can better be obtained by taking only one or two terms in the expansion.

The Two-State Problem

Before we embark on a systematic presentation of the basic method, let us see how the expansion in λ might indeed be valid in the exactly soluble two-state problem we have encountered many times already. Suppose we have a Hamiltonian that can be written as

$$H = E_1^{(0)}|1^{(0)}\rangle\langle 1^{(0)}| + E_2^{(0)}|2^{(0)}\rangle\langle 2^{(0)}|$$
$$+ \lambda V_{12}|1^{(0)}\rangle\langle 2^{(0)}| + \lambda V_{21}|2^{(0)}\rangle\langle 1^{(0)}|, \qquad (5.1.5)$$

where $|1^{(0)}\rangle$ and $|2^{(0)}\rangle$ are the energy eigenkets for the $\lambda = 0$ problem, and we consider the case $V_{11} = V_{22} = 0$. In this representation the H may be represented by a square matrix as follows:

$$H = \begin{pmatrix} E_1^{(0)} & \lambda V_{12} \\ \lambda V_{21} & E_2^{(0)} \end{pmatrix}, \qquad (5.1.6)$$

where we have used the basis formed by the unperturbed energy eigenkets. The V matrix must, of course, be Hermitian; let us solve the case when V_{12} and V_{21} are real:

$$V_{12} = V_{12}^*, \qquad V_{21} = V_{21}^*; \qquad (5.1.7)$$

hence, by Hermiticity

$$V_{12} = V_{21}. \qquad (5.1.8)$$

This can always be done by adjusting the phase of $|2^{(0)}\rangle$ relative to that of $|1^{(0)}\rangle$. The problem of obtaining the energy eigenvalues here is completely analogous to that of solving the spin-orientation problem, where the analogue of (5.1.6) is

$$H = a_0 + \boldsymbol{\sigma} \cdot \mathbf{a} = \begin{pmatrix} a_0 + a_3 & a_1 \\ a_1 & a_0 - a_3 \end{pmatrix}, \qquad (5.1.9)$$

where we assume $\mathbf{a} = (a_1, 0, a_3)$ is small and a_0, a_1, a_3 are all real. The eigenvalues for this problem are known to be just

$$E = a_0 \pm \sqrt{a_1^2 + a_3^2} . \qquad (5.1.10)$$

By analogy the corresponding eigenvalues for (5.1.6) are

$$\begin{Bmatrix} E_1 \\ E_2 \end{Bmatrix} = \frac{(E_1^{(0)} + E_2^{(0)})}{2} \pm \sqrt{\left[\frac{(E_1^{(0)} - E_2^{(0)})^2}{4} + \lambda^2 |V_{12}|^2 \right]}. \qquad (5.1.11)$$

Let us suppose $\lambda|V_{12}|$ is small compared with the relevant energy scale, the difference of the energy eigenvalues of the unperturbed problem:

$$\lambda|V_{12}| \ll |E_1^{(0)} - E_2^{(0)}|. \qquad (5.1.12)$$

We can then use

$$\sqrt{1 + \varepsilon} = 1 + \frac{1}{2}\varepsilon - \frac{\varepsilon^2}{8} + \cdots \qquad (5.1.13)$$

to obtain the expansion of the energy eigenvalues in the presence of perturbation $\lambda|V_{12}|$, namely,

$$E_1 = E_1^{(0)} + \frac{\lambda^2|V_{12}|^2}{\left(E_1^{(0)} - E_2^{(0)}\right)} + \cdots$$

$$(5.1.14)$$

$$E_2 = E_2^{(0)} + \frac{\lambda^2|V_{12}|^2}{\left(E_2^{(0)} - E_1^{(0)}\right)} + \cdots.$$

These are expressions that we can readily obtain using the general formalism to be developed shortly. It is also possible to write down the energy eigenkets in analogy with the spin-orientation problem.

The reader might be led to believe that a perturbation expansion always exists for a sufficiently weak perturbation. Unfortunately this is not necessarily the case. As an elementary example, consider a one-dimensional problem involving a particle of mass m in a very weak square-well potential of depth V_0 ($V = -V_0$ for $-a < x < a$, $V = 0$ for $|x| > a$). This problem admits one bound state of energy,

$$E = -(2ma^2/\hbar^2)|\lambda V|^2, \quad \lambda > 0 \text{ for attraction.} \qquad (5.1.15)$$

We might regard the square well as a very weak perturbation to be added to the free-particle Hamiltonian and interpret result (5.1.15) as the energy shift in the ground state from zero to $|\lambda V|^2$. Specifically, because (5.1.15) is quadratic in V, we might be tempted to associate this as the energy shift of the ground state computed according to second-order perturbation theory. However, this view is false because if this were the case, the system would also admit an $E < 0$ state for a repulsive potential case with λ negative, which would be sheer nonsense.

Let us now examine the radius of convergence of series expansion (5.1.14). If we go back to the exact expression of (5.1.11) and regard it as a function of a *complex* variable λ, we see that as $|\lambda|$ is increased from zero, branch points are encountered at

$$\lambda|V_{12}| = \frac{\pm i\left(E_1^{(0)} - E_2^{(0)}\right)}{2}. \qquad (5.1.16)$$

The condition for the convergence of the series expansion for the $\lambda = 1$ full-strength case is

$$|V_{12}| < \frac{|E_1^{(0)} - E_2^{(0)}|}{2}. \qquad (5.1.17)$$

If this condition is not met, perturbation expansion (5.1.14) is meaningless.*

---

*See the discussion on convergence following (5.1.44), under general remarks.

Formal Development of Perturbation Expansion

We now state in more precise terms the basic problem we wish to solve. Suppose we know completely and exactly the energy eigenkets and energy eigenvalues of

$$H_0|n^{(0)}\rangle = E_n^{(0)}|n^{(0)}\rangle. \tag{5.1.18}$$

The set $\{|n^{(0)}\rangle\}$ is complete in the sense that the closure relation $1 = \Sigma_n|n^{(0)}\rangle\langle n^{(0)}|$ holds. Furthermore, we assume here that the energy spectrum is nondegenerate; in the next section we will relax this assumption. We are interested in obtaining the energy eigenvalues and eigenkets for the problem defined by (5.1.4). To be consistent with (5.1.18) we should write (5.1.4) as

$$(H_0 + \lambda V)|n\rangle_\lambda = E_n^{(\lambda)}|n\rangle_\lambda \tag{5.1.19}$$

to denote the fact that the energy eigenvalues $E_n^{(\lambda)}$ and energy eigenkets $|n\rangle_\lambda$ are functions of the continuous parameter λ; however, we will usually dispense with this correct but more cumbersome notation.

As the continuous parameter λ is increased from zero, we expect the energy eigenvalue E_n for the nth eigenket to depart from its unperturbed value $E_n^{(0)}$, so we define the energy shift for the nth level as follows:

$$\Delta_n \equiv E_n - E_n^{(0)}. \tag{5.1.20}$$

The basic Schrödinger equation to be solved (approximately) is

$$\left(E_n^{(0)} - H_0\right)|n\rangle = (\lambda V - \Delta_n)|n\rangle. \tag{5.1.21}$$

We may be tempted to invert the operator $E_n^{(0)} - H_0$; however, in general, the inverse operator $1/(E_n^{(0)} - H_0)$ is ill defined because it may act on $|n^{(0)}\rangle$. Fortunately in our case $(\lambda V - \Delta_n)|n\rangle$ has no component along $|n^{(0)}\rangle$, as can easily be seen by multiplying both sides of (5.1.21) by $\langle n^{(0)}|$ on the left:

$$\langle n^{(0)}|(\lambda V - \Delta_n)|n\rangle = 0. \tag{5.1.22}$$

Suppose we define the complementary projection operator

$$\phi_n \equiv 1 - |n^{(0)}\rangle\langle n^{(0)}| = \sum_{k \neq n} |k^{(0)}\rangle\langle k^{(0)}|. \tag{5.1.23}$$

The inverse operator $1/(E_n^{(0)} - H_0)$ is well defined when it multiplies ϕ_n on the right. Explicitly,

$$\frac{1}{E_n^{(0)} - H_0}\phi_n = \sum_{k \neq n} \frac{1}{E_n^{(0)} - E_k^{(0)}}|k^{(0)}\rangle\langle k^{(0)}|. \tag{5.1.24}$$

Also from (5.1.22) and (5.1.23), it is evident that

$$(\lambda V - \Delta_n)|n\rangle = \phi_n(\lambda V - \Delta_n)|n\rangle. \tag{5.1.25}$$

We may therefore be tempted to rewrite (5.1.21) as

$$|n\rangle \overset{?}{=} \frac{1}{E_n^{(0)} - H_0} \phi_n (\lambda V - \Delta_n)|n\rangle. \tag{5.1.26}$$

However, this cannot be correct because as $\lambda \to 0$, we must have $|n\rangle \to |n^{(0)}\rangle$ and $\Delta_n \to 0$. Nevertheless, even for $\lambda \neq 0$, we can always add to $|n\rangle$ a solution to the homogeneous equation (5.1.18), namely, $c_n|n^{(0)}\rangle$, so a suitable final form is

$$|n\rangle = c_n(\lambda)|n^{(0)}\rangle + \frac{1}{E_n^{(0)} - H_0} \phi_n (\lambda V - \Delta_n)|n\rangle, \tag{5.1.27}$$

where

$$\lim_{\lambda \to 0} c_n(\lambda) = 1. \tag{5.1.28}$$

Note that

$$c_n(\lambda) = \langle n^{(0)}|n\rangle. \tag{5.1.29}$$

For reasons we will see later, it is convenient to depart from the usual normalization convention

$$\langle n|n\rangle = 1. \tag{5.1.30}$$

Rather, we set

$$\langle n^{(0)}|n\rangle = c_n(\lambda) = 1, \tag{5.1.31}$$

even for $\lambda \neq 0$. We can always do this if we are not worried about the overall normalization because the only effect of setting $c_n \neq 1$ is to introduce a common multiplicative factor. Thus, if desired, we can always normalize the ket at the very end of the calculation. It is also customary to write

$$\frac{1}{E_n^{(0)} - H_0} \phi_n \to \frac{\phi_n}{E_n^{(0)} - H_0} \tag{5.1.32}$$

and similarly

$$\frac{1}{E_n^{(0)} - H_0} \phi_n = \phi_n \frac{1}{E_n^{(0)} - H_0} = \phi_n \frac{1}{E_n^{(0)} - H_0} \phi_n, \tag{5.1.33}$$

so we have

$$|n\rangle = |n^{(0)}\rangle + \frac{\phi_n}{E_n^{(0)} - H_0} (\lambda V - \Delta_n)|n\rangle. \tag{5.1.34}$$

We also note from (5.1.22) and (5.1.31) that

$$\Delta_n = \lambda \langle n^{(0)}|V|n\rangle. \tag{5.1.35}$$

Everything depends on the two equations in (5.1.34) and (5.1.35). Our basic strategy is to expand $|n\rangle$ and Δ_n in the powers of λ and then match the appropriate coefficients. This is justified because (5.1.34) and (5.1.35) are identities which hold for all values of λ between 0 and 1. We begin by writing

$$|n\rangle = |n^{(0)}\rangle + \lambda|n^{(1)}\rangle + \lambda^2|n^{(2)}\rangle + \cdots$$

$$\Delta_n = \lambda\Delta_n^{(1)} + \lambda^2\Delta_n^{(2)} + \cdots. \tag{5.1.36}$$

Substituting (5.1.36) into (5.1.35) and equating the coefficient of various powers of λ, we obtain

$$O(\lambda^1): \quad \Delta_n^{(1)} = \langle n^{(0)}|V|n^{(0)}\rangle$$

$$O(\lambda^2): \quad \Delta_n^{(2)} = \langle n^{(0)}|V|n^{(1)}\rangle$$

$$\vdots \qquad \vdots \tag{5.1.37}$$

$$O(\lambda^N): \quad \Delta_n^{(N)} = \langle n^{(0)}|V|n^{(N-1)}\rangle,$$

so to evaluate the energy shift up to order λ^N it is sufficient to know $|n\rangle$ only up to order λ^{N-1}. We now look at (5.1.34); when it is expanded using (5.1.36), we get

$$|n^{(0)}\rangle + \lambda|n^{(1)}\rangle + \lambda^2|n^{(2)}\rangle + \cdots$$

$$= |n^{(0)}\rangle + \frac{\phi_n}{E_n^{(0)} - H_0}\left(\lambda V - \lambda\Delta_n^{(1)} - \lambda^2\Delta_n^{(2)} - \cdots\right)$$

$$\times \left(|n^{(0)}\rangle + \lambda|n^{(1)}\rangle + \cdots\right). \tag{5.1.38}$$

Equating the coefficient of powers of λ, we have

$$O(\lambda): \quad |n^{(1)}\rangle = \frac{\phi_n}{E_n^{(0)} - H_0}V|n^{(0)}\rangle, \tag{5.1.39}$$

where we have used $\phi_n\Delta_n^{(1)}|n^{(0)}\rangle = 0$. Armed with $|n^{(1)}\rangle$, it is now profitable for us to go back to our earlier expression for $\Delta_n^{(2)}$ [see (5.1.37)]:

$$\Delta_n^{(2)} = \langle n^{(0)}|V\frac{\phi_n}{E_n^{(0)} - H_0}V|n^{(0)}\rangle. \tag{5.1.40}$$

Knowing $\Delta_n^{(2)}$, we can work out the λ^2-term in ket equation (5.1.38) also using (5.1.39) as follows:

$$O(\lambda^2): \quad |n^{(2)}\rangle = \frac{\phi_n}{E_n^{(0)} - H_0}V\frac{\phi_n}{E_n^{(0)} - H_0}V|n^{(0)}\rangle$$

$$- \frac{\phi_n}{E_n^{(0)} - H_0}\langle n^{(0)}|V|n^{(0)}\rangle\frac{\phi_n}{E_n^{(0)} - H_0}V|n^{(0)}\rangle.$$

$$\tag{5.1.41}$$

Clearly, we can continue in this fashion as long as we wish. Our operator method is very compact; it is not necessary to write down the indices each time. Of course, to do practical calculations we must use at the end the explicit form of ϕ_n as given by (5.1.23).

To see how all this works, we write down the explicit expansion for the energy shift

$$\Delta_n \equiv E_n - E_n^{(0)}$$

$$= \lambda V_{nn} + \lambda^2 \sum_{k \neq n} \frac{|V_{nk}|^2}{E_n^{(0)} - E_k^{(0)}} + \cdots, \qquad (5.1.42)$$

where

$$V_{nk} \equiv \langle n^{(0)} | V | k^{(0)} \rangle \neq \langle n | V | k \rangle, \qquad (5.1.43)$$

that is, the matrix elements are taken with respect to *unperturbed* kets. Notice that when we apply the expansion to the two-state problem we recover the earlier expression (5.1.14). The expansion for the perturbed ket goes as follows:

$$|n\rangle = |n^{(0)}\rangle + \lambda \sum_{k \neq n} |k^{(0)}\rangle \frac{V_{kn}}{E_n^{(0)} - E_k^{(0)}}$$

$$+ \lambda^2 \left(\sum_{k \neq n} \sum_{l \neq n} \frac{|k^{(0)}\rangle V_{kl} V_{ln}}{\left(E_n^{(0)} - E_k^{(0)}\right)\left(E_n^{(0)} - E_l^{(0)}\right)} - \sum_{k \neq n} \frac{|k^{(0)}\rangle V_{nn} V_{kn}}{\left(E_n^{(0)} - E_k^{(0)}\right)^2} \right)$$

$$+ \cdots. \qquad (5.1.44)$$

Equation (5.1.44) says that the nth level is no longer proportional to the unperturbed ket $|n^{(0)}\rangle$ but acquires components along other unperturbed energy kets; stated another way, the perturbation V mixes various unperturbed energy eigenkets.

A few general remarks are in order. First, to obtain the first-order energy shift it is sufficient to evaluate the expectation value of V with respect to the unperturbed kets. Second, it is evident from the expression of the second-order energy shift (5.1.42) that two energy levels, say the ith level and the jth level, when connected by V_{ij} tend to repel each other; the lower one, say the ith level, tends to get depressed as a result of mixing with the higher jth level by $|V_{ij}|^2/(E_j^{(0)} - E_i^{(0)})$, while the energy of the jth level goes up by the same amount. This is a special case of the **no-level crossing theorem**, which states that a pair of energy levels connected by perturbation do not cross as the strength of the perturbation is varied.

Suppose there is more than one pair of levels with appreciable matrix elements but the ket $|n\rangle$, whose energy we are concerned with, refers to the ground state; then each term in (5.1.42) for the second-order energy shift is negative. This means that the second-order energy shift is always negative for the ground state; the lowest state tends to get even lower as a result of mixing.

It is clear that perturbation expansions (5.1.42) and (5.1.44) will converge if $|V_{il}/(E_i^{(0)} - E_l^{(0)})|$ is sufficiently "small." A more specific criterion can be given for the case in which H_0 is simply the kinetic-energy operator (then this Rayleigh-Schrödinger perturbation expansion is just the Born series): At an energy $E_0 < 0$, the Born series converges if and only if neither $H_0 + V$ nor $H_0 - V$ has bound states of energy $E \le E_0$ (R. G. Newton 1982, p. 233).

Wave-function Renormalization

We are in a position to look at the normalization of the perturbed ket. Recalling the normalization convention we use, (5.1.31), we see that the perturbed ket $|n\rangle$ is not normalized in the usual manner. We can renormalize the perturbed ket by defining

$$|n\rangle_N = Z_n^{1/2}|n\rangle, \tag{5.1.45}$$

where Z_n is simply a constant with $_N\langle n|n\rangle_N = 1$. Multiplying $\langle n^{(0)}|$ on the left we obtain [because of (5.1.31)]

$$Z_n^{1/2} = \langle n^{(0)}|n\rangle_N. \tag{5.1.46}$$

What is the physical meaning of Z_n? Because $|n\rangle_N$ satisfies the usual normalization requirement (5.1.30), Z_n can be regarded as the probability for the perturbed energy eigenstate to be found in the corresponding unperturbed energy eigenstate. Noting

$$_N\langle n|n\rangle_N = Z_n\langle n|n\rangle = 1, \tag{5.1.47}$$

we have

$$Z_n^{-1} = \langle n|n\rangle = (\langle n^{(0)}| + \lambda\langle n^{(1)}| + \lambda^2\langle n^{(2)}| + \cdots)$$

$$\times (|n^{(0)}\rangle + \lambda|n^{(1)}\rangle + \lambda^2|n^{(2)}\rangle + \cdots)$$

$$= 1 + \lambda^2\langle n^{(1)}|n^{(1)}\rangle + 0(\lambda^3)$$

$$= 1 + \lambda^2 \sum_{k \neq n} \frac{|V_{kn}|^2}{(E_n^{(0)} - E_k^{(0)})^2} + 0(\lambda^3), \tag{5.1.48a}$$

so up to order λ^2, we get for the probability of the perturbed state to be found in the corresponding unperturbed state

$$Z_n \simeq 1 - \lambda^2 \sum_{k \neq n} \frac{|V_{kn}|^2}{(E_n^0 - E_k^0)^2}. \tag{5.1.48b}$$

The second term in (5.1.48b) is to be understood as the probability for "leakage" to states other than $|n^{(0)}\rangle$. Notice that Z_n is less than 1, as expected on the basis of the probability interpretation for Z.

It is also amusing to note from (5.1.42) that to order λ^2, Z is related to the derivative of E_n with respect to $E_n^{(0)}$ as follows:

$$Z_n = \frac{\partial E_n}{\partial E_n^{(0)}}. \tag{5.1.49}$$

We understand, of course, that in taking the partial derivative of E_n with respect to $E_n^{(0)}$, we must regard the matrix elements of V as fixed quantities. Result (5.1.49) is actually quite general and not restricted to second-order perturbation theory.

Elementary Examples

To illustrate the perturbation method we have developed, let us look at two examples. The first one concerns a simple harmonic oscillator whose unperturbed Hamiltonian is the usual one:

$$H_0 = \frac{p^2}{2m} + \frac{1}{2}m\omega^2 x^2. \tag{5.1.50}$$

Suppose the spring constant $k = m\omega^2$ is changed slightly. We may represent the modification by adding an extra potential

$$V = \tfrac{1}{2}\varepsilon m\omega^2 x^2, \tag{5.1.51}$$

where ε is a dimensionless parameter such that $\varepsilon \ll 1$. From a certain point of view this is the silliest problem in the world to which to apply perturbation theory; the exact solution is immediately obtained just by changing ω as follows:

$$\omega \to \sqrt{1+\varepsilon}\,\omega, \tag{5.1.52}$$

yet this is an instructive example because it affords a comparison between the perturbation approximation and the exact approach.

We are concerned here with the new ground-state ket $|0\rangle$ in the presence of V and the ground-state energy shift Δ_0:

$$|0\rangle = |0^{(0)}\rangle + \sum_{k \neq 0} |k^{(0)}\rangle \frac{V_{k0}}{E_0^{(0)} - E_k^{(0)}} + \cdots \tag{5.1.53a}$$

and

$$\Delta_0 = V_{00} + \sum_{k \neq 0} \frac{|V_{k0}|^2}{E_0^{(0)} - E_k^{(0)}} + \cdots. \tag{5.1.53b}$$

The relevant matrix elements are (see Problem 5 in this chapter)

$$V_{00} = \left(\frac{\varepsilon m\omega^2}{2}\right)\langle 0^{(0)}|x^2|0^{(0)}\rangle = \frac{\varepsilon\hbar\omega}{4}$$

$$V_{20} = \left(\frac{\varepsilon m\omega^2}{2}\right)\langle 2^{(0)}|x^2|0^{(0)}\rangle = \frac{\varepsilon\hbar\omega}{2\sqrt{2}}. \tag{5.1.54}$$

All other matrix elements of form V_{k0} vanish. Noting that the nonvanishing energy denominators in (5.1.53a) and (5.1.53b) are $-2\hbar\omega$, we can combine everything to obtain

$$|0\rangle = |0^{(0)}\rangle - \frac{\varepsilon}{4\sqrt{2}}|2^{(0)}\rangle + 0(\varepsilon^2) \qquad (5.1.55a)$$

and

$$\Delta_0 = E_0 - E_0^{(0)} = \hbar\omega\left[\frac{\varepsilon}{4} - \frac{\varepsilon^2}{16} + 0(\varepsilon^3)\right]. \qquad (5.1.55b)$$

Notice that as a result of perturbation, the ground-state ket, when expanded in terms of original unperturbed energy eigenkets $\{|n^{(0)}\rangle\}$, acquires a component along the second excited state. The absence of a component along the first excited state is not surprising because our *total H* is invariant under parity; hence, an energy eigenstate is expected to be a parity eigenstate.

   A comparison with the exact method can easily be made for the energy shift as follows:

$$\frac{\hbar\omega}{2} \to \left(\frac{\hbar\omega}{2}\right)\sqrt{1+\varepsilon} = \left(\frac{\hbar\omega}{2}\right)\left[1 + \frac{\varepsilon}{2} - \frac{\varepsilon^2}{8} + \cdots\right], \qquad (5.1.56)$$

in complete agreement with (5.1.55b). As for the perturbed ket, we look at the change in the wave function. In the absence of V the ground-state wave function is

$$\langle x|0^{(0)}\rangle = \frac{1}{\pi^{1/4}}\frac{1}{\sqrt{x_0}}e^{-x^2/2x_0^2}, \qquad (5.1.57)$$

where

$$x_0 \equiv \sqrt{\frac{\hbar}{m\omega}} \qquad (5.1.58)$$

Substitution (5.1.52) leads to

$$x_0 \to \frac{x_0}{(1+\varepsilon)^{1/4}}; \qquad (5.1.59)$$

hence,

$$\langle x|0^{(0)}\rangle \to \frac{1}{\pi^{1/4}\sqrt{x_0}}(1+\varepsilon)^{1/8}\exp\left[-\left(\frac{x^2}{2x_0^2}\right)(1+\varepsilon)^{1/2}\right]$$

$$\approx \frac{1}{\pi^{1/4}}\frac{1}{\sqrt{x_0}}e^{-x^2/2x_0^2} + \frac{\varepsilon}{\pi^{1/4}\sqrt{x_0}}e^{-x^2/2x_0^2}\left[\frac{1}{8} - \frac{1}{4}\frac{x^2}{x_0^2}\right]$$

$$= \langle x|0^{(0)}\rangle - \frac{\varepsilon}{4\sqrt{2}}\langle x|2^{(0)}\rangle, \qquad (5.1.60)$$

where we have used

$$\langle x|2^{(0)}\rangle = \frac{1}{2\sqrt{2}} \langle x|0^{(0)}\rangle H_2\left(\frac{x}{x_0}\right)$$

$$= \frac{1}{2\sqrt{2}} \frac{1}{\pi^{1/4}} \frac{1}{\sqrt{x_0}} e^{-x^2/2x_0^2}\left[-2 + 4\left(\frac{x}{x_0}\right)^2\right], \quad (5.1.61)$$

and $H_2(x/x_0)$ is a Hermite polynomial of order 2.

As another illustration of nondegenerate perturbation theory, we discuss the **quadratic Stark effect**. A one-electron atom—the hydrogen atom or a hydrogenlike atom with one valence electron outside the closed (spherically symmetrical) shell—is subjected to a uniform electric field in the positive z-direction. The Hamiltonian H is split into two parts,

$$H_0 = \frac{\mathbf{p}^2}{2m} + V_0(r) \quad \text{and} \quad V = -e|\mathbf{E}|z \quad (e < 0 \text{ for the electron}). \quad (5.1.62)$$

[*Editor's Note:* Since the perturbation $V \to -\infty$ as $z \to -\infty$, particles bound by H_0 can, of course, escape now, and all formerly bound states acquire a finite lifetime. However, we can still formally use perturbation theory to calculate the shift in the energy. (The imaginary part of this shift, which we shall ignore here, would give us the lifetime of the state or the width of the corresponding resonance.)]

It is assumed that the energy eigenkets and the energy spectrum for the unperturbed problem (H_0 only) are completely known. The electron spin turns out to be irrelevant in this problem, and we assume that with spin degrees of freedom ignored, no energy level is degenerate. This assumption does not hold for $n \neq 1$ levels of the hydrogen atoms, where V_0 is the pure Coulomb potential; we will treat such cases later. The energy shift is given by

$$\Delta_k = -e|\mathbf{E}|z_{kk} + e^2|\mathbf{E}|^2 \sum_{j \neq k} \frac{|z_{kj}|^2}{E_k^{(0)} - E_j^{(0)}} + \cdots, \quad (5.1.63)$$

where we have used k rather than n to avoid confusion with the principal quantum number n. With no degeneracy, $|k^{(0)}\rangle$ is espected to be a parity eigenstate; hence,

$$z_{kk} = 0, \quad (5.1.64)$$

as we saw in Section 4.2. Physically speaking, there can be no linear Stark effect, that is, there is no term in the energy shift proportional to $|\mathbf{E}|$ because the atom possesses a vanishing permanent electric dipole, so the energy shift is *quadratic* in $|\mathbf{E}|$ if terms of order $e^3|\mathbf{E}|^3$ or higher are ignored.

Let us now look at z_{kj}, which appears in (5.1.63), where k (or j) is the **collective index** that stands for (n, l, m) and (n', l', m'). First, we recall the selection rule [see (3.10.39)]

$$\langle n', l'm'|z|n, lm\rangle = 0 \quad \text{unless} \begin{cases} l' = l \pm 1 \\ m' = m \end{cases} \quad (5.1.65)$$

that follows from angular momentum (the Wigner-Eckart theorem with $T_{q=0}^{(1)}$) and parity considerations.

There is another way to look at the m-selection rule. In the presence of V, the full spherical symmetry of the Hamiltonian is destroyed by the external electric field that selects the positive z-direction, but V (hence the total H) is still invariant under rotation around the z-axis; in other words, we still have a cylindrical symmetry. Formally this is reflected by the fact that

$$[V, L_z] = 0. \tag{5.1.66}$$

This means that L_z is still a good quantum number even in the presence of V. As a result, the perturbation can be written as a superposition of eigenkets of L_z with the same $m - m = 0$ in our case. This statement is true for all orders, in particular, for the first-order ket. Also, because the second-order energy shift is obtained from the first-order ket [see (5.1.40)], we can understand why only the $m = 0$ terms contribute to the sum.

The polarizability α of an atom is defined in terms of the energy shift of the atomic state as follows:

$$\Delta = -\tfrac{1}{2}\alpha|\mathbf{E}|^2. \tag{5.1.67}$$

Let us consider the special case of the ground state of the hydrogen atom. Even though the spectrum of the hydrogen atom is degenerate for excited states, the ground state (with spin ignored) is nondegenerate, so the formalism of nondegenerate perturbation theory can be applied. The ground state $|0^{(0)}\rangle$ is denoted in the (n, l, m) notation by $(1, 0, 0)$, so

$$\alpha = -2e^2 \sum_{k \neq 0}^{\infty} \frac{|\langle k^{(0)}|z|1,0,0\rangle|^2}{\left[E_0^{(0)} - E_k^{(0)} \right]}, \tag{5.1.68}$$

where the sum over k includes not only all bound states $|n, l, m\rangle$ (for $n > 1$) but also the positive-energy continuum states of hydrogen.

There are many ways to estimate approximately or evaluate exactly the sum in (5.1.68) with various degrees of sophistication. We present here the simplest of all the approaches. Suppose the denominator in (5.1.68) were constant. Then we could obtain the sum by considering

$$\sum_{k \neq 0} |\langle k^{(0)}|z|1,0,0\rangle|^2 = \sum_{\text{all } k} |\langle k^{(0)}|z|1,0,0\rangle|^2$$

$$= \langle 1,0,0|z^2|1,0,0\rangle, \tag{5.1.69}$$

where we have used the completeness relation in the last step. But we can easily evaluate $\langle z^2 \rangle$ for the ground state as follows:

$$\langle z^2 \rangle = \langle x^2 \rangle = \langle y^2 \rangle = \tfrac{1}{3}\langle r^2 \rangle, \tag{5.1.70}$$

and using the explicit form for the wave function we obtain

$$\langle z^2 \rangle = a_0^2,$$

where a_0 stands for the Bohr radius. Unfortunately the expression for polarizability α involves the energy denominator that depends on $E_k^{(0)}$; but we know that the inequality

$$- E_0^{(0)} + E_k^{(0)} \geq - E_0^{(0)} + E_1^{(0)} = \frac{e^2}{2a_0}\left[1 - \frac{1}{4}\right] \tag{5.1.71}$$

holds for every energy denominator in (5.1.68). As a result, we can obtain an upper limit for the polarizability of the ground state of the hydrogen atom, namely,

$$\alpha < \frac{16a_0^3}{3} \simeq 5.3a_0^3. \tag{5.1.72}$$

It turns out that we can evaluate exactly the sum in (5.1.68) using a method due to A. Dalgarno and J. T. Lewis (Merzbacher 1970, 424, for example), which also agrees with the experimentally measured value. This gives

$$\alpha = \frac{9a_0^3}{2} = 4.5a_0^3. \tag{5.1.73}$$

We obtain the same result (without using perturbation theory) by solving the Schrödinger equation exactly using parabolic coordinates.

5.2. TIME-INDEPENDENT PERTURBATION THEORY: THE DEGENERATE CASE

The perturbation method we developed in the previous section fails when the unperturbed energy eigenkets are degenerate. The method of the previous section assumes that there is a unique and well-defined unperturbed ket of energy $E_n^{(0)}$ which the perturbed ket approaches as $\lambda \to 0$. With degeneracy present, however, any linear combination of unperturbed kets has the same unperturbed energy; in such a case it is not a priori obvious to what linear combination of the unperturbed kets the perturbed ket is reduced in the limit $\lambda \to 0$. Here specifying just the energy eigenvalue is not enough; some other observable is needed to complete the picture. To be more specific, with degeneracy we can take as our base kets simultaneous eigenkets of H_0 and some other observable A, and we can continue labeling the unperturbed energy eigenket by $|k^{(0)}\rangle$, where k now symbolizes a collective index that stands for both the energy eigenvalue *and* the A eigenvalue. When the perturbation operator V does not commute with A, the **zeroth-order** eigenkets for H (including the perturbation) are in fact *not* A eigenkets.

From a more practical point of view, a blind application of formulas like (5.1.42) and (5.1.44) obviously runs into difficulty because

$$\frac{V_{nk}}{E_n^{(0)} - E_k^{(0)}} \tag{5.2.1}$$

becomes singular if V_{nk} is nonvanishing and $E_n^{(0)}$ and $E_k^{(0)}$ are equal. We must modify the method of the previous section to accommodate such a situation.

Whenever there is degeneracy we are free to choose our base set of unperturbed kets. We should, by all means, exploit this freedom. Intuitively we suspect that the catastrophe of vanishing denominators may be avoided by choosing our base kets in such a way that V has no off-diagonal matrix elements (such as $V_{nk} = 0$ in (5.2.1)). In other words, we should use the linear combinations of the degenerate unperturbed kets that diagonalize H in the subspace spanned by the degenerate unperturbed kets. This is indeed the correct procedure to use.

Suppose there is a g-fold degeneracy before the perturbation V is switched on. This means that there are g different eigenkets all with the same unperturbed energy $E_D^{(0)}$. Let us denote these kets by $\{|m^{(0)}\rangle\}$. In general, the perturbation removes the degeneracy in the sense that there will be g perturbed eigenkets all with different energies. Let them form a set $\{|l\rangle\}$. As λ goes to zero $|l\rangle \to |l^{(0)}\rangle$, and various $|l^{(0)}\rangle$ are eigenkets of H_0 all with the same energy $E_m^{(0)}$. However, the set $|l^{(0)}\rangle$ need not coincide with $\{|m^{(0)}\rangle\}$ even though the two sets of unperturbed eigenkets span the same degenerate subspace, which we call D. We can write

$$|l^{(0)}\rangle = \sum_{m \in D} \langle m^{(0)}|l^{(0)}\rangle |m^{(0)}\rangle,$$

where the sum is over the energy eigenkets in the degenerate subspace.

Before expanding in λ, there is a rearrangement of the Schrödinger equation that will make it much easier to carry out the expansion. Let P_0 be a projection operator onto the space defined by $\{|m^{(0)}\rangle\}$. We define $P_1 = 1 - P_0$ to be the projection onto the remaining states. We shall then write the Schrödinger equation for the states $|l\rangle$ as

$$0 = (E - H_0 - \lambda V)|l\rangle$$

$$= (E - E_D^{(0)} - \lambda V)P_0|l\rangle + (E - H_0 - \lambda V)P_1|l\rangle. \quad (5.2.2)$$

We next separate (5.2.2) into two equations by projecting from the left on (5.2.2) with P_0 and P_1,

$$(E - E_D^{(0)} - \lambda P_0 V)P_0|l\rangle - \lambda P_0 V P_1|l\rangle = 0 \quad (5.2.3)$$

$$-\lambda P_1 V P_0|l\rangle + (E - H_0 - \lambda P_1 V)P_1|l\rangle = 0. \quad (5.2.4)$$

We can solve (5.2.4) in the P_1 subspace because $P_1(E - H_0 - \lambda P_1 V P_1)$ is not singular in this subspace since E is close to $E_D^{(0)}$ and the eigenvalues of $P_1 H_0 P_1$ are all different from $E_D^{(0)}$. Hence we can write

$$P_1|l\rangle = P_1 \frac{\lambda}{E - H_0 - \lambda P_1 V P_1} P_1 V P_0|l\rangle \quad (5.2.5)$$

or written out explicitly to order λ when $|l\rangle$ is expanded as $|l\rangle = |l^{(0)}\rangle + \lambda|l^{(1)}\rangle + \cdots$.

$$P_1|l^{(1)}\rangle = \sum_{k \notin D} \frac{|k^{(0)}\rangle V_{kl}}{E_D^{(0)} - E_k^{(0)}}. \quad (5.2.6)$$

To calculate $P_0|l\rangle$, we substitute (5.2.5) into (5.2.3) to obtain

$$\left(E - E_D^{(0)} - \lambda P_0 V P_0 - \lambda^2 P_0 V P_1 \frac{1}{E - H_0 - \lambda V} P_1 V P_0\right) P_0|l\rangle = 0. \quad (5.2.7)$$

Although there is a term of order λ^2 in (5.2.7) that results from the substitution, we shall find that it produces a term of order λ in the state $P_0|l\rangle$. To order λ we obtain the equation for the energies to order λ and eigenfunctions to order zero,

$$(E - E_D^{(0)} - \lambda P_0 V P_0)(P_0|l^{(0)}\rangle) = 0. \quad (5.2.8)$$

This is an equation in the g dimensional degenerate subspace and clearly means that the eigenvectors are just the eigenvectors of the $g \times g$ matrix $P_0 V P_0$ and the eigenvalues $E^{(1)}$ are just the roots of the secular equation

$$\det[V - (E - E_D^{(0)})] = 0 \quad (5.2.9)$$

where $V =$ matrix of $P_0 V P_0$ with matrix elements $\langle m^{(0)}|V|m'^{(0)}\rangle$. Explicitly in matrix form we have

$$\begin{pmatrix} V_{11} & V_{12} & \cdots \\ V_{21} & V_{22} & \cdots \\ \vdots & \vdots & \ddots \end{pmatrix} \begin{pmatrix} \langle 1^{(0)}|l^{(0)}\rangle \\ \langle 2^{(0)}|l^{(0)}\rangle \\ \vdots \end{pmatrix} = \Delta_l^{(1)} \begin{pmatrix} \langle 1^{(0)}|l^{(0)}\rangle \\ \langle 2^{(0)}|l^{(0)}\rangle \\ \vdots \end{pmatrix}. \quad (5.2.10)$$

The roots determine the eigenvalues $\Delta_l^{(1)}$—there are g altogether—and by substituting them into (5.2.10), we can solve for $\langle m^{(0)}|l^{(0)}\rangle$ for each l up to an overall normalization constant. Thus by solving the eigenvalue problem, we obtain in one stroke both the first-order energy shifts and the correct zeroth-order eigenkets. Notice that the zeroth-order kets we obtain as $\lambda \to 0$ are just the linear combinations of the various $|m^{(0)}\rangle$'s that diagonalize the perturbation V, the diagonal elements immediately giving the first-order shift

$$\Delta_l^{(1)} = \langle l^{(0)}|V|l^{(0)}\rangle. \quad (5.2.11)$$

Note also that if the degenerate subspace were the whole space, we would have solved the problem exactly in this manner. The presence of unperturbed "distant" eigenkets not belonging to the degenerate subspace will show up only in higher orders—first order and higher for the energy eigenkets and second order and higher for the energy eigenvalues.

Expression (5.2.11) looks just like the first-order energy shift [see (5.1.37)] in the nondegenerate case except that here we have to make sure that the base kets used are such that V does not have nonvanishing off-diagonal matrix elements in the subspace spanned by the degenerate unperturbed eigenkets. If the V operator is already diagonal in the base ket representation we are using, we can immediately write down the first-order shift by taking the expectation value of V, just as in the nondegenerate case.

Let us now look at (5.2.7). To be safe we keep all terms in the $g \times g$ effective Hamiltonian that appears in (5.2.7) to order λ^2 although we want $P_0|l\rangle$ only to order λ. We find

$$\left(E - E_D^{(0)} - \lambda P_0 V P_0 - \lambda^2 P_0 V P_1 \frac{1}{E_D^{(0)} - H_0} P_1 V P_0\right)P_0|l\rangle = 0. \quad (5.2.12)$$

Let us call the eigenvalues of the $g \times g$ matrix $P_0 V P_0 v_i$ and the eigenvectors $P_0|l_i^{(0)}\rangle$. The eigen energies to first order are $E_i^{(1)} = E_D^{(0)} + \lambda v_i$. We assume that the degeneracy is completely resolved so that $E_i^{(1)} - E_j^{(1)} = \lambda(v_i - v_j)$ are all non-zero. We can now apply non-degenerate perturbation theory (5.1.39) to the $g \times g$ dimensional Hamiltonian that appears in (5.2.12). The resulting correction to the eigenvectors $P_0|l_i^{(0)}\rangle$ is

$$P_0|l_i^{(1)}\rangle = \sum_{j \neq i} \lambda \frac{P_0|l_j^{(0)}\rangle}{v_j - v_i} \langle l_j^{(0)}|VP_1 \frac{1}{E_D^{(0)} - H_0} P_1 V|l_i^{(0)}\rangle$$

or more explicitly

$$P_0|l_i^{(1)}\rangle = \sum_{j \neq i} \lambda \frac{P_0|l_j^{(0)}\rangle}{v_j - v_i} \sum_{k \notin D} \langle l_j^{(0)}|V|k\rangle \frac{1}{E_D^{(0)} - E_k^{(0)}} \langle k|V|l_i^{(0)}\rangle. \quad (5.2.14)$$

Thus, although the third term in the effective Hamiltonian that appears in (5.2.12) is of order λ^2, it is divided by energy denominators of order λ in forming the correction to the eigenvector, which then gives terms of order λ in the vector. If we add together (5.2.6) and (5.2.14), we get the eigenvector accurate to order λ.

As in the nondegenerate case, it is convenient to adopt the normalization convention $\langle l^{(0)}|l\rangle = 1$. We then have, from (5.2.3) and (5.2.4), $\lambda \langle l^{(0)}|V|l\rangle = \Delta_l = \lambda \Delta_l^{(1)} + \lambda^2 \Delta_l^{(2)} + \cdots$. The λ-term just reproduces (5.2.11). As for the λ^2-term, we obtain $\Delta_l^{(2)} = \langle l^{(0)}|V|l^{(1)}\rangle = \langle l^{(0)}|V|P_1 l^{(1)}\rangle + \langle l^{(0)}|V|P_0 l_i^{(1)}\rangle$. Since the vectors $P_0|l_j^{(0)}\rangle$ are eigenvectors of V, the correction to the vector, (5.2.14), gives no contribution to the second-order energy shift, so we find using (5.2.6)

$$\Delta_l^{(2)} = \sum_{k \in D} \frac{|V_{kl}|^2}{E_D^{(0)} - E_k^{(0)}} \quad (5.2.15)$$

Our procedure works provided that there is no degeneracy in the roots of secular equation (5.2.9). Otherwise we still have an ambiguity as to which linear contribution of the degenerate unperturbed kets the perturbed kets are reduced in the limit $\lambda \to 0$. Put in another way, if our method is to work, the degeneracy should be removed completely in first order. A challenge for the experts: How must we proceed if the degeneracy is not removed in first order, that is, if some of the roots of the secular equation are equal? (See Problem 12 of this chapter.)

Let us now summarize the basic procedure of degenerate perturbation theory:

1. Identify degenerate unperturbed eigenkets and construct the perturbation matrix V, a $g \times g$ matrix if the degeneracy is g-fold.
2. Diagonalize the perturbation matrix by solving, as usual, the appropriate secular equation.
3. Identify the roots of the secular equation with the first-order energy shifts; the base kets that diagonalize the V matrix are the correct zeroth-order kets to which the perturbed kets approach in the limit $\lambda \to 0$.
4. For higher orders use the formulas of the corresponding nondegenerate perturbation theory except in the summations, where we exclude all contributions from the unperturbed kets in the degenerate subspace D.

Linear Stark Effect

As an example of degenerate perturbation theory, let us study the effect of a uniform electric field on excited states of the hydrogen atom. As is well known, in the Schrödinger theory with a pure Coulomb potential with no spin dependence, the bound state energy of the hydrogen atom depends only on the principal quantum number n. This leads to degeneracy for all but the ground state because the allowed values of l for a given n satisfy

$$0 \le l < n. \tag{5.2.16}$$

To be specific, for the $n = 2$ level, there is an $l = 0$ state called $2s$ and three $l = 1$ ($m = \pm 1, 0$) states called $2p$, all with the same energy, $- e^2/8a_0$. As we apply a uniform electric field in the z-direction, the appropriate perturbation operator is given by

$$V = -ez|\mathbf{E}|, \tag{5.2.17}$$

which we must now diagonalize. Before we evaluate the matrix elements in detail using the usual (nlm) basis, let us note that the perturbation (5.2.17) has nonvanishing matrix elements only between states of opposite parity, that is, between $l = 1$ and $l = 0$ in our case. Furthermore, in order for the matrix element to be nonvanishing, the m-values must be the same because z behaves like a spherical tensor of rank one with spherical component (*magnetic quantum number*) zero. So the only nonvanishing matrix elements are between $2s$ ($m = 0$ necessarily) and $2p$ with $m = 0$. Thus

$$
V = \begin{array}{cccc}
2s & 2p \;\; m=0 & 2p \;\; m=1 & 2p \;\; m=-1 \\
\end{array}
$$

$$
V = \begin{pmatrix}
0 & \langle 2s|V|2p, m=0 \rangle & 0 & 0 \\
\langle 2p, m=0|V|2s \rangle & 0 & 0 & 0 \\
0 & 0 & 0 & 0 \\
0 & 0 & 0 & 0
\end{pmatrix}
$$

$$\tag{5.2.18}$$

Explicitly,

$$\langle 2s|V|2p, m = 0\rangle = \langle 2p, m = 0|V|2s\rangle$$

$$= 3ea_0|\mathbf{E}|. \qquad (5.2.19)$$

It is sufficient to concentrate our attention on the upper left-hand corner of the square matrix. It then looks very much like the σ_x matrix, and we can immediately write down the answer—for the energy shifts we get

$$\nabla_{\pm}^{(1)} = \pm\, 3ea_0|\mathbf{E}|, \qquad (5.2.20)$$

where the subscripts $\pm$ refer to the zeroth-order kets that diagonalize V:

$$|\pm\rangle = \frac{1}{\sqrt{2}}\,(|2s,m = 0\rangle \pm |2p,m = 0\rangle). \qquad (5.2.21)$$

Schematically the energy levels are as shown in Figure 5.1.

Notice that the shift is *linear* in the applied electric field strength, hence the term the **linear Stark effect**. One way we can visualize the existence of this effect is to note that the energy eigenkets (5.2.21) are not parity eigenstates and are therefore allowed to have nonvanishing electric permanent dipole moments, as we can easily see by explicitly evaluating $\langle z \rangle$. Quite generally, for an energy state that we can write as a superposition of opposite parity states, it is permissible to have a nonvanishing permanent electric dipole moment, which gives rise to the linear Stark effect.

An interesting question can now be asked. If we look at the "real" hydrogen atom, the $2s$ level and $2p$ level are not really degenerate. Due to the spin orbit force, $2p_{3/2}$ is separated from $2p_{1/2}$, as we will show in the next section, and even the degeneracy between the $2s_{1/2}$ and $2p_{1/2}$ levels that persists in the single particle Dirac theory is removed by quantum electrodynamics effects (the *Lamb shift*). We might therefore ask, Is it realistic to apply degenerate perturbation theory to this problem? A comparison with the exact result shows that if the perturbation matrix elements

FIGURE 5.1. Schematic energy-level diagram for the linear Stark effect as an example of degenerate perturbation theory.

are much larger when compared to the Lamb shift splitting, then the energy shift is linear in $|\mathbf{E}|$ for all practical purposes and the formalism of degenerate perturbation theory is applicable. On the opposite extreme, if the perturbation matrix elements are small compared to the Lamb shift splitting, then the energy shift is quadratic and we can apply nondegenerate perturbation theory; see Problem 13 of this chapter. This incidentally shows that the formalism of degenerate perturbation theory is still useful when the energy levels are almost degenerate compared to the energy scale defined by the perturbation matrix element. In intermediate cases we must work harder; it is safer to attempt to diagonalize the Hamiltonian exactly in the space spanned by all the nearby levels.

5.3. HYDROGENLIKE ATOMS: FINE STRUCTURE AND THE ZEEMAN EFFECT

Spin-Orbit Interaction and Fine Structure

In this section we study the atomic levels of hydrogenlike atoms, that is, atoms with one valence electron outside the closed shell. Alkali atoms such as sodium (Na) and potassium (K) belong to this category.

The central (spin-independent) potential $V_c(r)$ appropriate for the valence electron is no longer of the pure Coulomb form. This is because the electrostatic potential $\phi(r)$ that appears in

$$V_c(r) = e\phi(r) \tag{5.3.1}$$

is no longer due just to the nucleus of electric charge $|e|Z$; we must take into account the cloud of negatively charged electrons in the inner shells. A precise form of $\phi(r)$ does not concern us here. We simply remark that the degeneracy characteristics of the pure Coulomb potential are now removed in such a way that the higher l states lie higher for a given n. Physically this arises from the fact that the higher l states are more susceptible to the repulsion due to the electron cloud.

Instead of studying the details of $V_c(r)$, which determines the gross structure of hydrogenlike atoms, we discuss the effect of the spin-orbit $(\mathbf{L} \cdot \mathbf{S})$ interaction that gives rise to *fine structure*. We can understand the existence of this interaction in a qualitative fashion as follows. Because of the central force part (5.3.1), the valence electron experiences the electric field

$$\mathbf{E} = -\left(\frac{1}{e}\right)\nabla V_c(r). \tag{5.3.2}$$

But whenever a moving charge is subjected to an electric field, it "feels" an effective magnetic field given by

$$\mathbf{B}_{\text{eff}} = -\left(\frac{\mathbf{v}}{c}\right) \times \mathbf{E}. \tag{5.3.3}$$

Because the electron has a magnetic moment μ given by

$$\mu = \frac{e\mathbf{S}}{m_e c}, \tag{5.3.4}$$

we suspect a spin-orbit potential V_{LS} contribution to H as follows:

$$H_{LS} \stackrel{?}{=} -\mu \cdot \mathbf{B}_{\text{eff}}$$

$$= \mu \cdot \left(\frac{\mathbf{v}}{c} \times \mathbf{E} \right)$$

$$= \left(\frac{e\mathbf{S}}{m_e c} \right) \cdot \left[\frac{\mathbf{p}}{m_e c} \times \left(\frac{\mathbf{x}}{r} \right) \frac{1}{(-e)} \frac{dV_c}{dr} \right]$$

$$= \frac{1}{m_e^2 c^2} \frac{1}{r} \frac{dV_c}{dr} (\mathbf{L} \cdot \mathbf{S}). \tag{5.3.5}$$

When this expression is compared with the observed spin-orbit interaction, it is seen to have the correct sign, but the magnitude turns out to be too large by a factor of two. There is a classical explanation for this due to spin precession (*Thomas precession* after L. H. Thomas), but we shall not bother with that (Jackson 1975, for example). We simply treat the spin-orbit interaction phenomenologically and take V_{LS} to be one-half of (5.3.5). The correct quantum-mechanical explanation for this discrepancy must await the Dirac (relativistic) theory of the electron (Sakurai 1967, for instance).

We are now in a position to apply perturbation theory to hydrogenic atoms using V_{LS} as the perturbation (V of Sections 5.1 and 5.2). The unperturbed Hamiltonian H_0 is taken to be

$$H_0 = \frac{\mathbf{p}^2}{2m} + V_c(r), \tag{5.3.6}$$

where the central potential V_c is no longer of the pure Coulomb form for alkali atoms. With just H_0 we have freedom in choosing the base kets:

Set 1:   The eigenkets of $\mathbf{L}^2, L_z, \mathbf{S}^2, S_z$.

Set 2:   The eigenkets of $\mathbf{L}^2, \mathbf{S}^2, \mathbf{J}^2, J_z$. $\qquad$ (5.3.7)

Without V_{LS} (or H_{LS}) either set is satisfactory in the sense that the base kets are also energy eigenkets. With H_{LS} added it is far superior to use set 2 of (5.3.7) because $\mathbf{L} \cdot \mathbf{S}$ does not commute with L_z and S_z, while it does commute with $\mathbf{J}^2$ and J_z. Remember the cardinal rule: Choose unperturbed kets that diagonalize the perturbation. You have to be either a fool or a masochist to use the L_z, S_z eigenkets [set 1 of (5.3.7)] as the base kets for this problem; if we proceeded to apply blindly the method of degenerate perturbation theory starting with set 1 as our base kets, we would be forced to diagonalize the $V_{LS}(H_{LS})$ matrix written in the L_z, S_z representation. The results of this, after a lot of hard algebra, give us just the $\mathbf{J}^2$, J_z eigenkets as the zeroth-order unperturbed kets to be used!

In degenerate perturbation theory, if the perturbation is already diagonal in the representation we are using, all we need to do for the first-order energy shift is to take the expectation value. The wave function in the two-component form is explicitly written as

$$\psi_{nlm} = R_{nl}(r) \, \mathcal{Y}_l^{j=l\pm 1/2, m} \tag{5.3.8}$$

where $\mathcal{Y}_l^{j=l\pm 1/2, m}$ is the spin-angular function of Section 3.7 [see (3.7.64)]. For the first-order shift, we obtain

$$\Delta_{nlj} = \frac{1}{2m_e^2 c^2} \left\langle \frac{1}{r} \frac{dV_c}{dr} \right\rangle_{nl} \frac{\hbar^2}{2} \left\{ \begin{matrix} l \\ [-(l+1)] \end{matrix} \right\} \quad \begin{matrix} j = l + \frac{1}{2} \\ \\ j = l - \frac{1}{2} \end{matrix}$$

$$\left\langle \frac{1}{r} \frac{dV_c}{dr} \right\rangle_{nl} \equiv \int_0^\infty R_{nl} \frac{1}{r} \frac{dV_c}{dr} R_{nl} r^2 \, dr \tag{5.3.9}$$

where we have used the m-independent identity [see (3.7.65)]

$$\int \mathcal{Y}^\dagger \mathbf{S} \cdot \mathbf{L} \mathcal{Y} \, d\Omega = \frac{1}{2}\left[j(j+1) - l(l+1) - \frac{3}{4} \right]\hbar^2 = \frac{\hbar^2}{2}\left\{ \begin{matrix} l \\ -(l+1) \end{matrix} \right\} \quad \begin{matrix} j = l + \frac{1}{2} \\ \\ j = l - \frac{1}{2} \end{matrix}$$

$$\tag{5.3.10}$$

Equation (5.3.9) is known as **Lande's interval rule**.

To be specific, consider a sodium atom. From standard atomic spectroscopy notation, the ground-state configuration is

$$(1s)^2 (2s)^2 (2p)^6 (3s). \tag{5.3.11}$$

The inner 10 electrons can be visualized to form a spherically symmetrical electron cloud. We are interested in the excitation of the eleventh electron from $3s$ to a possible higher state. The nearest possibility is excitation to $3p$. Because the central potential is no longer of the pure Coulomb form, $3s$ and $3p$ are now split. The fine structure brought about by V_{LS} refers to even a finer split within $3p$, between $3p_{1/2}$ and $3p_{3/2}$, where the subscript refers to j. Experimentally, we observe two closely separated yellow lines—known as the **sodium D lines**—one at 5896 Å, the other at 5890 Å; see Figure 5.2. Notice that $3p_{3/2}$ lies higher because the radial integral in (5.3.9) is positive.

To appreciate the order of magnitude of the fine-structure splitting, let us note that for $Z \simeq 1$

$$\left\langle \frac{1}{r} \frac{dV_c}{dr} \right\rangle_{nl} \sim \frac{e^2}{a_0^3} \tag{5.3.12}$$

FIGURE 5.2. Schematic diagram of $3s$ and $3p$ lines. The $3s$ and $3p$ degeneracy is lifted because $V_c(r)$ is now the screened Coulomb potential due to core electrons rather than pure Coulombic; V_{LS} then removes the $3p_{1/2}$ and $3p_{3/2}$ degeneracy.

just on the basis of dimensional considerations. So the fine-structure splitting is of order $(e^2/a_0^3)(\hbar/m_ec)^2$, which is to be compared with Balmer splittings of order e^2/a_0. It is useful to recall here that the classical radius of the electron, the Compton wavelength of the electron, and the Bohr radius are related in the following way:

$$\frac{e^2}{m_ec^2} : \frac{\hbar}{m_ec} : a_0 :: 1 : 137 : (137)^2, \qquad (5.3.13)$$

where we have used

$$\frac{e^2}{\hbar c} = \frac{1}{137}. \qquad (5.3.14)$$

Typically, fine-structure splittings are then related to typical Balmer splittings via

$$\left(\frac{e^2}{a_0^3} \frac{\hbar^2}{m_e^2c^2} \right) : \left(\frac{e^2}{a_0} \right) :: \left(\frac{1}{137} \right)^2 : 1, \qquad (5.3.15)$$

which explains the origin of the term *fine structure*. There are other effects of similar orders of magnitude. Specifically, the relativistic mass correction arising from the expansion

$$\sqrt{m_e^2c^4 + p^2c^2} - m_ec^2 \approx \frac{\mathbf{p}^2}{2m_e} - \frac{\mathbf{p}^4}{8m_e^3c^2} \qquad (5.3.16)$$

is of the same order.

The Zeeman Effect

We now discuss hydrogen or hydrogenlike (one-electron) atoms in a uniform magnetic field—the **Zeeman effect**, sometimes called the *anomalous Zeeman effect* with the electron spin taken into account. Recall that a uniform magnetic field B is derivable from a vector potential

$$\mathbf{A} = \tfrac{1}{2}(\mathbf{B} \times \mathbf{r}). \tag{5.3.17}$$

For $\mathbf{B}$ in the positive z-direction ($\mathbf{B} = B\hat{\mathbf{z}}$),

$$\mathbf{A} = -\tfrac{1}{2}(By\hat{\mathbf{x}} - Bx\hat{\mathbf{y}}) \tag{5.3.18}$$

suffices where B stands for $|\mathbf{B}|$. Apart from the spin term, the interaction Hamiltonian is generated by the substitution

$$\mathbf{p} \to \mathbf{p} - \frac{e\mathbf{A}}{c}. \tag{5.3.19}$$

We therefore have

$$H = \frac{\mathbf{p}^2}{2m_e} + V_c(r) - \frac{e}{2m_ec}(\mathbf{p}\cdot\mathbf{A} + \mathbf{A}\cdot\mathbf{p}) + \frac{e^2\mathbf{A}^2}{2m_ec^2}. \tag{5.3.20}$$

Because

$$\begin{aligned}
\langle \mathbf{x}'|\mathbf{p}\cdot\mathbf{A}(\mathbf{x})|\rangle &= -i\hbar\nabla'\cdot\left[\mathbf{A}(\mathbf{x}')\langle\mathbf{x}'|\ \rangle\right] \\
&= \langle\mathbf{x}'|\mathbf{A}(\vec{\mathbf{x}})\cdot\mathbf{p}|\ \rangle + \langle\mathbf{x}'|\ \rangle\left[-i\hbar\nabla'\cdot\mathbf{A}(\mathbf{x}')\right],
\end{aligned} \tag{5.3.21}$$

it is legitimate to replace $\mathbf{p}\cdot\mathbf{A}$ by $\mathbf{A}\cdot\mathbf{p}$ whenever

$$\nabla\cdot\mathbf{A}(\mathbf{x}) = 0, \tag{5.3.22}$$

which is the case for the vector potential of (5.3.18). Noting

$$\begin{aligned}
\mathbf{A}\cdot\mathbf{p} &= |\mathbf{B}|\left(-\tfrac{1}{2}yp_x + \tfrac{1}{2}xp_y\right) \\
&= \tfrac{1}{2}|\mathbf{B}|L_z
\end{aligned} \tag{5.3.23}$$

and

$$\mathbf{A}^2 = \tfrac{1}{4}|\mathbf{B}|^2(x^2 + y^2), \tag{5.3.24}$$

we obtain for (5.3.20)

$$H = \frac{\mathbf{p}^2}{2m_e} + V_c(r) - \frac{e}{2m_ec}|\mathbf{B}|L_z + \frac{e^2}{8m_ec^2}|\mathbf{B}|^2(x^2 + y^2). \tag{5.3.25}$$

To this we may add the spin magnetic-moment interaction

$$-\boldsymbol{\mu}\cdot\mathbf{B} = \frac{-e}{m_ec}\mathbf{S}\cdot\mathbf{B} = \frac{-e}{m_ec}|\mathbf{B}|S_z. \tag{5.3.26}$$

The quadratic $|\mathbf{B}|^2(x^2 + y^2)$ is unimportant for a one-electron atom; the analogous term is important for the ground state of the helium atom where $L_z^{(\text{tot})}$ and $S_z^{(\text{tot})}$ both vanish. The reader may come back to this problem when he or she computes diamagnetic susceptibilities in Problems 18 and 19 of this chapter.

To summarize, omitting the quadratic term, the total Hamiltonian is made up of the following three terms:

$$H_0 = \frac{\mathbf{p}^2}{2m_e} + V_c(r) \tag{5.3.27a}$$

$$H_{LS} = \frac{1}{2m_e^2 c^2} \frac{1}{r} \frac{dV_c(r)}{dr} \mathbf{L} \cdot \mathbf{S} \tag{5.3.27b}$$

$$H_B = \frac{-e|\mathbf{B}|}{2m_e c}(L_z + 2S_z). \tag{5.3.27c}$$

Notice the factor 2 in front of S_z; this reflects the fact that the g-factor of the electron is 2.

Suppose H_B is treated as a small perturbation. We can study the effect of H_B using the eigenkets of $H_0 + H_{LS}$—the $\mathbf{J}^2$, J_z eigenkets—as our base kets. Noting

$$L_z + 2S_z = J_z + S_z, \tag{5.3.28}$$

the first-order shift can be written as

$$\frac{-e|\mathbf{B}|}{2m_e c}\langle J_z + S_z \rangle_{j=l\pm 1/2,\, m}. \tag{5.3.29}$$

The expectation value of J_z immediately gives $m\hbar$. As for $\langle S_z \rangle$, we first recall

$$\left| j = l \pm \frac{1}{2}, m \right\rangle = \pm \sqrt{\frac{l \pm m + \frac{1}{2}}{2l+1}}$$

$$\times \left| m_l = m - \frac{1}{2},\ m_s = \frac{1}{2} \right\rangle + \sqrt{\frac{l \mp m + \frac{1}{2}}{2l+1}} \left| m_l = m + \frac{1}{2},\ m_s = -\frac{1}{2} \right\rangle. \tag{5.3.30}$$

The expectation value of S_z can then easily be computed:

$$\langle S_z \rangle_{j=l\pm 1/2,\, m} = \frac{\hbar}{2}\left(|c_+|^2 - |c_-|^2\right)$$

$$= \frac{\hbar}{2} \frac{1}{(2l+1)}\left[\left(l \pm m + \frac{1}{2}\right) - \left(l \mp m + \frac{1}{2}\right)\right] = \pm \frac{m\hbar}{(2l+1)}. \tag{5.3.31}$$

In this manner we obtain Lande's formula for the energy shift (due to $\mathbf{B}$ field),

$$\Delta E_B = \frac{-e\hbar B}{2m_e c} m \left[1 \pm \frac{1}{(2l+1)}\right]. \tag{5.3.32}$$

We see that the energy shift of (5.3.32) is proportional to m. To understand the physical origin for this, we present another method for deriving (5.3.31). We recall that the expectation value of S_z can also be obtained using the projection theorem of Section 3.10. We get [see (3.10.45)]

$$\langle S_z \rangle_{j=l\pm 1/2, m} = \left[\langle \mathbf{S} \cdot \mathbf{J} \rangle_{j=l\pm 1/2} \right] \frac{m\hbar}{\hbar^2 j(j+1)}$$

$$= \frac{m \langle \mathbf{J}^2 + \mathbf{S}^2 - \mathbf{L}^2 \rangle_{j=l\pm 1/2}}{2\hbar j(j+1)}$$

$$= m\hbar \left[\frac{(l \pm \frac{1}{2})(l \pm \frac{1}{2}+1) + \frac{3}{4} - l(l+1)}{2(l \pm \frac{1}{2})(l \pm \frac{1}{2}+1)} \right]$$

$$= \pm \frac{m\hbar}{(2l+1)}, \qquad (5.3.33)$$

which is in complete agreement with (5.3.31).

In the foregoing discussion the magnetic field is treated as a small perturbation. We now consider the opposite extreme—the **Paschen-Back limit**—with a magnetic field so intense that the effect of H_B is far more important than that of H_{LS}, which we later add as a small perturbation. With $H_0 + H_B$ only, the good quantum numbers are L_z and S_z. Even $\mathbf{J}^2$ is no good because spherical symmetry is completely destroyed by the strong **B** field that selects a particular direction in space, the z-direction. We are left with cylindrical symmetry only—that is, invariance under rotation around the z-axis. So the L_z, S_z eigenkets $|l, s = \frac{1}{2}, m_l, m_s\rangle$ are to be used as our base kets. The effect of the main term H_B can easily be computed:

$$\langle H_B \rangle_{m_l m_s} = \frac{-e|\mathbf{B}|\hbar}{2m_e c}(m_l + 2m_s). \qquad (5.3.34)$$

The $2(2l+1)$ degeneracy in m_l and m_s we originally had with H_0 [see (5.3.27a)] is now reduced by H_B to states with the same $(m_l)+(2m_s)$, namely, $(m_l)+(1)$ and $(m_l+2)+(-1)$. Clearly we must evaluate the expectation value of $\mathbf{L} \cdot \mathbf{S}$ with respect to $|m_l, m_s\rangle$:

$$\langle \mathbf{L} \cdot \mathbf{S} \rangle = \langle L_z S_z + \frac{1}{2}(L_+ S_- + L_- S_+) \rangle_{m_l m_s}$$

$$= \hbar^2 m_l m_s, \qquad (5.3.35)$$

where we have used

$$\langle L_\pm \rangle_{m_l} = 0, \qquad \langle S_\pm \rangle_{m_s} = 0. \qquad (5.3.36)$$

Hence,

$$\langle H_{LS} \rangle_{m_l m_s} = \frac{\hbar^2 m_l m_s}{2m_e^2 c^2} \left\langle \frac{1}{r} \frac{dV_c}{dr} \right\rangle. \qquad (5.3.37)$$

TABLE 5-1

	Dominant interaction	Almost good	No good	Always good
Weak **B**	H_{LS}	$\mathbf{J}^2$ (or $\mathbf{L\cdot S}$)	L_z, S_z*	
Strong **B**	H_B	L_z, S_z	$\mathbf{J}^2$ (or $\mathbf{L\cdot S}$)	$\mathbf{L}^2, \mathbf{S}^2, J_z$

*The exception is the stretched configuration, for example, $p_{3/2}$ with $m = \pm\frac{3}{2}$. Here L_z and S_z are both good; this is because magnetic quantum number J_z, $m = m_l + m_s$ can be satisfied in only one way.

In many elementary books there are pictorial interpretations of the weak-field result (5.3.32) and the strong-field result (5.3.34), but we do not bother with them here. We simply summarize our results in Table 5-1, where weak and strong **B** fields are "calibrated" by comparing their magnitudes $e\hbar B/2m_e c$ with $(1/137)^2 e^2/a_0$. In this table *almost good* simply means good to the extent that the less dominant interaction could be ignored.

Specifically, let us look at the level scheme of a p electron $l = 1$ ($p_{3/2}$, $p_{1/2}$). In the weak **B** case the energy shifts are linear in **B**, with slopes determined by

$$m\left[1 \pm \left(\frac{1}{2l+1}\right)\right].$$

As we now increase **B**, mixing becomes possible between states with the same m-value—for example, $p_{3/2}$ with $m = \pm\frac{1}{2}$ and $p_{1/2}$ with $m = \pm\frac{1}{2}$; in this connection note the operator $L_z + 2S_z$ that appears in H_B [(5.3.27c)] is a rank 1 tensor operator $T_{q=0}^{(k=1)}$ with spherical component $q = 0$. In the intermediate **B** region simple formulas like (5.3.32) and (5.3.34) for the expectation values are not possible; it is really necessary to diagonalize the appropriate 2×2 matrix (Gottfried 1966, 371–73). In the strong **B** limit the energy shifts are again proportional to $|\mathbf{B}|$; as we see in (5.3.34), the slopes are determined by $m_l + 2m_s$.

Van der Waals' Interaction

An important, nice application of the Rayleigh-Schrödinger perturbation theory is to calculate the long-range interaction, or **van der Waals' force**, between two hydrogen atoms in their ground states. It is easy to show that the energy between the two atoms for large separation r is attractive and varies as r^{-6}.

Consider the two protons of the hydrogen atoms to be *fixed* at a distance r (along the z-axis) with $\mathbf{r}_1$ the vector from the first proton to its electron and $\mathbf{r}_2$ the vector from the second proton to its electron; see Figure

FIGURE 5.3. Two hydrogen atoms with their protons $(+)$ separated by a fixed distance r and their electrons $(-)$ at displacements $\mathbf{r}_i$ from them.

5.3. Then the Hamiltonian H can be written as

$$H = H_0 + V$$

$$H_0 = -\frac{\hbar^2}{2m}\left(\nabla_1^2 + \nabla_2^2\right) - \frac{e^2}{r_1} - \frac{e^2}{r_2} \tag{5.3.38}$$

$$V = \frac{e^2}{r} + \frac{e^2}{|\mathbf{r} + \mathbf{r}_2 - \mathbf{r}_1|} - \frac{e^2}{|\mathbf{r} + \mathbf{r}_2|} - \frac{e^2}{|\mathbf{r} - \mathbf{r}_1|}$$

The lowest-energy solution of H_0 is simply the product of the ground-state wave functions of the noninteracting hydrogen atoms

$$U_0^{(0)} = U_{100}^{(0)}(\mathbf{r}_1)U_{100}^{(0)}(\mathbf{r}_2) \tag{5.3.39}$$

Now for large r ($\gg$ the Bohr radius a_0) expand the perturbation V in powers of $\mathbf{r}_i/r$ to obtain

$$V = \frac{e^2}{r^3}(x_1 x_2 + y_1 y_2 - 2z_1 z_2) + 0\left(\frac{1}{r^4}\right) + \cdots \tag{5.3.40}$$

The lowest-order r^{-3}-term in (5.3.40) corresponds to the interaction of two electric dipoles $e\mathbf{r}_1$ and $e\mathbf{r}_2$ separated by $\mathbf{r}$. The higher-order terms represent higher-order multipole interactions, and thus every term in V involves spherical harmonics Y_l^m with $l_i > 0$ for each hydrogen atom. Hence, for each term in (5.3.40) the first-order perturbation energy matrix element $V_{00} \simeq 0$, since the ground state $U_0^{(0)}$ wave function (5.3.39) has $l_i = 0$ (and $\int d\Omega\, Y_l^m(\Omega) = 0$ for l and $m \neq 0$). The second-order perturbation

$$E^{(2)}(r) = \frac{e^4}{r^6} \sum_{k \neq 0} \frac{|\langle k^{(0)}|x_1 x_2 + y_1 y_2 - 2z_1 z_2|0^{(0)}\rangle|^2}{E_0^{(0)} - E_k^{(0)}} \tag{5.3.41}$$

will be nonvanishing. We immediately see that this interaction varies as $1/r^6$; since $E_k^{(0)} > E_0^{(0)}$, it is negative. This $1/r^6$ long-range attractive van der Waals' potential is a general property of the interaction between two atoms in their ground state.*

_____
*See the treatment in Schiff (1968), pages 261–263, which gives a lower and upper bound on the magnitude of the van der Waals' potential from (5.3.41) and from a variational calculation. Also note the first footnote on page 263 of Schiff concerning retardation effects.

5.4. VARIATIONAL METHODS

The perturbation theory developed in the previous section is, of course, of no help unless we already know exact solutions to a problem whose Hamiltonian is sufficiently similar. The variational method we now discuss is very useful for estimating the ground state energy E_0 when such exact solutions are not available.

We attempt to guess the ground-state energy E_0 by considering a "trial ket" $|\tilde{0}\rangle$, which tries to imitate the true ground-state ket $|0\rangle$. To this end we first obtain a theorem of great practical importance. We define $\overline{H}$ such that

$$\overline{H} \equiv \frac{\langle \tilde{0}|H|\tilde{0}\rangle}{\langle \tilde{0}|\tilde{0}\rangle}, \qquad (5.4.1)$$

where we have accommodated the possibility that $|\tilde{0}\rangle$ might not be normalized. We can then prove the following.

Theorem.
$$\overline{H} \geq E_0. \qquad (5.4.2)$$

This means that we can obtain an *upper bound* to E_0 by considering various kinds of $|\tilde{0}\rangle$. The proof of this is very straightforward.

Proof. Even though we do not know the energy eigenket of the Hamiltonian H, we can imagine that $|\tilde{0}\rangle$ can be expanded as

$$|\tilde{0}\rangle = \sum_{k=0}^{\infty} |k\rangle\langle k|\tilde{0}\rangle \qquad (5.4.3)$$

where $|k\rangle$ is an *exact* energy eigenket of H:

$$H|k\rangle = E_k|k\rangle. \qquad (5.4.4)$$

The theorem (5.4.2) follows when we use $E_k = E_k - E_0 + E_0$ to evaluate $\overline{H}$ in (5.4.1). We have

$$\overline{H} = \frac{\sum_{k=0}^{\infty} |\langle k|\tilde{0}\rangle|^2 E_k}{\sum_{k=0}^{\infty} |\langle k|\tilde{0}\rangle|^2} \qquad (5.4.5a)$$

$$= \frac{\sum_{k=1}^{\infty} |\langle k|\tilde{0}\rangle|^2 (E_k - E_0)}{\sum_{k=0}^{\infty} |\langle k|\tilde{0}\rangle|^2} + E_0 \qquad (5.4.5b)$$

$$\geq E_0, \qquad (5.4.5c)$$

where we have used the fact that $E_k - E_0$ in the first sum of (5.4.5b) is necessarily positive. It is also obvious from this proof that the equality sign in (5.4.2) holds only if $|\tilde{0}\rangle$ coincides exactly with $|0\rangle$, that is, if the coefficients $\langle k|\tilde{0}\rangle$ all vanish for $k \neq 0$.   □

The theorem (5.4.2) is quite powerful because $\bar{H}$ provides an upper bound to the true ground-state energy. Furthermore, a relatively poor trial ket can give a fairly good energy estimate for the ground state because if

$$\langle k|\tilde{0}\rangle \sim 0(\varepsilon) \quad \text{for } k \neq 0, \tag{5.4.6}$$

then from (5.4.5) we have

$$\bar{H} - E_0 \sim 0(\varepsilon^2). \tag{5.4.7}$$

We see an example of this in a moment. Of course, the method does not say anything about the discrepancy between $\bar{H}$ and E_0; all we know is that $\bar{H}$ is larger than (or equal to) E_0.

Another way to state the theorem is to assert that $\bar{H}$ is stationary with respect to the variation

$$|\tilde{0}\rangle \rightarrow |\tilde{0}\rangle + \delta|\tilde{0}\rangle; \tag{5.4.8}$$

that is, $\delta\bar{H} = 0$ when $|\tilde{0}\rangle$ coincides with $|0\rangle$. By this we mean that if $|0\rangle + \delta|\tilde{0}\rangle$ is used in place of $|\tilde{0}\rangle$ in (5.4.5) and we calculate $\bar{H}$, then the error we commit in estimating the true ground-state energy involves $|\tilde{0}\rangle$ to order $(\delta|\tilde{0}\rangle)^2$.

The variational method per se does not tell us what kind of trial kets are to be used to estimate the ground-state energy. Quite often we must appeal to physical intuition—for example, the asymptotic behavior of wave function at large distances. What we do in practice is to characterize trial kets by one or more parameters $\lambda_1, \lambda_2, \ldots$, and compute $\bar{H}$ as a function of $\lambda_1, \lambda_2, \ldots$. We then minimize $\bar{H}$ by (1) setting the derivative with respect to the parameters all zero, namely,

$$\frac{\partial \bar{H}}{\partial \lambda_1} = 0, \qquad \frac{\partial \bar{H}}{\partial \lambda_2} = 0, \ldots, \tag{5.4.9}$$

(2) determining the optimum values of $\lambda_1, \lambda_2, \ldots$, and (3) substituting them back to the expression for $\bar{H}$.

If the wave function for the trial ket already has a functional form of the exact ground-state energy eigenfunction, we of course obtain the true ground-state energy function by this method. For example, suppose somebody has the foresight to guess that the wave function for the ground state of the hydrogen atom must be of the form

$$\langle \mathbf{x}|0\rangle \propto e^{-r/a}, \tag{5.4.10}$$

where a is regarded as a parameter to be varied. We then find, upon minimizing $\bar{H}$ with (5.4.10), the correct ground-state energy $-e^2/2a_0$. Not surprisingly, the minimum is achieved when a coincides with the Bohr radius a_0.

As a second example, we attempt to estimate the ground state of the infinite-well (one-dimensional box) problem defined by

$$V = \begin{cases} 0, & \text{for } |x| < a \\ \infty, & \text{for } |x| > a. \end{cases} \tag{5.4.11}$$

The exact solutions are, of course, well known:

$$\langle x|0 \rangle = \frac{1}{\sqrt{a}} \cos\left(\frac{\pi x}{2a}\right), \tag{5.4.12}$$

$$E_0 = \left(\frac{\hbar^2}{2m}\right)\left(\frac{\pi^2}{4a^2}\right).$$

But suppose we did not know these. Evidently the wave function must vanish at $x = \pm a$; furthermore, for the ground state the wave function cannot have any wiggles. The simplest analytic function that satisfies both requirements is just a parabola going through $x = \pm a$:

$$\langle x|\tilde{0} \rangle = a^2 - x^2, \tag{5.4.13}$$

where we have not bothered to normalize $|\tilde{0}\rangle$. Here there is no variational parameter. We can compute $\overline{H}$ as follows:

$$\overline{H} = \frac{\left(\dfrac{-\hbar^2}{2m}\right) \displaystyle\int_{-a}^{a} (a^2 - x^2)\dfrac{d^2}{dx^2}(a^2 - x^2)dx}{\displaystyle\int_{-a}^{a} (a^2 - x^2)^2 \, dx}$$

$$= \left(\frac{10}{\pi^2}\right)\left(\frac{\pi^2 \hbar^2}{8a^2 m}\right) \approx 1.0132 \, E_0. \tag{5.4.14}$$

It is remarkable that with such a simple trial function we can come within 1.3% of the true ground-state energy.

A much better result can be obtained if we use a more sophisticated trial function. We try

$$\langle x|\tilde{0} \rangle = |a|^\lambda - |x|^\lambda, \tag{5.4.15}$$

where λ is now regarded as a variational parameter. Straightforward algebra gives

$$\overline{H} = \left[\frac{(\lambda + 1)(2\lambda + 1)}{(2\lambda - 1)}\right]\left(\frac{\hbar^2}{4ma^2}\right), \tag{5.4.16}$$

which has a minimum at

$$\lambda = \frac{(1 + \sqrt{6})}{2} \approx 1.72, \tag{5.4.17}$$

not far from $\lambda = 2$ (a parabola) considered earlier. This gives

$$\bar{H}_{min} = \left(\frac{5 + 2\sqrt{6}}{\pi^2}\right) E_0 \simeq 1.00298 E_0. \tag{5.4.18}$$

So the variational method with (5.4.15) gives the correct ground-state energy within 0.3%—a fantastic result considering the simplicity of the trial function used.

How well does this trial function imitate the true ground-state wave function? It is amusing that we can answer this question without explicitly evaluating the overlap integral $\langle 0|\tilde{0}\rangle$. Assuming that $|\tilde{0}\rangle$ is normalized, we have [from (5.4.1)–(5.4.4)]

$$\bar{H}_{min} = \sum_{k=0}^{\infty} |\langle k|\tilde{0}\rangle|^2 E_k$$

$$\geq |\langle 0|\tilde{0}\rangle|^2 E_0 + 9 E_0 \left(1 - |\langle 0|\tilde{0}\rangle|^2\right) \tag{5.4.19}$$

where $9 E_0$ is the energy of the second excited state; the first excited state $(k = 1)$ gives no contribution by parity conservation. Solving for $|\langle 0|\tilde{0}\rangle|$ and using (5.4.18), we have

$$|\langle 0|\tilde{0}\rangle|^2 \geq \frac{9 E_0 - \bar{H}_{min}}{8 E_0} = 0.99963. \tag{5.4.20}$$

Departure from unity characterizes a component of $|\tilde{0}\rangle$ in a direction orthogonal to $|0\rangle$. If we are talking about "angle" θ defined by

$$\langle 0|\tilde{0}\rangle = \cos\theta, \tag{5.4.21}$$

then (5.4.20) corresponds to

$$\theta \leq 1.1°, \tag{5.4.22}$$

so $|0\rangle$ and $|\tilde{0}\rangle$ are nearly "parallel."

One of the earliest applications of the variational method involved the ground-state energy of the helium atom, which we will discuss in Section 6.1. We can also use the variational method to estimate the energies of first excited states; all we need to do is work with a trial ket orthogonal to the ground-state wave function—either exact, if known, or an approximate one obtained by the variational method.

5.5. TIME-DEPENDENT POTENTIALS: THE INTERACTION PICTURE

Statement of the Problem

So far in this book we have been concerned with Hamiltonians that do not contain time explicitly. In nature, however, there are many quantum-mechanical systems of importance with time dependence. In the remaining part of this chapter we show how to deal with situations with time-dependent potentials.

We consider a Hamiltonian H such that it can be split into two parts,

$$H = H_0 + V(t),$$
(5.5.1)

where H_0 does not contain time explicitly. The problem $V(t) = 0$ is assumed to be solved in the sense that the energy eigenkets $|n\rangle$ and the energy eigenvalues E_n defined by

$$H_0|n\rangle = E_n|n\rangle$$
(5.5.2)

are completely known.* We may be interested in situations where initially only one of the energy eigenstates of H_0—for example, $|i\rangle$—is populated. As time goes on, however, states other than $|i\rangle$ are populated because with $V(t) \neq 0$ we are no longer dealing with "stationary" problems; the time-evolution operator is no longer as simple as $e^{-iHt/\hbar}$ when H itself involves time. Quite generally the time-dependent potential $V(t)$ can cause transitions to states other than $|i\rangle$. The basic question we address is, What is the probability as a function of time for the system to be found in $|n\rangle$, with $n \neq i$?

More generally, we may be interested in how an arbitrary state ket changes as time goes on, where the total Hamiltonian is the sum of H_0 and $V(t)$. Suppose at $t = 0$, the state ket of a physical system is given by

$$|\alpha\rangle = \sum_n c_n(0)|n\rangle.$$
(5.5.3)

We wish to find $c_n(t)$ for $t > 0$ such that

$$|\alpha, t_0 = 0; t\rangle = \sum_n c_n(t)e^{-iE_nt/\hbar}|n\rangle$$
(5.5.4)

where the ket on the left side stands for the state ket in the Schrödinger picture at t of a physical system whose state ket at $t = 0$ was found to be $|\alpha\rangle$.

The astute reader may have noticed the manner in which we have separated the time dependence of the coefficient of $|n\rangle$ in (5.5.4). The factor $e^{-iE_nt/\hbar}$ is present even if V is absent. This way of writing the time dependence makes it clear that the time evolution of $c_n(t)$ is due solely to the presence of $V(t)$; $c_n(t)$ would be identically equal to $c_n(0)$ and hence independent of t if V were zero. As we shall see in a moment, this separation is convenient because $c_n(t)$ satisfies a relatively simple differential equation. The probability of finding $|n\rangle$ is found by evaluating $|c_n(t)|^2$.

---

*In (5.5.2) we no longer use the notation $|n^{(0)}\rangle$, $E_n^{(0)}$.

The Interaction Picture

Before we discuss the differential equation for $c_n(t)$, we discuss the interaction picture. Suppose we have a physical system such that its state ket coincides with $|\alpha\rangle$ at $t = t_0$, where t_0 is often taken to be zero. At a later time, we denote the state ket in the Schrödinger picture by $|\alpha, t_0; t\rangle_S$, where the subscript S reminds us that we are dealing with the state ket of the Schrödinger picture.

We now *define*

$$|\alpha, t_0; t\rangle_I = e^{iH_0 t/\hbar}|\alpha, t_0; t\rangle_S, \qquad (5.5.5)$$

where $|\ \rangle_I$ stands for a state ket that represents the same physical situation in the *interaction picture*. At $t = 0$, $|\ \rangle_I$ evidently coincides with $|\ \rangle_S$. For operators (representing observables) we define observables in the interaction picture as

$$A_I \equiv e^{iH_0 t/\hbar}A_S e^{-iH_0 t/\hbar}. \qquad (5.5.6)$$

In particular,

$$V_I = e^{iH_0 t/\hbar}V e^{-iH_0 t/\hbar} \qquad (5.5.7)$$

where V without a subscript is understood to be the time-dependent potential in the Schrödinger picture. The reader may recall here the connection between the Schrödinger picture and the Heisenberg picture:

$$|\alpha\rangle_H = e^{+iHt/\hbar}|\alpha, t_0 = 0; t\rangle_S \qquad (5.5.8)$$

$$A_H = e^{iHt/\hbar}A_S e^{-iHt/\hbar}. \qquad (5.5.9)$$

The basic difference between (5.5.8) and (5.5.9) on the one hand and (5.5.6) and (5.5.7) on the other is that H rather than H_0 appears in the exponential.

We now derive the fundamental differential equation that characterizes the time evolution of a state ket in the interaction picture. Let us take the time derivative of (5.5.5) with the full H given by (5.5.1):

$$i\hbar\frac{\partial}{\partial t}|\alpha, t_0; t\rangle_I = i\hbar\frac{\partial}{\partial t}\left(e^{iH_0 t/\hbar}|\alpha, t_0; t\rangle_S\right)$$

$$= -H_0 e^{iH_0 t/\hbar}|\alpha, t_0; t\rangle_S + e^{iH_0 t/\hbar}(H_0 + V)|\alpha, t_0; t\rangle_S$$

$$= e^{iH_0 t/\hbar}V e^{-iH_0 t/\hbar}e^{iH_0 t/\hbar}|\alpha, t_0; t\rangle_S. \qquad (5.5.10)$$

We thus see

$$i\hbar\frac{\partial}{\partial t}|\alpha, t_0; t\rangle_I = V_I|\alpha, t_0; t\rangle_I, \qquad (5.5.11)$$

which is a Schrödinger-like equation with the total H replaced by V_I. In other words $|\alpha, t_0; t\rangle_I$ would be a ket fixed in time if V_I were absent. We can also show for an observable A (that does not contain time t explicitly in the Schrödinger picture) that

$$\frac{dA_I}{dt} = \frac{1}{i\hbar}[A_I, H_0], \qquad (5.5.12)$$

which is a Heisenberg-like equation with H replaced by H_0.

TABLE 5.2

TABLE 5.2

	Heisenberg picture	Interaction picture	Schrödinger picture
State ket	No change	Evolution determined by V_I	Evolution determined by H
Observable	Evolution determined by H	Evolution determined by H_0	No change

In many respects, the interaction picture, or *Dirac picture*, is intermediate between the Schrödinger picture and the Heisenberg picture; This should be evident from Table 5.2.

In the interaction picture we continue using $|n\rangle$ as our base kets. Thus we expand $|\ \rangle_I$ as follows:

$$|\alpha, t_0; t\rangle_I = \sum_n c_n(t)|n\rangle. \qquad (5.5.13)$$

With t_0 set equal to 0, we see that the $c_n(t)$ appearing here are the same as the $c_n(t)$ introduced earlier in (5.5.4), as can easily be verified by multiplying both sides of (5.5.4) by $e^{iH_0t/\hbar}$ using (5.5.2).

We are finally in a position to write the differential equation for $c_n(t)$. Multiplying both sides of (5.5.11) by $\langle n|$ from the left, we obtain

$$i\hbar \frac{\partial}{\partial t}\langle n|\alpha, t_0; t\rangle_I = \sum_m \langle n|V_I|m\rangle\langle m|\alpha, t_0; t\rangle_I. \qquad (5.5.14)$$

This can also be written using

$$\langle n|e^{iH_0t/\hbar}V(t)e^{-iH_0t/\hbar}|m\rangle = V_{nm}(t)e^{i(E_n - E_m)t/\hbar}$$

and

$$c_n(t) = \langle n|\alpha, t_0; t\rangle_I$$

[from (5.5.13)] as

$$i\hbar \frac{d}{dt}c_n(t) = \sum_m V_{nm}e^{i\omega_{nm}t}c_m(t), \qquad (5.5.15)$$

where

$$\omega_{nm} \equiv \frac{(E_n - E_m)}{\hbar} = -\omega_{mn}. \qquad (5.5.16)$$

Explicitly,

$$i\hbar \begin{pmatrix} \dot{c}_1 \\ \dot{c}_2 \\ \dot{c}_3 \\ \vdots \end{pmatrix} = \begin{pmatrix} V_{11} & V_{12}e^{i\omega_{12}t} & \cdots \\ V_{21}e^{i\omega_{21}t} & V_{22} & \cdots \\ & & V_{33} \\ \vdots & \vdots & & \ddots \end{pmatrix} \begin{pmatrix} c_1 \\ c_2 \\ c_3 \\ \vdots \end{pmatrix}. \qquad (5.5.17)$$

This is the basic coupled differential equation that must be solved to obtain the probability of finding $|n\rangle$ as a function of t.

Time-Dependent Two-State Problems: Nuclear Magnetic Resonance, Masers, and So Forth

Exact soluble problems with time-dependent potentials are rather rare. In most cases we have to resort to perturbation expansion to solve the coupled differential equations (5.5.17), as we will discuss in the next section. There is, however, a problem of enormous practical importance, which can be solved exactly—a two-state problem with a sinusoidal oscillating potential.

The problem is defined by

$$H_0 = E_1|1\rangle\langle 1| + E_2|2\rangle\langle 2| \quad (E_2 > E_1)$$
$$V(t) = \gamma e^{i\omega t}|1\rangle\langle 2| + \gamma e^{-i\omega t}|2\rangle\langle 1|, \tag{5.5.18}$$

where γ and ω are real and positive. In the language of (5.5.14) and (5.5.15), we have

$$V_{12} = V_{21}^* = \gamma e^{i\omega t}$$
$$V_{11} = V_{22} = 0. \tag{5.5.19}$$

We thus have a time-dependent potential that connects the two energy eigenstates of H_0. In other words, we can have a transition between the two states $|1\rangle \rightleftarrows |2\rangle$.

An exact solution to this problem is available. If initially—at $t = 0$ —only the lower level is populated so that [see (5.5.3)]

$$c_1(0) = 1, \qquad c_2(0) = 0, \tag{5.5.20}$$

then the probability for being found in each of the two states is given by (**Rabi's formula**, after I. I. Rabi, who is the father of molecular beam techniques)

$$|c_2(t)|^2 = \frac{\gamma^2/\hbar^2}{\gamma^2/\hbar^2 + (\omega - \omega_{21})^2/4} \sin^2\left\{\left[\frac{\gamma^2}{\hbar^2} + \frac{(\omega - \omega_{21})^2}{4}\right]^{1/2} t\right\} \tag{5.5.21a}$$

$$|c_1(t)|^2 = 1 - |c_2(t)|^2, \tag{5.5.21b}$$

where

$$\omega_{21} \equiv \frac{(E_2 - E_1)}{\hbar}, \tag{5.5.22}$$

as the reader may verify by working out Problem 30 of this chapter.

Let us now look at $|c_2|^2$ a little more closely. We see that the probability for finding the upper state E_2 exhibits an oscillatory time dependence with angular frequency, two times that of

$$\Omega = \sqrt{\left(\frac{\gamma^2}{\hbar^2}\right) + \frac{(\omega - \omega_{21})^2}{4}} \tag{5.5.23}$$

The amplitude of oscillation is very large when

$$\omega \simeq \omega_{21} = \frac{(E_2 - E_1)}{\hbar}, \tag{5.5.24}$$

that is, when the angular frequency of the potential—usually due to an externally applied electric or magnetic field—is nearly equal to the angular frequency characteristic of the two-state system. Equation (5.5.24) is therefore known as the **resonance condition**.

It is instructive to look at (5.5.21a) and (5.5.21b) a little closely exactly at resonance:

$$\omega = \omega_{21}, \qquad \Omega = \frac{\gamma}{\hbar}. \tag{5.5.25}$$

We can plot $|c_1(t)|^2$ and $|c_2(t)|^2$ as a function of t; see Figure 5.4. From $t = 0$ to $t = \pi\hbar/2\gamma$, the two-level system absorbs energy from the time-dependent potential $V(t)$; $|c_1(t)|^2$ decreases from unity as $|c_2(t)|^2$ grows. At $t = \pi\hbar/2\gamma$, only the upper state is populated. From $t = \pi\hbar/2\gamma$ to $t = \pi\hbar/\gamma$, the system gives up its excess energy [of the excited (upper) state] to $V(t)$; $|c_2|^2$ decreases and $|c_1|^2$ increases. This *absorption-emission cycle* is repeated indefinitely, as is also shown in Figure 5.4, so $V(t)$ can be regarded as a source or sink of energy; put in another way, $V(t)$ can cause a transition from $|1\rangle$ to $|2\rangle$ (absorption) or from $|2\rangle$ to $|1\rangle$ (emission). We will come back to this point of view when we discuss emission and absorption of radiation.

The absorption-emission cycle takes place even away from resonance. However, the amplitude of oscillation for $|2\rangle$ is now reduced; $|c_2(t)|^2_{\max}$ is no longer 1 and $|c_1(t)|^2$ does not go down all the way to 0. In Figure 5.5 we plot $|c_2(t)|^2_{\max}$ as a function of ω. This curve has a resonance peak centered around $\omega = \omega_{21}$, and the full width at half maxima is given by

FIGURE 5.4. Plot of $|c_1(t)|^2$ and $|c_2(t)|^2$ against time t exactly at resonance $\omega = \omega_{21}$ and $\Omega = \gamma/\hbar$. The graph also illustrates the back-and-forth behavior between $|1\rangle$ and $|2\rangle$.

FIGURE 5.5. Graph of $|c_2(t)|^2_{\max}$ as a function of ω, where $\omega = \omega_{21}$ corresponds to the resonant frequency.

$4\gamma/\hbar$. It is worth noting that the weaker the time-dependent potential (γ small), the narrower the resonance peak.

Spin Magnetic Resonance

The two-state problem defined by (5.5.18) has many physical applications. As a first example, consider a spin $\frac{1}{2}$ system—say a bound electron —subjected to a t-independent uniform magnetic field in the z-direction *and*, in addition, a t-dependent magnetic field rotating in the xy-plane:

$$\mathbf{B} = B_0\hat{z} + B_1(\hat{x}\cos\omega t + \hat{y}\sin\omega t) \qquad (5.5.26)$$

with B_0 and B_1 constant. We can treat the effect of the uniform t-independent field as H_0 and the effect of the rotating field as V. For

$$\mu = \frac{e}{m_e c}\mathbf{S} \qquad (5.5.27)$$

we have

$$H_0 = -\left(\frac{e\hbar B_0}{2m_e c}\right)(|+\rangle\langle+|-|-\rangle\langle-|)$$

$$V(t) = -\left(\frac{e\hbar B_1}{2m_e c}\right)[\cos\omega t(|+\rangle\langle-|+|-\rangle\langle+|)$$

$$+ \sin\omega t(-i|+\rangle\langle-|+i|-\rangle\langle+|)], \qquad (5.5.28)$$

where we have used the ket-bra forms of $2S_j/\hbar$ [see (3.2.1)]. With $e < 0, E_+$ has a higher energy than E_-, and we can identify

$$|+\rangle \rightarrow |2\rangle \quad \text{(upper level)}$$
$$|-\rangle \rightarrow |1\rangle \quad \text{(lower level)} \qquad (5.5.29)$$

to make correspondence with the notation of (5.5.18). The angular frequency characteristic of the two-state system is

$$\omega_{21} = \frac{|e|B_0}{m_e c},$$

(5.5.30)

which is just the spin-precession frequency for the $B_0 \neq 0$, $B_1 = 0$ problem already treated in Section 2.1. Even though the expectation values of $\langle S_{x,y} \rangle$ change due to spin precession in the counterclockwise direction (seen from the positive z-side), $|c_+|^2$ and $|c_-|^2$ remain unchanged in the absence of the rotating field. We now add a new feature as a result of the rotating field: $|c_+|^2$ and $|c_-|^2$ do change as a function of time. This can be seen by identifying

$$\frac{-e\hbar B_1}{2m_e c} \to \gamma, \qquad \omega \to \omega$$

(5.5.31)

to make correspondence to the notation of (5.5.18); our time-dependent interaction (5.5.28) is precisely of form (5.5.18). The fact that $|c_+(t)|^2$ and $|c_-(t)|^2$ vary in the manner indicated by Figure 5.4 for $\omega = \omega_{21}$ and the correspondence (5.5.29), for example, implies that the spin $\frac{1}{2}$ system undergoes a succession of spin-flops, $|+\rangle \rightleftarrows |-\rangle$, in addition to spin precession. Semiclassically, spin-flops of this kind can be interpreted as being due to the driving torque exerted by rotating $\mathbf{B}$.

The resonance condition is satisfied whenever the frequency of the rotating magnetic field coincides with the frequency of spin precession determined by the strength of the uniform magnetic field. We see that the probability of spin-flops is particularly large.

In practice, a rotating magnetic field may be difficult to produce experimentally. Fortunately, a horizontally oscillating magnetic field—for instance, in the x-direction— is just as good. To see this, we first note that such an oscillating field can be decomposed into a counterclockwise component and a clockwise component as follows:

$$2B_1\hat{x}\cos\omega t = B_1(\hat{x}\cos\omega t + \hat{y}\sin\omega t) + B_1(\hat{x}\cos\omega t - \hat{y}\sin\omega t).$$

(5.5.32)

We can obtain the effect of the counterclockwise component simply by reversing the sign of ω. Suppose the resonance condition is met for the counterclockwise component

$$\omega \simeq \omega_{21}.$$

(5.5.33)

Under a typical experimental condition,

$$\frac{B_1}{B_0} \ll 1,$$

(5.5.34)

which implies from (5.5.30) and (5.5.31) that

$$\frac{\gamma}{\hbar} \ll \omega_{21}; \qquad (5.5.35)$$

as a result, whenever the resonance condition is met for the counterclockwise component, the effect of the clockwise component becomes completely negligible, since it amounts to $\omega \rightarrow -\omega$, and the amplitude becomes small in magnitude as well as very rapidly oscillating.

The resonance problem we have solved is of fundamental importance in interpreting atomic molecular beam and nuclear magnetic resonance experiments. By varying the frequency of oscillating field, it is possible to make a very precise measurement of magnetic moment. We have based our discussion on the solution to differential equations (5.5.17); this problem can also be solved, perhaps more elegantly, by introducing the *rotating axis representation* of Rabi, Schwinger, and Van Vleck.

Maser

As another application of the time-dependent two-state problem, let us consider a **maser**. Specifically, we consider an ammonia molecule NH_3, which—as we may recall from Section 4.2—has two parity eigenstates $|S\rangle$ and $|A\rangle$ lying close together such that $|A\rangle$ is slightly higher. Let μ_{el} be the electric dipole operator of the molecule. From symmetry considerations we expect that μ_{el} is proportional to x, the position operator for the N atom. The basic interaction is like $-\mu_{el} \cdot E$, where for a maser E is a time-dependent electric field in a microwave cavity:

$$E = |E|_{max} \hat{z} \cos \omega t. \qquad (5.5.36)$$

It is legitimate to ignore the spatial variation of E because the wavelength in the microwave region is far larger than molecular dimension. The frequency ω is tuned to the energy difference between $|A\rangle$ and $|S\rangle$:

$$\omega \simeq \frac{(E_A - E_S)}{\hbar}. \qquad (5.5.37)$$

The diagonal matrix elements of the dipole operator vanish by parity:

$$\langle A|\mu_{el}|A\rangle = \langle S|\mu_{el}|S\rangle = 0, \qquad (5.5.38)$$

but the off-diagonal elements are, in general, nonvanishing:

$$\langle S|x|A\rangle = \langle A|x|S\rangle \neq 0. \qquad (5.5.39)$$

This means that there is a time-dependent potential that connects $|S\rangle$ and $|A\rangle$, and the general two-state problem we discussed earlier is now applicable.

We are now in a position to discuss how masers work. Given a molecular beam of NH_3 containing both $|S\rangle$ and $|A\rangle$, we first eliminate the $|S\rangle$ component by letting the beam go through a region of time-independent inhomogeneous electric field. Such an electric field separates $|S\rangle$ from $|A\rangle$ in much the same way as the inhomogeneous magnetic field in the Stern-Gerlach experiment separates $|+\rangle$ from $|-\rangle$. A pure beam of $|A\rangle$ then enters a microwave cavity tuned to the energy difference $E_A - E_S$. The dimension of the cavity is such that the time spent by the molecule is just $(\pi/2)\hbar/\gamma$. As a result we stay in the first emission phase of Figure 5.4; we have $|A\rangle$ in and $|S\rangle$ out. The excess energy of $|A\rangle$ is given up to the time-dependent potential as $|A\rangle$ turns into $|S\rangle$ and the radiation (microwave) field gains energy. In this way we obtain Microwave Amplification by Stimulated Emission of Radiation, or MASER.

There are many other applications of the general time-dependent two-state problem, such as the atomic clock and optical pumping. In fact, it is amusing to see that as many as four Nobel Prizes in physics have been awarded to those who exploited time-dependent two-state systems of some form.*

5.6. TIME-DEPENDENT PERTURBATION THEORY

Dyson Series

With the exception of a few problems like the two-level time-dependent problem of the previous section, exact solutions to the differential equation for $c_n(t)$ are usually not available. We must be content with approximate solutions to (5.5.17) obtained by perturbation expansion:

$$c_n(t) = c_n^{(0)} + c_n^{(1)} + c_n^{(2)} + \cdots, \qquad (5.6.1)$$

where $c_n^{(1)}, c_n^{(2)}, \ldots$ signify amplitudes of first order, second order, and so on in the strength parameter of the time-dependent potential. The iteration method used to solve this problem is similar to what we did in time-independent perturbation theory. If initially only the state i is populated, we approximate c_n on the right-hand side of differential equation (5.5.17) by $c_n^{(0)} = \delta_{ni}$ (independent of t) and relate it to the time derivative of $c_n^{(1)}$, integrate the differential equation to obtain $c_n^{(1)}$, plug $c_n^{(1)}$ into the right-hand side [of (5.5.17)] again to obtain the differential equation for $c_n^{(2)}$, and so on. This is how Dirac developed time-dependent perturbation theory in 1927.

Instead of working with $c_n(t)$, we propose to look at the time evolution operator $U_I(t, t_0)$ in the interaction picture, which we will define later. We obtain a perturbation expansion for $U_I(t, t_0)$, and at the very end

---

*Nobel Prize winners who took advantage of resonance in the two-level systems are Rabi (1944) on molecular beams and nuclear magnetic resonance; Bloch and Purcell (1952) on **B** field in atomic nuclei and nuclear magnetic moments; Townes, Basov, and Prochorov (1964) on masers, lasers, and quantum optics; and Kastler (1966) on optical pumping.

we relate the matrix elements of U_I to $c_n(t)$. If we are interested only in solving simple problems in nonrelativistic quantum mechanics, all this might look superfluous; however, the operator formalism we develop is very powerful because it can immediately be applied to more-advanced problems, such as relativistic quantum field theory and many-body theory.

The time-evolution operator in the interaction picture is defined by

$$|\alpha, t_0; t\rangle_I = U_I(t, t_0)|\alpha, t_0; t_0\rangle_I. \tag{5.6.2}$$

Differential equation (5.5.11) for the state ket of the interaction picture is equivalent to

$$i\hbar \frac{d}{dt} U_I(t, t_0) = V_I(t) U_I(t, t_0). \tag{5.6.3}$$

We must solve this operator differential equation subject to the initial condition

$$U_I(t, t_0)|_{t=t_0} = 1. \tag{5.6.4}$$

First, let us note that the differential equation together with the initial condition is equivalent to the following integral equation:

$$U_I(t, t_0) = 1 - \frac{i}{\hbar} \int_{t_0}^{t} V_I(t') U_I(t', t_0) \, dt'. \tag{5.6.5}$$

We can obtain an approximate solution to this equation by iteration:

$$U_I(t, t_0) = 1 - \frac{i}{\hbar} \int_{t_0}^{t} V_I(t') \left[1 - \frac{i}{\hbar} \int_{t_0}^{t'} V_I(t'') U_I(t'', t_0) \, dt'' \right] dt'$$

$$= 1 - \frac{i}{\hbar} \int_{t_0}^{t} dt' \, V_I(t') + \left(\frac{-i}{\hbar} \right)^2 \int_{t_0}^{t} dt' \int_{t_0}^{t'} dt'' \, V_I(t') V_I(t'')$$

$$+ \cdots + \left(\frac{-i}{\hbar} \right)^n \int_{t_0}^{t} dt' \int_{t_0}^{t'} dt'' \cdots$$

$$\times \int_{t_0}^{t^{(n-1)}} dt^{(n)} V_I(t') V_I(t'') \cdots V_I(t^{(n)})$$

$$+ \cdots. \tag{5.6.6}$$

This series is known as the **Dyson series** after Freeman J. Dyson, who applied this method to covariant quantum electrodynamics (QED).* Setting aside the difficult question of convergence, we can compute $U_I(t, t_0)$ to any finite order of perturbation theory.

---

*Note that in QED, the time-ordered product $(t' > t'' > \cdots)$ is introduced, and then this perturbation series can be summed into an exponential form. This exponential form immediately gives $U(t, t_0) = U(t, t_1) U(t_1, t_0)$ (Bjorken and Drell 1965, 175–78).

Transition Probability

Once $U_I(t, t_0)$ is given, we can predict the time development of any state ket. For example, if the initial state at $t = 0$ is one of the energy eigenstates of H_0, then to obtain the initial state ket at a later time, all we need to do is multiply by $U_I(t, 0)$:

$$|i, t_0 = 0; t\rangle_I = U_I(t, 0)|i\rangle$$
$$= \sum_n |n\rangle\langle n|U_I(t, 0)|i\rangle. \qquad (5.6.7)$$

In fact, $\langle n|U_I(t, 0)|i\rangle$ is nothing more than what we called $c_n(t)$ earlier [see (5.5.13)]. We will say more about this later.

We earlier introduced the time-evolution operator $U(t, t_0)$ in the Schrödinger picture (see Section 2.2). Let us now explore the connection between $U(t, t_0)$ and $U_I(t, t_0)$. We note from (2.2.13) and (5.5.5) that

$$|\alpha, t_0; t\rangle_I = e^{iH_0 t/\hbar}|\alpha, t_0; t\rangle_S$$
$$= e^{iH_0 t/\hbar}U(t, t_0)|\alpha, t_0; t_0\rangle_S$$
$$= e^{iH_0 t/\hbar}U(t, t_0)e^{-iH_0 t_0/\hbar}|\alpha, t_0; t_0\rangle_I. \qquad (5.6.8)$$

So we have

$$U_I(t, t_0) = e^{iH_0 t/\hbar}U(t, t_0)e^{-iH_0 t_0/\hbar}. \qquad (5.6.9)$$

Let us now look at the matrix element of $U_I(t, t_0)$ between energy eigenstates of H_0:

$$\langle n|U_I(t, t_0)|i\rangle = e^{i(E_n t - E_i t_0)/\hbar}\langle n|U(t, t_0)|i\rangle. \qquad (5.6.10)$$

We recall from Section 2.2 that $\langle n|U(t, t_0)|i\rangle$ is defined to be the transition amplitude. Hence our $\langle n|U_I(t, t_0)|i\rangle$ here is not quite the same as the transition amplitude defined earlier. However, the transition *probability* defined as the square of the modulus of $\langle n|U(t, t_0)|i\rangle$ is the same as the analogous quantity in the interaction picture

$$|\langle n|U_I(t, t_0)|i\rangle|^2 = |\langle n|U(t, t_0)|i\rangle|^2. \qquad (5.6.11)$$

Parenthetically, we may remark that if the matrix elements of U_I are taken between initial and final states that are not energy eigenstates—for example, between $|a'\rangle$ and $|b'\rangle$ (eigenkets of A and B; respectively), where $[H_0, A] \neq 0$ and/or $[H_0, B] \neq 0$—we have, in general,

$$|\langle b'|U_I(t, t_0)|a'\rangle| \neq |\langle b'|U(t, t_0)|a'\rangle|,$$

as the reader may easily verify. Fortunately, in problems where the interaction picture is found to be useful, the initial and final states are usually taken to be H_0 eigenstates. Otherwise, all that is needed is to expand $|a'\rangle$, $|b'\rangle$, and so on in terms of the energy eigenkets of H_0.

Coming back to $\langle n|U_I(t,t_0)|i\rangle$, we illustrate by considering a physical situation where at $t=t_0$, the system is known to be in state $|i\rangle$. The state ket in the Schrödinger picture $|i,t_0;t\rangle_S$ is then equal to $|i\rangle$ up to a phase factor. In applying the interaction picture, it is convenient to choose the phase factor at $t=t_0$ so that

$$|i,t_0;t_0\rangle_S = e^{-iE_i t_0/\hbar}|i\rangle, \tag{5.6.12}$$

which means that in the interaction picture we have the simple equation

$$|i,t_0;t_0\rangle_I = |i\rangle. \tag{5.6.13}$$

At a later time we have

$$|i,t_0;t\rangle_I = U_I(t,t_0)|i\rangle. \tag{5.6.14}$$

Comparing this with the expansion

$$|i,t_0;t\rangle_I = \sum_n c_n(t)|n\rangle, \tag{5.6.15}$$

we see

$$c_n(t) = \langle n|U_I(t,t_0)|i\rangle. \tag{5.6.16}$$

We now go back to the perturbation expansion for $U_I(t,t_0)$ [see (5.6.6)]. We can also expand $c_n(t)$ as in (5.6.1), where $c_n^{(1)}$ is first order in $V_I(t)$, $c_n^{(2)}$ is second order in $V_I(t)$, and so on. Comparing the expansion of both sides of (5.6.16), we obtain [using (5.5.7)]

$$c_n^{(0)}(t) = \delta_{ni} \quad \text{(independent of } t\text{)}$$

$$c_n^{(1)}(t) = \frac{-i}{\hbar}\int_{t_0}^t \langle n|V_I(t')|i\rangle\, dt'$$

$$= \frac{-i}{\hbar}\int_{t_0}^t e^{i\omega_{ni}t'}V_{ni}(t')\, dt' \tag{5.6.17}$$

$$c_n^{(2)}(t) = \left(\frac{-i}{\hbar}\right)^2 \sum_m \int_{t_0}^t dt' \int_{t_0}^{t'} dt''\, e^{i\omega_{nm}t'}V_{nm}(t')e^{i\omega_{mi}t''}V_{mi}(t''),$$

where we have used

$$e^{i(E_n-E_i)t/\hbar} = e^{i\omega_{ni}t}. \tag{5.6.18}$$

The transition probability for $|i\rangle \rightarrow |n\rangle$ with $n \neq i$ is obtained by

$$P(i\rightarrow n) = |c_n^{(1)}(t) + c_n^{(2)}(t) + \cdots|^2. \tag{5.6.19}$$

Constant Perturbation

As an application of (5.6.17), let us consider a constant perturbation turned on at $t=0$:

$$V(t) = \begin{cases} 0, & \text{for } t < 0 \\ V \quad \text{(independent of } t\text{)}, & \text{for } t \geq 0. \end{cases} \tag{5.6.20}$$

Even though the operator V has no explicit dependence on time, it is, in general, made up of operators like $\mathbf{x}$, $\mathbf{p}$, and $\mathbf{s}$. Now suppose at $t = 0$, we have only $|i\rangle$. With t_0 taken to be zero, we obtain

$$c_n^{(0)} = c_n^{(0)}(0) = \delta_{in},$$

$$c_n^{(1)} = \frac{-i}{\hbar} V_{ni} \int_0^t e^{i\omega_{ni}t'} \, dt'$$

$$= \frac{V_{ni}}{E_n - E_i} (1 - e^{i\omega_{ni}t}), \tag{5.6.21}$$

or

$$|c_n^{(1)}|^2 = \frac{|V_{ni}|^2}{|E_n - E_i|^2} (2 - 2\cos\omega_{ni}t)$$

$$= \frac{4|V_{ni}|^2}{|E_n - E_i|^2} \sin^2\left[\frac{(E_n - E_i)t}{2\hbar}\right]. \tag{5.6.22}$$

The probability of finding $|n\rangle$ depends not only on $|V_{ni}|^2$ but also on the energy difference $E_n - E_i$, so let us try to see how (5.6.22) looks as a function of E_n. In practice, we are interested in this way of looking at (5.6.22) when there are many states with $E \sim E_n$ so that we can talk about a continuum of final states with nearly the same energy. To this end we define

$$\omega \equiv \frac{E_n - E_i}{\hbar} \tag{5.6.23}$$

and plot $4\sin^2(\omega t/2)/\omega^2$ as a function of ω for fixed t, the time interval during which the perturbation has been on; see Figure 5.6. We see that the height of the middle peak, centered around $\omega = 0$, is t^2 and the width is proportional to $1/t$. As t becomes large, $|c_n^{(1)}(t)|^2$ is appreciable only for those final states that satisfy

$$t \sim \frac{2\pi}{|\omega|} = \frac{2\pi\hbar}{|E_n - E_i|}. \tag{5.6.24}$$

If we call Δt the time interval during which the perturbation has been turned on, a transition with appreciable probability is possible only if

$$\Delta t \, \Delta E \sim \hbar, \tag{5.6.25}$$

where by ΔE we mean the energy change involved in a transition with appreciable probability. If Δt is small, we have a broader peak in Figure 5.6, and as a result we can tolerate a fair amount of energy nonconservation. On the other hand, if the perturbation has been on for a very long time, we have a very narrow peak, and approximate energy conservation is required for a transition with appreciable probability. Note that this "uncertainty relation" is fundamentally different from the $x - p$ uncertainty relation of

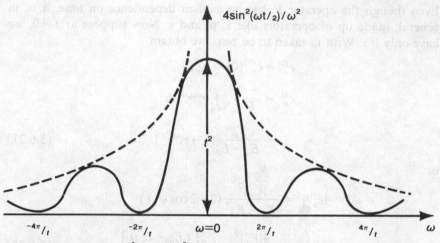

FIGURE 5.6. Plot of $4\sin^2(\omega t/2)/\omega^2$ versus ω for a fixed t, where in $\omega = (E_n - E_i)/\hbar$ we have regarded E_n as a continuous variable.

Section 1.6. There x and p are both observables. In contrast, time in nonrelativistic quantum mechanics is a parameter, not an observable.

For those transitions with exact energy conservation $E_n = E_i$, we have

$$|c_n^{(1)}(t)|^2 = \frac{1}{\hbar^2}|V_{ni}|^2 t^2. \qquad (5.6.26)$$

The probability of finding $|n\rangle$ after a time interval t is quadratic, *not* linear, in the time interval during which V has been on. This may appear intuitively unreasonable. There is no cause for alarm, however. In a realistic situation where our formalism is applicable, there is usually a group of final states, all with nearly the same energy as the energy of the initial state $|i\rangle$. In other words, a final state forms a continuous energy spectrum in the neighborhood of E_i. We give two examples along this line. Consider for instance, elastic scattering by some finite range potential (see Figure 5.7), which we will consider in detail in Chapter 7. The initial state is taken to be a plane wave state with its propagation direction oriented in the positive z-direction; the final state may also be a plane wave state of the same energy but with its propagation direction, in general, in a direction other than the positive z-direction. Another example of interest is the de-excitation of an excited atomic state via the emission of an Auger electron. The simplest example is a helium atom. The initial state may be $(2s)^2$, where both the electrons are excited; the final state may be $(1s)$ (that is, one of the electrons still bound) of the He^+ ion, while the second electron escapes with a positive energy E; see Figure 5.8. In such a case we are interested in the

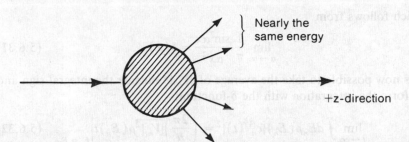

FIGURE 5.7. Elastic scattering of plane wave by some finite range potential.

FIGURE 5.8. Schematic diagram of two electron energy levels of helium atom.

total probability—that is, the transition probabilities summed over final states with $E_n \simeq E_i$:

$$\sum_{n,\, E_n \simeq E_i} |c_n^{(1)}|^2. \tag{5.6.27}$$

It is customary to define the density of final states as the number of states within energy interval $(E, E + dE)$ as

$$\rho(E)\, dE. \tag{5.6.28}$$

We can then write (5.6.27) as

$$\sum_{n,\, E_n \simeq E_i} |c_n^{(1)}|^2 \Rightarrow \int dE_n \rho(E_n) |c_n^{(1)}|^2$$

$$= 4 \int \sin^2\left[\frac{(E_n - E_i)t}{2\hbar}\right] \frac{|V_{ni}|^2}{|E_n - E_i|^2} \rho(E_n)\, dE_n. \tag{5.6.29}$$

As $t \to \infty$, we can take advantage of

$$\lim_{t \to \infty} \frac{1}{|E_n - E_i|^2} \sin^2\left[\frac{(E_n - E_i)t}{2\hbar}\right] = \frac{\pi t}{2\hbar} \delta(E_n - E_i), \tag{5.6.30}$$

which follows from

$$\lim_{\alpha \to \infty} \frac{1}{\pi} \frac{\sin^2 \alpha x}{\alpha x^2} = \delta(x). \tag{5.6.31}$$

It is now possible to take the average of $|V_{ni}|^2$ outside the integral sign and perform the integration with the δ-function:

$$\lim_{t \to \infty} \int dE_n \rho(E_n) |c_n^{(1)}(t)|^2 = \left(\frac{2\pi}{\hbar}\right) \overline{|V_{ni}|^2} \rho(E_n) t \bigg|_{E_n \simeq E_i}. \tag{5.6.32}$$

Thus the total transition probability *is* proportional to t for large values of t, which is quite reasonable. Notice that this linearity in t is a consequence of the fact that the total transition probability is proportional to the area under the peak of Figure 5.6, where the height varies as t^2 and the width varies as $1/t$.

It is conventional to consider the **transition rate**—that is, the transition probability per unit time. Expression (5.6.32) tells us that the total transition rate, defined by

$$\frac{d}{dt}\left(\sum_n |c_n^{(1)}|^2\right), \tag{5.6.33}$$

is constant in t for large t. Calling (5.6.33) $w_{i \to [n]}$, where $[n]$ stands for a group of final states with energy similar to i, we obtain

$$w_{i \to [n]} = \frac{2\pi}{\hbar} \overline{|V_{ni}|^2} \rho(E_n)_{E_n \simeq E_i} \tag{5.6.34}$$

independent of t, provided the first-order time-dependent perturbation theory is valid. This formula is of great practical importance; it is called **Fermi's golden rule** even though the basic formalism of t-dependent perturbation theory is due to Dirac.* We sometimes write (5.6.34) as

$$w_{i \to n} = \left(\frac{2\pi}{\hbar}\right) |V_{ni}|^2 \delta(E_n - E_i), \tag{5.6.35}$$

where it must be understood that this expression is integrated with $\int dE_n \rho(E_n)$.

We should also understand what is meant by $\overline{|V_{ni}|^2}$. If the final states $|n\rangle$ form a quasi-continuum, the matrix elements V_{ni} are often similar if $|n\rangle$ are similar. However, it may happen that all energy eigenstates with the same E_n do not necessarily have similar matrix elements. Consider, for example, elastic scattering. The $|V_{ni}|^2$ that determines the scattering cross section may depend on the final momentum direction. In such a case the

---

Editorial Note. Dr. Edward Teller, in teaching a quantum mechanics class at Berkeley in 1955 (in which the editor was in attendance), mentioned that this was actually Fermi's golden rule 2. Since Teller did not subscribe to golden rule 1, the class was not informed what rule 1 was. However, golden rule 1 is given in E. Fermi 1950, 136 and 148.

group of final states we should consider must have not only approximately the same energy, but they must also have approximately the same momentum direction. This point becomes clearer when we discuss the photoelectric effect.

Let us now look at the second-order term, still with the constant perturbation of (5.6.20). From (5.6.17) we have

$$c_n^{(2)} = \left(\frac{-i}{\hbar}\right)^2 \sum_m V_{nm}V_{mi} \int_0^t dt' e^{i\omega_{nm}t'} \int_0^{t'} dt'' e^{i\omega_{mi}t''}$$

$$= \frac{i}{\hbar} \sum_m \frac{V_{nm}V_{mi}}{E_m - E_i} \int_0^t \left(e^{i\omega_{ni}t'} - e^{i\omega_{nm}t'}\right) dt'. \qquad (5.6.36)$$

The first term on the right-hand side has the same t-dependence as $c_n^{(1)}$ [see (5.6.21)]. If this were the only term, we could then repeat the same argument as before and conclude that as $t \to \infty$, the only important contribution arises from $E_n \simeq E_i$. Indeed, when E_m differs from E_n and E_i, the second contribution gives rise to a rapid oscillation, which does not give a contribution to the transition probability that grows with t.

With $c^{(1)}$ and $c^{(2)}$ together, we have

$$w_{i \to [n]} = \frac{2\pi}{\hbar} \left| V_{ni} + \sum_m \frac{V_{nm}V_{mi}}{E_i - E_m} \right|^2 \rho(E_n) \Bigg|_{E_n \simeq E_i} \qquad (5.6.37)$$

The formula has the following physical interpretation. We visualize that the transition due to the second-order term takes place in two steps. First, $|i\rangle$ makes an energy nonconserving transition to $|m\rangle$; subsequently, $|m\rangle$ makes an energy nonconserving transition to $|n\rangle$, where between $|n\rangle$ and $|i\rangle$ there is overall energy conservation. Such energy nonconserving transitions are often called *virtual transitions*. Energy need not be conserved for those virtual transitions into (or from) virtual intermediate states. In contrast, the first-order term V_{ni} is often said to represent a direct energy-conserving "real" transition. A special treatment is needed if $V_{nm}V_{mi} \neq 0$ with $E_m \simeq E_i$. The best way to treat this is to use the slow-turn-on method $V \to e^{\eta t}V$, which we will discuss in Section 5.8 and Problem 31 of this chapter. The net result is to change the energy denominator in (5.6.37) as follows:

$$E_i - E_m \to E_i - E_m + i\varepsilon. \qquad (5.6.38)$$

Harmonic Perturbation

We now consider a sinusoidally varying time-dependent potential, commonly referred to as **harmonic perturbation**:

$$V(t) = \mathcal{V}e^{i\omega t} + \mathcal{V}^\dagger e^{-i\omega t}, \qquad (5.6.39)$$

where $\mathcal{V}$ may still depend on x, p, s, and so on. Actually, we have already encountered a time-dependent potential of this kind in Section 5.5 in discussing t-dependent two-level problems.

Again assume that only one of the eigenstates of H_0 is populated initially. Perturbation (5.6.39) is assumed to be turned on at $t = 0$, so

$$c_n^{(1)} = \frac{-i}{\hbar} \int_0^t \left(\mathscr{V}_{ni} e^{i\omega t'} + \mathscr{V}_{ni}^\dagger e^{-i\omega t'} \right) e^{i\omega_{ni} t'} \, dt'$$

$$= \frac{1}{\hbar} \left[\frac{1 - e^{i(\omega + \omega_{ni})t}}{\omega + \omega_{ni}} \mathscr{V}_{ni} + \frac{1 - e^{i(\omega_{ni} - \omega)t}}{-\omega + \omega_{ni}} \mathscr{V}_{ni}^\dagger \right] \qquad (5.6.40)$$

where $\mathscr{V}_{ni}^\dagger$ actually stands for $(\mathscr{V}^\dagger)_{ni}$. We see that this formula is similar to the constant perturbation case. The only change needed is

$$\omega_{ni} = \frac{E_n - E_i}{\hbar} \rightarrow \omega_{ni} \pm \omega. \qquad (5.6.41)$$

So as $t \rightarrow \infty$, $|c_n^{(1)}|^2$ is appreciable only if

$$\omega_{ni} + \omega \simeq 0 \quad \text{or} \quad E_n \simeq E_i - \hbar\omega \qquad (5.6.42a)$$

$$\omega_{ni} - \omega \simeq 0 \quad \text{or} \quad E_n \simeq E_i + \hbar\omega. \qquad (5.6.42b)$$

Clearly, whenever the first term is important because of (5.6.42a), the second term is unimportant, and vice versa. We see that we have no energy-conservation condition satisfied by the quantum-mechanical system alone; rather the apparent lack of energy conservation is compensated by the energy given out to—or energy taken away from—the "external" potential $V(t)$. Pictorially, we have Figure 5.9. In the first case (*stimulated emission*), the quantum-mechanical system gives up energy $\hbar\omega$ to V; this is clearly possible only if the initial state is excited. In the second case (*absorption*), the quantum-mechanical system receives energy $\hbar\omega$ from V and ends up as an excited state. Thus a time-dependent perturbation can be regarded as an inexhaustible source or sink of energy.

In complete analogy with (5.6.34), we have

$$w_{i \rightarrow [n]} = \frac{2\pi}{\hbar} |\mathscr{V}_{ni}|^2 \rho(E_n) \Big|_{E_n \simeq E_i - \hbar\omega}$$

$$\qquad (5.6.43)$$

$$w_{i \rightarrow [n]} = \frac{2\pi}{\hbar} |\mathscr{V}_{ni}^\dagger|^2 \rho(E_n) \Big|_{E_n \simeq E_i + \hbar\omega}$$

or, more commonly,

$$w_{i \rightarrow n} = \frac{2\pi}{\hbar} \left\{ \begin{matrix} |\mathscr{V}_{ni}|^2 \\ |\mathscr{V}_{ni}^\dagger|^2 \end{matrix} \right\} \delta(E_n - E_i \pm \hbar\omega). \qquad (5.6.44)$$

Note also that

$$|\mathscr{V}_{ni}|^2 = |\mathscr{V}_{in}^\dagger|^2, \qquad (5.6.45)$$

FIGURE 5.9. (i) Stimulated emission: Quantum-mechanical system gives up $\hbar\omega$ to V (possible only if initial state is excited). (ii) Absorption: Quantum mechanical system receives $\hbar\omega$ from V and ends up as an excited state.

which is a consequence of

$$\langle i|\mathscr{V}^\dagger|n\rangle = \langle n|\mathscr{V}|i\rangle^* \qquad (5.6.46)$$

(remember $\mathscr{V}^\dagger|n\rangle \overset{DC}{\leftrightarrow} \langle n|\mathscr{V}\rangle$). Combining (5.6.43) and (5.6.45), we have

$$\frac{\text{emission rate for } i \to [n]}{\text{density of final states for } [n]} = \frac{\text{absorption rate for } n \to [i]}{\text{density of final states for } [i]},$$

$$(5.6.47)$$

where in the absorption case we let i stand for final states. Equation (5.6.47), which expresses symmetry between emission and absorption, is known as **detailed balancing**.

To summarize, for constant perturbation, we obtain appreciable transition probability for $|i\rangle \to |n\rangle$ only if $E_n \simeq E_i$. In contrast, for harmonic perturbation we have appreciable transition probability only if $E_n \simeq E_i - \hbar\omega$ (stimulated emission) or $E_n \simeq E_i + \hbar\omega$ (absorption).

5.7. APPLICATIONS TO INTERACTIONS WITH THE CLASSICAL RADIATION FIELD

Absorption and Stimulated Emission

We apply the formalism of time-dependent perturbation theory to the interactions of atomic electron with the classical radiation field. By a **classical radiation field** we mean the electric or magnetic field derivable from a classical (as opposed to quantized) radiation field.

The basic Hamiltonian, with $|\mathbf{A}|^2$ omitted, is

$$H = \frac{\mathbf{p}^2}{2m_e} + e\phi(\mathbf{x}) - \frac{e}{m_e c}\mathbf{A}\cdot\mathbf{p}, \qquad (5.7.1)$$

which is justified if

$$\nabla\cdot\mathbf{A} = 0; \qquad (5.7.2)$$

specifically, we work with a monochromatic field of the plane wave for

$$\mathbf{A} = 2A_0\hat{\varepsilon}\cos\left(\frac{\omega}{c}\hat{\mathbf{n}}\cdot\mathbf{x} - \omega t\right) \tag{5.7.3}$$

where $\hat{\varepsilon}$ and $\hat{\mathbf{n}}$ are the (linear) polarization and propagation direction. Equation (5.7.3) obviously satisfies (5.7.2) because $\hat{\varepsilon}$ is perpendicular to the propagation direction $\hat{\mathbf{n}}$. We write

$$\cos\left(\frac{\omega}{c}\hat{\mathbf{n}}\cdot\mathbf{x} - \omega t\right) = \frac{1}{2}\left[e^{i(\omega/c)\hat{\mathbf{n}}\cdot\mathbf{x} - i\omega t} + e^{-i(\omega/c)\hat{\mathbf{n}}\cdot\mathbf{x} + i\omega t}\right] \tag{5.7.4}$$

and treat $-(e/m_e c)\mathbf{A}\cdot\mathbf{p}$ as time-dependent potential, where we express $\mathbf{A}$ in (5.7.3) as

$$\mathbf{A} = A_0\hat{\varepsilon}\left[e^{i(\omega/c)\hat{\mathbf{n}}\cdot\mathbf{x} - i\omega t} + e^{-i(\omega/c)\hat{\mathbf{n}}\cdot\mathbf{x} + i\omega t}\right]. \tag{5.7.5}$$

Comparing this result with (5.6.39), we see that the $e^{-i\omega t}$-term in

$$-\left(\frac{e}{m_e c}\right)\mathbf{A}\cdot\mathbf{p} = -\left(\frac{e}{m_e c}\right)A_0\hat{\varepsilon}\cdot\mathbf{p}\left[e^{i(\omega/c)\hat{\mathbf{n}}\cdot\mathbf{x} - i\omega t} + e^{-i(\omega/c)\hat{\mathbf{n}}\cdot\mathbf{x} + i\omega t}\right]$$

$$\tag{5.7.6}$$

is responsible for absorption, while the $e^{+i\omega t}$-term is responsible for stimulated emission.

Let us now treat the absorption case in detail. We have

$$\mathscr{V}_{ni}^{\dagger} = -\frac{eA_0}{m_e c}\left(e^{i(\omega/c)(\hat{\mathbf{n}}\cdot\mathbf{x})}\hat{\varepsilon}\cdot\mathbf{p}\right)_{ni} \tag{5.7.7}$$

and

$$w_{i\to n} = \frac{2\pi}{\hbar}\frac{e^2}{m_e^2 c^2}|A_0|^2|\langle n|e^{i(\omega/c)(\hat{\mathbf{n}}\cdot\mathbf{x})}\hat{\varepsilon}\cdot\mathbf{p}|i\rangle|^2\delta(E_n - E_i - \hbar\omega). \tag{5.7.8}$$

The meaning of the δ-function is clear. If $|n\rangle$ forms a continuum, we simply integrate with $\rho(E_n)$. But even if $|n\rangle$ is discrete, because $|n\rangle$ cannot be a ground state (albeit a bound-state energy level), its energy is not infinitely sharp; there may be a natural broadening due to a finite lifetime (see Section 5.8); there can also be a mechanism for broadening due to collisions. In such cases, we regard $\delta(\omega - \omega_{ni})$ as

$$\delta(\omega - \omega_{ni}) = \lim_{\gamma\to 0}\left(\frac{\gamma}{2\pi}\right)\frac{1}{\left[(\omega - \omega_{ni})^2 + \gamma^2/4\right]}. \tag{5.7.9}$$

Finally, the incident electromagnetic wave itself is not perfectly monochromatic; in fact, there is always a finite frequency width.

We derive an absorption cross section as

$$\frac{(\text{Energy/unit time}) \text{ absorbed by the atom } (i\to n)}{\text{Energy flux of the radiation field}}. \tag{5.7.10}$$

For the energy flux (energy per area per unit time), classical electromagnetic theory gives us

$$c\mathcal{U} = \frac{1}{2\pi} \frac{\omega^2}{c} |A_0|^2,$$ (5.7.11)

where we have used

$$\mathcal{U} = \frac{1}{2}\left(\frac{E_{\max}^2}{8\pi} + \frac{B_{\max}^2}{8\pi}\right)$$ (5.7.12)

for energy density (energy per unit volume) with

$$\mathbf{E} = -\frac{1}{c}\frac{\partial}{\partial t}\mathbf{A}, \qquad \mathbf{B} = \nabla \times \mathbf{A}.$$ (5.7.13)

Putting everything together, we get (remembering that $\hbar\omega =$ energy absorbed by atom for each absorption process)

$$
\begin{aligned}
\sigma_{abs} &= \frac{\hbar\omega(2\pi/\hbar)(e^2/m_e^2c^2)|A_0|^2 |\langle n|e^{i(\omega/c)(\hat{\mathbf{n}}\cdot\mathbf{x})}\hat{\boldsymbol{\varepsilon}}\cdot\mathbf{p}|i\rangle|^2 \delta(E_n - E_i - \hbar\omega)}{(1/2\pi)(\omega^2/c)|A_0|^2} \\
&= \frac{4\pi^2\hbar}{m_e^2\omega}\left(\frac{e^2}{\hbar c}\right)|\langle n|e^{i(\omega/c)(\hat{\mathbf{n}}\cdot\mathbf{x})}\hat{\boldsymbol{\varepsilon}}\cdot\mathbf{p}|i\rangle|^2 \delta(E_n - E_i - \hbar\omega).
\end{aligned}
$$ (5.7.14)

Equation (5.7.14) has the correct dimension $[1/(M^2/T)](M^2L^2/T^2)T = L^2$ if we recognize that $\alpha = e^2/\hbar c \simeq 1/137$ (dimensionless) and $\delta(E_n - E_i - \hbar\omega) = (1/\hbar)\delta(\omega_{ni} - \omega)$, where $\delta(\omega_{ni} - \omega)$ has time dimension T.

Electric Dipole Approximation

The *electric dipole approximation* (E1 approximation) is based on the fact that the wavelength of the radiation field is far longer than the atomic dimension, so that the series (remember $\omega/c = 1/\lambdabar$)

$$e^{i(\omega/c)\hat{\mathbf{n}}\cdot\mathbf{x}} = 1 + i\frac{\omega}{c}\hat{\mathbf{n}}\cdot\mathbf{x} + \cdots$$ (5.7.15)

can be approximated by its leading term, 1. The validity of this for a light atom is as follows: First, the $\hbar\omega$ of the radiation field must be of order of atomic level spacing, so

$$\hbar\omega \sim \frac{Ze^2}{(a_0/Z)} \simeq \frac{Ze^2}{R_{\text{atom}}}.$$ (5.7.16)

This leads to

$$\frac{c}{\omega} = \lambdabar \sim \frac{c\hbar R_{\text{atom}}}{Ze^2} \simeq \frac{137 R_{\text{atom}}}{Z}.$$ (5.7.17)

In other words,

$$\frac{1}{\lambdabar}R_{\text{atom}} \sim \frac{Z}{137} \ll 1$$ (5.7.18)

for light atoms (small Z). Because the matrix element of x is of order R_{atom}, that of x^2, of order R^2_{atom}, and so on, we see that the approximation of replacing (5.7.15) by its leading term is an excellent one.

Now we have

$$\langle n|e^{i(\omega/c)(\hat{\mathbf{n}}\cdot\mathbf{x})}\hat{\boldsymbol{\varepsilon}}\cdot\mathbf{p}|i\rangle \rightarrow \hat{\boldsymbol{\varepsilon}}\cdot\langle n|\mathbf{p}|i\rangle. \tag{5.7.19}$$

In particular, we take $\hat{\boldsymbol{\varepsilon}}$ along the x-axis (and $\hat{\mathbf{n}}$ along the z-axis). We must calculate $\langle n|p_x|i\rangle$. Using

$$[x, H_0] = \frac{i\hbar p_x}{m}, \tag{5.7.20}$$

we have

$$\langle n|p_x|i\rangle = \frac{m}{i\hbar}\langle n|[x, H_0]|i\rangle$$

$$= im\omega_{ni}\langle n|x|i\rangle. \tag{5.7.21}$$

Because of the approximation of the dipole operator, this approximation scheme is called the **electric dipole approximation**. We may here recall [see (3.10.39)] the selection rule for the dipole matrix element. Since $\mathbf{x}$ is a spherical tensor of rank 1 with $q = \pm 1$, we must have $m' - m = \pm 1$, $|j' - j| = 0,1$ (no $0 \rightarrow 0$ transition). If $\hat{\boldsymbol{\varepsilon}}$ is along the y-axis, the same selection rule applies. On the other hand, if $\hat{\boldsymbol{\varepsilon}}$ is in the z-direction, $q = 0$; hence, $m' = m$.

With the electric dipole approximation, the absorption cross section (5.7.14) now takes a simpler form upon using (5.7.19) and (5.7.21) as

$$\sigma_{abs} = 4\pi^2\alpha\omega_{ni}|\langle n|x|i\rangle|^2\delta(\omega - \omega_{ni}). \tag{5.7.22}$$

In other words, σ_{abs} treated as a function of ω exhibits a sharp δ-function-like peak whenever $\hbar\omega$ corresponds to the energy-level spacing at $\omega \simeq (E_n - E_i)/\hbar$. Suppose $|i\rangle$ is the ground state, then ω_{ni} is necessarily positive; integrating (5.7.22), we get

$$\int \sigma_{abs}(\omega)\, d\omega = \sum_n 4\pi^2\alpha\omega_{ni}|\langle n|x|i\rangle|^2. \tag{5.7.23}$$

In atomic physics we define **oscillator strength**, f_{ni}, as

$$f_{ni} \equiv \frac{2m\omega_{ni}}{\hbar}|\langle n|x|i\rangle|^2. \tag{5.7.24}$$

It is then straightforward (consider $[x,[x, H_0]]$) to establish the **Thomas-Reiche-Kuhn sum rule**,

$$\sum_n f_{ni} = 1. \tag{5.7.25}$$

In terms of the integration over the absorption cross section, we have

$$\int \sigma_{abs}(\omega)\, d\omega = \frac{4\pi^2\alpha\hbar}{2m_e} = 2\pi^2c\left(\frac{e^2}{m_e c^2}\right). \tag{5.7.26}$$

Notice how $\hbar$ has disappeared. Indeed, this is just the oscillation sum rule already known in classical electrodynamics (Jackson 1975, for instance). Historically, this was one of the first examples of how "new quantum mechanics" led to the correct classical result. This sum rule is quite remarkable because we did not specify in detail the form of the Hamiltonian.

Photoelectric Effect

We now consider the **photoelectric effect**—that is, the ejection of an electron when an atom is placed in the radiation field. The basic process is considered to be the transition from an atomic (bound) state to a continuum state $E > 0$. Therefore, $|i\rangle$ is the ket for an atomic state, while $|n\rangle$ is the ket for a continuum state, which can be taken to be a plane-wave state $|\mathbf{k}_f\rangle$, an approximation that is valid if the final electron is not too slow. Our earlier formula for $\sigma_{abs}(\omega)$ can still be used, except that we must now integrate $\delta(\omega_{ni} - \omega)$ together with the density of final states $\rho(E_n)$.

Our basic task is to calculate the number of final states per unit energy interval. As we will see in a moment, this is an example where the matrix element depends not only on the final state energy but also on the momentum *direction*. We must therefore consider a group of final states with both similar momentum directions and similar energies.

To count the number of states it is convenient to use the box normalization convention for plane-wave states. We consider a plane-wave state normalized if when we integrate the square modulus of its wave function for a cubic box of side L, we obtain unity. Furthermore, the state is assumed to satisfy the periodic boundary condition with periodicity of the side of the box. The wave function must then be of form

$$\langle \mathbf{x} | \mathbf{k}_f \rangle = \frac{e^{i\mathbf{k}_f \cdot \mathbf{x}}}{L^{3/2}}, \qquad (5.7.27)$$

where the allowed values of k_x must satisfy

$$k_x = \frac{2\pi n_x}{L}, \dots, \qquad (5.7.28)$$

with n_x a positive or negative integer. Similar restrictions hold for k_y and k_z. Notice that as $L \to \infty$, k_x, k_y, and k_z become continuous variables.

The problem of counting the number of states is reduced to that of counting the number of dots in three-dimensional lattice space. We define n such that

$$n^2 = n_x^2 + n_y^2 + n_z^2. \qquad (5.7.29)$$

As $L \to \infty$, it is a good approximation to treat n as a continuous variable; in fact it is just the magnitude of the radial vector in the lattice space. Let us consider a small-volume element such that the radial vector falls within n and $n + dn$ and the solid angle element $d\Omega$; clearly, it is of volume $n^2 \, dn \, d\Omega$. The energy of the final-state plane wave is related to k_f and hence to n; we have

$$E = \frac{\hbar^2 k_f^2}{2m_e} = \frac{\hbar^2}{2m_e} \frac{n^2 (2\pi)^2}{L^2}. \tag{5.7.30}$$

Furthermore, the direction of the radial vector in the lattice space is just the momentum direction of the final state, so the number of states in the interval between E and $E + dE$ with direction into $d\Omega$ being $\mathbf{k}_f$ is (remember $dE = (\hbar^2 k_f / m_e) \, dk_f$) given by*

$$n^2 \, d\Omega \frac{dn}{dE} \, dE = \left(\frac{L}{2\pi} \right)^3 \left(k_f^2 \right) \frac{dk_f}{dE} \, d\Omega \, dE$$

$$= \left(\frac{L}{2\pi} \right)^3 \frac{m_e}{\hbar^2} k_f \, dE \, d\Omega. \tag{5.7.31}$$

We can now put everything together to obtain an expression for the differential cross section for the photoelectric effect:

$$\frac{d\sigma}{d\Omega} = \frac{4\pi^2 \alpha \hbar}{m_e^2 \omega} |\langle \mathbf{k}_f | e^{i(\omega/c)(\hat{\mathbf{n}} \cdot \mathbf{x})} \hat{\boldsymbol{\epsilon}} \cdot \mathbf{p} | i \rangle|^2 \frac{m_e k_f L^3}{\hbar^2 (2\pi)^3}. \tag{5.7.32}$$

To be specific, let us consider the ejection of a K shell (the innermost shell) electron caused by absorption of light. The initial-state wave function is essentially the same as the ground-state hydrogen atom wave function except that the Bohr radius a_0 is replaced by a_0/Z. Thus

$$\langle \mathbf{k}_f | e^{i(\omega/c)(\hat{\mathbf{n}} \cdot \mathbf{x})} \hat{\boldsymbol{\epsilon}} \cdot \mathbf{p} | i \rangle = \hat{\boldsymbol{\epsilon}} \cdot \int d^3 x \frac{e^{-i\mathbf{k}_f \cdot \mathbf{x}}}{L^{3/2}} e^{i(\omega/c)(\hat{\mathbf{n}} \cdot \mathbf{x})}$$

$$\times (-i\hbar\nabla) \left[e^{-Zr/a_0} \left(\frac{Z}{a_0} \right)^{3/2} \right]. \tag{5.7.33}$$

Integrating by parts, we can pass ∇ to the left side. Furthermore,

$$\hat{\boldsymbol{\epsilon}} \cdot \left[\nabla e^{i(\omega/c)(\hat{\mathbf{n}} \cdot \mathbf{x})} \right] = 0 \tag{5.7.34}$$

because $\hat{\boldsymbol{\epsilon}}$ is perpendicular to $\hat{\mathbf{n}}$. On the other hand, ∇ acting on $e^{-i\mathbf{k}_f \cdot \mathbf{x}}$ brings down $-i\mathbf{k}_f$, which can be taken outside the integral. Thus to evaluate (5.7.33), all we need to do is take the Fourier transform of the atomic wave function with respect to

$$\mathbf{q} \equiv \mathbf{k}_f - \left(\frac{\omega}{c} \right) \hat{\mathbf{n}}. \tag{5.7.35}$$

---

*This is equivalent to taking one state per cube $d^3 x \, d^3 p / (2\pi\hbar)^3$ in phase space.

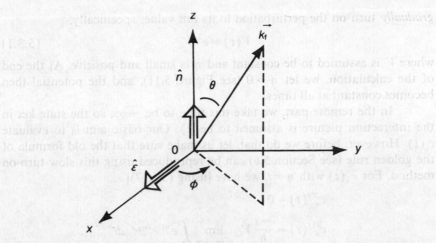

FIGURE 5.10. Polar coordinate system with $\boldsymbol{\varepsilon}$ and $\hat{n}$ along $0x$ and $0z$, respectively, and $\mathbf{k}_f = (k_f \sin\theta\cos\phi,\; k_f\sin\theta\sin\phi,\; k_f\cos\theta)$.

The final answer is (see Problem 39 of this chapter for the Fourier transform of the hydrogen atom wave function)

$$\frac{d\sigma}{d\Omega} = 32e^2 k_f \frac{\left(\hat{\boldsymbol{\varepsilon}}\cdot\mathbf{k}_f\right)^2}{mc\omega} \frac{Z^5}{a_0^5} \frac{1}{\left[\left(Z^2/a_0^2\right)+q^2\right]^4}. \tag{5.7.36}$$

If we introduce the coordinate system shown in Figure 5.10, we can write the differential cross section in terms of θ and ϕ using

$$\left(\hat{\boldsymbol{\varepsilon}}\cdot\mathbf{k}_f\right)^2 = k_f^2 \sin^2\theta\cos^2\phi$$

$$q^2 = k_f^2 - 2k_f\frac{\omega}{c}\cos\theta + \left(\frac{\omega}{c}\right)^2. \tag{5.7.37}$$

5.8. ENERGY SHIFT AND DECAY WIDTH

Our considerations so far have been restricted to the question of how states other than the initial state get populated. In other words, we have been concerned with the time development of the coefficient $c_n(t)$ with $n \neq i$. The question naturally arises, What happens to $c_i(t)$ itself?

To avoid the effect of a sudden change in the Hamiltonian, we propose to increase the perturbation very slowly. In the remote past $(t \to -\infty)$ the time-dependent potential is assumed to be zero. We then *gradually* turn on the perturbation to its full value; specifically,

$$V(t) = e^{\eta t} V \tag{5.8.1}$$

where V is assumed to be constant and η is small and positive. At the end of the calculation, we let $\eta \to 0$ (see Figure 5.11), and the potential then becomes constant at all times.

In the remote past, we take this time to be $-\infty$, so the state ket in the interaction picture is assumed to be $|i\rangle$. Our basic aim is to evaluate $c_i(t)$. However, before we do that, let us make sure that the old formula of the golden rule (see Section 5.6) can be reproduced using this slow-turn-on method. For $c_n(t)$ with $n \neq i$, we have [using (5.6.17)]

$$c_n^{(0)}(t) = 0$$

$$c_n^{(1)}(t) = \frac{-i}{\hbar} V_{ni} \lim_{t_0 \to -\infty} \int_{t_0}^{t} e^{\eta t'} e^{i\omega_{ni} t'} \, dt'$$

$$= \frac{-i}{\hbar} V_{ni} \frac{e^{\eta t + i\omega_{ni} t}}{\eta + i\omega_{ni}}. \tag{5.8.2}$$

To lowest nonvanishing order, the transition probability is therefore given by

$$|c_n(t)|^2 \simeq \frac{|V_{ni}|^2}{\hbar^2} \frac{e^{2\eta t}}{\eta^2 + \omega_{ni}^2}, \tag{5.8.3}$$

or

$$\frac{d}{dt} |c_n(t)|^2 \simeq \frac{2|V_{ni}|^2}{\hbar^2} \left(\frac{\eta e^{2\eta t}}{\eta^2 + \omega_{ni}^2} \right). \tag{5.8.4}$$

We now let $\eta \to 0$. Clearly, it is all right to replace $e^{\eta t}$ by unity, but note

$$\lim_{\eta \to 0} \frac{\eta}{\eta^2 + \omega_{ni}^2} = \pi \delta(\omega_{ni}) = \pi \hbar \delta(E_n - E_i). \tag{5.8.5}$$

FIGURE 5.11.   Plot of $V(t)$ versus t in the adiabatic (slow-turn-on) picture.

This leads to the golden rule,

$$w_{i \to n} \simeq \left(\frac{2\pi}{\hbar}\right)|V_{ni}|^2 \delta(E_n - E_i). \qquad (5.8.6)$$

Encouraged by this result, let us calculate $c_i^{(0)}$, $c_i^{(1)}$, and $c_i^{(2)}$, again using (5.6.17). We have

$$c_i^{(0)} = 1$$

$$c_i^{(1)} = \frac{-i}{\hbar} V_{ii} \lim_{t_0 \to -\infty} \int_{t_0}^t e^{\eta t'} dt' = \frac{-i}{\hbar \eta} V_{ii} e^{\eta t}$$

$$c_i^{(2)} = \left(\frac{-i}{\hbar}\right)^2 \sum_m |V_{mi}|^2 \lim_{t_0 \to -\infty} \int_{t_0}^t dt' e^{i\omega_{im} t' + \eta t'} \frac{e^{i\omega_{mi} t' + \eta t'}}{i(\omega_{mi} - i\eta)}$$

$$= \left(\frac{-i}{\hbar}\right)^2 |V_{ii}|^2 \frac{e^{2\eta t}}{2\eta^2} + \left(\frac{-i}{\hbar}\right) \sum_{m \neq i} \frac{|V_{mi}|^2 e^{2\eta t}}{2\eta(E_i - E_m + i\hbar\eta)}. \qquad (5.8.7)$$

Thus up to second order we have

$$c_i(t) \simeq 1 - \frac{i}{\hbar\eta} V_{ii} e^{\eta t} + \left(\frac{-i}{\hbar}\right)^2 |V_{ii}|^2 \frac{e^{2\eta t}}{2\eta^2} + \left(\frac{-i}{\hbar}\right) \sum_{m \neq i} \frac{|V_{mi}|^2 e^{2\eta t}}{2\eta(E_i - E_m + i\hbar\eta)}.$$

$$(5.8.8)$$

Now consider the time derivative of c_i [$dc_i(t)/dt \equiv \dot{c}_i$], which we have from (5.8.8). Upon dividing by c_i and letting $\eta \to 0$ (thus replacing $e^{\eta t}$ and $e^{2\eta t}$ by unity), we get

$$\frac{\dot{c}_i}{c_i} \simeq \frac{\dfrac{-i}{\hbar} V_{ii} + \left(\dfrac{-i}{\hbar}\right)^2 \dfrac{|V_{ii}|^2}{\eta} + \left(\dfrac{-i}{\hbar}\right) \displaystyle\sum_{m \neq i} \dfrac{|V_{mi}|^2}{(E_i - E_m + i\hbar\eta)}}{1 - \dfrac{i}{\hbar} \dfrac{V_{ii}}{\eta}}$$

$$\simeq \frac{-i}{\hbar} V_{ii} + \left(\frac{-i}{\hbar}\right) \sum_{m \neq i} \frac{|V_{mi}|^2}{E_i - E_m + i\hbar\eta}. \qquad (5.8.9)$$

Expansion (5.8.9) is formally correct up to second order in V. Note here that $\dot{c}_i(t)/c_i(t)$ is now independent of t. Equation (5.8.9) is a differential equation that is to hold *at all times*. Having obtained this, it is convenient to renormalize c_i so that $c_i(0) = 1$. We now try the ansatz

$$c_i(t) = e^{-i\Delta_i t/\hbar}, \qquad \frac{\dot{c}_i(t)}{c_i(t)} = \frac{-i}{\hbar} \Delta_i \qquad (5.8.10)$$

with Δ_i constant (in time) but not necessarily real. Clearly (5.8.10) is consistent with (5.8.9) because the right-hand side of (5.8.10) is constant. We can see the physical meaning of Δ_i by noting that $e^{-i\Delta_i t/\hbar}|i\rangle$ in the interaction picture implies $e^{-i\Delta_i t/\hbar - iE_i t/\hbar}|i\rangle$ in the Schrödinger picture. In other words,

$$E_i \rightarrow E_i + \Delta_i \qquad (5.8.11)$$

as a result of perturbation. That is, we have calculated the *level shift* using time-*dependent* perturbation theory. Now expand, as usual,

$$\Delta_i = \Delta_i^{(1)} + \Delta_i^{(2)} + \cdots , \qquad (5.8.12)$$

and compare (5.8.10) with (5.8.9); we get to first order

$$\Delta_i^{(1)} = V_{ii}. \qquad (5.8.13)$$

But this is just what we expect from *t-independent perturbation theory*. Before we look at $\Delta_i^{(2)}$, recall

$$\lim_{\varepsilon \to 0} \frac{1}{x + i\varepsilon} = \mathrm{Pr}. \frac{1}{x} - i\pi\delta(x). \qquad (5.8.14)$$

Thus

$$\mathrm{Re}(\Delta_i^{(2)}) = \mathrm{Pr}. \sum_{m \neq i} \frac{|V_{mi}|^2}{E_i - E_m} \qquad (5.8.15a)$$

$$\mathrm{Im}(\Delta_i^{(2)}) = -\pi \sum_{m \neq i} |V_{mi}|^2 \delta(E_i - E_m). \qquad (5.8.15b)$$

But the right-hand side of (5.8.15b) is familiar from the golden rule, so we can identify

$$\sum_{m \neq i} w_{i \to m} = \frac{2\pi}{\hbar} \sum_{m \neq i} |V_{mi}|^2 \delta(E_i - E_m) = -\frac{2}{\hbar} \mathrm{Im}[\Delta_i^{(2)}]. \qquad (5.8.16)$$

Coming back to $c_i(t)$, we can write (5.8.10) as

$$c_i(t) = e^{-(i/\hbar)[\mathrm{Re}(\Delta_i)t] + (1/\hbar)[\mathrm{Im}(\Delta_i)t]}. \qquad (5.8.17)$$

If we define

$$\frac{\Gamma_i}{\hbar} \equiv -\frac{2}{\hbar} \mathrm{Im}(\Delta_i), \qquad (5.8.18)$$

then

$$|c_i|^2 = e^{2\mathrm{Im}(\Delta_i)t/\hbar} = e^{-\Gamma_i t/\hbar}. \qquad (5.8.19)$$

Therefore, Γ_i characterizes the rate at which state $|i\rangle$ disappears.

It is worth checking the probability conservation up to second order in V for small t:

$$|c_i|^2 + \sum_{m \neq i} |c_m|^2 = (1 - \Gamma_i t/\hbar) + \sum_{m \neq i} w_{i \to m} t = 1, \qquad (5.8.20)$$

where (5.8.16) has been used. Thus the probabilities for finding the initial state and all other states add up to 1. Put in another way, the depletion of state $|i\rangle$ is compensated by the growth of states other than $|i\rangle$.

To summarize, the real part of the energy shift is what we usually associate with the level shift. The imaginary part of the energy shift is, apart from -2 [see (5.8.18)], the **decay width**. Note also

$$\frac{\hbar}{\Gamma_i} = \tau_i \tag{5.8.21}$$

where τ_i is the mean lifetime of state $|i\rangle$ because

$$|c_i|^2 = e^{-t/\tau_i}. \tag{5.8.22}$$

To see why Γ_i is called *width*, we look at the Fourier decomposition

$$\int f(E) e^{-iEt/\hbar} \, dE = e^{-i[E_i + \text{Re}(\Delta_i)]t/\hbar - \Gamma_i t/2\hbar}. \tag{5.8.23}$$

Using the Fourier inversion formula, we get

$$|f(E)|^2 \propto \frac{1}{\left\{ E - [E_i + \text{Re}(\Delta_i)] \right\}^2 + \Gamma_i^2/4} \tag{5.8.24}$$

Therefore, Γ_i has the usual meaning of full width at half maximum. Notice that we get the time-energy uncertainty relation from (5.8.21)

$$\Delta t \, \Delta E \sim \hbar, \tag{5.8.25}$$

where we identify the uncertainty in the energy with Γ_i and the mean lifetime with Δt.

Even though we discussed the subject of energy shift and decay width using the constant perturbation V obtained as the limit of (5.8.1) when $\eta \to 0$, we can easily generalize our considerations to the harmonic perturbation case discussed in Section 5.6. All we must do is to let

$$E_{n(m)} - E_i \to E_{n(m)} - E_i \pm \hbar\omega \tag{5.8.26}$$

in (5.8.2), (5.8.8), and (5.8.15), and so on. The quantum-mechanical description of unstable states we have developed here is originally due to Wigner and Weisskopf in 1930.

PROBLEMS

1. A simple harmonic oscillator (in one dimension) is subjected to a perturbation

$$\lambda H_1 = bx$$

where b is a real constant.

a. Calculate the energy shift of the ground state to *lowest nonvanishing order*.

b. Solve this problem *exactly* and compare with your result obtained in (a).

[You may assume without proof

$$\langle u_{n'}|x|u_n\rangle = \sqrt{\frac{\hbar}{2m\omega}}\left(\sqrt{n+1}\,\delta_{n',n+1} + \sqrt{n}\,\delta_{n',n-1}\right).\Bigr]$$

2. In nondegenerate time-independent perturbation theory, what is the probability of finding in a perturbed energy eigenstate ($|k\rangle$) the corresponding unperturbed eigenstate ($|k^{(0)}\rangle$)? Solve this up to terms of order g^2.

3. Consider a particle in a two-dimensional potential

$$V_0 = \begin{cases} 0 & \text{for } 0 \le x \le L, 0 \le y \le L, \\ \infty & \text{otherwise.} \end{cases}$$

Write the energy eigenfunctions for the ground and first excited states. We now add a time-independent perturbation of the form

$$V_1 = \begin{cases} \lambda xy & \text{for } 0 \le x \le L, 0 \le y \le L, \\ 0 & \text{otherwise.} \end{cases}$$

Obtain the zeroth-order energy eigenfunctions and the first-order energy shifts for the ground and first excited states.

4. Consider an isotropic harmonic oscillator in *two* dimensions. The Hamiltonian is given by

$$H_0 = \frac{p_x^2}{2m} + \frac{p_y^2}{2m} + \frac{m\omega^2}{2}(x^2 + y^2).$$

a. What are the energies of the three lowest-lying states? Is there any degeneracy?

b. We now apply a perturbation

$$V = \delta m\omega^2 xy,$$

where δ is a dimensionless real number much smaller than unity. Find the zeroth-order energy eigenket and the corresponding energy to first order [that is, the unperturbed energy obtained in (a) plus the first-order energy shift] for each of the three lowest-lying states.

c. Solve the $H_0 + V$ problem *exactly*. Compare with the perturbation results obtained in (b).

[You may use $\langle n'|x|n\rangle = \sqrt{\hbar/2m\omega}\,(\sqrt{n+1}\,\delta_{n',n+1} + \sqrt{n}\,\delta_{n',n-1}).$]

5. Establish (5.1.54) for the one-dimensional harmonic oscillator given by (5.1.50) with an additional perturbation $V = \frac{1}{2}\varepsilon m\omega^2 x^2$. Show that all other matrix elements V_{k0} vanish.

6. A slightly anisotropic three-dimensional harmonic oscillator has $\omega_z \approx \omega_x = \omega_y$. A charged particle moves in the field of this oscillator and is at the same time exposed to a uniform magnetic field in the x-direction. Assuming that the Zeeman splitting is comparable to the splitting produced by the anisotropy, but small compared to $\hbar\omega$, cal-

culate to first order the energies of the components of the first excited state. Discuss various limiting cases. (From Merzbacher, *Quantum Mechanics, 2/e,* © 1970. Reprinted by permission of Ellis Horwood, Ltd.).

7. A one-electron atom whose ground state is nondegenerate is placed in a uniform electric field in the z-direction. Obtain an approximate expression for the induced electric dipole moment of the ground state by considering the expectation value of ez with respect to the perturbed state vector computed to first order. Show that the same expression can also be obtained from the energy shift $\Delta = -\alpha|E|^2/2$ of the ground state computed to second order. (*Note:* α stands for the polarizability.) Ignore spin.

8. Evaluate the matrix elements (or expectation values) given below. If any vanishes, explain why it vanishes using simple symmetry (or other) arguments.

   a. $\langle n = 2, l = 1, m = 0|x| n = 2, l = 0, m = 0\rangle$.

   b. $\langle n = 2, l = 1, m = 0|p_z| n = 2, l = 0, m = 0\rangle$.

   [In (a) and (b), $|nlm\rangle$ stands for the energy eigenket of a nonrelativistic hydrogen atom with spin ignored.]

   c. $\langle L_z \rangle$ for an electron in a central field with $j = \frac{9}{2}, m = \frac{7}{2}, l = 4$.

   d. $\langle$singlet, $m_s = 0|S_z^{(e-)} - S_z^{(e+)}|$triplet, $m_s = 0\rangle$ for an s-state positronium.

   e. $\langle S^{(1)} \cdot S^{(2)} \rangle$ for the ground state of a hydrogen *molecule*.

9. A p-orbital electron characterized by $|n, l = 1, m = \pm 1, 0\rangle$ (ignore spin) is subjected to a potential

$$V = \lambda(x^2 - y^2) \quad (\lambda = \text{constant}).$$

   a. Obtain the "correct" zeroth-order energy eigenstates that diagonalize the perturbation. You need not evaluate the energy shifts in detail, but show that the original threefold degeneracy is now completely removed.

   b. Because V is invariant under time reversal and because there is no longer any degeneracy, we expect each of the energy eigenstates obtained in (a) to go into itself (up to a phase factor or sign) under time reversal. Check this point explicitly.

10. Consider a spinless particle in a two-dimensional infinite square well:

$$V = \begin{cases} 0 & \text{for } 0 \leq x \leq a, 0 \leq y \leq a, \\ \infty & \text{otherwise.} \end{cases}$$

   a. What are the energy eigenvalues for the three lowest states? Is there any degeneracy?

   b. We now add a potential

$$V_1 = \lambda xy, \quad 0 \leq x \leq a, 0 \leq y \leq a.$$

Taking this as a weak perturbation, answer the following:
- (i) Is the energy shift due to the perturbation linear or quadratic in λ for each of the three states?
- (ii) Obtain expressions for the energy shifts of the three lowest states accurate to order λ. (You need not evaluate integrals that may appear.)
- (iii) Draw an energy diagram with and without the perturbation for the three energy states. Make sure to specify which unperturbed state is connected to which perturbed state.

11. The Hamiltonian matrix for a two-state system can be written as

$$\mathcal{H} = \begin{pmatrix} E_1^0 & \lambda\Delta \\ \lambda\Delta & E_2^0 \end{pmatrix}.$$

Clearly the energy eigenfunctions for the unperturbed problems ($\lambda = 0$) are given by

$$\phi_1^{(0)} = \begin{pmatrix} 1 \\ 0 \end{pmatrix}, \qquad \phi_2^{(0)} = \begin{pmatrix} 0 \\ 1 \end{pmatrix}.$$

a. Solve this problem *exactly* to find the energy eigenfunctions ψ_1 and ψ_2 and the energy eigenvalues E_1 and E_2.
b. Assuming that $\lambda|\Delta| \ll |E_1^0 - E_2^0|$, solve the same problem using time-independent perturbation theory up to first order in the energy eigenfunctions and up to second order in the energy eigenvalues. Compare with the exact results obtained in (a).
c. Suppose the two unperturbed energies are "almost degenerate," that is,

$$|E_1^0 - E_2^0| \ll \lambda|\Delta|.$$

Show that the exact results obtained in (a) closely resemble what you would expect by applying *degenerate* perturbation theory to this problem with E_1^0 set exactly equal to E_2^0.

12. (This is a tricky problem because the degeneracy between the first and the second state is not removed in first order. See also Gottfried 1966, 397, Problem 1.) This problem is from Schiff 1968, 295, Problem 4. A system that has three unperturbed states can be represented by the perturbed Hamiltonian matrix

$$\begin{pmatrix} E_1 & 0 & a \\ 0 & E_1 & b \\ a^* & b^* & E_2 \end{pmatrix}$$

where $E_2 > E_1$. The quantities a and b are to be regarded as perturbations that are of the same order and are small compared with $E_2 - E_1$. Use the second-order nondegenerate perturbation theory to calculate the perturbed eigenvalues. (Is this procedure correct?) Then diagonalize the matrix to find the exact eigenvalues. Finally, use the second-order degenerate perturbation theory. Compare the three results obtained.

13. Compute the Stark effect for the $2S_{1/2}$ and $2P_{1/2}$ levels of hydrogen for a field ε sufficiently weak so that $e\varepsilon a_0$ is small compared to the fine structure, but take the Lamb shift δ ($\delta = 1057$ MHz) into account (that is, ignore $2P_{3/2}$ in this calculation). Show that for $e\varepsilon a_0 \ll \delta$, the energy shifts are quadratic in ε, whereas for $e\varepsilon a_0 \gg \delta$ they are linear in ε. (The radial integral you need is $\langle 2s|r|2p \rangle = 3\sqrt{3}\, a_0$.) Briefly discuss the consequences (if any) of time reversal for this problem. This problem is from Gottfried 1966, Problem 7-3.

14. Work out the Stark effect to lowest nonvanishing order for the $n = 3$ level of the hydrogen atom. Ignoring the spin-orbit force and relativistic correction (Lamb shift), obtain not only the energy shifts to lowest nonvanishing order but also the corresponding zeroth-order eigenket.

15. Suppose the electron had a very small intrinsic *electric* dipole moment analogous to the spin magnetic moment (that is, μ_{el} proportional to σ). Treating the hypothetical $-\mu_{el}\cdot\mathbf{E}$ interaction as a small perturbation, discuss qualitatively how the energy levels of the Na atom ($Z = 11$) would be altered in the absence of any external electromagnetic field. Are the level shifts first order or second order? State explicitly which states get mixed with each other. Obtain an expression for the energy shift of the lowest level that is affected by the perturbation. Assume throughout that only the valence electron is subjected to the hypothetical interaction.

16. Consider a particle bound to a fixed center by a spherically symmetric potential $V(r)$.
    a. Prove
    $$|\psi(0)|^2 = \left(\frac{m}{2\pi\hbar^2}\right)\left\langle \frac{dV}{dr} \right\rangle$$
    for all s states, ground and excited.
    b. Check this relation for the ground state of a three-dimensional isotropic oscillator, the hydrogen atom, and so on.
    (*Note*: This relation has actually been found to be useful in guessing the form of the potential between a quark and an antiquark.)

17. a. Suppose the Hamiltonian of a rigid rotator in a magnetic field perpendicular to the axis is of the form (Merzbacher 1970, Problem 17-1)
    $$A\mathbf{L}^2 + BL_z + CL_y$$
    if terms quadratic in the field are neglected. Assuming $B \gg C$, use perturbation theory to lowest nonvanishing order to get approximate energy eigenvalues.

b. Consider the matrix elements

$$\langle n'l'm'_l m'_s|(3z^2 - r^2)|nlm_l m_s\rangle,$$

$$\langle n'l'm'_l m'_s|xy|nlm_l m_s\rangle$$

of a one-electron (for example, alkali) atom. Write the selection rules for Δl, Δm_l, and Δm_s. Justify your answer.

18. Work out the *quadratic* Zeeman effect for the ground-state hydrogen atom $[\langle \mathbf{x}|0\rangle = (1/\sqrt{\pi a_0^3})e^{-r/a_0}]$ due to the usually neglected $e^2 \mathbf{A}^2/2m_e c^2$-term in the Hamiltonian taken to first order. Write the energy shift as

$$\Delta = -\tfrac{1}{2}\chi \mathbf{B}^2$$

and obtain an expression for *diamagnetic susceptibility*, χ. (The following definite integral may be useful:

$$\int_0^\infty e^{-\alpha r} r^n \, dr = \frac{n!}{\alpha^{n+1}}.)$$

19. (Merzbacher 1970, 448, Problem 11.) For the He wave function, use

$$\psi(\mathbf{x}_1, \mathbf{x}_2) = \left(Z_{\text{eff}}^3/\pi a_0^3\right)\exp\left[\frac{-Z_{\text{eff}}(r_1 + r_2)}{a_0}\right]$$

with $Z_{\text{eff}} = 2 - \frac{5}{16}$, as obtained by the variational method. The measured value of the diamagnetic susceptibility is 1.88×10^{-6} cm^3/mole.

Using the Hamiltonian for an atomic electron in a magnetic field, determine, for a state of zero angular momentum, the energy change to order B^2 if the system is in a uniform magnetic field represented by the vector potential $\mathbf{A} = \tfrac{1}{2}\mathbf{B} \times \mathbf{r}$.

Defining the atomic diamagnetic susceptibility χ by $E = -\tfrac{1}{2}\chi B^2$, calculate χ for a helium atom in the ground state and compare the result with the measured value.

20. Estimate the ground-state energy of a one-dimensional simple harmonic oscillator using

$$\langle x|\tilde{0}\rangle = e^{-\beta|x|}$$

as a trial function with β to be varied. (You may use

$$\int_0^\infty e^{-\alpha x} x^n \, dx = \frac{n!}{\alpha^{n+1}}.)$$

21. Estimate the lowest eigenvalue (λ) of the differential equation

$$\frac{d^2\psi}{dx^2} + (\lambda - |x|)\psi = 0, \qquad \psi \to 0 \text{ for } |x| \to \infty$$

using the variational method with

$$\psi = \begin{cases} c(\alpha - |x|), & \text{for } |x| < \alpha \\ 0, & \text{for } |x| > \alpha \end{cases} \qquad (\alpha \text{ to be varied})$$

as a trial function. (*Caution*: $d\psi/dx$ is discontinuous at $x = 0$.) Numerical data that may be useful for this problem are:

$$3^{1/3} = 1.442, \qquad 5^{1/3} = 1.710, \qquad 3^{2/3} = 2.080, \qquad \pi^{2/3} = 2.145.$$

The *exact* value of the lowest eigenvalue can be shown to be 1.019.

22. Consider a one-dimensional simple harmonic oscillator whose classical angular frequency is ω_0. For $t < 0$ it is known to be in the ground state. For $t > 0$ there is also a time-dependent potential

$$V(t) = F_0 x \cos \omega t$$

where F_0 is constant in both space and time. Obtain an expression for the expectation value $\langle x \rangle$ as a function of time using time-dependent perturbation theory to lowest nonvanishing order. Is this procedure valid for $\omega \simeq \omega_0$? [You may use $\langle n'|x|n \rangle = \sqrt{\hbar/2m\omega_0} (\sqrt{n+1}\, \delta_{n',n+1} + \sqrt{n}\, \delta_{n',n-1})$.]

23. A one-dimensional harmonic oscillator is in its ground state for $t < 0$. For $t \geq 0$ it is subjected to a time-dependent but spatially uniform *force* (not potential!) in the x-direction,

$$F(t) = F_0 e^{-t/\tau}.$$

a. Using time-dependent perturbation theory to first order, obtain the probability of finding the oscillator in its first excited state for $t > 0$. Show that the $t \to \infty$ (τ finite) limit of your expression is independent of time. Is this reasonable or surprising?

b. Can we find higher excited states?

[You may use

$$\langle n'|x|n \rangle = \sqrt{\hbar/2m\omega} (\sqrt{n}\, \delta_{n',n-1} + \sqrt{n+1}\, \delta_{n',n+1}).]$$

24. Consider a particle bound in a simple harmonic oscillator potential. Initially ($t < 0$), it is in the ground state. At $t = 0$ a perturbation of the form

$$H'(x,t) = Ax^2 e^{-t/\tau}$$

is switched on. Using time-dependent perturbation theory, calculate the probability that, after a sufficiently long time ($t \gg \tau$), the system will have made a transition to a given excited state. Consider all final states.

25. The unperturbed Hamiltonian of a two-state system is represented by

$$H_0 = \begin{pmatrix} E_1^0 & 0 \\ 0 & E_2^0 \end{pmatrix}.$$

There is, in addition, a time-dependent perturbation

$$V(t) = \begin{pmatrix} 0 & \lambda \cos \omega t \\ \lambda \cos \omega t & 0 \end{pmatrix} \qquad (\lambda \text{ real}).$$

a. At $t = 0$ the system is known to be in the first state, represented by

$$\begin{pmatrix} 1 \\ 0 \end{pmatrix}.$$

Using time-dependent perturbation theory and assuming that $E_1^0 - E_2^0$ is *not* close to $\pm \hbar \omega$, derive an expression for the probability that the system be found in the second state represented by

$$\begin{pmatrix} 0 \\ 1 \end{pmatrix}$$

as a function of t $(t > 0)$.
b. Why is this procedure not valid when $E_1^0 - E_2^0$ is close to $\pm \hbar \omega$?

26. A one-dimensional simple harmonic oscillator of angular frequency ω is acted upon by a spatially uniform but time-dependent force (*not* potential)

$$F(t) = \frac{(F_0 \tau / \omega)}{(\tau^2 + t^2)}, \quad -\infty < t < \infty.$$

At $t = -\infty$, the oscillator is known to be in the ground state. Using the time-dependent perturbation theory to first order, calculate the probability that the oscillator is found in the first excited state at $t = +\infty$.

Challenge for experts: $F(t)$ is so normalized that the impulse

$$\int F(t)\, dt$$

imparted to the oscillator is always the same—that is, independent of τ; yet for $\tau \gg 1/\omega$, the probability for excitation is essentially negligible. Is this reasonable? [Matrix element of x: $\langle n'|x|n \rangle = (\hbar / 2m\omega)^{1/2}$ $(\sqrt{n}\, \delta_{n', n-1} + \sqrt{n+1}\, \delta_{n', n+1})$.]

27. Consider a particle in one dimension moving under the influence of some time-independent potential. The energy levels and the corresponding eigenfunctions for this problem are assumed to be known. We now subject the particle to a traveling pulse represented by a time-dependent potential,

$$V(t) = A\delta(x - ct).$$

a. Suppose at $t = -\infty$ the particle is known to be in the ground state whose energy eigenfunction is $\langle x|i \rangle = u_i(x)$. Obtain the probability for finding the system in some excited state with energy eigenfunction $\langle x|f \rangle = u_f(x)$ at $t = +\infty$.
b. Interpret your result in (a) physically by regarding the δ-function pulse as a superposition of harmonic perturbations; recall

$$\delta(x - ct) = \frac{1}{2\pi c} \int_{-\infty}^{\infty} d\omega\, e^{i\omega[(x/c)-t]}.$$

Emphasize the role played by energy conservation, which holds even quantum mechanically as long as the perturbation has been on for a very long time.

28. A hydrogen atom in its ground state $[(n, l, m) = (1,0,0)]$ is placed between the plates of a capacitor. A time-dependent but spatial uniform electric field (not potential!) is applied as follows:

$$\mathbf{E} = \begin{cases} 0 & \text{for } t < 0, \\ \mathbf{E}_0 e^{-t/\tau} & \text{for } t > 0 \end{cases} \quad (\mathbf{E}_0 \text{ in the positive } z\text{-direction}).$$

Using first-order time-dependent perturbation theory, compute the probability for the atom to be found at $t \gg \tau$ in each of the three $2p$ states: $(n, l, m) = (2, 1, \pm 1 \text{ or } 0)$. Repeat the problem for the $2s$ state: $(n, l, m) = (2, 0, 0)$. You need not attempt to evaluate radial integrals, but perform all other integrations (with respect to angles and time).

29. Consider a composite system made up of two spin $\frac{1}{2}$ objects. For $t < 0$, the Hamiltonian does not depend on spin and can be taken to be zero by suitably adjusting the energy scale. For $t > 0$, the Hamiltonian is given by

$$H = \left(\frac{4\Delta}{\hbar^2}\right)\mathbf{S}_1 \cdot \mathbf{S}_2.$$

Suppose the system is in $|+ -\rangle$ for $t \le 0$. Find, as a function of time, the probability for being found in each of the following states $|+ +\rangle$, $|+ -\rangle$, $|- +\rangle$, and $|- -\rangle$:
a. By solving the problem exactly.
b. By solving the problem assuming the validity of first-order time-dependent perturbation theory with H as a perturbation switched on at $t = 0$. Under what condition does (b) give the correct results?

30. Consider a two-level system with $E_1 < E_2$. There is a time-dependent potential that connects the two levels as follows:

$$V_{11} = V_{22} = 0, \quad V_{12} = \gamma e^{i\omega t}, \quad V_{21} = \gamma e^{-i\omega t} \quad (\gamma \text{ real}).$$

At $t = 0$, it is known that only the lower level is populated—that is, $c_1(0) = 1$, $c_2(0) = 0$.
a. Find $|c_1(t)|^2$ and $|c_2(t)|^2$ for $t > 0$ by *exactly* solving the coupled differential equation

$$i\hbar \dot{c}_k = \sum_{n=1}^{2} V_{kn}(t) e^{i\omega_{kn}t} c_n, \quad (k = 1, 2).$$

b. Do the same problem using time-dependent perturbation theory to lowest nonvanishing order. Compare the two approaches for small values of γ. Treat the following two cases separately: (i) ω very different from ω_{21} and (ii) ω close to ω_{21}.

Answer for (a): (Rabi's formula)

$$|c_2(t)|^2 = \frac{\gamma^2/\hbar^2}{\gamma^2/\hbar^2 + (\omega - \omega_{21})^2/4} \sin^2\left\{\left[\frac{\gamma^2}{\hbar^2} + \frac{(\omega - \omega_{21})^2}{4}\right]^{1/2} t\right\},$$

$$|c_1(t)|^2 = 1 - |c_2(t)|^2.$$

31. Show that the slow-turn-on of perturbation $V \to V e^{\eta t}$ (see Baym 1969, 257) can generate contribution from the second term in (5.6.36).

32. a. Consider the positronium problem you solved in Chapter 3, Problem 3. In the presence of a uniform and static magnetic field B along the z-axis, the Hamiltonian is given by

$$H = A\mathbf{S}_1 \cdot \mathbf{S}_2 + \left(\frac{eB}{m_e c}\right)(S_{1z} - S_{2z}).$$

Solve this problem to obtain the energy levels of all four states *using degenerate time-independent perturbation theory* (instead of diagonalizing the Hamiltonian matrix). Regard the first and the second terms in the expression for H as H_0 and V, respectively. Compare your results with the exact expressions

$$E = -\left(\frac{\hbar^2 A}{4}\right)\left[1 \pm 2\sqrt{1 + 4\left(\frac{eB}{m_e c \hbar A}\right)^2}\right] \quad \text{for} \begin{cases} \text{singlet } m = 0 \\ \text{triplet } m = 0 \end{cases}$$

$$E = \frac{\hbar^2 A}{4} \qquad\qquad\qquad\qquad \text{for triplet } m = \pm 1,$$

where *triplet (singlet)* $m = 0$ stands for the state that becomes a pure triplet (singlet) with $m = 0$ as $B \to 0$.

b. We now attempt to cause transitions (via stimulated emission and absorption) between the two $m = 0$ states by introducing an oscillating magnetic field of the "right" frequency. Should we orient the magnetic field along the z-axis or along the x- (or y-) axis? Justify your choice. (The original static field is assumed to be along the z-axis throughout.)

c. Calculate the eigenvectors to first order.

32'. Repeat Problem 32 above, but with the atomic hydrogen Hamiltonian

$$H = A\mathbf{S}_1 \cdot \mathbf{S}_2 + \left(\frac{eB}{m_e c}\right)\mathbf{S}_1 \cdot \mathbf{B}$$

where in the hyperfine term $A\mathbf{S}_1' \cdot \mathbf{S}_2$, $\mathbf{S}_1$ is the electron spin, while $\mathbf{S}_2$ is the proton spin. [Note the problem here has less symmetry than that of the positronium case].

33. Consider the spontaneous emission of a photon by an excited atom.

The process is known to be an $E1$ transition. Suppose the magnetic quantum number of the atom decreases by one unit. What is the angular distribution of the emitted photon? Also discuss the polarization of the photon with attention to angular-momentum conservation for the whole (atom plus photon) system.

34. Consider an atom made up of an electron and a singly charged $(Z=1)$ triton (^{3}H). Initially the system is in its ground state $(n=1, l=0)$. Suppose the nuclear charge *suddenly increases* by one unit (realistically by emitting an electron and an antineutrino). This means that the triton nucleus turns into a helium $(Z=2)$ nucleus of mass 3 (^{3}He). Obtain the probability for the system to be found in the ground state of the resulting helium ion. The hydrogenic wave function is given by

$$\psi_{n=1, l=0}(\mathbf{x}) = \frac{1}{\sqrt{\pi}} \left(\frac{Z}{a_0} \right)^{3/2} e^{-Zr/a_0}.$$

35. The ground state of a hydrogen atom $(n=1, l=0)$ is subjected to a time-dependent potential as follows:

$$V(\mathbf{x}, t) = V_0 \cos(kz - \omega t).$$

Using time-dependent perturbation theory, obtain an expression for the transition rate at which the electron is emitted with momentum $\mathbf{p}$. Show, in particular, how you may compute the angular distribution of the ejected electron (in terms of θ and ϕ defined with respect to the z-axis). Discuss *briefly* the similarities and the differences between this problem and the (more realistic) photoelectric effect. (*Note:* For the initial wave function see Problem 34. If you have a normalization problem, the final wave function may be taken to be

$$\psi_f(\mathbf{x}) = \left(\frac{1}{L^{3/2}} \right) e^{i\mathbf{p} \cdot \mathbf{x}/\hbar}$$

with L very large, but you should be able to show that the observable effects are independent of L.)

36. Derive an expression for the density of free particle states in *two* dimensions, that is, the two-dimensional analog of

$$\rho(E)\, dE\, d\Omega = \left(\frac{L}{2\pi} \right)^3 \left(\frac{mk}{\hbar^2} \right) dE\, d\Omega, \quad \left(\mathbf{k} \equiv \frac{\mathbf{p}}{\hbar}, E = \frac{p^2}{2m} \right).$$

Your answer should be written as a function of k (or E) times $dE\, d\phi$, where ϕ is the polar angle that characterizes the momentum direction in two dimensions.

37. A particle of mass m constrained to move in one dimension is confined

within $0 < x < L$ by an infinite-wall potential

$$V = \infty \quad \text{for } x < 0, x > L,$$
$$V = 0 \quad \text{for } 0 \le x \le L.$$

Obtain an expression for the density of states (that is, the number of states per unit energy interval) for *high* energies as a function of E. (Check your dimension!)

38. Linearly polarized light of angular frequency ω is incident on a one-electron "atom" whose wave function can be approximated by the ground state of a three-dimensional isotropic harmonic oscillator of angular frequency ω_0. Show that the differential cross section for the ejection of a photoelectron is given by

$$\frac{d\sigma}{d\Omega} = \frac{4\alpha\hbar^2 k_f^3}{m^2 \omega \omega_0} \sqrt{\frac{\pi\hbar}{m\omega_0}} \exp\left\{-\frac{\hbar}{m\omega_0}\left[k_f^2 + \left(\frac{\omega}{c}\right)^2\right]\right\}$$

$$\times \sin^2\theta \cos^2\phi \exp\left[\left(\frac{2\hbar k_f \omega}{m\omega_0 c}\right)\cos\theta\right]$$

provided the ejected electron of momentum $\hbar k_f$ can be regarded as being in a plane-wave state. (The coordinate system used is shown in Figure 5.10.)

39. Find the probability $|\phi(\mathbf{p}')|^2 d^3 p'$ of the particular momentum $\mathbf{p}'$ for the ground-state hydrogen atom. (This is a nice exercise in three-dimensional Fourier transforms. To perform the angular integration choose the z-axis in the direction of $\mathbf{p}$.)

40. Obtain an expression for $\tau(2p \rightarrow 1s)$ for the hydrogen atom. Verify that it is equal to 1.6×10^{-9} s.

CHAPTER 6

Identical Particles

This short chapter is devoted to a discussion of some striking quantum-mechanical effects arising from the identity of particles. We also consider some applications to atoms more complex than hydrogen or hydrogenlike atoms.

6.1. PERMUTATION SYMMETRY

In classical physics it is possible to keep track of individual particles even though they may look alike. When we have particle 1 and particle 2 considered as a system, we can, in principle, follow the trajectory of 1 and that of 2 separately at each instant of time. For bookkeeping purposes, you may color one of them blue and the other red and then examine how the red particle moves and how the **blue particle** moves as time passes.

In quantum mechanics, however, identical particles are truly indistinguishable. This is because **we cannot** specify more than a complete set of commuting observables for each of the particles; in particular, we cannot label the particle by coloring it blue. Nor can we follow the trajectory because that would entail a position measurement at each instant of time, which necessarily disturbs the system; in particular the two situations (a) and (b) shown in Figure 6.1 cannot be distinguished—not even in principle.

For simplicity consider just two particles. Suppose one of the particles, which we call particle 1, is characterized by $|k'\rangle$, where k' is a

FIGURE 6.1. Two different paths, (a) and (b), of a two-electron system, for example, in which we cannot assert even in principle through which of the paths the electrons pass.

collective index for a complete set of observables. Likewise, we call the ket of the remaining particle $|k''\rangle$. The state ket for the two particles can be written in product form,

$$|k'\rangle|k''\rangle, \tag{6.1.1}$$

where it is understood that the first ket refers to particle 1 and the second ket to particle 2. We can also consider

$$|k''\rangle|k'\rangle, \tag{6.1.2}$$

where particle 1 is characterized by $|k''\rangle$ and particle 2 by $|k'\rangle$. Even though the two particles are indistinguishable, it is worth noting that mathematically (6.1.1) and (6.1.2) are *distinct* kets for $k' \neq k''$. In fact, with $k' \neq k''$, they are orthogonal to each other.

Suppose we make a measurement on the two-particle system. We may obtain k' for one particle and k'' for the other. However, we do not know a priori whether the state ket is $|k'\rangle|k''\rangle$, $|k''\rangle|k'\rangle$, or—for that matter—any linear combination of the two. Put in another way, all kets of form

$$c_1|k'\rangle|k''\rangle + c_2|k''\rangle|k'\rangle \tag{6.1.3}$$

lead to an identical set of eigenvalues when measurement is performed. This is known as **exchange degeneracy**. Exchange degeneracy presents a difficulty because, unlike the single particle case, a specification of the eigenvalue of a complete set of observables does not completely determine the state ket. The way nature avoids this difficulty is quite ingenious. But before proceeding further, let us develop the mathematics of permutation symmetry.

We define the permutation operator P_{12} by

$$P_{12}|k'\rangle|k''\rangle = |k''\rangle|k'\rangle. \tag{6.1.4}$$

Clearly,

$$P_{21} = P_{12} \quad \text{and} \quad P_{12}^2 = 1. \tag{6:1.5}$$

Under P_{12}, particle 1 having k' becomes particle 1 having k''; particle 2 having k'' becomes particle 2 having k'. In other words, it has the effect of interchanging 1 and 2.

In practice we often encounter an observable that has particle labels. For example in $\mathbf{S}_1 \cdot \mathbf{S}_2$ for a two-electron system, $\mathbf{S}_1$ ($\mathbf{S}_2$) stands for the spin operator of particle 1 (2). For simplicity we consider a specific case where the two-particle state ket is completely specified by the eigenvalues of a single observable A for each of the particles:

$$A_1|a'\rangle|a''\rangle = a'|a'\rangle|a''\rangle \tag{6.1.6a}$$

and

$$A_2|a'\rangle|a''\rangle = a''|a'\rangle|a''\rangle, \tag{6.1.6b}$$

where the subscripts on A denote the particle labels, and A_1 and A_2 are thus the observables A for particles 1 and 2, respectively. Applying P_{12} to both sides of (6.1.6a), we have

$$P_{12}A_1P_{12}^{-1}P_{12}|a'\rangle|a''\rangle = a'P_{12}|a'\rangle|a''\rangle$$

$$= P_{12}A_1P_{12}^{-1}|a''\rangle|a'\rangle = a'|a''\rangle|a'\rangle. \tag{6.1.7}$$

This is consistent with (6.1.6b) only if

$$P_{12}A_1P_{12}^{-1} = A_2. \tag{6.1.8}$$

It follows that P_{12} must change the particle labels of observables.

Let us now consider the Hamiltonian of a system of two identical particles. The observables, such as momentum and position operators, must necessarily appear symmetrically in the Hamiltonian—for example,

$$H = \frac{\mathbf{p}_1^2}{2m} + \frac{\mathbf{p}_2^2}{2m} + V_{\text{pair}}(|\mathbf{x}_1 - \mathbf{x}_2|) + V_{\text{ext}}(\mathbf{x}_1) + V_{\text{ext}}(\mathbf{x}_2). \tag{6.1.9}$$

Here we have separated the mutual interaction between the two particles from their interaction with some other external potential. Clearly, we have

$$P_{12}HP_{12}^{-1} = H \tag{6.1.10}$$

for H made up of observables for two identical particles. Because P_{12} commutes with H, we can say that P_{12} is a constant of the motion. The eigenvalues of P_{12} allowed are $+1$ and -1 because of (6.1.5). It therefore follows that if the two-particle state ket is symmetric (antisymmetric) to start with, it remains so at all times.

If we insist on eigenkets of P_{12}, two particular linear combinations are selected:

$$|k'k''\rangle_+ \equiv \frac{1}{\sqrt{2}}(|k'\rangle|k''\rangle + |k''\rangle|k'\rangle), \tag{6.1.11a}$$

and

$$|k'k''\rangle_- \equiv \frac{1}{\sqrt{2}}\left(|k'\rangle|k''\rangle - |k''\rangle|k'\rangle\right).\tag{6.1.11b}$$

We can define the symmetrizer and antisymmetrizer as follows:

$$S_{12} \equiv \tfrac{1}{2}(1 + P_{12}), \qquad A_{12} \equiv \tfrac{1}{2}(1 - P_{12}).\tag{6.1.12}$$

If we apply $S_{12}(A_{12})$ to an arbitrary linear combination of $|k'\rangle|k''\rangle$ and $|k''\rangle|k'\rangle$, the resulting ket is necessarily symmetric (antisymmetric). This can easily be seen as follows:

$$\begin{Bmatrix} S_{12} \\ A_{12} \end{Bmatrix}\left[c_1|k'\rangle|k''\rangle + c_2|k''\rangle|k'\rangle\right]$$

$$= \tfrac{1}{2}\left(c_1|k'\rangle|k''\rangle + c_2|k''\rangle|k'\rangle\right) \pm \tfrac{1}{2}\left(c_1|k''\rangle|k'\rangle + c_2|k'\rangle|k''\rangle\right)$$

$$= \frac{c_1 \pm c_2}{2}\left(|k'\rangle|k''\rangle \pm |k''\rangle|k'\rangle\right).\tag{6.1.13}$$

Our consideration can be extended to a system made up of many identical particles. We define

$$P_{ij}|k'\rangle|k''\rangle \cdots |k^i\rangle|k^{i+1}\rangle \cdots |k^j\rangle \cdots$$
$$= |k'\rangle|k''\rangle \cdots |k^j\rangle|k^{i+1}\rangle \cdots |k^i\rangle \ldots .\tag{6.1.14}$$

Clearly,

$$P_{ij}^2 = 1\tag{6.1.15}$$

just as before, and the allowed eigenvalues of P_{ij} are $+1$ and -1. It is important to note, however, that in general

$$[P_{ij}, P_{kl}] \neq 0.\tag{6.1.16}$$

It is worth explicitly working out a system of three identical particles. First, there are $3! = 6$ possible kets of form

$$|k'\rangle|k''\rangle|k'''\rangle\tag{6.1.17}$$

where k', k'', and k''' are all different. Thus there is sixfold exchange degeneracy. Yet if we insist that the state be *totally* symmetrical or *totally* antisymmetrical, we can form only one linear combination each. Explicitly, we have

$$|k'k''k'''\rangle_\pm \equiv \frac{1}{\sqrt{6}}\left\{|k'\rangle|k''\rangle|k'''\rangle \pm |k''\rangle|k'\rangle|k'''\rangle\right.$$

$$+ |k''\rangle|k'''\rangle|k'\rangle \pm |k'''\rangle|k''\rangle|k'\rangle$$

$$\left. + |k'''\rangle|k'\rangle|k''\rangle \pm |k'\rangle|k'''\rangle|k''\rangle\right\}.\tag{6.1.18}$$

These are both simultaneous eigenkets of P_{12}, P_{23}, and P_{13}. We remarked that there are altogether six independent state kets. It therefore follows that there are four independent kets that are neither totally symmetrical nor totally antisymmetrical. We could also introduce the operator P_{123} by defining

$$P_{123}(|k'\rangle|k''\rangle|k'''\rangle) = |k''\rangle|k'''\rangle|k'\rangle. \qquad (6.1.19)$$

Note that $P_{123} = P_{12}P_{13}$ because

$$P_{12}P_{13}(|k'\rangle|k''\rangle|k'''\rangle) = P_{12}(|k'''\rangle|k''\rangle|k'\rangle) = |k''\rangle|k'''\rangle|k'\rangle. \qquad (6.1.20)$$

In writing (6.1.18) we assumed that k', k'', and k''' are all different. If two of the three indices coincide, it is impossible to have a totally antisymmetrical state. The totally symmetrical state is given by

$$|k'k'k''\rangle_+ = \frac{1}{\sqrt{3}}\big(|k'\rangle|k'\rangle|k''\rangle + |k'\rangle|k''\rangle|k'\rangle + |k''\rangle|k'\rangle|k'\rangle\big), \qquad (6.1.21)$$

where the normalization factor is understood to be $\sqrt{2!/3!}$. For more-general cases we have a normalization factor

$$\sqrt{\frac{N_1!N_2!\cdots N_n!}{N!}}, \qquad (6.1.22)$$

where N is the total number of particles and N_i the number of times $|k^{(i)}\rangle$ occurs.

6.2. SYMMETRIZATION POSTULATE

So far we have not discussed whether nature takes advantage of totally symmetrical or totally antisymmetrical states. It turns out that systems containing N identical particles are either totally symmetrical under the interchange of any pair, in which case the particles are said to satisfy **Bose-Einstein** (B-E) **statistics**, hence known as **bosons**, or totally antisymmetrical, in which case the particles are said to satisfy **Fermi-Dirac** (F-D) **statistics**, hence known as **fermions**. Thus

$$P_{ij}|N \text{ identical bosons}\rangle = +|N \text{ identical bosons}\rangle \qquad (6.2.1a)$$

$$P_{ij}|N \text{ identical fermions}\rangle = -|N \text{ identical fermions}\rangle, \qquad (6.2.1b)$$

where P_{ij} is the permutation operator that interchanges the ith and the jth particle, with i and j arbitrary. It is an empirical fact that a mixed symmetry does not occur.

Even more remarkable is that there is a connection between the spin of a particle and the statistics obeyed by it:

Half-integer spin particles are fermions;   (6.2.2a)

Integer spin particles are bosons.   (6.2.2b)

Here particles can be composite; for example, a ^{3}He nucleus is a fermion just as the e^- or the proton; a ^{4}He nucleus is a boson just as the $\pi^\pm, \pi^0$ meson.

This spin-statistics connection is, as far as we know, an exact law of nature with no known exceptions. In the framework of nonrelativistic quantum mechanics, this principle must be accepted as an empirical postulate. In the relativistic quantum theory, however, it can be proved that half-integer spin particles cannot be bosons and integer spin particles cannot be fermions.

An immediate consequence of the electron being a fermion is that the electron must satisfy the **Pauli exclusion principle**, which states that no two electrons can occupy the same state. This follows because a state like $|k'\rangle|k'\rangle$ is necessarily symmetrical, which is not possible for a fermion. As is well known, the Pauli exclusion principle is the cornerstone of atomic and molecular physics as well as the whole of chemistry.

To illustrate the dramatic differences between fermions and bosons, let us consider two particles, each of which can occupy only two states, characterized by k' and k''. For a system of two fermions, we have no choice; there is only one possibility:

$$\frac{1}{\sqrt{2}}\left(|k'\rangle|k''\rangle - |k''\rangle|k'\rangle\right).$$ (6.2.3)

For bosons there are three states possible:

$$|k'\rangle|k'\rangle, \qquad |k''\rangle|k''\rangle, \qquad \frac{1}{\sqrt{2}}\left(|k'\rangle|k''\rangle + |k''\rangle|k'\rangle\right).$$ (6.2.4)

In contrast, for "classical" particles satisfying **Maxwell-Boltzmann** (M-B) **statistics** with no restriction on symmetry, we have altogether four independent states:

$$|k'\rangle|k''\rangle, \qquad |k''\rangle|k'\rangle, \qquad |k'\rangle|k'\rangle, \qquad |k''\rangle|k''\rangle.$$ (6.2.5)

We see that in the fermion case it is impossible for both particles to occupy the same state. In the boson case, for two out of the three allowed kets, both particles occupy the same state. In the classical (M-B) statistics case, both particles occupy the same state for two out of the four allowed kets. In this sense fermions are the least sociable; they avoid each other to make sure that they are not in the same state; in contrast, bosons are the most sociable, they really love to be in the same state, even more so than classical particles obeying M-B statistics.

The difference between fermions and bosons show up most dramatically at low temperatures; a system made up of bosons, such as liquid ^{4}He, exhibits a tendency for all particles to get down to the same ground state at extremely low temperatures. This is known as **Bose-Einstein condensation**, a feature not shared by a system made up of fermions.

6.3. TWO-ELECTRON SYSTEM

Let us now consider specifically a two-electron system. The eigenvalue of the permutation operator is necessarily -1. Suppose the base kets we use may be specified by x_1, x_2, m_{s1}, and m_{s2}, where m_{s1} and m_{s2} stand for the spin-magnetic quantum numbers of electron 1 and electron 2, respectively.

We can express the wave function for a two-electron system as a linear combination of the state ket with eigenbras of x_1, x_2, m_{s1}, and m_{s2} as follows:

$$\psi = \sum_{m_{s1}} \sum_{m_{s2}} C(m_{s1}, m_{s2})\langle x_1, m_{s1}; x_2, m_{s2}|\alpha\rangle. \tag{6.3.1}$$

If the Hamiltonian commutes with S_{tot}^2,

$$\left[S_{\text{tot}}^2, H\right] = 0, \tag{6.3.2}$$

then the energy eigenfunction is expected to be an eigenfunction of S_{tot}^2, and if ψ is written as

$$\psi = \phi(x_1, x_2)\chi, \tag{6.3.3}$$

then the spin function χ is expected to be one of the following:

$$\chi(m_{s1}, m_{s2}) = \begin{cases} \left. \begin{array}{l} \chi_{++} \\ \dfrac{1}{\sqrt{2}}(\chi_{+-} + \chi_{-+}) \\ \chi_{--} \end{array} \right\} & \text{triplet (symmetrical)} \\[2em] \dfrac{1}{\sqrt{2}}(\chi_{+-} - \chi_{-+}) & \text{singlet (antisymmetrical),} \end{cases}$$

$$\tag{6.3.4}$$

where χ_{+-} corresponds to $\chi(m_{s1} = \tfrac{1}{2}, m_{s2} = -\tfrac{1}{2})$. Notice that the triplet spin functions are all symmetrical; this is reasonable because the ladder operator $S_{1-} + S_{2-}$ commutes with P_{12} and the $|+\rangle|+\rangle$ state is even under P_{12}.

We note

$$\langle x_1, m_{s1}; x_2, m_{s2}|P_{12}|\alpha\rangle = \langle x_2, m_{s2}; x_1, m_{s1}|\alpha\rangle. \tag{6.3.5}$$

Fermi-Dirac statistics thus requires

$$\langle x_1, m_{s1}; x_2, m_{s2}|\alpha\rangle = -\langle x_2, m_{s2}; x_1, m_{s1}|\alpha\rangle. \tag{6.3.6}$$

Clearly, P_{12} can be written as

$$P_{12} = P_{12}^{(\text{space})} P_{12}^{(\text{spin})} \qquad (6.3.7)$$

where $P_{12}^{(\text{space})}$ just interchanges the position coordinate, while $P_{12}^{(\text{spin})}$ just interchanges the spin states. It is amusing that we can express $P_{12}^{(\text{spin})}$ as

$$P_{12}^{(\text{spin})} = \frac{1}{2}\left(1 + \frac{4}{\hbar^2}\mathbf{S}_1 \cdot \mathbf{S}_2\right), \qquad (6.3.8)$$

which follows because

$$\mathbf{S}_1 \cdot \mathbf{S}_2 = \begin{cases} \dfrac{\hbar^2}{4} & (\text{triplet}) \\[2mm] \dfrac{-3\hbar^2}{4} & (\text{singlet}) \end{cases} \qquad (6.3.9)$$

It follows from (6.3.3) that letting

$$|\alpha\rangle \to P_{12}|\alpha\rangle \qquad (6.3.10)$$

amounts to

$$\phi(\mathbf{x}_1, \mathbf{x}_2) \to \phi(\mathbf{x}_2, \mathbf{x}_1), \qquad \chi(m_{s1}, m_{s2}) \to \chi(m_{s2}, m_{s1}). \quad (6.3.11)$$

This together with (6.3.6) implies that if the space part of the wave function is symmetrical (antisymmetrical) the spin part must be antisymmetrical (symmetrical). As a result, the spin triplet state has to be combined with an antisymmetrical space function and the spin singlet state has to be combined with a space symmetrical function.

The space part of the wave function $\phi(\mathbf{x}_1, \mathbf{x}_2)$ provides the usual probabilistic interpretation. The probability for finding electron 1 in a volume element d^3x_1 centered around $\mathbf{x}_1$ and electron 2 in a volume element d^3x_2 is

$$|\phi(\mathbf{x}_1, \mathbf{x}_2)|^2 d^3x_1 d^3x_2. \qquad (6.3.12)$$

To see the meaning of this more closely, let us consider the specific case where the mutual interaction between the two electrons [for example, $V_{\text{pair}}(|\mathbf{x}_1 - \mathbf{x}_2|), \mathbf{S}_1 \cdot \mathbf{S}_2]$ can be ignored. If there is no spin dependence, the wave equation for the energy eigenfunction ψ [see (6.1.9)],

$$\left[\frac{-\hbar^2}{2m}\nabla_1^2 - \frac{\hbar^2}{2m}\nabla_2^2 + V_{\text{ext}}(\mathbf{x}_1) + V_{\text{ext}}(\mathbf{x}_2)\right]\psi = E\psi, \qquad (6.3.13)$$

is now separable. We have a solution of the form $\omega_A(\mathbf{x}_1)\omega_B(\mathbf{x}_2)$ times the spin function. With no spin dependence $\mathbf{S}_{\text{tot}}^2$ necessarily (and trivially) commutes with H, so the spin part must be a triplet or a singlet, which have definite symmetry properties under $P_{12}^{(\text{spin})}$. The space part must then be written as a symmetrical and antisymmetrical combination of $\omega_A(\mathbf{x}_1)\omega_B(\mathbf{x}_2)$

and $\omega_A(x_2)\omega_B(x_1)$:

$$\phi(x_1,x_2) = \frac{1}{\sqrt{2}}\left[\omega_A(x_1)\omega_B(x_2)\pm\omega_A(x_2)\omega_B(x_1)\right] \qquad (6.3.14)$$

where the upper sign is for a spin singlet and the lower is for a spin triplet. The probability of observing electron 1 in d^3x_1 around x_1 and electron 2 in d^3x_2 around x_2 is given by

$$\tfrac{1}{2}\left\{|\omega_A(x_1)|^2|\omega_B(x_2)|^2 + |\omega_A(x_2)|^2|\omega_B(x_1)|^2\right.$$
$$\left. \pm 2\,\mathrm{Re}\left[\omega_A(x_1)\omega_B(x_2)\omega_A^*(x_2)\omega_B^*(x_1)\right]\right\}d^3x_1 d^3x_2. \qquad (6.3.15)$$

The last term in the curly bracket is known as the **exchange density**.

We immediately see that when the electrons are in a spin-triplet state, the probability of finding the second electron at the same point in space vanishes. Put another way, the electrons tend to avoid each other when their spins are in a triplet state. In contrast, when their spins are in a singlet state, there is enhanced probability of finding them at the same point in space because of the presence of the exchange density.

Clearly, the question of identity is important only when the exchange density is nonnegligible or when there is substantial overlap between function ω_A and function ω_B. To see this point clearly, let us take the extreme case where $|\omega_A(x)|^2$ (where x may refer to x_1 or x_2) is big only in region A and $|\omega_B(x)|^2$ is big only in region B such that the two regions are widely separated. Now choose d^3x_1 in region A and d^3x_2 in region B; see Figure 6.2. The only important term then is just the first term in (6.3.15),

$$|\omega_A(x_1)|^2|\omega_B(x_2)|^2, \qquad (6.3.16)$$

which is nothing more than the joint probability density expected for classical particles. In this connection, recall that classical particles are necessarily well localized and the question of identity simply does not arise. Thus the exchange-density term is unimportant if regions A and B do not overlap. There is no need to antisymmetrize if the electrons are far apart

FIGURE 6.2. Two widely separated regions A and B; $|\omega_A(x)|^2$ is large in region A while $|\omega_B(x)|^2$ is large in region B.

and the overlap is negligible. This is quite gratifying. We never have to worry about the question of antisymmetrization with 10 billion electrons, nor is it necessary to take into account the antisymmetrization requirement between an electron in Los Angeles and an electron in Beijing.

6.4. THE HELIUM ATOM

A study of the helium atom is rewarding for several reasons. First of all, it is the simplest realistic problem where the question of identity—which we encountered in Section 6.3—plays an important role. Second, even though it is a simple system, the two-particle Schrödinger equation cannot be solved analytically; therefore, this is a nice place to illustrate the use of perturbation theory and also the use of the variational method.

The basic Hamiltonian is given by

$$H = \frac{\mathbf{p}_1^2}{2m} + \frac{\mathbf{p}_2^2}{2m} - \frac{2e^2}{r_1} - \frac{2e^2}{r_2} + \frac{e^2}{r_{12}}, \quad (6.4.1)$$

where $r_1 \equiv |\mathbf{x}_1|$, $r_2 \equiv |\mathbf{x}_2|$, and $r_{12} \equiv |\mathbf{x}_1 - \mathbf{x}_2|$; see Figure 6.3. Suppose the e^2/r_{12}-term were absent. Then, with the identity question ignored, the wave function would be just the product of two hydrogen atom wave functions with $Z = 1$ changed into $Z = 2$. The total spin is a constant of the motion, so the spin state is either singlet or triplet. The space part of the wave function for the important case where one of the electrons is in the ground state and the other in an excited state characterized by (nlm) is

$$\phi(\mathbf{x}_1, \mathbf{x}_2) = \frac{1}{\sqrt{2}} \left[\psi_{100}(\mathbf{x}_1) \psi_{nlm}(\mathbf{x}_2) \pm \psi_{100}(\mathbf{x}_2) \psi_{nlm}(\mathbf{x}_1) \right] \quad (6.4.2)$$

where the upper (lower) sign is for the spin singlet (triplet). We will come back to this general form for an excited state later.

For the ground state, we need a special treatment. Here the configuration is characterized by $(1s)^2$, that is, both electrons in $n = 1$, $l = 0$.

Nucleus of charge $+2|e|$

FIGURE 6.3. Schematic diagram of the helium atom.

The space function must then necessarily be symmetric and only the spin singlet function is allowed. So we have

$$\psi_{100}(\mathbf{x}_1)\psi_{100}(\mathbf{x}_2)\chi_{\text{singlet}} = \frac{Z^3}{\pi a_0^3}e^{-Z(r_1+r_2)/a_0}\chi \qquad (6.4.3)$$

with $Z = 2$. Not surprisingly, this "unperturbed" wave function gives

$$E = 2 \times 4\left(-\frac{e^2}{2a_0}\right) \qquad (6.4.4)$$

for the ground-state energy, which is about 30% bigger than the experimental value.

This is just the starting point of our investigation because in obtaining the above form (6.4.3), we have completely ignored the last term in (6.4.1) that describes the interaction between the two electrons. One way to approach the problem of obtaining a better energy value is to apply first-order perturbation theory using (6.4.3) as the unperturbed wave function and e^2/r_{12} as the perturbation. We obtain

$$\Delta_{(1s)^2} = \left\langle\frac{e^2}{r_{12}}\right\rangle_{(1s)^2} = \int\int\frac{Z^6}{\pi^2 a_0^6}e^{-2Z(r_1+r_2)/a_0}\frac{e^2}{r_{12}}d^3x_1\,d^3x_2. \qquad (6.4.5)$$

To carry out the indicated integration we first note

$$\frac{1}{r_{12}} = \frac{1}{\sqrt{r_1^2 + r_2^2 - 2r_1 r_2\cos\gamma}} = \sum_{l=0}^{\infty}\frac{r_<^l}{r_>^{l+1}}P_l(\cos\gamma), \qquad (6.4.6)$$

where $r_>$ ($r_<$) is the larger (smaller) of r_1 and r_2 and γ is the angle between $\mathbf{x}_1$ and $\mathbf{x}_2$. The angular integration is easily performed by expressing $P_l(\cos\gamma)$ in terms of $Y_l^m(\theta_1,\phi_1)$ and $Y_l^m(\theta_2,\phi_2)$ using the addition theorem of spherical harmonics:

$$P_l(\cos\gamma) = \frac{4\pi}{2l+1}\sum_{m=-l}^{l}Y_l^{m*}(\theta_1,\phi_1)Y_l^m(\theta_2,\phi_2). \qquad (6.4.7)$$

The angular integration is now trivial:

$$\int Y_l^m(\theta_i,\phi_i)\,d\Omega_i = \frac{1}{\sqrt{4\pi}}(4\pi)\delta_{l0}\delta_{m0}. \qquad (6.4.8)$$

The radial integration is elementary (but involves tedious algebra!); it leads to

$$\int_0^{\infty}\left[\int_0^{r_1}\frac{1}{r_1}e^{-(2Z/a_0)(r_1+r_2)}r_2^2\,dr_2 + \int_{r_1}^{\infty}\frac{1}{r_2}e^{-(2Z/a_0)(r_1+r_2)}r_2^2\,dr_2\right]r_1^2\,dr_1$$

$$= \frac{5}{128}\frac{a_0^5}{Z^5}. \qquad (6.4.9)$$

Combining everything, we have (for $Z = 2$)

$$\Delta_{(1s)^2} = \left(\frac{Z^6 e^2}{\pi^2 a_0^6}\right) 4\pi (\sqrt{4\pi})^2 \left(\frac{5}{128}\right) \left(\frac{a_0^5}{Z^5}\right)$$

$$= \left(\frac{5}{2}\right) \left(\frac{e^2}{2a_0}\right). \tag{6.4.10}$$

Adding this energy shift to (6.4.4), we have

$$E_{cal} = \left(-8 + \frac{5}{2}\right) \left(\frac{e^2}{2a_0}\right) \simeq -74.8 \text{ eV}. \tag{6.4.11}$$

Compare this with the experimental value,

$$E_{exp} = -78.8 \text{ eV}. \tag{6.4.12}$$

    This is not bad, but we can do better! We propose to use the variational method with Z, which we call Z_{eff}, as a variational parameter. The physical reason for this choice is that the effective Z seen by one of the electrons is smaller than 2 because the positive charge of 2 units at the origin (see Figure 6.3) is "screened" by the negatively charged cloud of the other electron; in other words, the other electron tends to neutralize the positive charge due to the helium nucleus at the center. For the normalized trial function we use

$$\langle \mathbf{x}_1, \mathbf{x}_2 | \tilde{0} \rangle = \left(\frac{Z_{eff}^3}{\pi a_0^3}\right) e^{-Z_{eff}(r_1 + r_2)/a_0}. \tag{6.4.13}$$

From this we obtain

$$\overline{H} = \left\langle \tilde{0} \left| \frac{\mathbf{p}_1^2}{2m} + \frac{\mathbf{p}_2^2}{2m} \right| \tilde{0} \right\rangle - \left\langle \tilde{0} \left| \frac{Ze^2}{r_1} + \frac{Ze^2}{r_2} \right| \tilde{0} \right\rangle + \left\langle \tilde{0} \left| \frac{e^2}{r_{12}} \right| \tilde{0} \right\rangle$$

$$= \left(2 \frac{Z_{eff}^2}{2} - 2Z Z_{eff} + \frac{5}{8} Z_{eff}\right) \left(\frac{e^2}{a_0}\right). \tag{6.4.14}$$

We easily see that the minimization of $\overline{H}$ is at

$$Z_{eff} = 2 - \tfrac{5}{16} = 1.6875. \tag{6.4.15}$$

This is smaller than 2, as anticipated. Using this value for Z_{eff} we get

$$E_{cal} = -77.5 \text{ eV}, \tag{6.4.16}$$

which is already very close considering the crudeness of the trial wave function.

    Historically, this achievement was considered to be one of the earliest signs that Schrödinger's wave mechanics was on the right track. We

$$E_{100} + E_{nlm}$$

FIGURE 6.4. Schematic diagram for the energy-level splittings of $(1s)(nl)$ for the helium atom.

cannot get this kind of number by the purely algebraic (operator) method. The helium calculation was first done by A. Unsöld in 1927.*

Let us briefly consider excited states. This is more interesting from the point of view of illustrating quantum-mechanical effects due to identity. We consider just $(1s)(nl)$. We write the energy of this state as

$$E = E_{100} + E_{nlm} + \Delta E. \tag{6.4.17}$$

In first-order perturbation theory, ΔE is obtained by evaluating the expectation value of e^2/r_{12}. We can write

$$\left\langle \frac{e^2}{r_{12}} \right\rangle = I \pm J, \tag{6.4.18}$$

where I and J, known respectively as the direct integral and the exchange integral, are given by

$$I = \int d^3x_1 \int d^3x_2 |\psi_{100}(\mathbf{x}_1)|^2 |\psi_{nlm}(\mathbf{x}_2)|^2 \frac{e^2}{r_{12}}, \tag{6.4.19a}$$

$$J = \int d^3x_1 \int d^3x_2 \psi_{100}(\mathbf{x}_1)\psi_{nlm}(\mathbf{x}_2) \frac{e^2}{r_{12}} \psi_{100}^*(\mathbf{x}_2)\psi_{nlm}^*(\mathbf{x}_1). \tag{6.4.19b}$$

The upper (lower) sign goes with the spin singlet (triplet) state. Obviously, I is positive; we can also show that J is positive. So the net result is such that for the same configuration, the spin singlet state lies higher, as shown in Figure 6.4.

The physical interpretation for this is as follows: In the singlet case the space function is symmetric and the electrons have a tendency to come close to each other. Therefore, the effect of the electrostatic repulsion is more serious; hence, a higher energy results. In the triplet case, the space function is antisymmetric and the electrons tend to avoid each other. Helium in spin-singlet states is known as **parahelium**, while helium in spin-triplet states is known as **orthohelium**. Each configuration splits into

*A. Unsöld, Ann. Phys. **82** (1927) 355.

FIGURE 6.5. Schematic energy level diagram for low-lying configurations of the helium atom.

the para state and the ortho state, the para state lying higher. For the ground state only parahelium is possible. See Figure 6.5 for a schematic energy level diagram of the helium atom.

It is very important to recall that the original Hamiltonian is spin-independent because the potential is made up of just three Coulomb terms. There was no $S_1 \cdot S_2$-term whatsoever. Yet there is a spin-dependent effect—the electrons with parallel spins have a lower energy—that arises from Fermi-Dirac statistics.

This explanation of the apparent spin dependence of the helium atom energy levels is due to Heisenberg. The physical origin of ferromagnetism—alignment of the electron spins extended over microscopic distances—is also believed to be essentially the same, but the properties of ferromagnets are much harder to calculate quantitatively from first principles.

6.5. PERMUTATION SYMMETRY AND YOUNG TABLEAUX

In keeping track of the requirement imposed by permutation symmetry, there is an extremely convenient bookkeeping technique known as **Young tableaux**, after A. Young, an English clergyman who published a fundamental paper on this subject in 1901. This section is meant to be an introduction to Young tableaux for the practical-minded reader. We do not necessarily present all derivations; this is one of those cases where the rules are simpler than the derivations.

To illustrate the basic techniques involved, we consider once again the spin states of a two-electron system. We have three symmetric states corresponding to the three possible orientations of the spin-triplet state and an antisymmetric state corresponding to the spin singlet. The spin state of an *individual* electron is to be represented by a box. We use $\boxed{1}$ for spin up and $\boxed{2}$ for spin down. These boxes are the basic *primitive objects* of SU(2). A single box represents a doublet.

We define a symmetric tableau, $\boxed{}\boxed{}$, and an antisymmetric tableau, $\begin{array}{c}\boxed{}\\\boxed{}\end{array}$ When applied to the spin states of a two-electron system, $\boxed{}\boxed{}$ is the Young tableau for a spin triplet, while $\begin{array}{c}\boxed{}\\\boxed{}\end{array}$ is the Young tableau for a spin singlet. Returning now to $\boxed{1}$ and $\boxed{2}$, we can build up the three-triplet states as follows:

$$\boxed{}\boxed{}\left\{\begin{array}{cc}\boxed{1}&\boxed{1}\\\boxed{1}&\boxed{2}\\\boxed{2}&\boxed{2}\end{array}\right. \tag{6.5.1}$$

We do not consider $\boxed{2}\boxed{1}$ because when we put boxes horizontally, symmetry is understood. So we deduce an important rule: Double counting is avoided if we require that the number (label) *not decrease* going from the left to the right.

As for the antisymmetric spin-singlet state,

$$\begin{array}{c}\boxed{1}\\\boxed{2}\end{array} \tag{6.5.2}$$

is the only possibility. Clearly $\begin{array}{c}\boxed{1}\\\boxed{1}\end{array}$ and $\begin{array}{c}\boxed{2}\\\boxed{2}\end{array}$ are impossible because of the requirement of antisymmetry; for a vertical tableau we cannot have a symmetric state. Furthermore, $\begin{array}{c}\boxed{2}\\\boxed{1}\end{array}$ is discarded to avoid double counting. To eliminate the unwanted symmetry states, we therefore require the number (label) to *increase* as we go down.

We take the following to be the general rule. In drawing Young tableau, going from left to right the number cannot decrease; going down the number must increase. We deduced this rule by considering the spin states of two electrons, but we can show this rule to be applicable to the construction of any tableau.

Consider now three electrons. We can construct totally symmetric spin states by the following rule:

$$\boxed{}\boxed{}\boxed{}\left\{\begin{array}{ccc}\boxed{1}&\boxed{1}&\boxed{1}\\\boxed{1}&\boxed{1}&\boxed{2}\\\boxed{1}&\boxed{2}&\boxed{2}\\\boxed{2}&\boxed{2}&\boxed{2}\end{array}\right. \tag{6.5.3}$$

This method gives four states altogether. This is just the multiplicity of the $j=\frac{3}{2}$ state, which is obviously symmetric as seen from the $m=\frac{3}{2}$ case, where all three spins are aligned in the positive z-direction.

What about the totally antisymmetric states? We may try vertical tableau like

$$\begin{array}{c}\boxed{1}\\\boxed{1}\\\boxed{1}\end{array}\quad\text{or}\quad\begin{array}{c}\boxed{1}\\\boxed{2}\\\boxed{2}\end{array}$$

But these are illegal, because the numbers must increase as we go down. This is not surprising because total antisymmetry is impossible for spin states of three electrons; quite generally, a necessary (but, of course, not sufficient) condition for total antisymmetry is that every state must be different. In fact, in SU(2) we cannot have three boxes in a vertical column.

We now define a mixed symmetry tableau that looks like this: ⊞. Such a tableau can be visualized as either a single box attached to a symmetric tableau [as in Equation (6.5.4a)] or a single box attached to an antisymmetric tableau [as in Equation (6.5.4b)].

$$(6.5.4a)$$

$$(6.5.4b)$$

If the spin function for three electrons is symmetric in two of the indices, neither of them can be antisymmetric with respect to a third index. For example,

$$(|+\rangle_1|-\rangle_2 + |-\rangle_1|+\rangle_2)|-\rangle_3 \qquad (6.5.5)$$

satisfies symmetry under $1 \leftrightarrow 2$, but it is neither symmetric nor antisymmetric with respect to $1 \leftrightarrow 3$ (or $2 \leftrightarrow 3$). We may try to enforce antisymmetry under $1 \leftrightarrow 3$ by subtracting the same thing from (6.5.5) with 1 and 3 interchanged:

$$|+\rangle_1|-\rangle_2|-\rangle_3 - |+\rangle_3|-\rangle_2|-\rangle_1 + |-\rangle_1|+\rangle_2|-\rangle_3 - |-\rangle_3|+\rangle_2|-\rangle_1 \qquad (6.5.6)$$
$$= (|+\rangle_1|-\rangle_3 - |-\rangle_1|+\rangle_3)|-\rangle_2.$$

This satisfies antisymmetry under $1 \leftrightarrow 3$, but we no longer have the original symmetry under $1 \leftrightarrow 2$. In any case the dimensionality of ⊞ is 2; that is, it represents a doublet ($j = \frac{1}{2}$). We can see this by noting that such a tableau corresponds to the angular momentum addition of a spin doublet (□) and a spin triplet (⊏⊐). We have used up the totally symmetric quartet ⊏⊏⊐, so the remainder must be a doublet. Alternatively, we may attach a doublet (□) to a singlet (⊟) as in (6.5.4b); the net product is obviously a doublet. So no matter how we consider it, ⊞ must represent a doublet. But this is precisely what the rule gives. If the number cannot decrease in the horizontal direction and must increase in the vertical direction, the only possibilities are

$$(6.5.7)$$

Because there are only two possibilities, ⊞ must correspond to a doublet. Notice that we do not consider ⊞.

We can consider Clebsch-Gordan series or angular-momentum addition as follows:

$$(2 \times 2 = 3 + 1)$$

$$(3 \times 2 = 4 + 2)$$ (6.5.8)

(Note: is impossible; $1 \times 2 = 2$.)

We now extend our consideration to three primitive objects. A box can assume three possibilities:

$$\square : \boxed{1}, \boxed{2}, \boxed{3}. \qquad (6.5.9)$$

The labels 1, 2, and 3 may stand for the magnetic quantum numbers of p-orbitals in atomic physics or charge states of the pion π^+, π^0, π^-, or the u, d, and s quarks in the SU(3) classification of elementary particles. We *assume* that the rule we inferred using two primitive objects can be generalized and work out such concepts as the dimensionality; we then check to see whether everything is reasonable.

(6.5.10)

These tableaux correspond to representations of SU(3).

			λ_1 boxes in first row
...	...	...	
...	...		λ_2 boxes in second row
...			λ_3 boxes in third row

$$(6.5.11)$$

For the purpose of figuring the dimensionality, it is legitimate to strike out

	...	
	---	---
	...	
	...	

$$(6.5.12)$$

a "singlet" at the left-hand side of (6.5.11). We can show the dimensionality to be

$$d(\lambda_1, \lambda_2, \lambda_3) = \frac{(p+1)(q+1)(p+q+2)}{2} \qquad (6.5.13)$$

where $p = \lambda_1 - \lambda_2$ and $q = \lambda_2 - \lambda_3$.

In the SU(3) language, a tableau corresponds to a definite irreducible representation of SU(3). On the other hand, when each box is interpreted to mean a $j = 1$ object, then a tableau does not correspond to an irreducible representation of the rotation group. Let us discuss this point more specifically. We start with putting together two boxes, where each box represents a $j = 1$ state.

$$\square \otimes \square = \square\square \oplus \begin{array}{c}\square\\\square\end{array}. \qquad (3 \times 3 = 6 + 3) \qquad (6.5.14)$$

The horizontal tableau has six states; the tableau is to be broken down into $j = 2$ (multiplicity 5) and $j = 0$ (multiplicity 1), both of which are symmetric. In fact this is just how we construct a symmetric second-rank tensor out of two vectors. The vertical tableau $\begin{array}{c}\square\\\square\end{array}$ corresponds to an antisymmetric $j = 1$ state behaving like $\mathbf{a} \times \mathbf{b}$.

To work out the addition of three angular momenta with $j_1 = j_2 = j_3 = 1$, let us first figure out

$$(6.5.15)$$

To see how $\square\square\square$ breaks down, we note that it must contain $j = 3$. However, this is not the only totally symmetric state; $\mathbf{a}(\mathbf{b} \cdot \mathbf{c}) + \mathbf{b}(\mathbf{c} \cdot \mathbf{a}) + \mathbf{c}(\mathbf{a} \cdot \mathbf{b})$ is also totally symmetric, and this has the transformation property of $j = 1$. So $\square\square\square$ contains both $j = 3$ (seven states) and $j = 1$ (three states). As for $\begin{array}{c}\square\square\\\square\end{array}$ with eight possibilities altogether, the argument is more involved, but we note that this **8** cannot be broken into **7 + 1** because **7** is totally symmetric, while **1** is totally antisymmetric when we know that **8** is of *mixed* symmetry. So the only other possibility is **8 = 5 + 3**—in other words $j = 2$ and $j = 1$.

Finally, therefore, we must have

$$\square \otimes \square \otimes \square = \square\square\square \oplus \begin{array}{c}\square\square\\\square\end{array} \oplus \begin{array}{c}\square\square\\\square\end{array} \oplus \begin{array}{c}\square\\\square\\\square\end{array}$$

$$3 \times 3 \quad \times 3 \;=\; \underset{\underset{7+3}{\uparrow}}{10} \;+\; \underset{\underset{5+3}{\uparrow}}{8} \;+\; \underset{\underset{5+3}{\uparrow}}{8} \;+1 \tag{6.5.16}$$

In terms of angular-momentum states, we have

$j = 3$ (dimension 7)   once   (totally symmetric)

$j = 2$ (dimension 5)   twice   (both mixed symmetry)

$j = 1$ (dimension 3)   three times (one totally symmetric,

two mixed symmetry)

$j = 0$ (dimension 1)   once   (totally antisymmetric)

$$\tag{6.5.17}$$

That the $j = 0$ state is unique corresponds to the fact that the only product of **a**, **b**, and **c** invariant under rotation is $\mathbf{a} \cdot (\mathbf{b} \times \mathbf{c})$, which is necessarily antisymmetric. We can also look at the $j = 1$ states using the tensor approach. We have three independent vectors constructed from **a**, **b**, and **c**: $\mathbf{a}(\mathbf{b} \cdot \mathbf{c})$, $\mathbf{b}(\mathbf{c} \cdot \mathbf{a})$, and $\mathbf{c}(\mathbf{a} \cdot \mathbf{b})$. From these we can construct only one totally symmetric combination,

$$\mathbf{a}(\mathbf{b} \cdot \mathbf{c}) + \mathbf{b}(\mathbf{c} \cdot \mathbf{a}) + \mathbf{c}(\mathbf{a} \cdot \mathbf{b}). \tag{6.5.18}$$

We can apply this consideration to the $(2p)^3$ configuration of the nitrogen atom, N ($Z = 7$, shell structure $(1s)^2(2s)^2(2p)^3$). There are altogether

$$\frac{6!}{3!3!} = \frac{6 \cdot 5 \cdot 4}{3 \cdot 2} = 20 \text{ states.} \tag{6.5.19}$$

The space function behaving like $\square\square\square$, which would have $l_{\text{tot}} = 3$, is actually impossible because it must be combined with a totally antisymmetric spin function. Remember

$$\begin{array}{c}\square\\\square\\\square\end{array},$$

where each box stands for spin up or down, is impossible for spin states of three electrons. In contrast the totally antisymmetric space function

$$\begin{array}{c}\square\\\square\\\square\end{array}$$

with $l_{\text{tot}} = 0$ is perfectly allowable if combined with a totally symmetric spin function $\square\square\square$, which has total spin angular momentum $\frac{3}{2}$; we have $^4S_{3/2}$ for this configuration. The mixed-symmetry space function $\begin{array}{c}\square\square\\\square\end{array}$ ($l_{\text{tot}} = 2, 1$) must be combined with a mixed-symmetry spin function, necessarily a spin doublet $\begin{array}{c}\square\square\\\square\end{array}$. So we have $^2D_{5/2,3/2}$ and $^2P_{3/2,1/2}$. The counting of states leads to the following:

$$j = \tfrac{5}{2} \qquad \text{6 states}$$
$$j = \tfrac{3}{2} \qquad 4 \times 3 \text{ states}$$
$$j = \tfrac{1}{2} \qquad \underline{2 \text{ states}} \qquad (6.5.20)$$
$$\overline{20 \text{ states}}$$

This agrees with the other way of counting.

Finally, we consider applications to elementary particle physics. Here we apply SU(3) considerations to the nonrelativistic quark model, where the primitive objects are u, d, s (up, down, and strange, where *up* and *down* refer to *isospin up* and *isospin down*). A box can now stand for u, d, or s. We look at the decuplet representation ▢▢▢ (**10**):

$$\Delta^{++, +, 0, -} \qquad ddd\,udd\,uud\,uuu \qquad I = \tfrac{3}{2},$$
$$\Sigma^{+, 0, -} \qquad dds\,uds\,uus \qquad I = 1,$$
$$\Xi^{0, -} \qquad dss\,uss \qquad I = \tfrac{1}{2}, \qquad (6.5.21)$$
$$\Omega^{-} \qquad sss \qquad I = 0,$$

where I stands for isospin.

Now all ten states are known to be spin $\tfrac{3}{2}$ objects. It is safe to assume that the space part is in a relative S-state for low-lying states of three quarks. We expect total symmetry in the spin degree of freedom. For instance, the $j = \tfrac{3}{2}$, $m = \tfrac{3}{2}$ state of Δ can be visualized to have quark spins all aligned.

But the quarks are spin $\tfrac{1}{2}$ objects; we expect total antisymmetry because of Fermi-Dirac statistics. Yet

Quark label (now called flavor): symmetric

Spin: symmetric   (6.5.22)

Space: symmetric

for the $j = \tfrac{3}{2}$ decuplet. But as is evident from (6.5.22), the total symmetry in this case is even! This led to the "statistics paradox," which was especially embarrassing because other aspects of the nonrelativistic quark model were so successful.

The way out of this dilemma is to postulate that there is actually an additional degree of freedom called *color* (red, blue, or yellow) and postulate that the observed hadrons (strongly interacting particles, including $J = \frac{3}{2}^{+}$ states considered here) are **color singlets**

$$\frac{1}{\sqrt{6}}(|RBY\rangle - |BRY\rangle + |BYR\rangle - |YBR\rangle + |YRB\rangle - |RYB\rangle). \quad (6.5.23)$$

This is in complete analogy with the unique

$$\begin{array}{|c|}\hline 1 \\\hline 2 \\\hline 3 \\\hline\end{array}$$

of (6.5.10), a totally antisymmetric combination in color space. The statistics problem is now solved because

$$P_{ij} = P_{ij}^{(\text{flavor})} P_{ij}^{(\text{spin})} P_{ij}^{(\text{space})} P_{ij}^{(\text{color})} \quad (6.5.24)$$
$$\quad (-) \qquad (+) \qquad (+) \qquad (+) \qquad (-)$$

One might argue that this is a cheap way to get out of the dilemma. Fortunately, there were also other pieces of evidence in favor of color, such as the decay rate of π^0 and the cross section for electron-positron annihilation into hadrons. In fact, this is a very good example of how attempts to overcome difficulties lead to nontrivial prediction of color.

PROBLEMS

1. a. N identical spin $\frac{1}{2}$ particles are subjected to a one-dimensional simple harmonic oscillator potential. What is the ground-state energy? What is the Fermi energy?

   b. What are the ground state and Fermi energies if we ignore the mutual interactions and assume N to be very large?

2. It is obvious that two nonidentical spin1 particles with no orbital angular momenta (that is, s-states for both) can form $j = 0$, $j = 1$, and $j = 2$. Suppose, however, that the two particles are *identical*. What restrictions do we get?

3. Discuss what would happen to the energy levels of a helium atom if the electron were a spinless boson. Be as quantitative as you can.

4. Three spin 0 particles are situated at the corners of an equilateral triangle. Let us define the z-axis to go through the center and in the direction normal to the plane of the triangle. The whole system is free to rotate about the z-axis. Using statistics considerations, obtain restrictions on the magnetic quantum numbers corresponding to J_z.

5. Consider three weakly interacting, identical spin 1 particles.
   a. Suppose the space part of the state vector is known to be symmetric
      under interchange of *any* pair. Using notation $|+\rangle|0\rangle|+\rangle$ for particle
      1 in $m_s = +1$, particle 2 in $m_s = 0$, particle 3 in $m_s = +1$, and so on,
      construct the normalized spin states in the following three cases:
      (i) All three of them in $|+\rangle$.
      (ii) Two of them in $|+\rangle$, one in $|0\rangle$.
      (iii) All three in different spin states.
      What is the total spin in each case?
   b. Attempt to do the same problem when the space part is antisymmetric
      under interchange of any pair.
6. Suppose the electron were a spin $\frac{3}{2}$ particle obeying Fermi-Dirac statistics. Write the configuration of a hypothetical Ne ($Z = 10$) atom made up
   of such "electrons" [that is, the analog of $(1s)^2(2s)^2(2p)^6$]. Show that
   the configuration is highly degenerate. What is the ground state (the
   lowest term) of the hypothetical Ne atom in spectroscopic notation
   ($^{2S+1}L_J$, where S, L, and J stand for the total spin, the total orbital
   angular momentum, and the total angular momentum, respectively) when
   exchange splitting and spin-orbit splitting are taken into account?
7. Two identical spin $\frac{1}{2}$ fermions move in one dimension under the influence of the infinite-wall potential $V = \infty$ for $x < 0$, $x > L$, and $V = 0$
   for $0 \leq x \leq L$.
   a. Write the ground-state wave function and the ground-state energy
      when the two particles are constrained to a triplet spin state (*ortho*
      state).
   b. Repeat (a) when they are in a singlet spin state (*para* state).
   c. Let us now suppose that the two particles interact mutually via a very
      short-range attractive potential that can be approximated by
      $$V = -\lambda\delta(x_1 - x_2) \quad (\lambda > 0).$$
   Assuming that perturbation theory is valid even with such a singular
   potential, discuss semiquantitatively what happens to the energy levels
   obtained in (a) and (b).

CHAPTER 7

Scattering Theory

This last chapter of the book is devoted to the theory of scattering and, more generally, collision processes. It is impossible to overemphasize the importance of this subject.

7.1. THE LIPPMANN-SCHWINGER EQUATION

We begin with a time-independent formulation of scattering processes. We assume that the Hamiltonian can be written as

$$H = H_0 + V \tag{7.1.1}$$

where H_0 stands for the kinetic-energy operator

$$H_0 = \frac{\mathbf{p}^2}{2m}. \tag{7.1.2}$$

In the absence of a scatterer, V would be zero, and an energy eigenstate would be just a free particle state $|\mathbf{p}\rangle$. The presence of V causes the energy eigenstate to be different from a free-particle state. However, if the scattering process is to be elastic—that is, no change in energy—we are interested in obtaining a solution to the full-Hamiltonian Schrödinger equation with the same energy eigenvalue. More specifically, let $|\phi\rangle$ be the energy eigenket of H_0:

$$H_0|\phi\rangle = E|\phi\rangle. \tag{7.1.3}$$

(We use $|\phi\rangle$ here rather than $|\mathbf{p}\rangle$ because we may later be interested in free-spherical wave rather than plane-wave states; $|\phi\rangle$ may stand for either.) The basic Schrödinger equation we wish to solve is

$$(H_0 + V)|\psi\rangle = E|\psi\rangle. \tag{7.1.4}$$

Both H_0 and $H_0 + V$ exhibit *continuous* energy spectra. We look for a solution to (7.1.4) such that, as $V \to 0$, we have $|\psi\rangle \to |\phi\rangle$, where $|\phi\rangle$ is the solution to the free-particle Schrödinger equation [(7.1.3)] with the *same* energy eigenvalue.

It may be argued that the desired solution is

$$|\psi\rangle = \frac{1}{E - H_0} V|\psi\rangle + |\phi\rangle, \tag{7.1.5}$$

apart from complications arising from the singular nature of the operator $1/(E - H_0)$. We can see this by noting that $E - H_0$ applied to (7.1.5) immediately gives the correct equation, (7.1.4). The presence of $|\phi\rangle$ is reasonable because $|\psi\rangle$ must reduce to $|\phi\rangle$ as V vanishes. However, without prescriptions for dealing with a singular operator, an equation of type (7.1.5) has no meaning. The trick we used in time-independent perturbation theory—inserting the complimentary projection operator, and so on (see Section 5.1)—does not work well here because both $|\phi\rangle$ and $|\psi\rangle$ exhibit continuous eigenvalues. Instead, this time the solution is specified by making E slightly complex:

$$|\psi^{(\pm)}\rangle = |\phi\rangle + \frac{1}{E - H_0 \pm i\varepsilon} V|\psi^{(\pm)}\rangle. \tag{7.1.6}$$

This is known as the **Lippmann-Schwinger equation**. The physical meaning of $\pm$ is to be discussed in a moment by looking at $\langle \mathbf{x}|\psi^{(\pm)}\rangle$ at large distances.

The Lippmann-Schwinger equation is a *ket equation* independent of particular representations. We now confine ourselves to the position basis by multiplying $\langle \mathbf{x}|$ from the left. Thus

$$\langle \mathbf{x}|\psi^{(\pm)}\rangle = \langle \mathbf{x}|\phi\rangle + \int d^3x' \left\langle \mathbf{x} \left| \frac{1}{E - H_0 \pm i\varepsilon} \right| \mathbf{x}' \right\rangle \langle \mathbf{x}'|V|\psi^{(\pm)}\rangle. \tag{7.1.7}$$

This is an **integral equation** for scattering because the unknown ket $|\psi^{(\pm)}\rangle$ appears under an integral sign. If $|\phi\rangle$ stands for a plane-wave state with momentum $\mathbf{p}$, we can write

$$\langle \mathbf{x}|\phi\rangle = \frac{e^{i\mathbf{p}\cdot\mathbf{x}/\hbar}}{(2\pi\hbar)^{3/2}} \tag{7.1.8}$$

[*Editor's Note:* In contrast to bound states, the plane-wave state (7.1.8) is, of course, not normalizable and not really a vector in Hilbert space. Dealing with such states is one of the inconveniences of time-independent scattering theory. The "normalization" in (7.1.8) is such that

$$\int d^3x \langle \mathbf{p}' | \mathbf{x} \rangle \langle \mathbf{x} | \mathbf{p} \rangle = \delta^{(3)}(\mathbf{p} - \mathbf{p}'). \qquad (7.1.9)]$$

If, on the other hand, the Lippman-Schwinger equation is written using the momentum basis, we obtain

$$\langle \mathbf{p} | \psi^{(\pm)} \rangle = \langle \mathbf{p} | \phi \rangle + \frac{1}{E - (p^2/2m) \pm i\varepsilon} \langle \mathbf{p} | V | \psi^{(\pm)} \rangle. \qquad (7.1.10)$$

We shall come back to this equation in Section 7.2.

Let us consider specifically the position basis and work with (7.1.7). To make any progress we must first evaluate the kernel of the integral equation defined by

$$G_\pm(\mathbf{x}, \mathbf{x}') \equiv \frac{\hbar^2}{2m} \left\langle \mathbf{x} \left| \frac{1}{E - H_0 \pm i\varepsilon} \right| \mathbf{x}' \right\rangle. \qquad (7.1.11)$$

We claim that $G_\pm(\mathbf{x}, \mathbf{x}')$ is given by

$$G_\pm(\mathbf{x}, \mathbf{x}') = -\frac{1}{4\pi} \frac{e^{\pm ik|\mathbf{x} - \mathbf{x}'|}}{|\mathbf{x} - \mathbf{x}'|} \qquad (7.1.12)$$

where $E \equiv \hbar^2 k^2/2m$. To show this, we evaluate (7.1.11) as follows:

$$\frac{\hbar^2}{2m} \left\langle \mathbf{x} \left| \frac{1}{E - H_0 \pm i\varepsilon} \right| \mathbf{x}' \right\rangle = \frac{\hbar^2}{2m} \int d^3p' \int d^3p'' \langle \mathbf{x} | \mathbf{p}' \rangle$$

$$\times \left\langle \mathbf{p}' \left| \frac{1}{E - (\mathbf{p}'^2/2m) \pm i\varepsilon} \right| \mathbf{p}'' \right\rangle \langle \mathbf{p}'' | \mathbf{x}' \rangle, \qquad (7.1.13)$$

where H_0 acts on $\langle \mathbf{p}' |$. Now use

$$\left\langle \mathbf{p}' \left| \frac{1}{E - (\mathbf{p}'^2/2m) \pm i\varepsilon} \right| \mathbf{p}'' \right\rangle = \frac{\delta^{(3)}(\mathbf{p}' - \mathbf{p}'')}{E - (\mathbf{p}'^2/2m) \pm i\varepsilon}$$

$$\langle \mathbf{x} | \mathbf{p}' \rangle = \frac{e^{i\mathbf{p}' \cdot \mathbf{x}/\hbar}}{(2\pi\hbar)^{3/2}}, \qquad \langle \mathbf{p}'' | \mathbf{x}' \rangle = \frac{e^{-i\mathbf{p}' \cdot \mathbf{x}'/\hbar}}{(2\pi\hbar)^{3/2}}. \qquad (7.1.14)$$

The right-hand side of (7.1.13) becomes

$$\frac{\hbar^2}{2m} \int \frac{d^3p'}{(2\pi\hbar)^3} \frac{e^{i\mathbf{p}' \cdot (\mathbf{x} - \mathbf{x}')/\hbar}}{[E - (\mathbf{p}'^2/2m) \pm i\varepsilon]}. \qquad (7.1.15)$$

Now write $E = \hbar^2 k^2 / 2m$ and set $\mathbf{p}' \equiv \hbar \mathbf{q}$. Equation (7.1.15) becomes

$$\frac{1}{(2\pi)^3} \int_0^\infty q^2 \, dq \int_0^{2\pi} d\phi \int_{-1}^{+1} \frac{d(\cos\theta) \, e^{i|\mathbf{q}||\mathbf{x}-\mathbf{x}'|\cos\theta}}{k^2 - q^2 \pm i\varepsilon}$$

$$= \frac{-1}{8\pi^2} \frac{1}{i|\mathbf{x}-\mathbf{x}'|} \int_{-\infty}^{+\infty} \frac{dq \, q\left(e^{iq|\mathbf{x}-\mathbf{x}'|} - e^{-iq|\mathbf{x}-\mathbf{x}'|} \right)}{q^2 - k^2 \mp i\varepsilon}$$

$$= -\frac{1}{4\pi} \frac{e^{\pm ik|\mathbf{x}-\mathbf{x}'|}}{|\mathbf{x}-\mathbf{x}'|}. \tag{7.1.16}$$

In the last step we used the method of residues, noting that the integrand has poles in the complex q-plane at

$$q = \pm k \sqrt{1 \pm \left(\frac{i\varepsilon}{k^2} \right)} \simeq \pm k \pm i\varepsilon'. \tag{7.1.17}$$

The reader may recognize that $G_\pm$ is nothing more than Green's function for the Helmholtz equation,

$$(\nabla^2 + k^2) G_\pm(\mathbf{x}, \mathbf{x}') = \delta^{(3)}(\mathbf{x} - \mathbf{x}'). \tag{7.1.18}$$

Armed with the explicit form of $G_\pm$ as in Equation (7.1.12), we can use (7.1.11) to write Equation (7.1.7) as

$$\langle \mathbf{x} | \psi^{(\pm)} \rangle = \langle \mathbf{x} | \phi \rangle - \frac{2m}{\hbar^2} \int d^3 x' \frac{e^{\pm ik|\mathbf{x}-\mathbf{x}'|}}{4\pi|\mathbf{x} - \mathbf{x}'|} \langle \mathbf{x}' | V | \psi^{(\pm)} \rangle. \tag{7.1.19}$$

Notice that the wave function $\langle \mathbf{x} | \psi^{(\pm)} \rangle$ in the presence of the scatterer is written as the sum of the wave function for the incident wave $\langle \mathbf{x} | \phi \rangle$ and a term that represents the effect of scattering. As we will see explicitly later, at sufficiently large distances the spatial dependence of the second term is $e^{\pm ikr}/r$ provided that the potential is of finite range. This means that the positive solution (negative solution) corresponds to the plane wave plus an outgoing (incoming) spherical wave. In most physical problems we are interested in the positive solution because it is difficult to prepare a system satisfying the boundary condition appropriate for the negative solution.

To see the behavior of $\langle \mathbf{x} | \psi^{(\pm)} \rangle$ more explicitly, let us consider the specific case where V is a local potential—that is, a potential diagonal in the x-representation. Potentials that are functions only of the position operator x belong to this category. In precise terms V is said to be **local** if it can be written as

$$\langle \mathbf{x}' | V | \mathbf{x}'' \rangle = V(\mathbf{x}') \delta^{(3)}(\mathbf{x}' - \mathbf{x}''). \tag{7.1.20}$$

As a result, we obtain

$$\langle \mathbf{x}'|V|\psi^{(\pm)}\rangle = \int d^3x'' \langle \mathbf{x}'|V|\mathbf{x}''\rangle\langle \mathbf{x}''|\psi^{(\pm)}\rangle$$

$$= V(\mathbf{x}')\langle \mathbf{x}'|\psi^{(\pm)}\rangle. \tag{7.1.21}$$

The integral equation (7.1.19) now simplifies as

$$\langle \mathbf{x}|\psi^{(\pm)}\rangle = \langle \mathbf{x}|\phi\rangle - \frac{2m}{\hbar^2}\int d^3x' \frac{e^{\pm ik|\mathbf{x}-\mathbf{x}'|}}{4\pi|\mathbf{x}-\mathbf{x}'|} V(\vec{x}')\langle \mathbf{x}'|\psi^{(\pm)}\rangle. \tag{7.1.22}$$

Let us attempt to understand the physics contained in this equation. The vector $\mathbf{x}$ is understood to be directed towards the observation point at which the wave function is evaluated. For a finite range potential, the region that gives rise to a nonvanishing contribution is limited in space. In scattering processes we are interested in studying the effect of the scatterer (that is, the finite range potential) at a point far outside the range of the potential. This is quite relevant from a practical point of view because we cannot put a detector at short distance near the scattering center. Observation is always made by a detector placed very far away from the scatterer at r greatly larger than the range of the potential. In other words, we can safely set

$$|\mathbf{x}| \gg |\mathbf{x}'|, \tag{7.1.23}$$

as depicted in Figure 7.1.

Introducing

$$r = |\mathbf{x}|$$
$$r' = |\mathbf{x}'| \tag{7.1.24}$$

and

$$\alpha = \angle(\mathbf{x}, \mathbf{x}'), \tag{7.1.25}$$

FIGURE 7.1. Finite-range scattering potential. The *observation point P* is where the wave function $\langle \mathbf{x}|\psi^{(\pm)}\rangle$ is to be evaluated, while the contribution to the integral in Equation (7.1.22) is for $|\mathbf{x}'|$ less than the range of the potential, as depicted by the shaded region of the figure.

we have for $r \gg r'$,

$$|\mathbf{x} - \mathbf{x}'| = \sqrt{r^2 - 2rr'\cos\alpha + r'^2}$$

$$= r\left(1 - \frac{2r'}{r}\cos\alpha + \frac{r'^2}{r^2}\right)^{1/2} \tag{7.1.26}$$

$$\simeq r - \hat{\mathbf{r}} \cdot \mathbf{x}'$$

where

$$\hat{\mathbf{r}} \equiv \frac{\mathbf{x}}{|\mathbf{x}|}. \tag{7.1.27}$$

Also define

$$\mathbf{k}' \equiv k\hat{\mathbf{r}}. \tag{7.1.28}$$

The motivation for this definition is that $\mathbf{k}'$ represents the propagation vector for waves reaching observation point $\mathbf{x}$. We then obtain

$$e^{\pm ik|\mathbf{x}-\mathbf{x}'|} \simeq e^{\pm ikr}e^{\mp i\mathbf{k}'\cdot\mathbf{x}'} \tag{7.1.29}$$

for large r. It is legitimate to replace $1/|\mathbf{x} - \mathbf{x}'|$ by just $1/r$. Furthermore, to get rid of the $\hbar$'s in expressions such as $1/(2\pi\hbar)^{3/2}$, it is convenient to use $|\mathbf{k}\rangle$ rather than $|\mathbf{p}_i\rangle$, where

$$\mathbf{k} \equiv \frac{\mathbf{p}_i}{\hbar}. \tag{7.1.30}$$

Because $|\mathbf{k}\rangle$ is normalized as

$$\langle\mathbf{k}|\mathbf{k}'\rangle = \delta^{(3)}(\mathbf{k} - \mathbf{k}') \tag{7.1.31}$$

we have

$$\langle\mathbf{x}|\mathbf{k}\rangle = \frac{e^{i\mathbf{k}\cdot\mathbf{x}}}{(2\pi)^{3/2}}. \tag{7.1.32}$$

So, finally,

$$\langle\mathbf{x}|\psi^{(+)}\rangle \xrightarrow{r \text{ large}} \langle\mathbf{x}|\mathbf{k}\rangle - \frac{1}{4\pi}\frac{2m}{\hbar^2}\frac{e^{ikr}}{r}\int d^3x' e^{-i\mathbf{k}'\cdot\mathbf{x}'}V(\mathbf{x}')\langle\mathbf{x}'|\psi^{(+)}\rangle$$

$$= \frac{1}{(2\pi)^{3/2}}\left[e^{i\mathbf{k}\cdot\mathbf{x}} + \frac{e^{ikr}}{r}f(\mathbf{k}',\mathbf{k})\right]. \tag{7.1.33}$$

This form makes it very clear that we have the original plane wave in propagation direction $\mathbf{k}$ plus an outgoing spherical wave with amplitude $f(\mathbf{k}',\mathbf{k})$ given by

$$f(\mathbf{k}',\mathbf{k}) \equiv -\frac{1}{4\pi}\frac{2m}{\hbar^2}(2\pi)^3\int d^3x' \frac{e^{-i\mathbf{k}'\cdot\mathbf{x}'}}{(2\pi)^{3/2}}V(\mathbf{x}')\langle\mathbf{x}'|\psi^{(+)}\rangle$$

$$= -\frac{1}{4\pi}(2\pi)^3\frac{2m}{\hbar^2}\langle\mathbf{k}'|V|\psi^{(+)}\rangle. \tag{7.1.34}$$

Similarly, we can readily show from (7.1.22) and (7.1.29) that $\langle \mathbf{x} | \psi^{(-)} \rangle$ corresponds to the original plane wave in propagation direction $\mathbf{k}$ plus an incoming spherical wave with spatial dependence e^{-ikr}/r and amplitude $-(1/4\pi)(2\pi)^3(2m/\hbar^2)\langle -\mathbf{k}' | V | \psi^{(-)} \rangle$.

To obtain the **differential cross section** $d\sigma/d\Omega$, we may consider a large number of identically prepared particles all characterized by the wave function (7.1.32). We can then ask, what is the number of incident particles crossing a plane perpendicular to the incident direction per unit area per unit time? This is just proportional to the probability flux due to the first term on the right-hand side in (7.1.33). Likewise we may ask, what is the number of scattered particles going into a small area $d\sigma$ subtending a differential solid-angle element $d\Omega$? Clearly,

$$\frac{d\sigma}{d\Omega} \, d\Omega = \frac{\text{number of particles scattered into } d\Omega \text{ per unit time}}{\text{number of incident particles crossing unit area per unit time}}$$

$$= \frac{r^2 |\mathbf{j}_{\text{scatt}}| d\Omega}{|\mathbf{j}_{\text{incid}}|} = |f(\mathbf{k}',\mathbf{k})|^2 d\Omega. \tag{7.1.35}$$

Hence the differential cross section is

$$\frac{d\sigma}{d\Omega} = |f(\mathbf{k}',\mathbf{k})|^2. \tag{7.1.36}$$

Wave-Packet Description

The reader may wonder here whether our time-independent formulation of scattering has anything to do with the motion of a particle being

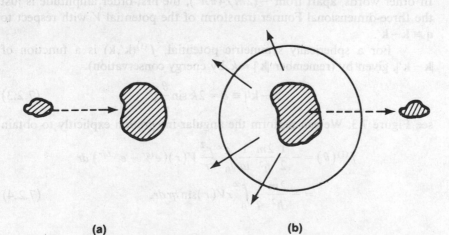

(a)   **(b)**

FIGURE 7.2. (a) Incident wave packet approaching scattering center initially. (b) Incident wave packet continuing to move in the original direction plus spherical outgoing wave front (after a long time duration).

bounced by a scattering center. The incident plane wave we have used is infinite in extent in both space and time. In a more realistic situation, we consider a wave packet (a difficult subject!) that approaches the scattering center.* After a long time we have both the original wave packet moving in the original direction plus a spherical wave front that moves outward, as in Figure 7.2. Actually the use of a plane wave is satisfactory as long as the dimension of the wave packet is much larger than the size of the scatterer (or range of V).

7.2. THE BORN APPROXIMATION

Equation (7.1.34) is still not directly useful in computing the differential cross section because in the expression for $f(\mathbf{k}', \mathbf{k})$ the unknown ket $|\psi^{(+)}\rangle$ appears. If the effect of the scatterer is not very strong, we may infer that it is not such a bad approximation to replace $\langle \mathbf{x}'|\psi^{(+)}\rangle$ (which appears under the integral sign) by $\langle \mathbf{x}'|\phi\rangle$—that is,

$$\langle \mathbf{x}'|\psi^{(+)}\rangle \to \langle \mathbf{x}'|\phi\rangle = \frac{e^{i\mathbf{k}\cdot\mathbf{x}'}}{(2\pi)^{3/2}}. \qquad (7.2.1)$$

We then obtain an approximate expression for $f(\mathbf{k}', \mathbf{k})$. Because we treat the potential V to first order, the approximate amplitude so obtained is known as the **first-order Born amplitude** and is denoted by $f^{(1)}$:

$$f^{(1)}(\mathbf{k}', \mathbf{k}) = -\frac{1}{4\pi} \frac{2m}{\hbar^2} \int d^3 x' e^{i(\mathbf{k}-\mathbf{k}')\cdot\mathbf{x}'} V(\mathbf{x}'). \qquad (7.2.2)$$

In other words, apart from $-(2m/4\pi\hbar^2)$, the first-order amplitude is just the three-dimensional Fourier transform of the potential V with respect to $\mathbf{q} \equiv \mathbf{k} - \mathbf{k}'$.

For a spherically symmetric potential, $f^{(1)}(\mathbf{k}', \mathbf{k})$ is a function of $|\mathbf{k} - \mathbf{k}'|$, given by (remember $|\mathbf{k}'| = k$ by energy conservation)

$$|\mathbf{k} - \mathbf{k}'| \equiv q = 2k \sin \frac{\theta}{2}; \qquad (7.2.3)$$

see Figure 7.3. We can perform the angular integration explicitly to obtain

$$f^{(1)}(\theta) = -\frac{1}{2} \frac{2m}{\hbar^2} \frac{1}{iq} \int_0^\infty \frac{r^2}{r} V(r) (e^{iqr} - e^{-iqr}) \, dr$$

$$= -\frac{2m}{\hbar^2} \frac{1}{q} \int_0^\infty r V(r) \sin qr \, dr. \qquad (7.2.4)$$

---

*For a fuller account of the wave-packet approach, see M. L. Goldberger and K. M. Watson, *Collision Theory*, Chapter 3 (New York: John Wiley, 1964); R. G. Newton, *Scattering Theory of Waves and Particles*, Chapter 6 (New York: McGraw-Hill, 1966).

FIGURE 7.3. Scattering through angle θ, where $\mathbf{q} = \mathbf{k} - \mathbf{k}'$.

An example is now in order. Consider scattering by a Yukawa potential

$$V(r) = \frac{V_0 e^{-\mu r}}{\mu r}, \tag{7.2.5}$$

where V_0 is independent of r and $1/\mu$ corresponds, in a certain sense, to the range of the potential. Notice that V goes to zero very rapidly for $r \gg 1/\mu$. For this potential we obtain [from (7.2.4)]

$$f^{(1)}(\theta) = -\left(\frac{2mV_0}{\mu \hbar^2}\right) \frac{1}{q^2 + \mu^2}, \tag{7.2.6}$$

where we have used

$$\mathrm{Im}\left[\int_0^\infty e^{-\mu r} e^{iqr}\, dr\right] = -\mathrm{Im}\left(\frac{1}{-\mu + iq}\right)$$

$$= \frac{q}{\mu^2 + q^2}. \tag{7.2.7}$$

Notice also that

$$q^2 = 4k^2 \sin^2\frac{\theta}{2} = 2k^2(1 - \cos\theta). \tag{7.2.8}$$

So, in the first Born approximation, the differential cross section for scattering by a Yukawa potential is given by

$$\left(\frac{d\sigma}{d\Omega}\right) \simeq \left(\frac{2mV_0}{\mu \hbar^2}\right)^2 \frac{1}{\left[2k^2(1 - \cos\theta) + \mu^2\right]^2}. \tag{7.2.9}$$

It is amusing to observe here that as $\mu \to 0$, the Yukawa potential is reduced to the Coulomb potential, provided the ratio V_0/μ is fixed—for example, to be $ZZ'e^2$—in the limiting process. We see that the first Born differential cross section obtained in this manner becomes

$$\left(\frac{d\sigma}{d\Omega}\right) \simeq \frac{(2m)^2(ZZ'e^2)^2}{\hbar^4} \frac{1}{16k^4 \sin^4(\theta/2)}. \tag{7.2.10}$$

Even the $\hbar$ disappears if $\hbar k$ is identified as $|\mathbf{p}|$, so

$$\left(\frac{d\sigma}{d\Omega}\right) = \frac{1}{16}\left(\frac{ZZ'e^2}{E_{KE}}\right)^2 \frac{1}{\sin^4(\theta/2)}, \qquad (7.2.11)$$

where $E_{KE} = |\mathbf{p}|^2/2m$; this is precisely the Rutherford scattering cross section that can be obtained *classically*.

Coming back to (7.2.4), the Born amplitude with a spherically symmetric potential, there are several general remarks we can make if $f(\mathbf{k}',\mathbf{k})$ can be approximated by the corresponding first Born amplitude, $f^{(1)}$.

1. $d\sigma/d\Omega$, or $f(\theta)$, is a function of q only; that is, $f(\theta)$ depends on the energy $(\hbar^2 k^2/2m)$ and θ only through the combination $2k^2(1 - \cos\theta)$.
2. $f(\theta)$ is always real.
3. $d\sigma/d\Omega$ is independent of the sign of V.
4. For small k (q necessarily small),

$$f^{(1)}(\theta) = -\frac{1}{4\pi}\frac{2m}{\hbar^2}\int V(r)\,d^3x$$

    involving a volume integral independent of θ.
5. $f(\theta)$ is small for large q due to rapid oscillation of the integrand.

Let us now discuss the validity of the first-order Born approximation. It is clear from the derivation that if the Born approximation is to be applicable, $\langle \mathbf{x}|\psi^{(+)}\rangle$ should not be too different from $\langle \mathbf{x}|\phi\rangle$ inside the range of potential—that is, in the region where $V(\mathbf{x})$ is appreciable. Otherwise, it is not legitimate to replace $|\psi^{(+)}\rangle$ by $|\phi\rangle$. In other words, the distortion of the incident wave must be small. Going back to the .exact expression (7.1.22), we note that the condition that $\langle \mathbf{x}|\psi^{(+)}\rangle$ be not too different from $\langle \mathbf{x}|\phi\rangle$ at the center of the scattering potential $\mathbf{x} \simeq 0$ is seen to be

$$\left|\frac{2m}{\hbar^2}\frac{1}{4\pi}\int d^3x'\,\frac{e^{ikr'}}{r'}V(\mathbf{x}')\,e^{i\mathbf{k}\cdot\mathbf{x}'}\right| \ll 1. \qquad (7.2.12)$$

We now consider what the special case of the Yukawa potential in (7.2.5) may imply. At low energies—that is, for small k ($k \ll \mu$)—it is legitimate to replace $e^{ikr'}$ by 1. So we must have

$$\frac{2m}{\hbar^2}\frac{|V_0|}{\mu^2} \ll 1. \qquad (7.2.13)$$

This requirement may be compared with the condition for the Yukawa potential to develop a bound state, which we can show to be

$$\frac{2m}{\hbar^2\mu^2}|V_0| \geq 2.7 \qquad (7.2.14)$$

with V_0 negative. In other words, if the potential is strong enough to develop a bound state, the Born approximation will probably give a misleading result. In the opposite high k-limit, the condition that the second term in (7.1.22) is small can be shown to imply

$$\frac{2m}{\hbar^2}\frac{|V_0|}{\mu k}\ln\left(\frac{k}{\mu}\right) \ll 1. \tag{7.2.15}$$

As k becomes larger, this inequality is more easily satisfied. Quite generally, the Born approximation tends to get better at higher energies.

The Higher-Order Born Approximation

Let us now consider the higher-order Born approximation. Here, it is more compact to use the symbolic approach. For the transition operator T, we define T such that

$$V|\psi^{(+)}\rangle = T|\phi\rangle. \tag{7.2.16}$$

Multiplying the Lippmann-Schwinger equation (7.1.6) by V, we obtain

$$T|\phi\rangle = V|\phi\rangle + V\frac{1}{E - H_0 + i\varepsilon}T|\phi\rangle. \tag{7.2.17}$$

This is supposed to hold for $|\phi\rangle$ taken to be any plane-wave state; furthermore, we know that these momentum eigenkets are complete. Therefore, we must have the following operator equation satisfied:

$$T = V + V\frac{1}{E - H_0 + i\varepsilon}T. \tag{7.2.18}$$

The scattering amplitude of (7.1.34) can now be written as [using (7.2.16) with the $|\phi\rangle$ as momentum eigenkets]

$$f(\mathbf{k}',\mathbf{k}) = -\frac{1}{4\pi}\frac{2m}{\hbar^2}(2\pi)^3\langle\mathbf{k}'|T|\mathbf{k}\rangle. \tag{7.2.19}$$

Thus to determine $f(\mathbf{k}',\mathbf{k})$, it is sufficient to know the transition operator T. We can obtain an iterative solution for T as follows:

$$T = V + V\frac{1}{E - H_0 + i\varepsilon}V + V\frac{1}{E - H_0 + i\varepsilon}V\frac{1}{E - H_0 + i\varepsilon}V + \cdots. \tag{7.2.20}$$

Correspondingly, we can expand f as follows:

$$f(\mathbf{k}',\mathbf{k}) = \sum_{n=1}^{\infty} f^{(n)}(\mathbf{k}',\mathbf{k}), \tag{7.2.21}$$

FIGURE 7.4. Physical interpretation of the higher-order Born term $f^{(2)}(\mathbf{k}',\mathbf{k})$.

where n is the number of times the V operator enters. We have

$$f^{(1)}(\mathbf{k}',\mathbf{k}) = -\frac{1}{4\pi}\frac{2m}{\hbar^2}(2\pi)^3\langle\mathbf{k}'|V|\mathbf{k}\rangle$$

$$f^{(2)}(\mathbf{k}',\mathbf{k}) = -\frac{1}{4\pi}\frac{2m}{\hbar^2}(2\pi)^3\left\langle\mathbf{k}'\Big|V\frac{1}{E-H_0+i\varepsilon}V\Big|\mathbf{k}\right\rangle \qquad (7.2.22)$$

$$\vdots$$

If an explicit form is required for $f^{(2)}$, we can write it as

$$f^{(2)} = -\frac{1}{4\pi}\frac{2m}{\hbar^2}(2\pi)^3\int d^3x'\int d^3x''\langle\mathbf{k}'|\mathbf{x}'\rangle V(\mathbf{x}')$$

$$\times\left\langle\mathbf{x}'\Big|\frac{1}{E-H_0+i\varepsilon}\Big|\mathbf{x}''\right\rangle V(\mathbf{x}'')\langle\mathbf{x}''|\mathbf{k}\rangle$$

$$= -\frac{1}{4\pi}\frac{2m}{\hbar^2}\int d^3x'\int d^3x''\, e^{-i\mathbf{k}'\cdot\mathbf{x}'}V(\mathbf{x}')$$

$$\times\left[\frac{2m}{\hbar^2}G_+(\mathbf{x}',\mathbf{x}'')\right]V(\mathbf{x}'')e^{i\mathbf{k}\cdot\mathbf{x}''} \qquad (7.2.23)$$

A physical interpretation of (7.2.23) is given in Figure 7.4, where the incident wave interacts at $\mathbf{x}''$—which explains the appearance of $V(\mathbf{x}'')$—and then propagates from $\mathbf{x}''$ to $\mathbf{x}'$ via Green's function for the Helmholtz equation (7.1.18); subsequently, a second interaction occurs at $\mathbf{x}'$ —thus the appearance of $V(\mathbf{x}')$—and, finally, the wave is scattered into the direction $\mathbf{k}'$. In other words, $f^{(2)}$ corresponds to scattering viewed as a two-step process; likewise, $f^{(3)}$ is viewed as a three-step process, and so on.

7.3 OPTICAL THEOREM

There is a very famous relationship popularly attributed to Bohr, Peierls, and Placzek [*Editor's Note:* This relationship is in fact due to Eugene Feenberg* (*Phys. Rev.* **40**, 1932); see R. G. Newton (*Am. J. Phys.* **44**,

---

*As pointed out by Newton in his Review (c.f. Ref. 8 therein), Feenberg's paper is also remarkable for the fact that it was published on 1 April 1932, with a receipt date stated as 8 September 1932—thus violating causality!

639, 1976) for the historical background.] called the **optical theorem**, which relates the imaginary part of the forward scattering amplitude $f(\theta = 0)$ to the total cross section σ_{tot}, as follows:

Optical Theorem

$$\text{Im } f(\theta = 0) = \frac{k\sigma_{tot}}{4\pi} \qquad (7.3.1)$$

where

$$f(\theta = 0) \equiv f(\mathbf{k}, \mathbf{k}), \qquad (7.3.2)$$

the setting of $\mathbf{k}' \equiv \mathbf{k}$ imposes scattering in the forward direction, and

$$\sigma_{tot} \equiv \int \frac{d\sigma}{d\Omega} \, d\Omega. \qquad (7.3.3)$$

Proof. From (7.2.19) we have

$$f(\theta = 0) = f(\mathbf{k}, \mathbf{k}) = -\frac{1}{4\pi} \frac{2m}{\hbar^2} (2\pi)^3 \langle \mathbf{k} | T | \mathbf{k} \rangle. \qquad (7.3.4)$$

We next evaluate $\text{Im}\langle \mathbf{k} | T | \mathbf{k} \rangle$ using (7.2.16), (7.1.6), and the hermiticity of V:

$$\text{Im}\langle \mathbf{k} | T | \mathbf{k} \rangle = \text{Im}\langle \mathbf{k} | V | \psi^{(+)} \rangle$$

$$= \text{Im}\left[\left(\langle \psi^{(+)} | - \langle \psi^{(+)} | V \frac{1}{E - H_0 - i\varepsilon} \right) V | \psi^{(+)} \rangle \right]. \qquad (7.3.5)$$

Now we use the well-known relation

$$\frac{1}{E - H_0 - i\varepsilon} = \text{Pr.} \left(\frac{1}{E - H_0} \right) + i\pi\delta(E - H_0)$$

to reduce the right-hand side of (7.3.5) to the form

$$\text{Im}(\langle \psi^{(+)} | V | \psi^{(+)} \rangle) - \text{Im}\langle \psi^{(+)} | V \text{ Pr.} \frac{1}{E - H_0} V | \psi^{(+)} \rangle$$

$$- \text{Im}\langle \psi^{(+)} | V i\pi\delta(E - H_0) V | \psi^{(+)} \rangle. \qquad (7.3.6)$$

The first two terms of (7.3.6) vanish because of the hermiticity of V and $V \text{ Pr.}[1/(E - H_0)]V$; hence (7.3.6) reduces to

$$- \pi\langle \psi^{(+)} | V \delta(E - H_0) V | \psi^{(+)} \rangle. \qquad (7.3.7)$$

Again, we can recast (7.3.7) using (7.2.16) and $|\phi\rangle = |\mathbf{k}\rangle$ as

$$\text{Im}\langle \mathbf{k} | T | \mathbf{k} \rangle = - \pi\langle \mathbf{k} | T^\dagger \delta(E - H_0) T | \mathbf{k} \rangle$$

$$= - \pi \int d^3 k' \, \langle \mathbf{k} | T^\dagger | \mathbf{k}' \rangle \langle \mathbf{k}' | T | \mathbf{k} \rangle \delta\left(E - \frac{\hbar^2 k'^2}{2m} \right)$$

$$= - \pi \int d\Omega' \frac{mk}{\hbar^2} |\langle \mathbf{k}' | T | \mathbf{k} \rangle|^2, \qquad (7.3.8)$$

where we have used $d^3k' = k'^2 dE(dk'/dE) d\Omega'$, the δ-function constraint $E = \hbar^2 k'^2/2m$ [hence $dE = (\hbar^2 k'/m) dk'$], and—finally—$k' = k$. From (7.3.4) and (7.3.8), we have

$$\text{Im}\, f(0) = -\frac{1}{4\pi} \frac{2m}{\hbar^2} (2\pi)^3 \left(-\frac{\pi mk}{\hbar^2} \int d\Omega' |\langle \mathbf{k}'|T|\mathbf{k}\rangle|^2 \right)$$

$$= \frac{k\sigma_{\text{tot}}}{4\pi}, \tag{7.3.9}$$

where in the last step we have used (7.1.36), (7.2.19), and (7.3.3). $\square$

We can appreciate the physical significance of the optical theorem after we discuss shadow scattering.

7.4. EIKONAL APPROXIMATION

This approximation covers a situation in which $V(\mathbf{x})$ varies very little over a distance of order of wavelength λ (which can be regarded as "small"). Note that V itself need not be weak as long as $E \gg |V|$; hence the domain of validity here is different from the Born approximation. Under these conditions, the semiclassical path concept becomes applicable, and we replace the exact wave function $\psi^{(+)}$ by the semiclassical wave function [see (2.4.18) and (2.4.22)], namely,

$$\psi^{(+)} \sim e^{iS(\mathbf{x})/\hbar}. \tag{7.4.1}$$

This leads to the Hamilton-Jacobi equation for S,

$$\frac{(\nabla S)^2}{2m} + V = E = \frac{\hbar^2 k^2}{2m}, \tag{7.4.2}$$

as discussed in Section 2.4. We propose to compute S from (7.4.2) by making the further approximation that the classical trajectory is a straight-line path, which should be satisfactory for small deflection at high energy.* Consider the situation depicted in Figure 7.5, where the straight-line trajectory is along the z-direction. Integrating (7.4.2) we have

$$\frac{S}{\hbar} = \int_{-\infty}^{z} \left[k^2 - \frac{2m}{\hbar^2} V\left(\sqrt{b^2 + z'^2}\right) \right]^{1/2} dz' + \text{constant}. \tag{7.4.3}$$

The additive constant is to be chosen in such a way that

$$\frac{S}{\hbar} \to kz \quad \text{as} \quad V \to 0 \tag{7.4.4}$$

so that the plane-wave form for (7.4.1) is reproduced in this zero-potential

---

*Needless to say, solution of (7.4.2) to *determine* the classical trajectory would be a forbidding task in general.

limit. We can then write Equation (7.4.3) as

$$\frac{S}{\hbar} = kz + \int_{-\infty}^{z} \left[\sqrt{k^2 - \frac{2m}{\hbar^2} V\left(\sqrt{b^2 + z'^2}\right)} - k \right] dz'$$

$$\cong kz - \frac{m}{\hbar^2 k} \int_{-\infty}^{z} V\left(\sqrt{b^2 + z'^2}\right) dz' \qquad (7.4.5)$$

where for $E \gg V$, we have used

$$\sqrt{k^2 - \frac{2m}{\hbar^2} V\left(\sqrt{b^2 + z'^2}\right)} \sim k - \frac{mV}{\hbar^2 k}$$

at high $E = \hbar^2 k^2 / 2m$. So

$$\psi^{(+)}(\mathbf{x}) = \psi^{(1)}(\mathbf{b} + z\hat{\mathbf{z}}) \simeq \frac{1}{(2\pi)^{3/2}} e^{ikz} \exp\left[\frac{-im}{\hbar^2 k} \int_{-\infty}^{z} V\left(\sqrt{b^2 + z'^2}\right) dz' \right].$$

$$(7.4.6)$$

Though (7.4.6) does not have the correct asymptotic form appropriate for an incident plus spherical outgoing wave (that is, it is not of form $e^{i\vec{\mathbf{k}} \cdot \vec{\mathbf{x}}} + f(\theta)(e^{ikr}/r)$ and indeed refers only to motion along the original direction), it can nevertheless still be used in (7.1.34) to obtain an approximate expression for $f(\mathbf{k}', \mathbf{k})$, to wit,

$$f(\mathbf{k}', \mathbf{k}) = -\frac{1}{4\pi} \frac{2m}{\hbar^2} \int d^3x' e^{-i\mathbf{k}' \cdot \mathbf{x}'} V\left(\sqrt{b^2 + z'^2}\right) e^{i\mathbf{k} \cdot \mathbf{x}'}$$

$$\times \exp\left[-\frac{im}{\hbar^2 k} \int_{-\infty}^{z'} V\left(\sqrt{b^2 + z''^2}\right) dz'' \right]. \qquad (7.4.7)$$

Note that without the last factor, exp [...], (7.4.7) is just like the first-order Born amplitude in (7.2.2). We perform the three-dimensional (d^3x') integration in (7.4.7) by introducing cylindrical coordinates $d^3x' = b\,db\,d\phi_b\,dz'$ (see

FIGURE 7.5. Schematic diagram of eikonal approximation scattering where the classical straight line trajectory is along the z-direction, $|\mathbf{x}| = r$, and $b = |\mathbf{b}|$ is the impact parameter.

Figure 7.5) and noting that

$$(\mathbf{k} - \mathbf{k}') \cdot \mathbf{x}' = (\mathbf{k} - \mathbf{k}') \cdot (\mathbf{b} + z'\hat{\mathbf{z}}) \simeq -\mathbf{k}' \cdot \mathbf{b}, \qquad (7.4.8)$$

where we have used $\mathbf{k} \perp \mathbf{b}$ and $(\mathbf{k} - \mathbf{k}') \cdot \hat{\mathbf{z}} \sim 0(\theta^2)$, which can be ignored for small deflection θ. Without loss of generality we choose scattering to be in the xz-plane and write

$$\mathbf{k}' \cdot \mathbf{b} = (k \sin\theta \hat{\mathbf{x}} + k \cos\theta \hat{\mathbf{z}}) \cdot (b \cos\phi_b \hat{\mathbf{x}} + b \sin\phi_b \hat{\mathbf{y}}) = kb\theta \cos\phi_b.$$

$$(7.4.9)$$

The expression for $f(\mathbf{k}', \mathbf{k})$ becomes

$$f(\mathbf{k}', \mathbf{k}) = -\frac{1}{4\pi} \frac{2m}{\hbar^2} \int_0^\infty b\,db \int_0^{2\pi} d\phi_b\, e^{-ikb\theta\cos\phi_b}$$

$$\times \int_{-\infty}^{+\infty} dz\, V \exp\left[\frac{-im}{\hbar^2 k} \int_{-\infty}^z V\,dz'\right]. \qquad (7.4.10)$$

We next use the following identities:

$$\int_0^{2\pi} d\phi_b\, e^{-ikb\theta\cos\phi_b} = 2\pi J_0(kb\theta) \qquad (7.4.11)$$

and

$$\int_{-\infty}^{+\infty} dz\, V \exp\left[\frac{-im}{\hbar^2 k} \int_{-\infty}^z V\,dz'\right] = \frac{i\hbar^2 k}{m} \exp\left[\frac{-im}{\hbar^2 k} \int_{-\infty}^z V\,dz'\right]\Bigg|_{z=-\infty}^{z=+\infty},$$

$$(7.4.12)$$

where, of course, the contribution from $z = -\infty$ on the right-hand side of (7.4.12) vanishes in the exponent. So, finally

$$f(\mathbf{k}', \mathbf{k}) = -ik \int_0^\infty db\, b J_0(kb\theta)[e^{2i\Delta(b)} - 1], \qquad (7.4.13)$$

where

$$\Delta(b) \equiv \frac{-m}{2k\hbar^2} \int_{-\infty}^{+\infty} V(\sqrt{b^2 + z^2})\,dz. \qquad (7.4.14)$$

In (7.4.14) we fix the impact parameter b and integrate along the straight-line path z, shown in Figure 7.5. There is no contribution from $[e^{2i\Delta(b)} - 1]$ in (7.4.13) if b is greater than the range of V.

It can be shown in a straightforward manner that the eikonal approximation satisfies the optical theorem (7.3.1). This proof plus some interesting applications—for example, when V is a Gaussian potential $\Delta(b)$ becomes Gaussian in b-space—are discussed in the literature (Gottfried 1966). For the case where V is a Yukawa potential, see Problem 7 in this chapter.

7.5. FREE-PARTICLE STATES: PLANE WAVES VERSUS SPHERICAL WAVES

In considering scattering by a spherically symmetric potential, we often examine how states with definite angular momenta are affected by the scatterer. Such considerations lead to the method of partial waves, to be discussed in detail in Section 7.6. However, before discussing the angular momentum decomposition of scattering states, let us first talk about free-particle states, which are also eigenstates of angular momentum.

For a free particle the Hamiltonian is just the kinetic-energy operator, which obviously commutes with the momentum operator. It is for this reason that in Section 7.1 we also took $|\phi\rangle$, an eigenket of the free-particle Hamiltonian, to be a momentum eigenket or a plane-wave state $|\mathbf{k}\rangle$, where the eigenvalue of the momentum operator is $\hbar\mathbf{k}$. We note, however, that the free-particle Hamiltonian also commutes with $\mathbf{L}^2$ and L_z. Thus it is possible to consider a simultaneous eigenket of H_0, $\mathbf{L}^2$, and L_z. Ignoring spin, such a state is denoted by $|E, l, m\rangle$, often called a **spherical-wave state**.

More generally, the most general free-particle state can be regarded as a superposition of $|E, l, m\rangle$ with various E, l, and m in much the same way as the most general free-particle state can be regarded as a superposition of $|\mathbf{k}\rangle$ with different $\mathbf{k}$, different in both magnitude and direction. Put in another way, a free-particle state can be analysed using either the plane-wave basis $\{|\mathbf{k}\rangle\}$ or the spherical-wave basis $\{|E, l, m\rangle\}$.

We now derive the transformation function $\langle\mathbf{k}|E, l, m\rangle$ that connects the plane-wave basis with the spherical-wave basis. We can also regard this quantity as the momentum-space wave function for the spherical wave characterized by E, l, and m. We adopt the normalization convention for the spherical-wave eigenket as follows:

$$\langle E', l', m'|E, l, m\rangle = \delta_{ll'}\delta_{mm'}\delta(E - E'). \qquad (7.5.1)$$

In analogy with the position-space wave function, we may guess the angular dependence:

$$\langle\mathbf{k}|E, l, m\rangle = g_{lE}(k)Y_l^m(\hat{\mathbf{k}}). \qquad (7.5.2)$$

To prove this rigorously, we proceed as follows. First, consider the momentum eigenket $|k\hat{\mathbf{z}}\rangle$—that is, a plane-wave state whose propagation direction is along the positive z-axis. An important property of this state is that it has no orbital angular-momentum component in the z-direction:

$$L_z|k\hat{\mathbf{z}}\rangle = (xp_y - yp_x)|k_x = 0, k_y = 0, k_z = k\rangle = 0. \qquad (7.5.3)$$

Actually this is plausible from classical considerations: The angular-momentum component must vanish in the direction of propagation because $\mathbf{L}\cdot\mathbf{p} = (\mathbf{x}\times\mathbf{p})\cdot\mathbf{p} = 0$. Because of (7.5.3)—and since $\langle E', l', m'|k\hat{\mathbf{z}}\rangle = 0$ for

$m' \neq 0$—we must be able to expand $|k\hat{z}\rangle$ as follows:

$$|k\hat{z}\rangle = \sum_{l'} \int dE' |E', l', m' = 0\rangle \langle E', l', m' = 0|k\hat{z}\rangle. \qquad (7.5.4)$$

Notice that there is no m' sum; m' is always zero. We can obtain the most general momentum eigenket, with the direction of $\mathbf{k}$ specified by θ and ϕ, from $|k\hat{z}\rangle$ by just applying the appropriate rotation operator as follows [see Figure 3.3 and (3.6.47)]:

$$|\mathbf{k}\rangle = \mathscr{D}(\alpha = \phi, \beta = \theta, \gamma = 0)|k\hat{z}\rangle. \qquad (7.5.5)$$

Multiplying (7.5.5) by $\langle E, l, m|$ on the left, we obtain

$$\langle E, l, m|\mathbf{k}\rangle = \sum_{l'} \int dE' \langle E, l, m|\mathscr{D}(\alpha = \phi, \beta = \theta, \gamma = 0)|E', l', m' = 0\rangle$$

$$\times \langle E', l', m' = 0|k\hat{z}\rangle$$

$$= \sum_{l'} \int dE' \mathscr{D}_{m0}^{(l')}(\alpha = \phi, \beta = \theta, \gamma = 0)$$

$$\times \delta_{ll'}\delta(E - E')\langle E', l', m' = 0|k\hat{z}\rangle$$

$$= \mathscr{D}_{m0}^{(l)}(\alpha = \phi, \beta = \theta, \gamma = 0)\langle E, l, m = 0|k\hat{z}\rangle. \qquad (7.5.6)$$

Now $\langle E, l, m = 0|k\hat{z}\rangle$ is independent of the orientation of $\mathbf{k}$—that is, independent of θ and ϕ—and we may as well call it $\sqrt{\dfrac{2l + 1}{4\pi}}\, g_{lE}^*(k)$. So we can write, using (3.6.51),

$$\langle \mathbf{k}|E, l, m\rangle = g_{lE}(k)\, Y_l^m(\hat{\mathbf{k}}). \qquad (7.5.7)$$

Let us determine $g_{lE}(k)$. First, we note that

$$(H_0 - E)|E, l, m\rangle = 0. \qquad (7.5.8)$$

But we also let $H_0 - E$ operate on a momentum eigenbra $\langle \mathbf{k}|$ as follows:

$$\langle \mathbf{k}|(H_0 - E) = \left(\frac{\hbar^2 k^2}{2m} - E\right)\langle \mathbf{k}|. \qquad (7.5.9)$$

Multiplying (7.5.9) with $|E, l, m\rangle$ on the right, we obtain

$$\left(\frac{\hbar^2 k^2}{2m} - E\right)\langle \mathbf{k}|E, l, m\rangle = 0. \qquad (7.5.10)$$

This means that $\langle \mathbf{k}|E, l, m\rangle$ can be nonvanishing only if $E = \hbar^2 k^2/2m$; so we must be able to write $g_{lE}(k)$ as

$$g_{lE}(k) = N\delta\left(\frac{\hbar^2 k^2}{2m} - E\right). \qquad (7.5.11)$$

To determine N we go back to our normalization convention (7.5.1). We obtain

$$\langle E', l', m'|E, l, m\rangle = \int d^3k'' \langle E', l', m'|\mathbf{k}''\rangle\langle \mathbf{k}''|E, l, m\rangle$$

$$= \int k''^2\, dk'' \int d\Omega_{\mathbf{k}''} |N|^2 \delta\left(\frac{\hbar^2 k''^2}{2m} - E'\right)$$

$$\times \delta\left(\frac{\hbar^2 k''^2}{2m} - E\right) Y_{l'}^{m'*}(\hat{\mathbf{k}}'') Y_l^m(\hat{\mathbf{k}}'')$$

$$= \int \frac{k''^2\, dE''}{dE''/dk''} \int d\Omega_{\mathbf{k}''} |N|^2 \delta\left(\frac{\hbar^2 k''^2}{2m} - E'\right)\delta\left(\frac{\hbar^2 k''^2}{2m} - E\right)$$

$$\times Y_{l'}^{m'*}(\hat{\mathbf{k}}'') Y_l^m(\hat{\mathbf{k}}'')$$

$$= |N|^2 \frac{mk'}{\hbar^2} \delta(E - E')\delta_{ll'}\delta_{mm'}, \tag{7.5.12}$$

where we have defined $E'' = \hbar^2 k''^2/2m$ to change k''-integration into E''-integration. Comparing this with (7.5.1), we see that $N = \hbar/\sqrt{mk}$ will suffice. Therefore, we can finally write

$$g_{lE}(k) = \frac{\hbar}{\sqrt{mk}} \delta\left(\frac{\hbar^2 k^2}{2m} - E\right); \tag{7.5.13}$$

hence

$$\langle \mathbf{k}|E, l, m\rangle = \frac{\hbar}{\sqrt{mk}} \delta\left(\frac{\hbar^2 k^2}{2m} - E\right) Y_l^m(\hat{\mathbf{k}}). \tag{7.5.14}$$

From (7.5.14) we infer that the plane-wave state $|\mathbf{k}\rangle$ can be expressed as a superposition of free spherical-wave states with all possible l-values; in particular,

$$|\mathbf{k}\rangle = \sum_l \sum_m \int dE |E, l, m\rangle\langle E, l, m|\mathbf{k}\rangle$$

$$= \sum_{l=0}^\infty \sum_{m=-l}^l |E, l, m\rangle\bigg|_{E = \hbar^2 k^2/2m} \left(\frac{\hbar}{\sqrt{mk}} Y_l^{m*}(\hat{\mathbf{k}})\right). \tag{7.5.15}$$

Because the transverse dimension of the plane wave is infinite, we expect that the plane wave must contain all possible values of impact parameter b (semiclassically, the impact parameter $b \simeq l\hbar/p$). From this point of view it is no surprise that the momentum eigenstates $|\mathbf{k}\rangle$, when analyzed in terms of spherical-wave states, contain all possible values of l.

We have derived the wave function for $|E, l, m\rangle$ in momentum space. Next, we consider the corresponding wave function in position space.

From wave mechanics, the reader should be familiar with the fact that the wave function for a free spherical wave is $j_l(kr)Y_l^m(\hat{\mathbf{r}})$, where $j_l(kr)$ is the spherical Bessel function of order l (see Appendix A). The second solution $n_l(kr)$, although it satisfies the appropriate differential equation, is inadmissible because it is singular at the origin. So we can write

$$\langle \mathbf{x}|E,l,m\rangle = c_l j_l(kr)Y_l^m(\hat{\mathbf{r}}). \tag{7.5.16}$$

To determine c_l, all we have to do is compare

$$\langle \mathbf{x}|\mathbf{k}\rangle = \frac{e^{i\mathbf{k}\cdot\mathbf{x}}}{(2\pi)^{3/2}} = \sum_l \sum_m \int dE \langle \mathbf{x}|E,l,m\rangle\langle E,l,m|\mathbf{k}\rangle$$

$$= \sum_l \sum_m \int dE\, c_l j_l(kr)Y_l^m(\hat{\mathbf{r}})\frac{\hbar}{\sqrt{mk}}\delta\!\left(E - \frac{\hbar^2 k^2}{2m}\right)Y_l^{m*}(\hat{\mathbf{k}})$$

$$= \sum_l \frac{(2l+1)}{4\pi}P_l(\hat{\mathbf{k}}\cdot\hat{\mathbf{r}})\frac{\hbar}{\sqrt{mk}}c_l j_l(kr), \tag{7.5.17}$$

where we have used the addition theorem

$$\sum_m Y_l^m(\hat{\mathbf{r}})Y_l^{m*}(\hat{\mathbf{k}}) = [(2l+1)/4\pi]P_l(\hat{\mathbf{k}}\cdot\hat{\mathbf{r}})$$

in the last step. Now $\langle \mathbf{x}|\mathbf{k}\rangle = e^{i\mathbf{k}\cdot\mathbf{x}}/(2\pi)^{3/2}$ can also be written as

$$\frac{e^{i\mathbf{k}\cdot\mathbf{x}}}{(2\pi)^{3/2}} = \frac{1}{(2\pi)^{3/2}}\sum_l (2l+1)i^l j_l(kr)P_l(\hat{\mathbf{k}}\cdot\hat{\mathbf{r}}), \tag{7.5.18}$$

which can be proved by using the following integral representation for $j_l(kr)$:

$$j_l(kr) = \frac{1}{2i^l}\int_{-1}^{+1}e^{ikr\cos\theta}P_l(\cos\theta)\,d(\cos\theta). \tag{7.5.19}$$

Comparing (7.5.17) with (7.5.18), we have

$$c_l = \frac{i^l}{\hbar}\sqrt{\frac{2mk}{\pi}}. \tag{7.5.20}$$

To summarize, we have

$$\langle \mathbf{k}|E,l,m\rangle = \frac{\hbar}{\sqrt{mk}}\delta\!\left(E - \frac{\hbar^2 k^2}{2m}\right)Y_l^m(\hat{\mathbf{k}}) \tag{7.5.21a}$$

$$\langle \mathbf{x}|E,l,m\rangle = \frac{i^l}{\hbar}\sqrt{\frac{2mk}{\pi}}j_l(kr)Y_l^m(\hat{\mathbf{r}}). \tag{7.5.21b}$$

These expressions are extremely useful in developing the partial-wave expansion discussed in the next section.

We conclude this section by applying (7.5.21a) to a decay process. Suppose a parent particle of spin j disintegrates into two spin-zero particles A (spin j) $\rightarrow B$ (spin 0) $+ C$ (spin 0). The basic Hamiltonian responsible for such a decay process is, in general, very complicated. However, we do know that angular momentum is conserved because the basic Hamiltonian must be rotationally invariant. So the momentum-space wave function for the final state must be of the form (7.5.21a), with l identified with the spin of the parent particle. This immediately enables us to compute the angular distribution of the decay product because the momentum-space wave function is nothing more than the probability amplitude for finding the decay product with relative momentum direction $\mathbf{k}$.

As a concrete example from nuclear physics, let us consider the decay of an excited nucleus, Ne^{20*}:

$$Ne^{20*} \rightarrow O^{16} + He^4. \qquad (7.5.22)$$

Both O^{16} and He^4 are known to be spinless particles. Suppose the magnetic quantum number of the parent nucleus is ± 1, relative to some direction z. Then the angular distribution of the decay product is proportional to $|Y_1^{\pm 1}(\theta, \phi)|^2 = (3/8\pi)\sin^2\theta$, where (θ, ϕ) are the polar angles defining the relative direction $\mathbf{k}$ of the decay product. On the other hand, if the magnetic quantum number is 0 for a parent nucleus with spin 1, the decay angular distribution varies as $|Y_1^0(\theta, \phi)|^2 = (3/4\pi)\cos^2\theta$.

For a general spin orientation we obtain

$$\sum_{m=-1}^{1} w(m)|Y_{l=1}^m|^2. \qquad (7.5.23)$$

For an unpolarized nucleus the various $w(m)$ are all equal, and we obtain an isotropic distribution; this is not surprising because there is no preferred direction if the parent particle is unpolarized.

For a higher spin object, the angular distribution of the decay is more involved; the higher the spin of the parent decaying system, the greater the complexity of the angular distribution of the decay products. Quite generally, through a study of the angular distribution of the decay products, it is possible to determine the spin of the parent nucleus.

7.6. METHOD OF PARTIAL WAVES

Partial-Wave Expansion

Let us now come back to the case $V \neq 0$. We assume that the potential is spherically symmetric, that is, invariant under rotations in three dimensions. It then follows that the transition operator T, which is given by (7.2.20), commutes with $\mathbf{L}^2$ and $\mathbf{L}$. In other words, T is a scalar operator.

It is now useful to use the spherical-wave basis because the Wigner-Eckart theorem [see (3.10.38)], applied to a scalar operator, immediately gives

$$\langle E', l', m'|T|E, l, m\rangle = T_l(E)\delta_{ll'}\delta_{mm'}. \tag{7.6.1}$$

In other words, T is diagonal both in l and in m; furthermore, the (nonvanishing) diagonal element depends on E and l but not on m. This leads to an enormous simplification, as we will see shortly.

Let us now look at the scattering amplitude (7.2.19):

$$
\begin{aligned}
f(\mathbf{k}',\mathbf{k}) &= -\frac{1}{4\pi}\frac{2m}{\hbar^2}(2\pi)^3\langle\mathbf{k}'|T|\mathbf{k}\rangle \\
&= -\frac{1}{4\pi}\frac{2m}{\hbar^2}(2\pi)^3\sum_l\sum_m\sum_{l'}\sum_{m'}\int dE\int dE'\langle\mathbf{k}'|E'l'm'\rangle \\
&\qquad \times\langle E'l'm'|T|Elm\rangle\langle Elm|\mathbf{k}\rangle \\
&= -\frac{1}{4\pi}\frac{2m}{\hbar^2}(2\pi)^3\frac{\hbar^2}{mk}\sum_l\sum_m T_l(E)\bigg|_{E=\hbar^2k^2/2m}Y_l^m(\hat{\mathbf{k}}')Y_l^{m*}(\hat{\mathbf{k}}) \\
&= -\frac{4\pi^2}{k}\sum_l\sum_m T_l(E)\bigg|_{E=\hbar^2k^2/2m}Y_l^m(\hat{\mathbf{k}}')Y_l^{m*}(\hat{\mathbf{k}}). \tag{7.6.2}
\end{aligned}
$$

To obtain the angular dependence of the scattering amplitude, let us choose the coordinate system in such a way that $\mathbf{k}$, as usual, is in the positive z-direction. We then have [see (3.6.50)]

$$Y_l^m(\hat{\mathbf{k}}) = \sqrt{\frac{2l+1}{4\pi}}\,\delta_{m0}, \tag{7.6.3}$$

where we have used $P_l(1)=1$; hence only the terms $m=0$ contribute. Taking θ to be the angle between $\mathbf{k}'$ and $\mathbf{k}$, we can write

$$Y_l^0(\hat{\mathbf{k}}') = \sqrt{\frac{2l+1}{4\pi}}\,P_l(\cos\theta). \tag{7.6.4}$$

It is customary here to define the **partial-wave amplitude** $f_l(k)$ as follows:

$$f_l(k) \equiv -\frac{\pi T_l(E)}{k}. \tag{7.6.5}$$

For (7.6.2) we then have

$$f(\mathbf{k}',\mathbf{k}) = f(\theta) = \sum_{l=0}^{\infty}(2l+1)f_l(k)P_l(\cos\theta), \tag{7.6.6}$$

where $f(\theta)$ still depends on k (or the incident energy) even though k is suppressed.

To appreciate the physical significance of $f_l(k)$, let us study the large-distance behavior of the wave function $\langle\mathbf{x}|\psi^{(+)}\rangle$ given by (7.1.33). Using the expansion of a plane wave in terms of spherical waves [(7.5.18)] and noting that (Appendix A)

$$j_l(kr) \xrightarrow{\text{large } r} \frac{e^{i(kr-(l\pi/2))} - e^{-i(kr-(l\pi/2))}}{2ikr}, \qquad (i^l = e^{i(\pi/2)l}) \quad (7.6.7)$$

and that $f(\theta)$ is given by (7.6.6), we have

$$\langle \mathbf{x} | \psi^{(+)} \rangle \xrightarrow{\text{large } r} \frac{1}{(2\pi)^{3/2}} \left[e^{ikz} + f(\theta) \frac{e^{ikr}}{r} \right]$$

$$= \frac{1}{(2\pi)^{3/2}} \left[\sum_l (2l+1) P_l(\cos\theta) \left(\frac{e^{ikr} - e^{-i(kr-l\pi)}}{2ikr} \right) \right.$$

$$\left. + \sum_l (2l+1) f_l(k) P_l(\cos\theta) \frac{e^{ikr}}{r} \right]$$

$$= \frac{1}{(2\pi)^{3/2}} \sum_l (2l+1) \frac{P_l}{2ik} \left[[1+2ikf_l(k)] \frac{e^{ikr}}{r} - \frac{e^{-i(kr-l\pi)}}{r} \right].$$

$$(7.6.8)$$

The physics of scattering is now clear. When the scatterer is absent, we can analyze the plane wave as the sum of a spherically outgoing wave behaving like e^{ikr}/r and a spherically incoming wave behaving like $-e^{-i(kr-l\pi)}/r$ for each l. The presence of the scatterer changes only the coefficient of the outgoing wave, as follows:

$$1 \to 1 + 2ikf_l(k). \qquad (7.6.9)$$

The incoming wave is completely unaffected.

Unitarity and Phase Shifts

We now examine the consequences of probability conservation, or unitarity. In a time-independent formulation, the flux current density $\mathbf{j}$ must satisfy

$$\nabla \cdot \mathbf{j} = -\frac{\partial |\psi|^2}{\partial t} = 0. \qquad (7.6.10)$$

Let us now consider a spherical surface of very large radius. By Gauss's theorem, we must have

$$\int_{\substack{\text{spherical} \\ \text{surface}}} \mathbf{j} \cdot d\mathbf{S} = 0. \qquad (7.6.11)$$

Physically (7.6.10) and (7.6.11) mean that there is no source or sink of particles. The outgoing flux must equal the incoming flux. Furthermore, because of angular-momentum conservation, this must hold for each partial wave separately. In other words, the coefficient of e^{ikr}/r must be the same in magnitude as the coefficient of e^{-ikr}/r. Defining $S_l(k)$ to be

$$S_l(k) \equiv 1 + 2ikf_l(k), \tag{7.6.12}$$

this means [from (7.6.9)] that

$$|S_l(k)| = 1, \tag{7.6.13}$$

that is, the most that can happen is a change in the phase of the outgoing wave. Equation (7.6.13) is known as the **unitarity relation** for the lth partial wave. In a more advanced treatment of scattering, $S_l(k)$ can be regarded as the lth diagonal element of the S operator, which is required to be unitary as a consequence of probability conservation.

We thus see that the only change in the wave function at a large distance as a result of scattering is to change the *phase* of the outgoing wave. Calling this phase $2\delta_l$ (the factor of 2 here is conventional), we can write

$$S_l = e^{2i\delta_l}, \tag{7.6.14}$$

with δ_l real. It is understood here that δ_l is a function of k even though we do not explicitly write δ_l as $\delta_l(k)$. Returning to f_l, we can write [from (7.6.12)]

$$f_l = \frac{(S_l - 1)}{2ik} \tag{7.6.15}$$

or, explicitly in terms of δ_l,

$$f_l = \frac{e^{2i\delta_l} - 1}{2ik} = \frac{e^{i\delta_l}\sin\delta_l}{k} = \frac{1}{k\cot\delta_l - ik}, \tag{7.6.16}$$

whichever is convenient. For the full scattering amplitude we have

$$f(\theta) = \sum_{l=0} (2l+1)\left(\frac{e^{2i\delta_l} - 1}{2ik}\right) P_l(\cos\theta)$$

$$= \frac{1}{k}\sum_{l=0} (2l+1)e^{i\delta_l}\sin\delta_l P_l(\cos\theta) \tag{7.6.17}$$

with δ_l real. This expression for $f(\theta)$ rests on the twin principles of **rotational invariance** and **probability conservation**. In many books on wave mechanics, (7.6.17) is obtained by explicitly solving the Schrödinger equation with a real, spherically symmetric potential; our derivation of (7.6.17) may be of interest because it can be generalized to situations when the potential described in the context of nonrelativistic quantum mechanics may fail.

The differential cross section $d\sigma/d\Omega$ can be obtained [see (7.1.36)] by just taking the modulus squared of (7.6.17). To obtain the total cross section we have

$$\sigma_{tot} = \int |f(\theta)|^2 \, d\Omega$$

$$= \frac{1}{k^2} \int_0^{2\pi} d\phi \int_{-1}^{+1} d(\cos\theta) \sum_l \sum_{l'} (2l+1)(2l'+1)$$

$$\times e^{i\delta_l}\sin\delta_l e^{-i\delta_{l'}}\sin\delta_{l'} P_l P_{l'}$$

$$= \frac{4\pi}{k^2} \sum_l (2l+1)\sin^2\delta_l. \tag{7.6.18}$$

We can check the optical theorem (7.3.1), which we obtained earlier using a more general argument. All we need to do is note from (7.6.17) that

$$\mathrm{Im}\, f(\theta=0) = \sum_l \frac{(2l+1)\mathrm{Im}\left[e^{i\delta_l}\sin\delta_l\right]}{k} P_l(\cos\theta)\bigg|_{\theta=0}$$

$$= \sum_l \frac{(2l+1)}{k}\sin^2\delta_l, \tag{7.6.19}$$

which is the same as (7.6.18) except for $4\pi/k$.

As a function of energy, δ_l changes; hence $f_l(k)$ changes also. The unitarity relation of (7.6.13) is a restriction on the manner in which f_l can vary. This can be most conveniently seen by drawing an Argand diagram for kf_l. We plot kf_l in a complex plane, as shown in Figure 7.6, which is

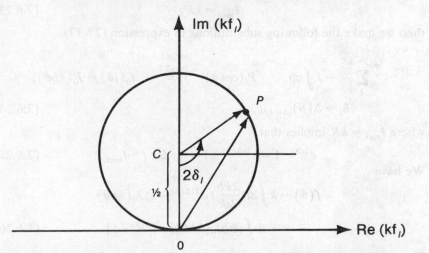

FIGURE 7.6. Argand diagram for kf_l. OP is the magnitude of kf_l, while CO and CP are each radii of length $\frac{1}{2}$ on the unitary circle; angle $OCP = 2\delta_l$.

self-explanatory if we note from (7.6.16) that

$$kf_l = \frac{i}{2} + \frac{1}{2}e^{-(i\pi/2)+2i\delta_l}. \tag{7.6.20}$$

Notice that there is a circle of radius $\frac{1}{2}$, known as the **unitary circle**, on which kf_l must lie.

We can see many important features from Figure 7.6. Suppose δ_l is small. Then f_l must stay near the bottom of the circle. It may be positive or negative, but f_l is almost purely real:

$$f_l = \frac{e^{i\delta_l}\sin\delta_l}{k} \simeq \frac{(1+i\delta_l)\delta_l}{k} \simeq \frac{\delta_l}{k}. \tag{7.6.21}$$

On the other hand, if δ_l is near $\pi/2$, kf_l is almost purely imaginary, and the magnitude of kf_l is maximal. Under such a condition the lth partial wave may be in resonance, a concept to be discussed in some detail in Section 7.8. Note that the maximum partial cross section

$$\sigma_{max}^{(l)} = 4\pi\lambdabar^2(2l+1) \tag{7.6.22}$$

is achieved [see (7.6.18)] when $\sin^2\delta_l = 1$.

Connection with the Eikonal Approximation

The eikonal approximation discussed in 7.4 is valid at high energies ($\lambdabar \ll$ range R); hence many partial waves contribute. We may regard l as a continuous variable. As an aside we note the semiclassical argument that $l = bk$ (because angular momentum $l\hbar = bp$, where b is the impact parameter and momentum $p = \hbar k$). We take

$$l_{max} = kR; \tag{7.6.23}$$

then we make the following substitutions in expression (7.6.17):

$$\sum_l^{l_{max}=kR} \to k\int db, \qquad P_l(\cos\theta) \overset{\substack{\text{large } l,\\ \text{small } \theta}}{\simeq} J_0(l\theta) = J_0(kb\theta),$$

$$\delta_l \to \Delta(b)|_{b=l/k}, \tag{7.6.24}$$

where $l_{max} = kR$ implies that

$$e^{2i\delta_l} - 1 = e^{2i\Delta(b)} - 1 = 0 \quad \text{for } l > l_{max}. \tag{7.6.25}$$

We have

$$f(\theta) \to k\int db \frac{2kb}{2ik}(e^{2i\Delta(b)}-1)J_0(kb\theta)$$

$$= -ik\int db\, bJ_0(kb\theta)[e^{2i\Delta(b)}-1]. \tag{7.6.26}$$

The computation of δ_l can be done by using the explicit form for $\Delta(b)$ given by (7.4.14) (see Problem 7 in this chapter).

Determination of Phase Shifts

Let us now consider how we may actually determine the phase shifts given a potential V. We assume that V vanishes for $r > R$, R being the range of the potential. Outside (that is, for $r > R$) the wave function must be that of a free spherical wave. This time, however, there is no reason to exclude $n_l(r)$ because the origin is excluded from our consideration. The wave function is therefore a linear combination of $j_l(kr)P_l(\cos\theta)$ and $n_l(kr)P_l(\cos\theta)$ or, equivalently, $h_l^{(1)}P_l$ and $h_l^{(2)}P_l$, where $h_l^{(1)}$ and $h_l^{(2)}$ are the spherical Hankel functions defined by

$$h_l^{(1)} = j_l + in_l, \qquad h_l^{(2)} = j_l - in_l; \tag{7.6.27}$$

these have the asymptotic behavior (see Appendix A)

$$h_l^{(1)} \xrightarrow{r \text{ large}} \frac{e^{i(kr-(l\pi/2))}}{ikr}, \qquad h_l^{(2)} \xrightarrow{r \text{ large}} -\frac{e^{-i(kr-(l\pi/2))}}{ikr}. \tag{7.6.28}$$

The full-wave function at any r can then be written as:

$$\langle \mathbf{x}|\psi^{(+)}\rangle = \frac{1}{(2\pi)^{3/2}} \sum i^l (2l+1) A_l(r) P_l(\cos\theta) \quad (r > R). \tag{7.6.29}$$

For $r > R$ we have (for the radial-wave function)

$$A_l = c_l^{(1)} h_l^{(1)}(kr) + c_l^{(2)} h_l^{(2)}(kr), \tag{7.6.30}$$

where the coefficient that multiplies A_l in (7.6.29) is chosen so that, for $V = 0$, $A_l(r)$ coincides with $j_l(kr)$ everywhere. Using (7.6.28), we can compare the behavior of the wave function for large r given by (7.6.29) and (7.6.30) with

$$\frac{1}{(2\pi)^{3/2}} \sum_l (2l+1) P_l \left[\frac{e^{2i\delta_l}e^{ikr}}{2ikr} - \frac{e^{-i(kr-l\pi)}}{2ikr} \right]. \tag{7.6.31}$$

Clearly, we must have

$$c_l^{(1)} = \tfrac{1}{2} e^{2i\delta_l}, \qquad c_l^{(2)} = \tfrac{1}{2}. \tag{7.6.32}$$

So the radial-wave function for $r > R$ is now written as

$$A_l(r) = e^{i\delta_l} [\cos\delta_l \, j_l(kr) - \sin\delta_l \, n_l(kr)]. \tag{7.6.33}$$

Using this, we can evaluate the logarithmic derivative at $r = R$—that is, just outside the range of the potential—as follows:

$$\beta_l \equiv \left(\frac{r}{A_l} \frac{dA_l}{dr} \right)_{r=R}$$

$$= kR \left[\frac{j_l'(kR)\cos\delta_l - n_l'(kR)\sin\delta_l}{j_l(kR)\cos\delta_l - n_l(kR)\sin\delta_l} \right], \tag{7.6.34}$$

where $j_l'(kR)$ stands for the derivative of j_l with respect to kr evaluated at

$kr = kR$. Conversely, knowing the logarithmic derivative at R, we can obtain the phase shift as follows:

$$\tan \delta_l = \frac{kRj_l'(kR) - \beta_l j_l(kR)}{kRn_l'(kR) - \beta_l n_l(kR)}. \tag{7.6.35}$$

The problem of determining the phase shift is thus reduced to that of obtaining β_l.

We now look at the solution to the Schrödinger equation for $r < R$ —that is, inside the range of the potential. For a spherically symmetric potential, we can solve the Schrödinger equation in three dimensions by looking at the equivalent one-dimensional equation

$$\frac{d^2 u_l}{dr^2} + \left(k^2 - \frac{2m}{\hbar^2} V - \frac{l(l+1)}{r^2} \right) u_l = 0, \tag{7.6.36}$$

where

$$u_l = rA_l(r) \tag{7.6.37}$$

subject to the boundary condition

$$u_l\big|_{r=0} = 0. \tag{7.6.38}$$

We integrate this one-dimensional Schrödinger equation—if necessary, numerically—up to $r = R$, starting at $r = 0$. In this way we obtain the logarithmic derivative at R. By continuity we must be able to match the logarithmic derivative for the inside and outside solutions at $r = R$:

$$\beta_l\big|_{\text{inside solution}} = \beta_l\big|_{\text{outside solution}}, \tag{7.6.39}$$

where the left-hand side is obtained by integrating the Schrödinger equation up to $r = R$, while the right-hand side is expressible in terms of the phase shifts that characterize the large-distance behavior of the wave function. This means that the phase shifts are obtained simply by substituting β_l for the inside solution into $\tan \delta_l$ [(7.6.35)]. For an alternative approach it is possible to derive an integral equation for $A_l(r)$, from which we can obtain phase shifts (see Problem 8 of this chapter).

Hard-Sphere Scattering

Let us work out a specific example. We consider scattering by a hard, or rigid, sphere

$$V = \begin{cases} \infty & \text{for } r < R \\ 0 & \text{for } r > R. \end{cases} \tag{7.6.40}$$

In this problem we need not even evaluate β_l (which is actually ∞). All we need to know is that the wave function must vanish at $r = R$ because the

sphere is impenetrable. Therefore,

$$A_l(r)|_{r=R} = 0 \qquad (7.6.41)$$

or, from (7.6.33),

$$j_l(kR)\cos\delta_l - n_l(kR)\sin\delta_l = 0 \qquad (7.6.42)$$

or

$$\tan\delta_l = \frac{j_l(kR)}{n_l(kR)}. \qquad (7.6.43)$$

Thus the phase shifts are now known for any l. Notice that no approximations have been made so far.

To appreciate the physical significance of the phase shifts, let us consider the $l=0$ case (S-wave scattering) specifically. Equation (7.6.43) becomes, for $l=0$,

$$\tan\delta_0 = \frac{\sin kR/kR}{-\cos kR/kR} = -\tan kR, \qquad (7.6.44)$$

or $\delta_0 = -kR$. The radial-wave function (7.6.33) with $e^{i\delta_0}$ omitted varies as

$$A_{l=0}(r) \propto \frac{\sin kr}{kr}\cos\delta_0 + \frac{\cos kr}{kr}\sin\delta_0 = \frac{1}{kr}\sin(kr + \delta_0). \quad (7.6.45)$$

Therefore, if we plot $rA_{l=0}(r)$ as a function of distance r, we obtain a sinusoidal wave, which is shifted when compared to the free sinusoidal wave by amount R; see Figure 7.7.

FIGURE 7.7. Plot of $rA_{l=0}(r)$ versus r (with the $e^{i\delta_0}$ factor removed). The dashed curve for $V=0$ behaves like $\sin kr$, while the solid curve is for S-wave hard-sphere scattering, shifted by $R = -\delta_0/k$ from the case $V=0$.

Let us now study the low and high energy limits of $\tan \delta_l$. Low energy means kR small, $kR \ll 1$. We can then use (see Appendix A)

$$j_l(kr) \simeq \frac{(kr)^l}{(2l+1)!!}$$

$$n_l(kr) \simeq -\frac{(2l-1)!!}{(kr)^{l+1}}$$

(7.6.46)

to obtain

$$\tan \delta_l = \frac{-(kR)^{2l+1}}{\left\{ (2l+1) \left[(2l-1)!! \right]^2 \right\}}.$$

(7.6.47)

It is therefore all right to ignore δ_l with $l \neq 0$. In other words, we have S-wave scattering only, which is actually expected for almost any finite-range potential at low energy. Because $\delta_0 = -kR$ regardless of whether k is large or small, we obtain

$$\frac{d\sigma}{d\Omega} = \frac{\sin^2 \delta_0}{k^2} \simeq R^2 \quad \text{for } kR \ll 1.$$

(7.6.48)

It is interesting that the total cross section, given by

$$\sigma_{\text{tot}} = \int \frac{d\sigma}{d\Omega} \, d\Omega = 4\pi R^2,$$

(7.6.49)

is *four* times the *geometric cross section* πR^2. By geometric cross section we mean the area of the disc of radius R that blocks the propagation of the plane wave (and has the same cross section area as that of a hard sphere). Low-energy scattering, of course, means a very large wavelength scattering, and we do not necessarily expect a classically reasonable result.

One might conjecture that the geometric cross section is reasonable to expect for high-energy scattering because at high energies the situation might look similar to the semiclassical situation. At high energies many l-values contribute, up to $l_{\text{max}} \simeq kR$, a reasonable assumption. The total cross section is therefore given by

$$\sigma_{\text{tot}} = \frac{4\pi}{k^2} \sum_{l=0}^{l \simeq kR} (2l+1) \sin^2 \delta_l.$$

(7.6.50)

But using (7.6.43), we have

$$\sin^2 \delta_l = \frac{\tan^2 \delta_l}{1 + \tan^2 \delta_l} = \frac{[j_l(kR)]^2}{[j_l(kR)]^2 + [n_l(kR)]^2} \simeq \sin^2 \left(kR - \frac{\pi l}{2} \right),$$

(7.6.51)

where we have used

$$j_l(kr) \sim \frac{1}{kr}\sin\left(kr - \frac{l\pi}{2}\right)$$

$$n_l(kr) \sim -\frac{1}{kr}\cos\left(kr - \frac{l\pi}{2}\right).$$

(7.6.52)

We see that δ_l decreases by 90° each time l increases by one unit. Thus, for an adjacent pair of partial waves, $\sin^2\delta_l + \sin^2\delta_{l+1} = \sin^2\delta_l + \sin^2(\delta_l - \pi/2)$ $= \sin^2\delta_l + \cos^2\delta_l = 1$, and with so many l-values contributing to (7.6.50), it is legitimate to replace $\sin^2\delta_l$ by its average value, $\frac{1}{2}$. The number of terms in the l-sum is roughly kR, as is the average of $2l+1$. Putting all the ingredients together, (7.6.50) becomes

$$\sigma_{\text{tot}} = \frac{4\pi}{k^2}(kR)^2\frac{1}{2} = 2\pi R^2,$$

(7.6.53)

which is not the geometric cross section πR^2 either! To see the origin of the factor of 2, we may split (7.6.17) into two parts:

$$f(\theta) = \frac{i}{2ik}\sum_{l=0}^{kR}(2l+1)e^{2i\delta_l}P_l(\cos\theta) + \frac{i}{2k}\sum_{l=0}^{kR}(2l+1)P_l(\cos\theta)$$

$$= f_{\text{reflection}} + f_{\text{shadow}}.$$

(7.6.54)

In evaluating $\int|f_{\text{refl}}|^2\,d\Omega$, the orthogonality of the $P_l(\cos\theta)$'s ensures that there is no interference amongst contributions from different l, and we obtain the sum of the square of partial-wave contributions:

$$\int|f_{\text{refl}}|^2\,d\Omega = \frac{2\pi}{4k^2}\sum_{l=0}^{l_{\text{max}}}\int_{-1}^{+1}(2l+1)^2[P_l(\cos\theta)]^2\,d(\cos\theta)$$

$$= \frac{\pi l_{\text{max}}^2}{k^2} = \pi R^2.$$

(7.6.55)

Turning our attention to f_{shad}, we note that it is pure imaginary. It is particularly strong in the forward direction because $P_l(\cos\theta) = 1$ for $\theta = 0$, and the contributions from various l-values all add up coherently—that is, with the same phase, pure imaginary and positive in our case. We can use the small-angle approximation for P_l [see (7.6.24)] to obtain

$$f_{\text{shad}} \simeq \frac{i}{2k}\sum(2l+1)J_0(l\theta)$$

$$\simeq ik\int_0^R b\,db\,J_0(kb\theta)$$

$$= \frac{iRJ_1(kR\theta)}{\theta}$$

(7.6.56)

But this is just the formula for Fraunhofer diffraction in optics with a strong peaking near $\theta \simeq 0$. Letting $\xi = kR\theta$ and $d\xi/\xi = d\theta/\theta$, we can evaluate

$$\int |f_{shad}|^2 \, d\Omega = 2\pi \int_{-1}^{+1} \frac{R^2 [J_1(kR\theta)]^2}{\theta^2} \, d(\cos\theta)$$

$$\simeq 2\pi R^2 \int_0^\infty \frac{[J_1(\xi)]^2}{\xi} \, d\xi$$

$$\simeq \pi R^2. \tag{7.6.57}$$

Finally, the interference between f_{shad} and f_{refl} vanishes:

$$\mathrm{Re}\left(f_{shad}^* f_{refl} \right) \simeq 0 \tag{7.6.58}$$

because the phase of f_{refl} oscillates ($2\delta_{l+1} = 2\delta_l - \pi$), approximately averaging to zero, while f_{shad} is pure imaginary. Thus

$$\sigma_{tot} = \underset{\underset{\sigma_{refl}}{\uparrow}}{\pi R^2} + \underset{\underset{\sigma_{shad}}{\uparrow}}{\pi R^2}. \tag{7.6.59}$$

The second term (coherent contribution in the forward direction) is called a *shadow* because for hard-sphere scattering at high energies, waves with impact parameter less than R must be deflected. So, just *behind* the scatterer there must be zero probability for finding the particle and a shadow must be created. In terms of wave mechanics, this shadow is due to destructive interference between the original wave (which would be there even if the scatterer were absent) and the newly scattered wave. Thus we need scattering in order to create a shadow. That this shadow amplitude must be pure imaginary may be seen by recalling from (7.6.8) that the coefficient of $e^{ikr}/2ikr$ for the lth partial wave behaves like $1 + 2ikf_l(k)$, where the 1 would be present even without the scatterer; hence there must be a positive imaginary term in f_l to get cancellation. In fact, this gives a physical interpretation of the optical theorem, which can be checked explicitly. First note that

$$\frac{4\pi}{k} \mathrm{Im}\, f(0) \simeq \frac{4\pi}{k} \mathrm{Im}[f_{shad}(0)] \tag{7.6.60}$$

because $\mathrm{Im}[f_{refl}(0)]$ averages to zero due to oscillating phase. Using (7.6.54), we obtain

$$\frac{4\pi}{k} \mathrm{Im}\, f_{shad}(0) = \frac{4\pi}{k} \mathrm{Im}\left[\frac{i}{2k} \sum_{l=0}^{kR} (2l+1) P_l(1) \right] = 2\pi R^2 \tag{7.6.61}$$

which is indeed equal to σ_{tot}.

7.7. LOW-ENERGY SCATTERING AND BOUND STATES

At low energies—or, more precisely, when $\lambdabar = 1/k$ is comparable to or larger than the range R—partial waves for higher l are, in general, unimportant. This point may be obvious classically because the particle cannot penetrate the centrifugal barrier; as a result the potential inside has no effect. In terms of quantum mechanics, the effective potential for the lth partial wave is given by

$$V_{\text{eff}} = V(r) + \frac{\hbar^2}{2m} \frac{l(l+1)}{r^2};\qquad (7.7.1)$$

unless the potential is strong enough to accommodate $l \neq 0$ bound states near $E \simeq 0$, the behavior of the radial-wave function is largely determined by the centrifugal barrier term, which means that it must resemble $j_l(kr)$. More quantitatively, it is possible to estimate the behavior of the phase shift using the integral equation for the partial wave (see Problem 8 of this chapter):

$$\frac{e^{i\delta_l}\sin\delta_l}{k} = -\frac{2m}{\hbar^2}\int_0^\infty j_l(kr)V(r)A_l(r)r^2\,dr.\qquad (7.7.2)$$

If $A_l(r)$ is not too different from $j_l(kr)$ and $1/k$ is much larger than the range of the potential, the right-hand side would vary as k^{2l}; for small δ_l, the left-hand side must vary as δ_l/k. Hence, the phase shift k goes to zero as

$$\delta_l \sim k^{2l+1}\qquad (7.7.3)$$

for small k. This is known as **threshold behavior**.

It is therefore clear that at low energies with a finite range potential, S-wave scattering is important.

Rectangular Well or Barrier

To be specific let us consider S-wave scattering by

$$V = \begin{cases} V_0 = \text{constant} & \text{for } r < R \\ 0 & \text{otherwise} \end{cases} \quad \begin{cases} V_0 > 0 & \text{repulsive} \\ V_0 < 0 & \text{attractive} \end{cases}\qquad (7.7.4)$$

Many of the features we obtain here are common to more-complicated finite range potentials.

We have already seen that the outside-wave function [see (7.6.33) and (7.6.45)] must behave like

$$e^{i\delta_0}[j_0(kr)\cos\delta_0 - n_0(kr)\sin\delta_0] \simeq \frac{e^{i\delta_0}\sin(kr+\delta_0)}{kr}.\qquad (7.7.5)$$

The inside solution can also easily be obtained for V_0 a constant:

$$u \equiv rA_{l=0}(r) \propto \sin k'r,\qquad (7.7.6)$$

with k' determined by

$$E - V_0 = \frac{\hbar^2 k'^2}{2m},\qquad (7.7.7)$$

where we have used the boundary condition $u = 0$ at $r = 0$. In other words, the inside wave function is also sinusoidal as long as $E > V_0$. The curvature of the sinusoidal wave is different than in the free-particle case; as a result the wave function can be pushed in ($\delta_0 > 0$) or pulled out ($\delta_0 < 0$) depending on whether $V_0 < 0$ (attractive) or $V_0 > 0$ (repulsive), as shown in Figure 7.8. Notice also that (7.7.6) and (7.7.7) hold even if $V_0 > E$, provided we understand sin to mean sinh—that is, the wave function behaves like

$$u(r) \propto \sinh[\kappa r], \qquad (7.7.6')$$

where

$$\frac{\hbar^2 \kappa^2}{2m} = (V_0 - E). \qquad (7.7.7')$$

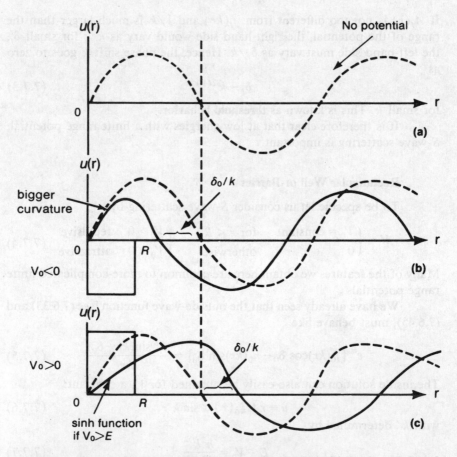

FIGURE 7.8 Plot of $u(r)$ versus r. (a) For $V = 0$ (dashed line). (b) For $V_0 < 0$, $\delta_0 > 0$ with the wave function (solid line) pushed in. (c) For $V_0 > 0$, $\delta_0 < 0$ with the wave function (solid line) pulled out.

We now concentrate on the attractive case and imagine that the magnitude of V_0 is increased. Increased attraction will result in a wave function with a larger curvature. Suppose the attraction is such that the interval $[0, R]$ just accommodates one-fourth cycle of the sinusoidal wave. Working in the low energy $kR \ll 1$ limit, the phase shift is now $\delta_0 = \pi/2$, and this results in a maximal S-wave cross section for a given k because $\sin^2 \delta_0$ is unity. Now increase the well depth V_0 even further. Eventually the attraction is so strong that one-half cycle of the sinusoidal wave can be fitted within the range of the potential. The phase shift δ_0 is now π; in other words, the wave function outside R is 180° out of phase compared to the free-particle-wave function. What is remarkable is that the partial cross section vanishes ($\sin^2 \delta_0 = 0$),

$$\sigma_{l=0} = 0,\tag{7.7.8}$$

despite the very strong attraction of the potential. In addition, if the energy is low enough for $l \neq 0$ waves still to be unimportant, we then have an almost-perfect transmission of the incident wave. This kind of situation, known as the **Ramsauer-Townsend effect**, is actually observed experimentally for scattering of electrons by such rare gases as argon, krypton, and xenon. This effect was first observed in 1923 prior to the birth of wave mechanics and was considered to be a great mystery. Note the typical parameters here are $R \sim 2 \times 10^{-8}$ cm for electron kinetic energy of order $0.1 \mathrm{eV}$, leading to $kR \sim 0.324$.

Zero-Energy Scattering and Bound States

Let us consider scattering at extremely low energies ($k \simeq 0$). For $r > R$ and for $l = 0$, the outside radial-wave function satisfies

$$\frac{d^2 u}{dr^2} = 0.\tag{7.7.9}$$

The obvious solution to (7.7.9) is

$$u(r) = \mathrm{constant}(r - a),\tag{7.7.10}$$

just a straight line! This can be understood as an infinitely long wavelength limit of the usual expression for the outside-wave function [see (7.6.37) and (7.6.45)],

$$\lim_{k \to 0} \sin(kr + \delta_0) = \lim_{k \to 0} \sin\left[k\left(r + \frac{\delta_0}{k}\right)\right],\tag{7.7.11}$$

which looks like (7.7.10). We have

$$\frac{u'}{u} = k \cot\left[k\left(r + \frac{\delta_0}{k}\right)\right] \xrightarrow{k \to 0} \frac{1}{r - a}.\tag{7.7.12}$$

Setting $r = 0$ [even though at $r = 0$, (7.7.10) is not the true wave function], we obtain

$$\lim_{k \to 0} k \cot \delta_0 \xrightarrow{k \to 0} -\frac{1}{a}.\tag{7.7.13}$$

The quantity a is known as the **scattering length**. The limit of the total cross section as $k \to 0$ is given by [see (7.6.16)]

$$\sigma_{tot} = \sigma_{l=0} = 4\pi \lim_{k \to 0} \left| \frac{1}{k \cot \delta_0 - ik} \right|^2 = 4\pi a^2. \qquad (7.7.14)$$

Even though a has the same dimension as the range of the potential R, a and R can differ by orders of magnitude. In particular, for an attractive potential, it is possible for the magnitude of the scattering length to be far greater than the range of the potential. To see the physical meaning of a, we note that a is nothing more than the intercept of the outside-wave function. For a repulsive potential, $a > 0$ and is roughly of order of R, as seen in Figure 7.9a. However, for an attractive potential, the intercept is on the negative side (Figure 7.9b). If we *increase* the attraction, the outside-wave function can again cross the r-axis on the positive side (Figure 7.9c).

The sign change resulting from increased attraction is related to the development of a bound state. To see this point quantitatively, we note from Figure 7.9c that for a very large and positive, the wave function is essentially flat for $r > R$. But (7.7.10) with a very large is not too different from $e^{-\kappa r}$ with κ essentially zero. Now $e^{-\kappa r}$ with $\kappa \simeq 0$ is just a bound-state-wave function for $r > R$ with energy E infinitesimally negative. The inside-wave function ($r < R$) for the $E = 0+$ case (scattering with zero kinetic energy) and the $E = 0-$ case (bound state with infinitesimally small binding energy) are essentially the same because in both cases k' in $\sin k'r$ [(7.7.6)] is determined by

$$\frac{\hbar^2 k'^2}{2m} = E - V_0 \simeq |V_0| \qquad (7.7.15)$$

with E infinitesimal (positive or negative).

Because the inside-wave functions are the same for the two physical situations ($E = 0+$ and $E = 0-$), we can equate the logarithmic derivative of the bound-state-wave function with that of the solution involving zero kinetic-energy scattering,

$$- \left. \frac{\kappa e^{-\kappa r}}{e^{-\kappa r}} \right|_{r=R} = \left. \left(\frac{1}{r-a} \right) \right|_{r=R}, \qquad (7.7.16)$$

or, if $R \ll a$,

$$\kappa \simeq \frac{1}{a}. \qquad (7.7.17)$$

The binding energy satisfies

$$E_{BE} = - E_{\text{bound state}} = \frac{\hbar^2 \kappa^2}{2m} \simeq \frac{\hbar^2}{2ma^2}, \qquad (7.7.18)$$

FIGURE 7.9. Plot of $u(r)$ versus r for (a) repulsive potential, (b) attractive potential, and (c) deeper attraction. The intercept a of the zero-energy outside-wave function with the r-axis is shown for each of three cases.

and we have a relation between scattering length and bound-state energy. This is a remarkable result. To wit, if there is a loosely bound state, we can infer its binding energy by performing scattering experiments near zero kinetic energy, provided a is measured to be large compared with the range R of the potential. This connection between the scattering length and the bound-state energy was first pointed out by Wigner, who attempted to apply (7.7.18) to np-scattering.

Experimentally, the $^3S_1$-state of the np-system has a bound state, that is, the deuteron with

$$E_{\mathrm{BE}} = 2.22 \text{ MeV}. \qquad (7.7.19)$$

The scattering length is measured to be

$$a_{\text{triplet}} = 5.4 \times 10^{-13} \text{ cm,} \tag{7.7.20}$$

leading to the binding-energy prediction

$$\frac{\hbar^2}{2\mu a^2} = \frac{\hbar^2}{m_N a^2} = m_N c^2 \left(\frac{\hbar}{m_N ca} \right)^2$$

$$= (938 \text{ MeV}) \left(\frac{2.1 \times 10^{-14} \text{ cm}}{5.4 \times 10^{-13} \text{ cm}} \right)^2 = 1.4 \text{ MeV} \tag{7.7.21}$$

where μ is the reduced mass approximated by $m_{n,p}/2$. The agreement between (7.7.19) and (7.7.21) is not too satisfactory. The discrepancy is due to the fact that the inside-wave functions are not exactly the same and that $a_{\text{triplet}} \gg R$ is not really such a good approximation for the deuteron. A better result can be obtained by keeping the next term in the expansion of $k \cot \delta$ as a function of k,

$$k \cot \delta_0 = -\frac{1}{a} + \frac{1}{2} r_0 k^2, \tag{7.7.22}$$

where r_0 is known as the effective range (see, for example, Preston 1962, 23).

Bound States as Poles of $S_l(k)$

We conclude this section by studying the analytic properties of the amplitude $S_l(k)$ for $l = 0$. Let us go back to (7.6.8) and (7.6.12), where the radial wave function for $l = 0$ at large distance was found to be proportional to

$$S_{l=0}(k) \frac{e^{ikr}}{r} - \frac{e^{-ikr}}{r}. \tag{7.7.23}$$

Compare this with the wave function for a bound state at large distance,

$$\frac{e^{-\kappa r}}{r}. \tag{7.7.24}$$

The existence of a bound state implies that a nontrivial solution to the Schrödinger equation with $E < 0$ exists only for a particular (discrete) value of κ. We may argue that $e^{-\kappa r}/r$ is like e^{ikr}/r, except that k is now purely imaginary. Apart from k being imaginary, the important difference between (7.7.23) and (7.7.24) is that in the bound-state case, $e^{-\kappa r}/r$ is present even without the analogue of the incident wave. Quite generally only the ratio of the coefficient of e^{ikr}/r to that of e^{-ikr}/r is of physical interest, and this is given by $S_l(k)$. In the bound-state case we can sustain the outgoing wave (with imaginary k) even without an incident wave. So the ratio is ∞, which means that $S_{l=0}(k)$, regarded as a function of a complex variable k, has a

FIGURE 7.10. The complex k-plane with bound-state pole at $k = +i\kappa$.

pole at $k = i\kappa$. Thus a bound state implies a pole (which can be shown to be a simple pole) on the positive imaginary axis of the complex k-plane; see Figure 7.10. For k real and positive, we have the region of physical scattering. Here we must require [compare with (7.6.14)]

$$S_{l=0} = e^{2i\delta_0} \tag{7.7.25}$$

with δ_0 real. Furthermore, as $k \to 0$, $k \cot \delta_0$ has a limiting value $-1/a$ [(7.7.13)], which is finite, so δ_0 must behave as follows:

$$\delta_0 \to 0, \pm \pi, \ldots. \tag{7.7.26}$$

Hence $S_{l=0} = e^{2i\delta_0} \to 1$ as $k \to 0$.

Now let us attempt to construct a simple function satisfying:

1. Pole at $k = i\kappa$ (existence of bound state).
2. $|S_{l=0}| = 1$ for $k > 0$ real (unitarity).   (7.7.27)
3. $S_{l=0} = 1$ at $k = 0$ (threshold behavior).

The simplext function that satisfies all three conditions of (7.7.27) is

$$S_{l=0}(k) = \frac{-k - i\kappa}{k - i\kappa}. \tag{7.7.28}$$

[*Editor's Note:* Equation (7.7.28) is chosen for simplicity rather than as a physically realistic example. For reasonable potentials (not hard spheres!) the phase shift vanishes as $k \to \infty$.]

An assumption implicit in choosing this form is that there is no other singularity that is important apart from the bound-state pole. We can then use (7.6.15) to obtain, for $f_{l=0}(k)$,

$$f_{l=0} = \frac{S_{l=0} - 1}{2ik} = \frac{1}{-\kappa - ik}. \tag{7.7.29}$$

Comparing this with (7.6.16),

$$f_{l=0} = \frac{1}{k \cot \delta_0 - ik}, \tag{7.7.30}$$

we see that

$$\lim_{k \to 0} k \cot \delta_0 = -\frac{1}{a} = -\kappa, \qquad (7.7.31)$$

precisely the relation between bound state and scattering length [(7.7.17)].

It thus appears that by exploiting unitarity and analyticity of $S_l(k)$ in the k-plane, we may obtain the kind of information that can be secured by solving the Schrödinger equation explicitly. This kind of technique can be very useful in problems where the details of the potential are not known.

7.8. RESONANCE SCATTERING

In atomic, nuclear, and particle physics, we often encounter a situation where the scattering cross section for a given partial wave exhibits a pronounced peak. This section is concerned with the dynamics of such a **resonance**.

We continue to consider a finite-ranged potential $V(r)$. The *effective* potential appropriate for the radial wave function of the *l*th partial wave is $V(r)$ plus the centrifugal barrier term as given by (7.7.1). Suppose $V(r)$ itself is attractive. Because the second term,

$$\frac{\hbar^2}{2m} \frac{l(l+1)}{r^2}$$

is repulsive, we have a situation where the effective potential has an attractive well followed by a repulsive barrier at larger distances, as shown in Figure 7.11.

Suppose the barrier were infinitely high. It would then be possible for particles to be trapped inside, which is another way of saying that we expect bound states, with energy $E > 0$. They are *genuine* bound states in the sense that they are eigenstates of the Hamiltonian with definite values of E. In other words, they are *stationary* states with infinite lifetime.

FIGURE 7.11. $V_{eff} = V(r) + (\hbar^2/2m)[l(l+1)/r^2]$ versus r. For $l \neq 0$ the barrier can be due to $(\hbar^2/2m)[l(l+1)/r^2]$; for $l = 0$ barrier must be due to V itself.

  In the more realistic case of a finite barrier, the particle can be trapped inside, but it cannot be trapped forever. Such a trapped state has a finite lifetime due to quantum-mechanical tunneling. In other words, a particle leaks through the barrier to the outside region. Let us call such a state **quasi-bound state** because it would be an honest bound state if the barrier were infinitely high.

  The corresponding scattering phase shift δ_l rises through the value $\pi/2$ as the incident energy rises through that of the quasi-bound state, and at the same time the corresponding partial-wave cross section passes through its maximum possible value $4\pi(2l + 1)/k^2$. [*Editor's Note:* Such a sharp rise in the phase shift is, in the time-dependent Schrödinger equation, associated with a delay of the emergence of the trapped particles, rather than an unphysical advance, as would be the case for a sharp decrease through $\pi/2$.]

  It is instructive to verify this point with explicit calculations for some known potential. The result of a numerical calculation shows that a resonance behavior is in fact possible for $l \neq 0$ with a spherical-well potential.

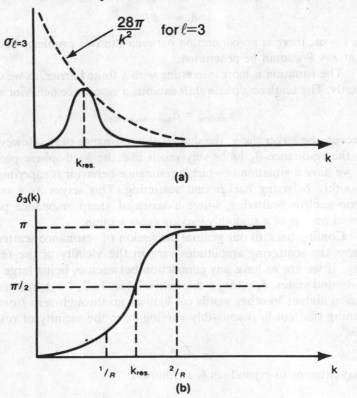

FIGURE 7.12. Plots of (a) $\sigma_{l=3}$ versus k, where at resonance $\delta_3(k_{res}) = \pi/2$ and $\sigma_{l=3} = (4\pi/k_{res}^2) \times 7 = 28\pi/k_{res}^2$ and (b) $\delta_3(k)$ versus k. The curves are for a spherical well with $2mV_0 R^2/\hbar^2 = 5.5$.

To be specific we show the results for a spherical well with $2mV_0R^2/\hbar^2 = 5.5$ and $l = 3$ in Figure 7.12. The phase shift (Figure 7.12b), which is small at extremely low energies, starts increasing rapidly past $k = 1/R$, and goes through $\pi/2$ around $k = 1.3/R$.

Another very instructive example is provided by a repulsive δ-shell potential that is exactly soluble (see Problem 9 in this chapter):

$$\frac{2m}{\hbar^2} V(r) = \gamma \delta(r - R). \tag{7.8.1}$$

Here resonances are possible for $l = 0$ because the δ-shell potential itself can trap the particle in the region $0 < r < R$. For the case $\gamma = \infty$, we expect a series of bound states in the region $r < R$ with

$$kR = \pi, 2\pi, \ldots; \tag{7.8.2}$$

this is because the radial wave function for $l = 0$ must vanish not only at $r = 0$ but also at $r = R-$ in this case. For the region $r > R$, we simply have hard-sphere scattering with the S-wave phase shift, given by

$$\delta_0 = -kR. \tag{7.8.3}$$

With $\gamma = \infty$, there is no connection between the two problems because the wall at $r = R$ cannot be penetrated.

The situation is more interesting with a finite barrier, as we can show explicitly. The scattering phase shift exhibits a resonance behavior whenever

$$E_{\text{incident}} \simeq E_{\text{quasi-bound state}}. \tag{7.8.4}$$

Moreover, the larger the γ, the sharper the resonance peak. However, away from the resonance δ_0 looks very much like the hard-sphere phase shift. Thus we have a situation in which a resonance behavior is superimposed on a smoothly behaving background scattering. This serves as a model for neutron-nucleus scattering, where a series of sharp resonance peaks are observed on top of a smoothly varying cross section.

Coming back to our general discussion of resonance scattering, we ask how the scattering amplitudes vary in the vicinity of the resonance energy. If we are to have any connection between σ_l being large and the quasi-bound states, δ_l *must go through* $\pi/2$ (*or* $3\pi/2, \ldots$) *from below*, as discussed above. In other words $\cot \delta_l$ must go through zero from above. Assuming that $\cot \delta_l$ is smoothly varying near the vicinity of resonance, that is,

$$E \simeq E_r, \tag{7.8.5}$$

we may attempt to expand $\cot \delta_l$ as follows:

$$\cot \delta_l = \underbrace{\cot \delta_l|_{E=E_r}}_{0} - c(E - E_r) + 0\left[(E - E_r)^2\right]. \tag{7.8.6}$$

This leads to

$$f_l(k) = \frac{1}{k \cot \delta_l - ik} = \frac{1}{k} \frac{1}{[-c(E - E_r) - i]}$$

$$= -\frac{\Gamma/2}{k\left[(E - E_r) + \frac{i\Gamma}{2}\right]}, \tag{7.8.7}$$

where we have defined the *width* Γ by

$$\frac{d(\cot \delta_l)}{dE}\bigg|_{E = E_r} = -c \equiv -\frac{2}{\Gamma} \tag{7.8.8}$$

Notice that Γ is very small if $\cot \delta_l$ varies rapidly. If a simple resonance dominates the lth partial-wave cross section, we obtain a one-level resonance formula (the Breit-Wigner formula):

$$\sigma_l = \frac{4\pi}{k^2} \frac{(2l + 1)(\Gamma/2)^2}{(E - E_r)^2 + \Gamma^2/4}. \tag{7.8.9}$$

So it is legitimate to regard Γ as the full width at half-maximum, provided the resonance is reasonably narrow so that variation in $1/k^2$ can be ignored.

7.9. IDENTICAL PARTICLES AND SCATTERING

As an example to illustrate the phase of the scattering amplitude, let us consider the scattering of two identical spinless charged particles via the Coulomb potential (which we discuss further in Section 7.13). The space-wave function must now be symmetric, so the asymptotic wave function must look like

$$e^{i\mathbf{k}\cdot\mathbf{x}} + e^{-i\mathbf{k}\cdot\mathbf{x}} + [f(\theta) + f(\pi - \theta)]\frac{e^{ikr}}{r}, \tag{7.9.1}$$

where $\mathbf{x} = \mathbf{x}_1 - \mathbf{x}_2$ is the relative position vector between the two particles 1 and 2. This results in a differential cross section,

$$\frac{d\sigma}{d\Omega} = |f(\theta) + f(\pi - \theta)|^2$$

$$= |f(\theta)|^2 + |f(\pi - \theta)|^2 + 2\text{Re}[f(\theta)f^*(\pi - \theta)]. \tag{7.9.2}$$

The cross section is enhanced through constructive interference at $\theta \simeq \pi/2$.

In contrast, for spin $\frac{1}{2}$ – spin $\frac{1}{2}$ scattering with unpolarized beam and V independent of spin, we have the spin-singlet scattering going with space-symmetrical function and the spin triplet going with space-antisymmetrical wave function (see Section 6.3). If the initial beam is unpolarized, we have the statistical contribution $\frac{1}{4}$ for spin singlet and $\frac{3}{4}$ for spin triplet; hence

$$\frac{d\sigma}{d\Omega} = \frac{1}{4}|f(\theta) + f(\pi - \theta)|^2 + \frac{3}{4}|f(\theta) - f(\pi - \theta)|^2$$

$$= |f(\theta)|^2 + |f(\pi - \theta)|^2 - \text{Re}[f(\theta)f^*(\pi - \theta)]. \qquad (7.9.3)$$

In other words, we expect destructive interference at $\theta \simeq \pi/2$. This has, in fact, been observed.

7.10. SYMMETRY CONSIDERATIONS IN SCATTERING

Suppose V and H_0 are both invariant under some symmetry operation. We may ask what this implies for the matrix element of T or for the scattering amplitude $f(\mathbf{k}', \mathbf{k})$.

If the symmetry operator is unitary (for example, rotation and parity), everything is quite straightforward. Using the explicit form of T as given by (7.2.20), we see that

$$UH_0U^\dagger = H_0, \qquad UVU^\dagger = V \qquad (7.10.1)$$

implies that T is also invariant under U—that is,

$$UTU^\dagger = T. \qquad (7.10.2)$$

We define

$$|\tilde{\mathbf{k}}\rangle \equiv U|\mathbf{k}\rangle, \qquad |\tilde{\mathbf{k}}'\rangle \equiv U|\mathbf{k}'\rangle. \qquad (7.10.3)$$

Then

$$\langle \tilde{\mathbf{k}}'|T|\tilde{\mathbf{k}}\rangle = \langle \mathbf{k}'|U^\dagger UTU^\dagger U|\mathbf{k}\rangle$$

$$= \langle \mathbf{k}'|T|\mathbf{k}\rangle. \qquad (7.10.4)$$

As an example, we consider the specific case where U stands for the parity operator

$$\pi|\mathbf{k}\rangle = |-\mathbf{k}\rangle, \qquad \pi|-\mathbf{k}\rangle = |\mathbf{k}\rangle. \qquad (7.10.5)$$

Thus invariance of H_0 and V under parity would mean

$$\langle -\mathbf{k}'|T|-\mathbf{k}\rangle = \langle \mathbf{k}'|T|\mathbf{k}\rangle. \qquad (7.10.6)$$

Pictorially, we have the situation illustrated in Figure 7.13a.

We exploited the consequence of angular-momentum conservation when we developed the method of partial waves. The fact that T is diagonal in the $|Elm\rangle$ representation is a direct consequence of T being invariant under rotation. Notice also that $\langle \mathbf{k}'|T|\mathbf{k}\rangle$ depends only on the relative orientation of $\mathbf{k}$ and $\mathbf{k}'$, as depicted in Figure 7.13b.

When the symmetry operation is antiunitary (as in time reversal), we must be more careful. First, we note that the requirement that V as well as

(a) **(b)**

FIGURE 7.13. (a) Equality of T matrix elements between $\mathbf{k} \to \mathbf{k}'$ and $-\mathbf{k} \to -\mathbf{k}'$. (b) Equality of T matrix elements under rotation.

H_0 be invariant under time reversal invariance requires that

$$\Theta T \Theta^{-1} = T^{\dagger}. \tag{7.10.7}$$

This is because the antiunitary operator changes

$$\frac{1}{E - H_0 + i\varepsilon} \quad \text{into} \quad \frac{1}{E - H_0 - i\varepsilon} \tag{7.10.8}$$

in (7.2.20). We also recall that for an antiunitary operator [see (4.4.11)],

$$\langle \beta | \alpha \rangle = \langle \tilde{\alpha} | \tilde{\beta} \rangle, \tag{7.10.9}$$

where

$$|\tilde{\alpha}\rangle \equiv \Theta |\alpha\rangle \quad \text{and} \quad |\tilde{\beta}\rangle \equiv \Theta |\beta\rangle. \tag{7.10.10}$$

Let us consider

$$|\alpha\rangle = T|\mathbf{k}\rangle, \qquad \langle \beta | = \langle \mathbf{k}'|; \tag{7.10.11}$$

then

$$|\tilde{\alpha}\rangle = \Theta T |\mathbf{k}\rangle = \Theta T \Theta^{-1} \Theta |\mathbf{k}\rangle = T^{\dagger} |-\mathbf{k}\rangle$$

$$|\tilde{\beta}\rangle = \Theta |\mathbf{k}\rangle = |-\mathbf{k}'\rangle. \tag{7.10.12}$$

As a result (7.10.9) becomes

$$\langle \mathbf{k}'|T|\mathbf{k}\rangle = \langle -\mathbf{k}|T|-\mathbf{k}'\rangle. \tag{7.10.13}$$

Notice that the initial and final momenta are interchanged, in addition to the fact that the directions of the momenta have been reversed.

It is also interesting to combine the requirements of time reversal [(7.10.13)] and parity [(7.10.6)]:

$$\langle \mathbf{k}'|T|\mathbf{k}\rangle \overset{\text{under } \Theta}{=} \langle -\mathbf{k}|T|-\mathbf{k}'\rangle \overset{\text{under } \pi}{=} \langle \mathbf{k}|T|\mathbf{k}'\rangle; \tag{7.10.14}$$

that is, from (7.2.19) and (7.2.22) we have

$$f(\mathbf{k}, \mathbf{k}') = f(\mathbf{k}', \mathbf{k}), \tag{7.10.15}$$

which results in

$$\frac{d\sigma}{d\Omega}(\mathbf{k} \rightarrow \mathbf{k}') = \frac{d\sigma}{d\Omega}(\mathbf{k}' \rightarrow \mathbf{k}). \tag{7.10.16}$$

Equation (7.10.16) is known as **detailed balance**.

It is more interesting to look at the analogue of (7.10.14) when we have spin. Here we may characterize the initial free-particle ket by $|\mathbf{k}, m_s\rangle$, and we exploit (4.4.79) for the time-reversal portion:

$$\langle \mathbf{k}', m'_s | T | \mathbf{k}, m_s \rangle = i^{-2m_s + 2m_{s'}} \langle -\mathbf{k}, -m_s | T | -\mathbf{k}', -m'_s \rangle$$

$$= i^{-2m_s + 2m_{s'}} \langle \mathbf{k}, -m_s | T | \mathbf{k}', -m'_s \rangle. \tag{7.10.17}$$

For unpolarized initial states, we sum over the initial spin states and divide by $(2s + 1)$; if the final polarization is not observed, we must sum over final states. We then obtain detailed balance in the form

$$\overline{\frac{d\sigma}{d\Omega}}(\mathbf{k} \rightarrow \mathbf{k}') = \overline{\frac{d\sigma}{d\Omega}}(\mathbf{k}' \rightarrow \mathbf{k}), \tag{7.10.18}$$

where we understand the bar on the top of $d\sigma/d\Omega$ in (7.10.18) to mean that we average over the initial spin states and sum over the final spin states.

7.11. TIME-DEPENDENT FORMULATION OF SCATTERING

Our discussion of scattering so far has been based on the time-independent formulation. It is also possible to develop a formalism of scattering based on the time-dependent Schrödinger equation. We show that this formalism leads to the same Lippmann-Schwinger equation, (7.1.6).

In the time-dependent formulation we conceive of a scattering process as a change in the state ket from a free-particle ket to a state ket influenced by the presence of the potential V. The basic equation of motion is

$$\left(i\hbar \frac{\partial}{\partial t} - H_0 \right) |\psi; t\rangle = V|\psi; t\rangle, \tag{7.11.1}$$

where $|\psi; t\rangle$ is the time-dependent Schrödinger ket in the presence of V. The boundary condition appropriate for the scattering problem is that in the remote past $(t \rightarrow -\infty)$, the particle was free. This requirement is automatically accomplished if we turn on the potential adiabatically—that is, very slowly—as in Section 5.8:

$$V \rightarrow \lim_{\eta \to 0} V e^{\eta t}. \tag{7.11.2}$$

Just as the partial differential equation with an inhomogeneous term is solved by introducing a Green's function [see (7.1.18)], the operator

Schrödinger equation (7.11.1) is solved by introducing the Green's operator $G_+(t, t')$ satisfying

$$\left(i\hbar \frac{\partial}{\partial t} - H_0\right) G_+(t, t') = \delta(t - t'). \tag{7.11.3}$$

The *causality* requirement we impose on G_+ is that the interaction of a particle at t' has an effect only for $t > t'$. We therefore impose the *retarded* boundary condition

$$G_+(t, t') = 0 \quad \text{for } t < t'. \tag{7.11.4}$$

We claim that the solution to (7.11.3) and (7.11.4) is

$$G_+(t, t') = -\frac{i}{\hbar}\theta(t - t')e^{-iH_0(t-t')/\hbar}. \tag{7.11.5}$$

For $t > t'$, a constant times $e^{-iH_0(t-t')/\hbar}$ clearly satisfies the differential equation (7.11.3) because the δ-function on the right-hand side is inoperative. For $t < t'$, we obviously have the desired condition (7.11.4) because $G_+(t,t')$ here is identically zero. At $t = t'$, we note that there is an extra contribution due to the discontinuity of the θ-function that just balances the right-hand side of (7.11.3):

$$i\hbar \frac{\partial}{\partial t}\left[-\frac{i}{\hbar}\theta(t - t')\right] = \delta(t - t'). \tag{7.11.6}$$

The solution to the full problem can now be written as follows:

$$|\psi^{(+)}; t\rangle = |\phi; t\rangle + \int_{-\infty}^{+\infty} G_+(t, t')V|\psi^{(+)}; t'\rangle \, dt', \tag{7.11.7}$$

where

$$\left(i\hbar\frac{\partial}{\partial t} - H_0\right)|\phi; t\rangle = 0 \tag{7.11.8}$$

and the upper limit of the integration in (7.11.7) may as well be t because G_+ vanishes for $t' > t$. As $t \to -\infty$, $|\psi^{(+)}; t\rangle$ coincides with $|\phi; t\rangle$ just as required; this is because $G_+(t, t')$ vanishes as $t \to -\infty$ for any finite value of t'. To see that (7.11.7) satisfies the t-dependent Schrödinger equation (7.11.1), we merely apply the operator $[i\hbar(\partial/\partial t) - H_0]$ to $|\psi^{(+)}; t\rangle$. The $|\phi; t\rangle$ ket makes no contribution; as for its effect on the second term, $[i\hbar(\partial/\partial t) - H_0]$ acting on G_+ just gives $\delta(t - t')$, by means of which the integration is immediately evaluated to be $V|\psi^{(+)}; t\rangle$.

So far we have not even required $|\psi^{(+)}; t\rangle$ to be an energy eigenket. If it is, we can separate the time dependence as usual:

$$|\phi; t\rangle = |\phi\rangle e^{-iEt/\hbar} \tag{7.11.9}$$
$$|\psi; t\rangle = |\psi\rangle e^{-iEt/\hbar}.$$

Here there is the implicit assumption that E does not change if V is switched on adiabatically according to (7.11.2). Equations (7.11.5) and (7.11.7), evaluated at $t = 0$, now yield

$$|\psi^{(+)}\rangle = |\phi\rangle - \frac{i}{\hbar} \int_{-\infty}^{0} dt' e^{iH_0t'/\hbar} e^{-iEt'/\hbar} V |\psi^{(+)}\rangle. \qquad (7.11.10)$$

The integral may appear to oscillate indefinitely. However, we recall that V is really to be understood as $V e^{\eta t}$. As a result, the time integration is straightforward:

$$|\psi^{(+)}\rangle = |\phi\rangle - \frac{i}{\hbar} \lim_{t'' \to -\infty} \int_{t''}^{0} dt' e^{i(H_0 - E - i\eta\hbar)t'/\hbar} V |\psi^{(+)}\rangle$$

$$= |\phi\rangle - \frac{1}{H_0 - E - i\eta\hbar} \left[1 - \lim_{t'' \to -\infty} e^{[i(H_0 - E)/\hbar + \eta]t''} \right] V |\psi^{(+)}\rangle.$$

$$(7.11.11)$$

But as $t'' \to -\infty$, this is just the Lippmann-Schwinger equation (7.1.6).

The reader should note carefully how the $i\varepsilon$ prescription appears in the two formalisms. Earlier, using the time-independent formalism we saw that the choice of positive sign of the $i\varepsilon$-term (see Section 7.1) corresponds to the statement that the scatterer affects only outgoing spherical waves. In the t-dependent formulation presented here, the presence of $i\varepsilon$ ($\varepsilon = \eta\hbar$) in (7.11.11) arises from the requirement that the particle was free in the remote past.

One may argue that the slow switch-on of the potential (7.11.2) on which we have relied is somewhat artificial. But let us suppose that we are using a wave-packet formalism to describe scattering. When the wave packet is well outside the range of the potential, it does not matter whether the potential is zero or finite. In particular, V may be zero in the remote past, which then leads to no difficulty.

Connection With Time-Dependent Perturbation Theory

Inasmuch as scattering can be discussed using the time-dependent formulation, which is based on the time-dependent Schrödinger equation (7.11.1), we should be able to apply an approximation scheme based on (7.11.1). In particular we should be able to deploy the methods of time-dependent perturbation theory developed earlier in Section 5.6 to the scattering problem—provided, of course, the potential can be regarded as weak in some sense.

First we will show how the golden rule can be applied to compute $d\sigma/d\Omega$, leading to the results of the Born approximation of Section 7.2.

We assume in the remote past that the state ket is represented by a momentum eigenket $|k\rangle$. When the interaction is slowly switched on, as in (7.11.2), momentum eigenkets other than $|k\rangle$—for example, $|k'\rangle$—are populated. As we have seen (see Section 5.6), the transition probability is (to first order) evaluated in the following manner. First we write

$$\langle \mathbf{k}'|U_I^{(1)}(t,-\infty)|\mathbf{k}\rangle = -\frac{i}{\hbar}\int_{-\infty}^t \langle \mathbf{k}'|V_I(t')|\mathbf{k}\rangle \, dt', \quad (7.11.12)$$

where $V_I(t') = e^{iH_0 t'/\hbar} V e^{-iH_0 t'/\hbar} e^{\eta t'}$ and $E_k = \hbar^2 k^2/2m$. The transition probability of finding $|\mathbf{k}'\rangle$ at time t is then

$$|\langle \mathbf{k}'|U_I^{(1)}(t,-\infty)|\mathbf{k}\rangle|^2 = \frac{|\langle \mathbf{k}'|V|\mathbf{k}\rangle|^2}{\hbar^2} \frac{e^{2\eta t}}{\left[(E_k - E_{k'})^2/\hbar^2 + \eta^2\right]}.$$

$$(7.11.13)$$

As $\eta \to 0$ (t finite), the transition rate is just what we expect from the golden rule:

$$\frac{d}{dt}|\langle \mathbf{k}'|U_I^{(1)}(t,-\infty)|\mathbf{k}\rangle|^2 = \frac{2\pi}{\hbar}|\langle \mathbf{k}'|V|\mathbf{k}\rangle|^2 \delta(E_k - E_{k'}), \quad (7.11.14)$$

where we have used (5.8.5). Note that the right-hand side of .(7.11.14) is independent of t.

It is important here to review the normalization conventions used for plane-wave states. In Section 1.7 we used the δ-function normalization

$$\langle \mathbf{k}'|\mathbf{k}\rangle = \delta^{(3)}(\mathbf{k}-\mathbf{k}'). \quad (7.11.15)$$

The completeness relation is then written as

$$1 = \int d^3k \, |\mathbf{k}\rangle\langle\mathbf{k}|. \quad (7.11.16)$$

In applying t-dependent perturbation theory to scattering processes, it is more helpful to use box normalization,

$$\langle \mathbf{k}'|\mathbf{k}\rangle = \delta_{\mathbf{k}',\mathbf{k}}, \quad (7.11.17)$$

where the allowed values for $\mathbf{k}$ are given by

$$k_{x,y,z} = \frac{2\pi n_{x,y,z}}{L}. \quad (7.11.18)$$

The wave function is given by

$$\langle \mathbf{x}|\mathbf{k}\rangle = \frac{1}{L^{3/2}} e^{i\mathbf{k}\cdot\mathbf{x}} \quad (7.11.19)$$

instead of $[1/(2\pi)^{3/2}]e^{i\mathbf{k}\cdot\mathbf{x}}$. The completeness relation is

$$1 = \sum_{\mathbf{k}} |\mathbf{k}\rangle\langle\mathbf{k}|, \quad (7.11.20)$$

but for a very large box we might as well treat the variables $k_{x,y,z}$ as continuous, so

$$1 = \left(\frac{L}{2\pi}\right)^3 \int d^3k |\mathbf{k}\rangle\langle\mathbf{k}|. \tag{7.11.21}$$

This looks like (7.11.16) except for the presence of $(L/2\pi)^3$. A very useful relation that enables us to go from the δ-function normalization convention to that of box normalization is

$$(2\pi)^3 \underset{\substack{\delta - fn \\ \text{normalization}}}{\langle\mathbf{k}'|V|\mathbf{k}\rangle} = L^3 \underset{\substack{\text{box} \\ \text{normalization}}}{\langle\mathbf{k}'|V|\mathbf{k}\rangle} \tag{7.11.22}$$

as the reader may easily verify by inserting a complete set of states in the position representation.

The box normalization is very convenient for evaluating the density of states. For this reason it is used more often in a treatment of scattering based on time-dependent perturbation theory. Thus if we are interested in scattering into the solid angle $d\Omega$, the relevant formula is

$$n^2 \, dn \, d\Omega = \left(\frac{L}{2\pi}\right)^3 \frac{km}{\hbar^2} dE \, d\Omega \tag{7.11.23}$$

[see (5.7.31)].

Coming back to scattering, which we view as a transition rate w from $|\mathbf{k}\rangle$ into a group of states $|\mathbf{k}'\rangle$ subtending the solid-angle element $d\Omega$, we have w given by (for elastic scattering $k' = k$)

$$w = \frac{2\pi}{\hbar} |\langle\mathbf{k}'|V|\mathbf{k}\rangle|^2 \left(\frac{L}{2\pi}\right)^3 \frac{km}{\hbar^2} d\Omega \tag{7.11.24}$$

from the golden rule (5.6.34) and (7.11.14). This must be equated to

$$(\text{Incident flux}) \times \frac{d\sigma}{d\Omega} d\Omega. \tag{7.11.25}$$

As for the incident flux, we obtain [from $\mathbf{j} = (\hbar/m)\text{Im}(\psi^* \nabla \psi)$]

$$|\mathbf{j}| = \frac{\hbar}{m} \left| \text{Im}\left(\frac{e^{-i\mathbf{k}\cdot\mathbf{x}}}{L^{3/2}} \nabla \frac{e^{i\mathbf{k}\cdot\mathbf{x}}}{L^{3/2}} \right) \right| = \frac{\hbar k}{mL^3}. \tag{7.11.26}$$

Alternatively, incident flux = velocity/volume = $\hbar k/mL^3$. Putting everything together

$$\frac{d\sigma}{d\Omega} = \left(\frac{mL^3}{\hbar k}\right)\left(\frac{2\pi}{\hbar}\right)\left(\frac{L}{2\pi}\right)^3\left(\frac{km}{\hbar^2}\right)\left|\frac{1}{L^3}\int d^3x \, V(\mathbf{x}) e^{i(\mathbf{k}-\mathbf{k}')\cdot\mathbf{x}}\right|^2$$

$$= \left|\frac{1}{4\pi}\frac{2m}{\hbar^2}\int d^3x \, V(\mathbf{x}) e^{i(\mathbf{k}-\mathbf{k}')\cdot\mathbf{x}}\right|^2. \tag{7.11.27}$$

But this is precisely the result of the first-order Born approximation [(7.2.22)]. Higher-order Born terms can be obtained in a similar manner.

To sum up, the time-dependent formulation based on the time-dependent Schrödinger equation [(7.11.1)] enables us to derive easily the results we obtained earlier using the time-independent formalism—the Lippmann-Schwinger equation, the Born approximation, and so on. Furthermore, it turns out that the time-dependent formalism is more suitable for discussing more-general reaction processes other than elastic scattering. As a concrete example to illustrate this point, we now turn to a discussion of the inelastic scattering of electrons by atoms.

7.12. INELASTIC ELECTRON-ATOM SCATTERING

Let us consider the interactions of electron beams with atoms assumed to be in their ground states. The incident electron may get scattered elastically with final atoms unexcited:

$$e^- + \text{atom (ground state)} \to e^- + \text{atom (ground state)}. \quad (7.12.1)$$

This is an example of *elastic scattering*. To the extent that the atom can be regarded as infinitely heavy, the kinetic energy of the electron does not change. It is also possible for the target atom to get excited:

$$e^- + \text{atom (ground state)} \to e^- + \text{atom (excited state)}. \quad (7.12.2)$$

In this case we talk about **inelastic scattering** because the kinetic energy of the final outgoing electron is now less than that of the initial incoming electron, the difference being used to excite the target atom.

The initial ket of the electron plus the atomic system is written as

$$|\mathbf{k}, 0\rangle \quad (7.12.3)$$

where $\mathbf{k}$ refers to the wave vector of the incident electron and 0 stands for the atomic ground state. Strictly speaking (7.12.3) should be understood as the direct product of the incident electron ket $|\mathbf{k}\rangle$ and the ground-state atomic ket $|0\rangle$. The corresponding wave function is

$$\frac{1}{L^{3/2}} e^{i\mathbf{k} \cdot \mathbf{x}} \psi_0(\mathbf{x}_1, \mathbf{x}_2, \dots, \mathbf{x}_z) \quad (7.12.4)$$

where we use the box normalization for the plane wave.

We may be interested in a final-state electron with a definite wave vector $\mathbf{k}'$. The final-state ket and the corresponding wave function are

$$|\mathbf{k}', n\rangle \quad \text{and} \quad \frac{1}{L^{3/2}} e^{i\mathbf{k}' \cdot \mathbf{x}} \psi_n(\mathbf{x}_1, \dots, \mathbf{x}_z), \quad (7.12.5)$$

where $n = 0$ for elastic scattering and $n \neq 0$ for inelastic scattering.

Assuming that time-dependent perturbation theory is applicable, we can immediately write the differential cross section, as in the previous section:

$$\frac{d\sigma}{d\Omega}(0 \to n) = \frac{1}{(\hbar k/m_e L^3)} \frac{2\pi}{\hbar} |\langle \mathbf{k}'n|V|\mathbf{k}0\rangle|^2 \left(\frac{L}{2\pi}\right)^3 \left(\frac{k'm_e}{\hbar^2}\right)$$

$$= \left(\frac{k'}{k}\right) L^6 \left|\frac{1}{4\pi} \frac{2m_e}{\hbar^2} \langle \mathbf{k}', n|V|\mathbf{k},0\rangle\right|^2. \qquad (7.12.6)$$

Everything is similar, including the cancellation of terms such as L^3, with one important exception: $k' \equiv |\mathbf{k}'|$ is not, in general, equal to $k \equiv |\mathbf{k}|$ for inelastic scattering.

The next question is, What V is appropriate for this problem? The incident electron can interact with the nucleus, assumed to be situated at the origin; it can also interact with each of the atomic electrons. So V is to be written as

$$V = -\frac{Ze^2}{r} + \sum_i \frac{e^2}{|\mathbf{x} - \mathbf{x}_i|}. \qquad (7.12.7)$$

Here complications may arise because of the identity of the incident electron with one of the atomic electrons; to treat this rigorously is a nontrivial task. Fortunately, for a relatively fast electron we can legitimately ignore the question of identity; this is because there is little overlap between the bound-state electron and the incident electron in *momentum* space. We must evaluate the matrix element $\langle \mathbf{k}'n|V|\mathbf{k}0\rangle$, which, when explicitly written, is

$$\langle \mathbf{k}'n|V|\mathbf{k}0\rangle = \frac{1}{L^3} \int d^3x e^{i\mathbf{q}\cdot\mathbf{x}} \langle n| - \frac{Ze^2}{r} + \sum_i \frac{e^2}{|\mathbf{x} - \mathbf{x}_i|} |0\rangle$$

$$= \frac{1}{L^3} \int d^3x e^{i\mathbf{q}\cdot\mathbf{x}} \prod_i^z \int d^3x_i \, \psi_n^*(\mathbf{x}_1, \dots, \mathbf{x}_z) \left[-\frac{Ze^2}{r} + \sum_i \frac{e^2}{|\mathbf{x} - \mathbf{x}_i|} \right]$$

$$\times \psi_0(\mathbf{x}_1, \dots, \mathbf{x}_z) \qquad (7.12.8)$$

with $\mathbf{q} \equiv \mathbf{k} - \mathbf{k}'$.

Let us see how to evaluate the matrix element of the first term, $-Ze^2/r$, where r actually means $|\mathbf{x}|$. First we note that this is a potential between the incident electron and the nucleus, which is independent of the atomic electron coordinates. So it can be taken outside the integration

$$\prod_i^z \int d^3x_i$$

in (7.12.8); we simply obtain

$$\langle n|0\rangle = \delta_{n0} \qquad (7.12.9)$$

for the remainder. In other words, this term contributes only to the elastic-scattering case, where the target atom remains unexcited. In the elastic case we must still integrate $e^{i\mathbf{q}\cdot\mathbf{x}}/r$ with respect to $\mathbf{x}$, which amounts to taking the Fourier transform of the Coulomb potential; this can readily be done because we already evaluated in Section 7.2 the Fourier transform of the Yukawa potential [see (7.2.6) in conjunction with (7.2.2)]. Hence

$$\int d^3x \frac{e^{i\mathbf{q}\cdot\mathbf{x}}}{r} = \lim_{\mu \to 0} \int \frac{d^3x e^{i\mathbf{q}\cdot\mathbf{x}-\mu r}}{r} = \frac{4\pi}{q^2}. \tag{7.12.10}$$

As for the second term in (7.12.8), we can evaluate the Fourier transform of $1/|\mathbf{x}-\mathbf{x}_i|$. We can accomplish this by shifting the coordinate variables $\mathbf{x} \to \mathbf{x}+\mathbf{x}_i$:

$$\sum_i \int \frac{d^3x e^{i\mathbf{q}\cdot\mathbf{x}}}{|\mathbf{x}-\mathbf{x}_i|} = \sum_i \int \frac{d^3x e^{i\mathbf{q}\cdot(\mathbf{x}+\mathbf{x}_i)}}{|\mathbf{x}|} = \frac{4\pi}{q^2} \sum_i e^{i\mathbf{q}\cdot\mathbf{x}_i}. \tag{7.12.11}$$

Notice that this is just the Fourier transform of the Coulomb potential multiplied by the Fourier transform of the electron density due to the atomic electrons situated at $\mathbf{x}_i$:

$$\rho_{\text{atom}}(\mathbf{x}) = \sum_i \delta^{(3)}(\mathbf{x}-\mathbf{x}_i). \tag{7.12.12}$$

We customarily define the **form factor** $F_n(\mathbf{q})$ for excitation $|0\rangle$ to $|n\rangle$ as follows:

$$ZF_n(\mathbf{q}) \equiv \langle n | \sum_i e^{i\mathbf{q}\cdot\mathbf{x}_i} | 0 \rangle, \tag{7.12.13}$$

which is made of coherent—in the sense of definite phase relationships—contributions from the various electrons. Notice that as $q \to 0$, we have

$$\frac{1}{Z} \langle n | \sum_i e^{i\mathbf{q}\cdot\mathbf{x}_i} | 0 \rangle \to 1$$

for $n = 0$; hence the form factor approaches unity in the elastic-scattering case. For $n \neq 0$ (inelastic scattering), $F_n(\mathbf{q}) \to 0$ as $\mathbf{q} \to 0$ by orthogonality between $|n\rangle$ and $|0\rangle$. We can then write the matrix element in (7.12.8) as

$$\int d^3x e^{i\mathbf{q}\cdot\mathbf{x}} \langle n | \left(-\frac{Ze^2}{r} + \sum_i \frac{e^2}{|\mathbf{x}-\mathbf{x}_i|} \right) | 0 \rangle = \frac{4\pi Ze^2}{q^2} [-\delta_{n0} + F_n(\mathbf{q})]$$

$$\tag{7.12.14}$$

We are finally in a position to write the differential cross section for inelastic (or elastic) scattering of electrons by atoms:

$$\frac{d\sigma}{d\Omega} (0 \to n) = \left(\frac{k'}{k}\right) \left| \frac{1}{4\pi} \frac{2m_e}{\hbar^2} \frac{4\pi Ze^2}{q^2} [-\delta_{n0} + F_n(\mathbf{q})] \right|^2$$

$$= \frac{4m_e^2}{\hbar^4} \frac{(Ze^2)^2}{q^4} \left(\frac{k'}{k}\right) |-\delta_{n0} + F_n(\mathbf{q})|^2. \tag{7.12.15}$$

For inelastic scattering the δ_{n0}-term does not contribute, and it is customary to write the differential cross section in terms of the Bohr radius,

$$a_0 = \frac{\hbar^2}{e^2 m_e}, \tag{7.12.16}$$

as follows:

$$\frac{d\sigma}{d\Omega}(0 \to n) = 4Z^2 a_0^2 \left(\frac{k'}{k}\right) \frac{1}{(qa_0)^4} |F_n(\mathbf{q})|^2. \tag{7.12.17}$$

Quite often $d\sigma/dq$ is used in place of $d\sigma/d\Omega$; using

$$q^2 = |\mathbf{k} - \mathbf{k}'|^2 = k^2 + k'^2 - 2kk'\cos\theta \tag{7.12.18}$$

and $dq = -d(\cos\theta)kk'/q$, we can write

$$\frac{d\sigma}{dq} = \frac{2\pi q}{kk'} \frac{d\sigma}{d\Omega}. \tag{7.12.19}$$

The inelastic cross section we have obtained can be used to discuss *stopping power* — the energy loss of a charged particle as it goes through matter. A number of people, including H. A. Bethe and F. Bloch, have discussed the quantum-mechanical derivation of stopping power from the point of view of the inelastic-scattering cross section. We are interested in the energy loss of a charged particle per unit length traversed by the incident charged particle. The collision rate per unit length is $N\sigma$, where N is the number of atoms per unit volume; at each collision process the energy lost by the charged particle is $E_n - E_0$. So dE/dx is written as

$$\frac{dE}{dx} = N \sum_n (E_n - E_0) \int \frac{d\sigma}{dq}(0 \to n) \, dq$$

$$= N \sum_n (E_n - E_0) \frac{4Z^2}{a_0^2} \int_{q_{min}}^{q_{max}} \frac{k'}{k} \frac{1}{q^4} \frac{2\pi q}{kk'} |F_n(\mathbf{q})|^2 \, dq$$

$$= \frac{8\pi N}{k^2 a_0^2} \sum_n (E_n - E_0) \int_{q_{min}}^{q_{max}} \left| \langle n | \sum_{i=1}^{z} e^{i\mathbf{q}\cdot\mathbf{x}_i} | 0 \rangle \right|^2 \frac{dq}{q^3}. \tag{7.12.20}$$

There are many papers written on how to evaluate the sum in (7.12.20).* The upshot of all this is to justify quantum mechanically Bohr's 1913 formula for stopping power,

$$\frac{dE}{dx} = \frac{4\pi N Z e^4}{m_e v^2} \ln\left(\frac{2m_e v^2}{I}\right), \tag{7.12.21}$$

where I is a semiempirical parameter related to the average excitation

---

*For a relatively elementary discussion, see K. Gottfried (1966) and H. A. Bethe and R. W. Jackiw (1968).

energy $\langle E_n - E_0 \rangle$. If the charged particle has electric charge $\pm ze$, we just replace Ze^4 by $z^2 Ze^4$. It is also important to note that even if the projectile is not an electron, the m_e that appears in (7.12.21) is still the electron mass, not the mass of the charged particle. So the energy loss is dependent on the charge and the velocity of the projectile but is independent of the mass of the projectile. This has an important application to the detection of charged particles.

Quantum mechanically, we view the energy loss of a charged particle as a series of inelastic-scattering processes. At each interaction between the charged particle and an atom, we may imagine that a "measurement" of the position of the charged particle is made. We may wonder why particle tracks in such media as cloud chambers and nuclear emulsions are nearly straight. The reason is that the differential cross section (7.12.17) is sharply peaked at small q; in an overwhelming number of collisions, the final direction of momentum is nearly the same as the incident electron due to the rapid falloff of q^{-4} and $F_n(\mathbf{q})$ for large q.

Nuclear Form Factor

The excitation of atoms due to inelastic scattering is important for $q \sim 10^9$ cm^{-1} to 10^{10} cm^{-1}. If q is too large, the contributions due to $F_0(\mathbf{q})$ or $F_n(\mathbf{q})$ drop off very rapidly. At extremely high q, where q is now of order $1/R_{\text{nucleus}} \sim 10^{12}$ cm^{-1}, the structure of the nucleus becomes important. The Coulomb potential due to the point nucleus must now be replaced by a Coulomb potential due to an extended object,

$$-\frac{Ze^2}{r} \rightarrow -Ze^2 \int \frac{d^3x' N(r')}{|\mathbf{x} - \mathbf{x}'|}, \qquad (7.12.22)$$

where $N(r)$ is a nuclear charge distribution, normalized so that

$$\int d^3x' N(r') = 1. \qquad (7.12.23)$$

The pointlike nucleus can now be regarded as a special case, with

$$N(r') = \delta^{(3)}(r'). \qquad (7.12.24)$$

We can evaluate the Fourier transform of the right-hand side of (7.12.22) in analogy with (7.12.10) as follows:

$$Ze^2 \int d^3x \int \frac{d^3x' e^{i\mathbf{q}\cdot\mathbf{x}} N(r')}{|\mathbf{x} - \mathbf{x}'|} = Ze^2 \int d^3x' e^{i\mathbf{q}\cdot\mathbf{x}'} N(r') \int \frac{d^3x e^{i\mathbf{q}\cdot\mathbf{x}}}{r}$$

$$= Ze^2 \frac{4\pi}{q^2} F_{\text{nucleus}}(\mathbf{q}) \qquad (7.12.25)$$

where we have shifted the coordinates $\mathbf{x} \to \mathbf{x} + \mathbf{x}'$ in the first step and

$$F_{\text{nucleus}} \equiv \int d^3 x e^{i\mathbf{q} \cdot \mathbf{x}} N(r). \tag{7.12.26}$$

We thus obtain the deviation from the Rutherford formula due to the finite size of the nucleus,

$$\frac{d\sigma}{d\Omega} = \left(\frac{d\sigma}{d\Omega} \right)_{\text{Rutherford}} |F(\mathbf{q})|^2, \tag{7.12.27}$$

where $(d\sigma/d\Omega)_{\text{Rutherford}}$ is the differential cross section for the electric scattering of electrons by a pointlike nucleus of charge $Z|e|$. For small q we have

$$F_{\text{nucleus}}(\mathbf{q}) = \int d^3 x \left(1 + i\mathbf{q} \cdot \mathbf{x} - \frac{1}{2} q^2 r^2 (\hat{\mathbf{q}} \cdot \hat{\mathbf{r}})^2 + \cdots \right) N(r)$$

$$= 1 - \frac{1}{6} q^2 \langle r^2 \rangle_{\text{nucleus}} + \cdots. \tag{7.12.28}$$

The $\mathbf{q} \cdot \mathbf{x}$-term vanishes because of spherical symmetry, and in the q^2-term we have used the fact that the angular average of $\cos^2 \theta$ (where θ is the angle between $\hat{\mathbf{q}}$ and $\hat{\mathbf{r}}$) is just $\frac{1}{3}$:

$$\frac{1}{2} \int_{-1}^{+1} d(\cos \theta) \cos^2 \theta = \frac{1}{3}. \tag{7.12.29}$$

The quantity $\langle r^2 \rangle_{\text{nucleus}}$ is known as the mean square radius of the nucleus. In this way it is possible to "measure" the size of the nucleus and also of the proton, as done by R. Hofstadter and coworkers. In the proton case the spin (magnetic moment) effect is also important.

7.13. COULOMB SCATTERING

This last section was not written even in preliminary form by Professor Sakurai, but it was listed as an item he would like to consider for *Modern Quantum Mechanics*. Professor Thomas Fulton of The Johns Hopkins University graciously offered to contribute his own lecture notes on Coulomb scattering for this section in honor of Professor Sakurai's memory. The editor deeply appreciates this gesture of friendship. However, the reader needs to be alerted that there could be stylistic and even notational changes here from the rest of the book.

In this revised edition, the material is somewhat reorganized; the principal results previously obtained are still given in the main text, while the mathematical details are now presented in Appendixes C.1 and C.2.

Much of this material is a slightly expanded version of Gottfried's treatment (Gottfried 1966, pp. 148–153) and uses the notation of this text. The treatment of Coulomb partial waves is original. The present discussion of Coulomb scattering differs from the standard treatment (see, for example, Bohm 1951, and Schiff 1968) by dealing directly with the asymptotic forms. The differential equation (7.13.7) is the standard form, which can also be obtained by separating variables in parabolic coordinates. It can be recognized as the differential equation for the confluent hypergeometric function,* and so the properties of this function (including asymptotic forms) can be applied to analyse this case. However, the present alternative approach can pass directly to the asymptotic limit by using Laplace transforms and complex variable techniques (see Appendixes C.1 and C.2), and thus avoid referring to the detailed properties of the confluent hypergeometric function. Clearly, this simpler approach, which can be understood without any reference to material outside the present textbook, loses information about the scattering wave function at the origin. Thus, for example, we can say nothing about the *Gamow factor*,[†] which is relevant for the study of many nuclear reaction rates. The interested reader is therefore encouraged to supplement his knowledge here with reading from other texts (e.g., Schiff 1968) that deal with the behavior of the Coulomb wave function at the origin via power series expansion of the associated confluent hypergeometric function.

Scattering Solutions of the Hamiltonian of the Coulomb Interaction

We start with the three-dimensional Schrödinger equation with Coulomb potential

$$V(r) = \frac{-Z_1 Z_2 e^2}{r} \qquad (7.13.1)$$

for a collision between particles of charges $Z_1 e$ and $-Z_2 e$, as follows:

$$\left(-\frac{\hbar^2}{2m} \nabla^2 - \frac{Z_1 Z_2 e^2}{r}\right)\psi(\mathbf{r}) = E\psi(\mathbf{r}), \qquad E > 0 \qquad (7.13.2a)$$

or

$$\left(\nabla^2 + k^2 + \frac{2\gamma k}{r}\right)\psi(\mathbf{r}) = 0 \qquad (7.13.2b)$$

where m is the reduced mass $m = m_1 m_2/(m_1 + m_2)$ for the particles $Z_1 e$

---

*See, for instance, E. T. Whittaker and G. N. Watson, *A Course of Modern Analysis*, 4th ed. (London: Cambridge University Press, 1935), Chapter XVI.

[†]G. Gamow, *Z. Phys.* Vol. *51*, no. 204 (1928); R. W. Gurney and E. U. Condon, *Phys. Rev.* Vol. *33*, no. 127 (1929).

and $-Z_2e$. The γk in (7.13.2b) is given by

$$\gamma k = \frac{Z_1 Z_2 e^2 m}{\hbar^2} \quad \text{or} \quad \gamma = \frac{Z_1 Z_2 e^2}{\hbar v} = \frac{\alpha Z_1 Z_2 c}{v}, \quad \alpha = \frac{e^2}{\hbar c} = \frac{1}{137.03608}.$$

$$(7.13.3)$$

Note that $\gamma > 0$ corresponds to attraction. As long as we are interested in a pure Coulomb field, it is possible to write our solution $\psi_\mathbf{k}(\mathbf{r})$ to (7.13.2) as

$$\psi_\mathbf{k}(\mathbf{r}) = e^{i\mathbf{k}\cdot\mathbf{r}}\chi(u)$$

$$u = ikr(1 - \cos\theta) = ik(r - z) = ikw \qquad (7.13.4)$$

$$\mathbf{k}\cdot\mathbf{r} = kz.$$

The separation of variables for $\psi_\mathbf{k}(\mathbf{r})$ in (7.13.4) is plausible if we recognize (1) that the solution will not involve the azimuthal angle ϕ because of the axial symmetry of the problem and (2) since $\psi_\mathbf{k}(\mathbf{r})$ represents the complete Coulomb-wave function (incident plus scattered wave), terms must exist in its dominant asymptotic form that contain $e^{i\mathbf{k}\cdot\mathbf{r}}$ and $r^{-1}e^{ikr}$. We will demonstrate shortly [see Equations (7.13.9a), (7.13.13), and (7.13.14)] that, with the choice of independent variables we are about to make, this will indeed be the case. (Another argument for our particular choice of variables is given by Gottfried 1966, 148.)

Let us choose independent variables (z, w, λ) where $w = r - z$ and λ can be taken to be ϕ, on which the solution $\psi_\mathbf{k}(\mathbf{r})$ does *not* depend. In changing our Cartesian coordinates (x, y, z) to (z, w, λ), use—for example—such expressions as

$$\frac{\partial}{\partial x} = \frac{\partial w}{\partial x}\frac{\partial}{\partial w} + \frac{\partial z}{\partial x}\frac{\partial}{\partial z} + \frac{\partial \lambda}{\partial x}\frac{\partial}{\partial \lambda}$$

$$= \frac{x}{r}\frac{\partial}{\partial w} + \frac{\partial \lambda}{\partial x}\frac{\partial}{\partial \lambda} \qquad (7.13.5)$$

Note that because $e^{ikz}\chi(u)$ is independent of λ, the operation $\partial/\partial\lambda$ makes no contribution. The reader will readily verify that, operating on $e^{ikz}\chi(u)$,

$$\frac{\partial^2}{\partial x^2} = \frac{x^2}{r^2}\frac{\partial^2}{\partial w^2} + \left(\frac{1}{r} - \frac{x^2}{r^3}\right)\frac{\partial}{\partial w}$$

$$\frac{\partial^2}{\partial y^2} = \frac{y^2}{r^2}\frac{\partial^2}{\partial w^2} + \left(\frac{1}{r} - \frac{y^2}{r^3}\right)\frac{\partial}{\partial w} \qquad (7.13.6)$$

$$\frac{\partial^2}{\partial z^2} = \frac{w^2}{r^2}\frac{\partial^2}{\partial w^2} + \left(\frac{w}{r^2} - \frac{w^2}{r^3}\right)\frac{\partial}{\partial w} - \frac{2w}{r}\frac{\partial^2}{\partial z\partial w} + \frac{w}{r^2}\frac{\partial}{\partial w} + \frac{\partial^2}{\partial z^2}.$$

Using (7.13.4)–(7.13.6) in (7.13.2), we have

$$\left[u \frac{d^2}{du^2} + (1 - u) \frac{d}{du} - i\gamma \right] \chi(u) = 0. \tag{7.13.7}$$

Our first attempt at the solution of (7.13.7) considers the asymptotic case—that is, solutions for *large* $r - z$ (away from the forward direction, since $r - z = r(1 - \cos \theta) = 0$ for $\theta = 0$). Let us try two types of solutions, (1) $\chi \sim u^\lambda$ and (2) $\chi \sim e^u$.

The first type of solution requires

$$(-\lambda - i\gamma)u^\lambda \simeq 0, \quad \text{or} \quad \lambda = -i\gamma \tag{7.13.8}$$

and, hence,

$$\chi(u) \sim u^{-i\gamma} \sim e^{-i\gamma \, \ln \, k(r-z)} \tag{7.13.9a}$$

$$\psi_\mathbf{k}(\mathbf{r}) \sim e^{i[\mathbf{k} \cdot \mathbf{r} - \gamma \, \ln \, k(r-z)]}. \tag{7.13.9b}$$

Equation (7.13.9b) clearly represents the incoming plane-wave piece. The second type of solution, $\chi \sim e^u$, manifestly satisfies $u(d^2\chi/du^2) - u(d\chi/du) = 0$, so heuristically we try for a solution that combines features of both solutions in product form,

$$\chi(u) \sim u^\lambda e^u, \tag{7.13.10}$$

and substitute into (7.13.7). The coefficient of $u^{\lambda+1}e^u$ obviously vanishes, while the coefficient of the $u^\lambda e^u$-term leads to the following relation:

$$2\lambda + (1 - \lambda) - i\gamma = 0, \quad \text{or} \quad \lambda = -1 + i\gamma. \tag{7.13.11}$$

Hence,

$$\chi(u) \simeq \frac{u^{i\gamma}e^u}{u} \simeq \frac{e^{ik(r-z)}}{k(r - z)} e^{i\gamma \, \ln \, k(r-z)} \tag{7.13.12}$$

and

$$\psi(\mathbf{r}) \sim \frac{e^{i[kr+\gamma \, \ln \, k(r-z)]}}{r - z}, \tag{7.13.13}$$

clearly an outgoing spherical wave. Combining the two solution pieces given by (7.13.9) and (7.13.13) linearly and noting that $r - z = r(1 - \cos \theta) = 2r \sin^2(\theta/2)$ while $\ln[2kr \sin^2(\theta/2)] = \ln(2kr) + 2 \ln \sin (\theta/2)$, we write the normalized wave function as

$$\psi_\mathbf{k}(\mathbf{r}) \xrightarrow[|u| \to \infty]{} \frac{1}{(2\pi)^{3/2}} \left\{ e^{i[\mathbf{k} \cdot \mathbf{r} - \gamma \, \ln(kr - \mathbf{k} \cdot \mathbf{r})]} + \frac{f_c(k, \theta)e^{i[kr+\gamma \, \ln \, 2kr]}}{r} \right\}. \tag{7.13.14}$$

There are extra phase effects at large r, which is due to the long range of the Coulomb interaction.

Now we must find the Coulomb scattering amplitude $f_c(k, \theta)$. Interestingly, aside from a factor of γ/k, the magnitude is just from $(r - z)$: $(1/2k \sin^2 \theta/2)$, which appears in the asymptotic form (7.13.13). But we have to work hard to get it! Because the details here are quite involved mathematically (c.f. Appendix C.1), the first-time reader is encouraged to focus only on the final results summarized below. The physical basis of our results are discussed later on in this section.

For the normalized $\psi_{\mathbf{k}}(\mathbf{r})$ we obtain

$$\psi_{\mathbf{k}}(\mathbf{r}) \sim \frac{1}{(2\pi)^{3/2}} \left[e^{i[kz - \gamma \ln k(r-z)]} + \frac{g_1^*(\gamma)}{g_1(\gamma)} \frac{\gamma}{2k \sin^2(\theta/2)} \frac{e^{i[kr + \gamma \ln k(r-z)]}}{r} \right].$$

$$(7.13.15)$$

This exhibits explicitly all the r- and k-dependent phases and leads to the identification from (7.13.14) that

$$f_c(k, \theta) = \frac{\gamma e^{i[\Theta(\gamma) + 2\gamma \ln \sin(\theta/2)]}}{2k \sin^2(\theta/2)} \qquad (7.13.16)$$

$$e^{i\Theta(\gamma)} = \frac{g_1^*(\gamma)}{g_1(\gamma)}.$$

Thus, as in (7.1.36), the differential cross section is

$$\frac{d\sigma_c(k, \theta)}{d\Omega} = |f_c(k, \theta)|^2 = \frac{\gamma^2}{4k^2 \sin^4(\theta/2)}, \qquad (7.13.17)$$

where γ is given by (7.13.3)—and we are back to the Rutherford formula of (7.2.11).

For the aficionados, we remind the reader of Hankel's formula

$$\int_{C_1} e^s s^{-z} ds = \frac{2\pi i}{\Gamma(z)} \qquad (7.13.18)$$

(which checks for $z = 1$ and $\Gamma(1) = 0! = 1$). Thus

$$g_1(\gamma) = \frac{1}{\Gamma(1 - i\gamma)}, \qquad e^{i\Theta(\gamma)} = \frac{\Gamma(1 - i\gamma)}{\Gamma(1 + i\gamma)}. \qquad (7.13.19)$$

Partial-Wave Analysis for the Coulomb Case

We can rewrite $\psi(\mathbf{r})$ from (7.13.4) and (C.1.5) as

$$\psi(\mathbf{r}) = e^{i\mathbf{k}\cdot\mathbf{r}} \chi(u)$$

$$= A e^{i\mathbf{k}\cdot\mathbf{r}} \int_C e^{ut} t^{i\gamma-1} (1 - t)^{-i\gamma} dt$$

$$= A \int_C e^{i\mathbf{k}\cdot\mathbf{r}} e^{ik(r-z)t}(1 - t)d(t, \gamma)dt$$

$$= A \int_C e^{ikrt} e^{i\mathbf{k}\cdot\mathbf{r}(1-t)}(1 - t)d(t, \gamma)dt \qquad (7.13.20)$$

where

$$d(t, \gamma) = t^{i\gamma-1}(1 - t)^{-i\gamma-1}. \qquad (7.13.21)$$

We perform the partial-wave expansion of the plane wave analogous to (7.5.18) as

$$\psi(\mathbf{r}) = \sum_{l=0}^{\infty} (2l + 1)i^l P_l(\cos\theta)A_l(kr), \qquad (7.13.22)$$

where

$$A_l(kr) = A \int_C e^{ikrt} j_l[kr(1 - t)](1 - t)d(t, \gamma)dt. \qquad (7.13.23)$$

Now, $j_l = \frac{1}{2}(h_l^{(1)} + h_l^{(1)*})$, where the $h_l^{(1)}$ are spherical Hankel functions (see Appendix A and Whittaker and Watson 1935), $h_l(\rho) = E_l(\rho)e^{i\rho}/\rho$,

l	0	1	2
$E_l(\rho)$	$-i$	$-\left(1 + \dfrac{i}{\rho}\right)$	$i\left(1 + \dfrac{3i}{\rho} - \dfrac{3}{\rho^2}\right),$

$$(7.13.24)$$

and, asymptotically, $E_l(\rho) = (-i)^{l+1} + 0(\rho^{-1})$. Hence, we write

$$A_l(kr) = A_l^{(1)}(kr) + A_l^{(2)}(kr), \qquad (7.13.25)$$

where $A_l^{(1)}$ and $A_l^{(2)}$ correspond to the contributions from h_l and h_l^*, respectively.

The explicit evaluation of $A_l^{(1)}(kr)$ and $A_l^{(2)}(kr)$ is given in Appendix C.2 and leads to the following results

$$A_l^{(1)}(kr) = 0 \qquad (7.13.26)$$

and

$$A_l^{(2)}(kr) \simeq -\frac{Ae^{\pi\gamma/2}}{2ikr}[2\pi i g_1(\gamma)]$$
$$\times \{e^{-i[kr - (l\pi/2) + \gamma \ln 2kr]} - e^{2i\eta_l(k)}e^{i[kr - (l\pi/2) + \gamma \ln 2kr]}\}, \qquad (7.13.27)$$

where we have optimistically introduced a real phase $\eta_l(k)$:

$$e^{2i\eta_l(k)} = \frac{g_3(\gamma)}{g_1(\gamma)} = \Gamma(1 - i\gamma)g_3(\gamma). \qquad (7.13.28)$$

Note that we write $\eta_l(k)$ because γ depends on k [see (7.13.3)].

Let us look briefly at some simple examples to demonstrate that $\eta_l(k)$ is indeed a real phase. For $l = 0$,

$$E_0^* = i, \qquad 2\pi i g_3(\gamma) = \int_{C_1} e^s s^{-i\gamma-1} ds = 2\pi i g_1^*(\gamma) = \frac{2\pi i}{\Gamma(1 + i\gamma)},$$

$$e^{2i\eta_0} = \frac{\Gamma(1 - i\gamma)}{\Gamma(1 + i\gamma)}. \tag{7.13.29}$$

For $l = 1$, we have

$$E_1^*(\rho) = -\left(1 - \frac{i}{\rho}\right), \qquad E_1^*\left(\frac{-s}{2i}\right) = -\left(1 - \frac{i}{-s/2i}\right) = -\left(1 - \frac{2}{s}\right)$$

$$2\pi i g_3(\gamma) = -\int_{C_1} e^s s^{-i\gamma-1}\left(1 - \frac{2}{s}\right) ds = -2\pi i\left[\frac{1}{\Gamma(1 + i\gamma)} - \frac{2}{\Gamma(2 + i\gamma)}\right]$$

$$= \frac{-2\pi i}{\Gamma(2 + i\gamma)}[(1 + i\gamma) - 2] = \frac{2\pi i(1 - i\gamma)}{\Gamma(2 + i\gamma)} \tag{7.13.30}$$

$$e^{2i\eta_1} = \frac{g_3(\gamma)}{g_1(\gamma)} = \frac{(1 - i\gamma)\Gamma(1 - i\gamma)}{\Gamma(2 + i\gamma)} = \frac{\Gamma(2 - i\gamma)}{\Gamma(2 + i\gamma)}.$$

The same pattern repeats for $l = 2, 3, \ldots$. Thus for a general l, we conjecture

$$e^{2i\eta_l} = \frac{\Gamma(1 + l - i\gamma)}{\Gamma(1 + l + i\gamma)}. \tag{7.13.31}$$

As a final summary we remark that the Coulomb partial-wave-scattering case differs from the general partial-wave case (see Section 7.6) only through the modification

$$-\frac{1}{2} h_l^{(1)}(kr) \cong -\frac{e^{i(kr - (l\pi/2))}}{2ikr} \to -\frac{e^{i(kr - (l\pi/2) + \gamma \ln 2kr)}}{2ikr} \tag{7.13.32}$$

$$e^{2i\delta_l} \to e^{2i\eta_l} = \frac{\Gamma(1 + l - i\gamma)}{\Gamma(1 + l + i\gamma)}.$$

Let us note that the asymptotic form of the Coulomb scattering wave function, Eq. (7.13.15), is different from that which appears in Eq. (7.1.33), written for large r as

$$\psi \to e^{ikz} + f(\theta) \frac{e^{ikr}}{r}. \tag{7.13.33}$$

The latter form is valid only for short-range forces, while the Coulomb force is a long-range one. The form (7.1.33') is modified as follows for the Coulomb interaction: The first term on the right-hand side of (7.13.15) contains not only the factor e^{ikz} as in (7.13.33), but also a modifying, coordinate dependent, multiplicative phase factor $e^{-i\gamma \ln k(r-z)}$. Hence, the incident plane wave is slightly distorted, irrespective of how far away the particle is from the origin. Analogously, the second term on the right-hand side of (7.13.15), corresponding to the outgoing spherical wave, contains the r dependent phase factor $e^{i\gamma \ln 2kr}$. Nevertheless, in spite of these long-range effects leading to phase factors that vary with distance, we can still define a scattering cross section for short-range forces because the distorting terms, although they alter physically observable quantities (e.g., the mean current), lead to alterations that vanish as r goes to infinity.

PROBLEMS

1. The Lippmann-Schwinger formalism can also be applied to a *one-dimensional* transmission-reflection problem with a finite-range potential, $V(x) \neq 0$ for $0 < |x| < a$ only.
   a. Suppose we have an incident wave coming from the left: $\langle x|\phi \rangle = e^{ikx}/\sqrt{2\pi}$. How must we handle the singular $1/(E - H_0)$ operator if we are to have a transmitted wave only for $x > a$ and a reflected wave and the original wave for $x < -a$? Is the $E \to E + i\varepsilon$ prescription still correct? Obtain an expression for the appropriate Green's function and write an integral equation for $\langle x|\psi^{(+)} \rangle$.
   b. Consider the special case of an attractive δ-function potential

   $$V = -\left(\frac{\gamma \hbar^2}{2m}\right)\delta(x) \quad (\gamma > 0).$$

   Solve the integral equation to obtain the transmission and reflection amplitudes. Check your results with Gottfried 1966, 52.
   c. The one-dimensional δ-function potential with $\gamma > 0$ admits one (and only one) bound state for any value of γ. Show that the transmission and reflection amplitudes you computed have bound-state poles at the expected positions when k is regarded as a complex variable.

2. Prove

$$\sigma_{tot} \simeq \frac{m^2}{\pi \hbar^4} \int d^3x \int d^3x' V(r)V(r') \frac{\sin^2 k|\mathbf{x} - \mathbf{x}'|}{k^2|\mathbf{x} - \mathbf{x}'|^2}$$

in each of the following ways.
   a. By integrating the differential cross section computed using the first-order Born approximation.
   b. By applying the optical theorem to the forward-scattering amplitude in the *second*-order Born approximation. [Note that $f(0)$ is real if the first-order Born approximation is used.]

3. Consider a potential

$$V = 0 \quad \text{for } r > R, \qquad V = V_0 = \text{constant} \quad \text{for } r < R.$$

where V_0 may be positive or negative. Using the method of partial waves, show that for $|V_0| \ll E = \hbar^2 k^2 / 2m$ and $kR \ll 1$ the differential cross section is isotropic and that the total cross section is given by

$$\sigma_{\text{tot}} = \left(\frac{16\pi}{9} \right) \frac{m^2 V_0^2 R^6}{\hbar^4}.$$

Suppose the energy is raised slightly. Show that the angular distribution can then be written as

$$\frac{d\sigma}{d\Omega} = A + B \cos \theta.$$

Obtain an approximate expression for B/A.

4. A spinless particle is scattered by a weak Yukawa potential

$$V = \frac{V_0 e^{-\mu r}}{\mu r}$$

where $\mu > 0$ but V_0 can be positive or negative. It was shown in the text that the first-order Born amplitude is given by

$$f^{(1)}(\theta) = -\frac{2mV_0}{\hbar^2 \mu} \frac{1}{\left[2k^2 (1 - \cos \theta) + \mu^2 \right]}.$$

a. Using $f^{(1)}(\theta)$ and assuming $|\delta_l| \ll 1$, obtain an expression for δ_l in terms of a Legendre function of the second kind,

$$Q_l(\zeta) = \frac{1}{2} \int_{-1}^{1} \frac{P_l(\zeta')}{\zeta - \zeta'} \, d\zeta'.$$

b. Use the expansion formula

$$Q_l(\zeta) = \frac{l!}{1 \cdot 3 \cdot 5 \cdots (2l+1)}$$

$$\times \left\{ \frac{1}{\zeta^{l+1}} + \frac{(l+1)(l+2)}{2(2l+3)} \frac{1}{\zeta^{l+3}} \right.$$

$$\left. + \frac{(l+1)(l+2)(l+3)(l+4)}{2 \cdot 4 \cdot (2l+3)(2l+5)} \frac{1}{\zeta^{l+5}} + \cdots \right\} \quad (|\zeta| > 1)$$

to prove each assertion.

(i) δ_l is negative (positive) when the potential is repulsive (attractive).

(ii) When the de Broglie wavelength is much longer than the range of the potential, δ_l is proportional to k^{2l+1}. Find the proportionality constant.

5. Check explicitly the $x - p_x$ uncertainty relation for the ground state of a particle confined inside a hard sphere: $V = \infty$ for $r > a$, $V = 0$ for $r < a$. (*Hint*: Take advantage of spherical symmetry.)

6. Consider the scattering of a particle by an impenetrable sphere

$$V(r) = \begin{cases} 0 & \text{for } r > a \\ \infty & \text{for } r < a. \end{cases}$$

   a. Derive an expression for the *s*-wave ($l = 0$) phase shift. (You need not know the detailed properties of the spherical Bessel functions to be able to do this simple problem!)

   b. What is the total cross section σ [$\sigma = \int (d\sigma/d\Omega) \, d\Omega$] in the extreme low-energy limit $k \to 0$? Compare your answer with the geometric cross section πa^2. You may assume without proof:

$$\frac{d\sigma}{d\Omega} = |f(\theta)|^2,$$

$$f(\theta) = \left(\frac{1}{k}\right) \sum_{l=0}^{\infty} (2l+1) e^{i\delta_l} \sin \delta_l P_l(\cos \theta).$$

7. Use $\delta_l = \Delta(b)|_{b=l/k}$ to obtain the phase shift δ_l for scattering at high energies by (a) the Gaussian potential, $V = V_0 \exp(-r^2/a^2)$, and (b) the Yukawa potential, $V = V_0 \exp(-\mu r)/\mu r$. Verify the assertion that δ_l goes to zero very rapidly with increasing l (k fixed) for $l \gg kR$, where R is the "range" of the potential. [The formula for $\Delta(b)$ is given in (7.4.14)].

8. a. Prove

$$\frac{\hbar^2}{2m} \langle \mathbf{x} | \frac{1}{E - H_0 + i\varepsilon} | \mathbf{x}' \rangle = -ik \sum_l \sum_m Y_l^m(\hat{\mathbf{r}}) Y_l^{m*}(\hat{\mathbf{r}}') j_l(kr_<) h_l^{(1)}(kr_>)$$

   where $r_<$ ($r_>$) stands for the smaller (larger) of r and r'.

   b. For spherically symmetric potentials, the Lippmann-Schwinger equation can be written for *spherical* waves:

$$|Elm(+)\rangle = |Elm\rangle + \frac{1}{E - H_0 + i\varepsilon} V |Elm(+)\rangle.$$

   Using (a), show that this equation, written in the x-representation, leads to an equation for the radial function, $A_l(k; r)$, as follows:

$$A_l(k; r) = j_l(kr) - \frac{2mik}{\hbar^2}$$

$$\times \int_0^{\infty} j_l(kr_<) h_l^{(1)}(kr_>) V(r') A_l(k; r') r'^2 \, dr'.$$

By taking r very large, also obtain

$$f_l(k) = e^{i\delta_l}\frac{\sin\delta_l}{k}$$

$$= -\left(\frac{2m}{\hbar^2}\right)\int_0^\infty j_l(kr)A_l(k;r)V(r)r^2\,dr.$$

9. Consider scattering by a repulsive δ-shell potential:

$$\left(\frac{2m}{\hbar^2}\right)V(r) = \gamma\delta(r-R), \quad (\gamma>0).$$

a. Set up an equation that determines the s-wave phase shift δ_0 as a function of k $(E=\hbar^2k^2/2m)$.

b. Assume now that γ is very large,

$$\gamma \gg \frac{1}{R}, k.$$

Show that if $\tan kR$ is *not* close to zero, the s-wave phase shift resembles the hard-sphere result discussed in the text. Show also that for $\tan kR$ close to (but not exactly equal to) zero, resonance behavior is possible; that is, $\cot\delta_0$ goes through zero from the positive side as k increases. Determine approximately the positions of the resonances keeping terms of order $1/\gamma$; compare them with the bound-state energies for a particle confined *inside* a spherical wall of the same radius,

$$V=0, \quad r<R; \qquad V=\infty, \quad r>R.$$

Also obtain an approximate expression for the resonance width Γ defined by

$$\Gamma = \frac{-2}{[d(\cot\delta_0)/dE]|_{E=E_r}}$$

and notice, in particular, that the resonances become extremely sharp as γ becomes large. (*Note*: For a different, more sophisticated approach to this problem see Gottfried 1966, 131–141, who discusses the analytic properties of the D_l-function defined by $A_l = j_l/D_l$.)

10. A spinless particle is scattered by a time-dependent potential

$$\mathscr{V}(\mathbf{r},t) = V(\mathbf{r})\cos\omega t.$$

Show that if the potential is treated to first order in the transition amplitude, the energy of the scattered particle is increased or decreased by $\hbar\omega$. Obtain $d\sigma/d\Omega$. Discuss qualitatively what happens if the higher-order terms are taken into account.

11. Show that the differential cross section for the elastic scattering of a fast

electron by the ground state of the hydrogen atom is given by

$$\frac{d\sigma}{d\Omega} = \left(\frac{4m^2 e^4}{\hbar^4 q^4}\right)\left\{1 - \frac{16}{\left[4 + (qa_0)^2\right]^2}\right\}^2.$$

(Ignore the effect of identity.)

12. Let the energy of a particle moving in a central field be $E(J_1 J_2 J_3)$, where (J_1, J_2, J_3) are the three action variables. How does the functional form of E specialize for the Coulomb potential? Using the recipe of the action-angle method, compare the degeneracy of the central field and the Coulomb problems and relate it to the vector $\mathbf{A}$.

If the Hamiltonian is

$$H = \frac{p^2}{2\mu} + V(r) + F(\mathbf{A}^2),$$

how are these statements changed?

Describe the corresponding degeneracies of the central field and Coulomb problems in quantum theory in terms of the usual quantum numbers (n, l, m) and also in terms of the quantum numbers (k, m, n). Here the second set, (k, m, n), labels the wave functions $\mathscr{D}^k_{mn}(\alpha\beta\gamma)$.

How are the wave functions $\mathscr{D}^k_{mn}(\alpha\beta\gamma)$ related to Laguerre times spherical harmonics?

APPENDIX A

Brief Summary of Elementary Solutions to Schrödinger's Wave Equation

Here we summarize the simple solutions to Schrödinger's wave equation for a variety of soluble potential problems.

A.1. FREE PARTICLES ($V = 0$)

The plane-wave, or momentum, eigenfunction is

$$\psi_k(\mathbf{x}, t) = \frac{1}{(2\pi)^{3/2}} e^{i\mathbf{k}\cdot\mathbf{x} - i\omega t}, \tag{A.1.1}$$

where

$$\mathbf{k} = \frac{\mathbf{p}}{\hbar}, \qquad \omega = \frac{E}{\hbar} = \frac{\mathbf{p}^2}{2m\hbar} = \frac{\hbar\mathbf{k}^2}{2m} \tag{A.1.2}$$

and our normalization is

$$\int \psi_{k'}^* \psi_k \, d^3x = \delta^{(3)}(\mathbf{k} - \mathbf{k}'). \tag{A.1.3}$$

The superposition of plane waves leads to the *wave-packet* description. In the one-dimensional case,

$$\psi(x, t) = \frac{1}{\sqrt{2\pi}} \int_{-\infty}^{\infty} dk \, A(k) e^{i(kx - \omega t)} \quad \left(\omega = \frac{\hbar k^2}{2m}\right). \tag{A.1.4}$$

For $|A(k)|$ sharply peaked near $k \simeq k_0$, the wave packet moves with a group velocity

$$v_g \simeq \left(\frac{d\omega}{dk}\right)_{k_0} = \frac{\hbar k_0}{m}. \tag{A.1.5}$$

The time evolution of a minimum wave packet can be described by

$$\psi(x, t) = \left[\frac{(\Delta x)_0^2}{2\pi^3}\right]^{1/4} \int_{-\infty}^{\infty} e^{-(\Delta x)_0^2(k-k_0)^2 + ikx - i\omega(k)t} \, dk, \quad \omega(k) = \frac{\hbar k^2}{2m}, \tag{A.1.6}$$

where

$$|\psi(x, t)|^2 = \left\{\frac{1}{2\pi(\Delta x)_0^2\left[1 + (\hbar^2 t^2/4m^2)(\Delta x)_0^{-4}\right]}\right\}^{1/2}$$

$$\times \exp\left\{-\frac{(x - \hbar k_0 t/m)^2}{2(\Delta x)_0^2\left[1 + (\hbar^2 t^2/4m^2)(\Delta x)_0^{-4}\right]}\right\}. \tag{A.1.7}$$

So the width of the wave packet expands as

$$(\Delta x)_0 \quad \text{at } t = 0 \rightarrow (\Delta x)_0\left[1 + \frac{\hbar^2 t^2}{4m^2}(\Delta x)_0^{-4}\right]^{1/2} \quad \text{at } t > 0. \tag{A.1.8}$$

A.2. PIECEWISE CONSTANT POTENTIALS IN ONE DIMENSION

The basic solutions are:

$$E > V = V_0: \quad \psi_E(x) = c_+ e^{ikx} + c_- e^{-ikx}, \quad k = \sqrt{\frac{2m(E - V_0)}{\hbar^2}}. \tag{A.2.1}$$

$E < V = V_0$ (classically forbidden region):

$$\psi_E(x) = c_+ e^{\kappa x} + c_- e^{-\kappa x}, \quad \kappa = \sqrt{\frac{2m(V_0 - E)}{\hbar^2}} \tag{A.2.2}$$

(c_+ must be set equal to 0 if $x = \pm\infty$ is included in the domain under discussion).

Rigid-Wall Potential (One-dimensional Box)

Here

$$V = \begin{cases} 0 & \text{for } 0 < x < L, \\ \infty & \text{otherwise.} \end{cases} \tag{A.2.3}$$

The wave functions and energy eigenstates are

$$\psi_E(x) = \sqrt{\frac{2}{L}} \sin\left(\frac{n\pi x}{L}\right), \quad n = 1, 2, 3\ldots,$$

$$E = \frac{\hbar^2 n^2 \pi^2}{2mL^2}. \tag{A.2.4}$$

Square-Well Potential

The potential V is

$$V = \begin{cases} 0 & \text{for } |x| > a \\ -V_0 & \text{for } |x| < a \quad (V_0 > 0) \end{cases} \tag{A.2.5}$$

The bound-state ($E < 0$) solutions are:

$$\psi_E \sim \begin{cases} e^{-\kappa|x|} & \text{for } |x| > a, \\ \left.\begin{array}{l} \cos kx \quad \text{(even parity)} \\ \sin kx \quad \text{(odd parity)} \end{array}\right\} & \text{for } |x| < a, \end{cases} \tag{A.2.6}$$

where

$$k = \sqrt{\frac{2m(-|E| + V_0)}{\hbar^2}}, \quad \kappa = \sqrt{\frac{2m|E|}{\hbar^2}}. \tag{A.2.7}$$

The allowed discrete values of energy $E = -\hbar^2\kappa^2/2m$ are to be determined by solving

$$\begin{aligned} ka \tan ka &= \kappa a \quad \text{(even parity)} \\ ka \cot ka &= -\kappa a \quad \text{(odd parity)}. \end{aligned} \tag{A.2.8}$$

Note also that κ and k are related by

$$\frac{2mV_0 a^2}{\hbar^2} = (k^2 + \kappa^2)a^2. \tag{A.2.9}$$

A.3. TRANSMISSION—REFLECTION PROBLEMS

In this discussion we define the transmission coefficient T to be the ratio of the flux of the transmitted wave to that of the incident wave. We consider these simple examples.

Square Well ($V = 0$ for $|x| > a$, $V = -V_0$ for $|x| < a$.)

$$\begin{aligned} T &= \frac{1}{\left\{1 + \left[(k'^2 - k^2)^2/4k^2 k'^2\right]\sin^2 2k'a\right\}} \\ &= \frac{1}{\left\{1 + \left[V_0^2/4E(E + V_0)\right]\sin^2\left(2a\sqrt{2m(E + V_0)/\hbar^2}\right)\right\}} \end{aligned} \tag{A.3.1}$$

where

$$k = \sqrt{\frac{2mE}{\hbar^2}}, \qquad k' = \sqrt{\frac{2m(E + V_0)}{\hbar^2}}. \qquad (A.3.2)$$

Note that resonances occur whenever

$$2a\sqrt{\frac{2m(E + V_0)}{\hbar^2}} = n\pi, \quad n = 1, 2, 3, \ldots . \qquad (A.3.3)$$

Potential Barrier ($V = 0$ for $|x| > a$, $V = V_0 > 0$ for $|x| < a$.)

Case 1: $E < V_0$.

$$
T = \frac{1}{\left\{ 1 + \left[(k^2 + \kappa^2)^2 / 4k^2\kappa^2 \right] \sinh^2 2\kappa a \right\}}
$$

$$
= \frac{1}{\left\{ 1 + \left[V_0^2 / 4E(V_0 - E) \right] \sinh^2 \left(2a\sqrt{2m(V_0 - E)/\hbar^2} \right) \right\}}. \qquad (A.3.4)
$$

Case 2: $E > V_0$. This case is the same as the square-well case with V_0 replaced by $-V_0$.

Potential Step ($V = 0$ for $x < 0$, $V = V_0$ for $x > 0$, and $E > V_0$.)

$$
T = \frac{4kk'}{(k + k')^2} = \frac{4\sqrt{(E - V_0)E}}{\left(\sqrt{E} + \sqrt{E - V_0} \right)^2} \qquad (A.3.5)
$$

with

$$k = \sqrt{\frac{2mE}{\hbar^2}}, \qquad k' = \sqrt{\frac{2m(E - V_0)}{\hbar^2}}. \qquad (A.3.6)$$

More General Potential Barrier [$V(x) > E$ for $a < x < b$, $V(x) < E$ outside range $[a, b]$.]

The approximate JWKB solution for T is

$$
T \simeq \exp\left\{ -2 \int_a^b dx \sqrt{\frac{2m[V(x) - E]}{\hbar^2}} \right\}, \qquad (A.3.7)
$$

where a and b are the classical turning points.*

---

*JWKB stand for Jeffreys-Wentzel-Kramers-Brillouin.

A.4. SIMPLE HARMONIC OSCILLATOR

Here the potential is

$$V(x) = \frac{m\omega^2 x^2}{2},$$ (A.4.1)

and we introduce a dimensionless variable

$$\xi = \sqrt{\frac{m\omega}{\hbar}}\, x.$$ (A.4.2)

The energy eigenfunctions are

$$\psi_E = (2^n n!)^{-1/2} \left(\frac{m\omega}{\pi\hbar}\right)^{1/4} e^{-\xi^2/2} H_n(\xi)$$ (A.4.3)

and the energy levels are

$$E = \hbar\omega\left(n + \frac{1}{2}\right), \quad n = 0,1,2,\dots.$$ (A.4.4)

The Hermite polynomials have the following properties:

$$H_n(\xi) = (-1)^n e^{\xi^2} \frac{\partial^n}{\partial\xi^n} e^{-\xi^2}$$

$$\int_{-\infty}^{\infty} H_{n'}(\xi)\, H_n(\xi)\, e^{-\xi^2}\, d\xi = \pi^{1/2} 2^n n! \delta_{nn'}.$$

$$\frac{d^2}{d\xi^2} H_n - 2\xi \frac{dH_n}{d\xi} + 2n H_n = 0$$

$$H_0(\xi) = 1, \quad H_1(\xi) = 2\xi,$$ (A.4.5)

$$H_2(\xi) = 4\xi^2 - 2, \; H_3(\xi) = 8\xi^3 - 12\xi,$$

$$H_4(\xi) = 16\xi^4 - 48\xi^2 + 12.$$

A.5. THE CENTRAL FORCE PROBLEM [SPHERICALLY SYMMETRICAL POTENTIAL $V = V(r)$.]

Here the basic differential equation is

$$-\frac{\hbar^2}{2m}\left[\frac{1}{r^2}\frac{\partial}{\partial r}\left(r^2 \frac{\partial\psi_E}{\partial r}\right) + \frac{1}{r^2 \sin\theta}\frac{\partial}{\partial\theta}\left(\sin\theta \frac{\partial\psi_E}{\partial\theta}\right)\right.$$

$$\left. + \frac{1}{r^2 \sin^2\theta}\frac{\partial^2\psi_E}{\partial\phi^2}\right] + V(r)\psi_E = E\psi_E$$ (A.5.1)

where our spherically symmetrical potential $V(r)$ satisfies

$$\lim_{r \to 0} r^2 V(r) \to 0.$$ (A.5.2)

The method of separation of variables,

$$\Psi_E(\mathbf{x}) = R(\bar{x})Y_l^m(\theta,\phi), \tag{A.5.3}$$

leads to the angular equation

$$-\left[\frac{1}{\sin\theta}\frac{\partial}{\partial\theta}\left(\sin\theta\frac{\partial}{\partial\theta}\right)+\frac{1}{\sin^2\theta}\frac{\partial^2}{\partial\phi^2}\right]Y_l^m = l(l+1)Y_l^m, \tag{A.5.4}$$

where the spherical harmonics

$$Y_l^m(\theta,\phi), \quad l = 0,1,2,\dots, m = -l, -l+1,\dots, +l \tag{A.5.5}$$

satisfy

$$-i\frac{\partial}{\partial\phi}Y_l^m = mY_l^m \tag{A.5.6}$$

and $Y_l^m(\theta,\phi)$ have the following properties:

$$Y_l^m(\theta,\phi) = (-1)^m\sqrt{\frac{2l+1}{4\pi}\frac{(l-m)!}{(l+m)!}}\,P_l^m(\cos\theta)e^{im\phi}$$

$$\text{for } m \geq 0,$$

$$Y_l^m(\theta,\phi) = (-1)^{|m|}Y_l^{|m|*}(\theta,\phi) \quad \text{for } m < 0,$$

$$P_l^m(\cos\theta) = (1-\cos^2\theta)^{m/2}\frac{d^m}{d(\cos\theta)^m}P_l(\cos\theta) \quad \text{for } m \geq 0,$$

$$P_l(\cos\theta) = \frac{(-1)^l}{2^l l!}\frac{d^l(1-\cos^2\theta)^l}{d(\cos\theta)^l},$$

$$Y_0^0 = \frac{1}{\sqrt{4\pi}}, \qquad Y_1^0 = \sqrt{\frac{3}{4\pi}}\cos\theta, \tag{A.5.7}$$

$$Y_1^{\pm 1} = \mp\sqrt{\frac{3}{8\pi}}(\sin\theta)e^{\pm i\phi},$$

$$Y_2^0 = \sqrt{\frac{5}{16\pi}}(3\cos^2\theta-1),$$

$$Y_2^{\pm 1} = \mp\sqrt{\frac{15}{8\pi}}(\sin\theta\cos\theta)e^{\pm i\phi},$$

$$Y_2^{\pm 2} = \sqrt{\frac{15}{32\pi}}(\sin^2\theta)e^{\pm 2i\phi}$$

$$\int Y_{l'}^{m'*}(\theta,\phi)Y_l^m(\theta,\phi)\,d\Omega = \delta_{ll'}\delta_{mm'} \left[\int d\Omega = \int_0^{2\pi}d\phi\int_{-1}^{+1}d(\cos\theta)\right].$$

For the radial piece of (A.5.3), let us define

$$u_E(r) = rR(r). \tag{A.5.8}$$

Then the radial equation is reduced to an equivalent one-dimensional problem, namely,

$$-\frac{\hbar^2}{2m}\frac{d^2 u_E}{dr^2}+\left[V(r)+\frac{l(l+1)\hbar^2}{2mr^2}\right]u_E = Eu_E$$

subject to the boundary condition

$$u_E(r)\big|_{r=0}=0. \tag{A.5.9}$$

For the case of *free* particles $[V(r)=0]$ in our spherical coordinates:

$$R(r)=c_1 j_l(\rho)+c_2 n_l(\rho) \quad (c_2=0 \text{ if the origin is included.}) \tag{A.5.10}$$

where ρ is a dimensionless variable

$$\rho \equiv kr, \qquad k=\sqrt{\frac{2mE}{\hbar^2}}. \tag{A.5.11}$$

We need to list the commonly used properties of the Bessel functions and spherical Bessel and Hankel functions. The spherical Bessel functions are

$$j_l(\rho)=\left(\frac{\pi}{2\rho}\right)^{1/2}J_{l+1/2}(\rho),$$

$$n_l(\rho)=(-1)^{l+1}\left(\frac{\pi}{2\rho}\right)^{1/2}J_{-l-1/2}(\rho),$$

$$j_0(\rho)=\frac{\sin\rho}{\rho}, \qquad\qquad n_0(\rho)=-\frac{\cos\rho}{\rho},$$

$$j_1(\rho)=\frac{\sin\rho}{\rho^2}-\frac{\cos\rho}{\rho}, \qquad n_1(\rho)=-\frac{\cos\rho}{\rho^2}-\frac{\sin\rho}{\rho}, \tag{A.5.12}$$

$$j_2(\rho)=\left(\frac{3}{\rho^3}-\frac{1}{\rho}\right)\sin\rho-\frac{3}{\rho^2}\cos\rho,$$

$$n_2(\rho)=-\left(\frac{3}{\rho^3}-\frac{1}{\rho}\right)\cos\rho-\frac{3}{\rho^2}\sin\rho.$$

For $\rho \to 0$, the leading terms are

$$j_l(\rho)\xrightarrow[\rho\to 0]{}\frac{\rho^l}{(2l+1)!!}, \qquad n_l(\rho)\xrightarrow[\rho\to 0]{}-\frac{(2l-1)!!}{\rho^{l+1}}, \tag{A.5.13}$$

where

$$(2l+1)!!\equiv(2l+1)(2l-1)\cdots 5\cdot 3\cdot 1. \tag{A.5.14}$$

In the large ρ-asymptotic limit, we have

$$j_l(\rho)\xrightarrow[\rho\to\infty]{}\frac{1}{\rho}\cos\left[\rho-\frac{(l+1)\pi}{2}\right],$$

$$n_l(\rho)\xrightarrow[\rho\to\infty]{}\frac{1}{\rho}\sin\left[\rho-\frac{(l+1)\pi}{2}\right]. \tag{A.5.15}$$

Because of constraints (A.5.8) and (A.5.9), $R(r)$ must be finite at $r = 0$; hence, from (A.5.10) and (A.5.13) we see that the $n_l(\rho)$-term must be deleted because of its singular behavior as $\rho \to 0$. Thus $R(r) = c_l j_l(\rho)$ [or, in the notation of Chapter VII, Section 7.6, $A_l(r) = R(r) = c_l j_l(\rho)$]. For a three-dimensional square-well potential, $V = -V_0$ for $r < R$ (with $V_0 > 0$), the desired solution is

$$R(r) = A_l(r) = \text{constant } j_l(\alpha r), \qquad (A.5.16)$$

where

$$\alpha = \left[\frac{2m(V_0 - |E|)}{\hbar^2} \right]^{1/2}, \quad r < R. \qquad (A.5.17)$$

As discussed in (7.6.30), the exterior solution for $r > R$, where $V = 0$, can be written as a linear combination of spherical Hankel functions. These are defined as follows:

$$h_l^{(1)}(\rho) = j_l(\rho) + i n_l(\rho)$$

$$h_l^{(1)*}(\rho) = h_l^{(2)}(\rho) = j_l(\rho) - i n_l(\rho) \qquad (A.5.18)$$

which, from (A.5.15), have the asymptotic forms for $\rho \to \infty$ as follows:

$$h_l^{(1)}(\rho) \xrightarrow[\rho \to \infty]{} \frac{1}{\rho} e^{i[\rho - (l+1)\pi/2]}$$

$$h_l^{(1)*}(\rho) = h_l^{(2)}(\rho) \xrightarrow[\rho \to \infty]{} \frac{1}{\rho} e^{-i[\rho - (l+1)\pi/2]}. \qquad (A.5.19)$$

If we are interested in the bound-state energy levels of the three-dimensional square-well potential, where $V(r) = 0$, $r > R$, we have

$$u_l(r) = r A_l(r) = \text{constant } e^{-\kappa r} f\left(\frac{1}{\kappa r} \right)$$

$$\kappa = \left(\frac{2m|E|}{\hbar^2} \right)^{1/2} \qquad (A.5.20)$$

To the extent that the asymptotic expansions, of which (A.5.19) give the leading terms, do not contain terms with exponent of opposite sign to that given, we have—for $r > R$—the desired solution from (A.5.20):

$$A_l(r) = \text{constant } h_l^{(1)}(i\kappa r) = \text{constant } [j_l(i\kappa r) + i n_l(i\kappa r)], \qquad (A.5.21)$$

where the first three of these functions are

$$h_0^{(1)}(i\kappa r) = -\frac{1}{\kappa r} e^{-\kappa r}$$

$$h_1^{(1)}(i\kappa r) = i \left(\frac{1}{\kappa r} + \frac{1}{\kappa^2 r^2} \right) e^{-\kappa r} \qquad (A.5.22)$$

$$h_2^{(1)}(i\kappa r) = \left(\frac{1}{\kappa r} + \frac{3}{\kappa^2 r^2} + \frac{3}{\kappa^3 r^3} \right) e^{-\kappa r}.$$

Finally, we note that in considering the shift from free particles $[V(r) = 0]$ to the case of the constant potential $V(r) = V_0$, we need only to replace the E in the free-particle solution [see (A.5.10) and (A.5.11) by $E - V_0$. Note, though, that if $E < V_0$, $h_l^{(1,2)}(i\kappa r)$ is to be used with $\kappa = \sqrt{2m(V_0 - E)/\hbar^2}$.

A.6. HYDROGEN ATOM

Here the potential is

$$V(r) = -\frac{Ze^2}{r} \tag{A.6.1}$$

and we introduce the dimensionless variable

$$\rho = \left(\frac{8m_e|E|}{\hbar^2}\right)^{1/2} r. \tag{A.6.2}$$

The energy eigenfunctions and eigenvalues (energy levels) are

$$\psi_{nlm} = R_{nl}(r) Y_l^m(\theta, \phi)$$

$$R_{nl}(r) = -\left\{\left(\frac{2Z}{na_0}\right)^3 \frac{(n-l-1)!}{2n[(n+l)!]^3}\right\}^{1/2} e^{-\rho/2}\rho^l L_{n+l}^{2l+1}(\rho)$$

$$E_n = \frac{-Z^2e^2}{2n^2a_0} \quad \text{(independent of } l \text{ and } m) \tag{A.6.3}$$

$$a_0 = \text{Bohr radius} = \frac{\hbar^2}{m_e e^2}$$

$$n \geq l+1, \qquad \rho = \frac{2Zr}{na_0}.$$

The associated Laguerre polynomials are defined as follows:

$$L_p^q(\rho) = \frac{d^q}{d\rho^q} L_p(\rho), \tag{A.6.4}$$

where—in particular—

$$L_p(\rho) = e^\rho \frac{d^p}{d\rho^p}(\rho^p e^{-\rho}) \tag{A.6.5}$$

and the normalization integral satisfies

$$\int e^{-\rho}\rho^{2l}\left[L_{n+l}^{2l+1}(\rho)\right]^2 \rho^2 \, d\rho = \frac{2n[(n+l)!]^3}{(n-l-1)!}. \tag{A.6.6}$$

The radial functions for low n are:

$$R_{10}(r) = \left(\frac{Z}{a_0}\right)^{3/2} 2e^{-Zr/a_0}$$

$$R_{20}(r) = \left(\frac{Z}{2a_0}\right)^{3/2} (2 - Zr/a_0)e^{-Zr/2a_0} \qquad (A.6.7)$$

$$R_{21}(r) = \left(\frac{Z}{2a_0}\right)^{3/2} \frac{Zr}{\sqrt{3}\, a_0} e^{-Zr/2a_0}.$$

The radial integrals are

$$\langle r^k \rangle \equiv \int_0^\infty dr \; r^{2+k} \, [R_{nl}(r)]^2,$$

$$\langle r \rangle = \left(\frac{a_0}{2Z}\right) [3n^2 - l(l+1)]$$

$$\langle r^2 \rangle = \left(\frac{a_0^2 n^2}{2Z^2}\right) [5n^2 + 1 - 3l(l+1)] \qquad (A.6.8)$$

$$\left\langle \frac{1}{r} \right\rangle = \frac{Z}{n^2 a_0},$$

$$\left\langle \frac{1}{r^2} \right\rangle = \frac{Z^2}{[n^3 a_0^2 \, (l + \frac{1}{2})]}.$$

APPENDIX B

Proof of the Angular-Momentum Addition Rule Given by Equation (3.7.38)

It will be instructive to discuss the angular-momentum addition rule from the quantum-mechanical point of view. Let us, for the moment, label our angular momenta, so that $j_1 \geqq j_2$. This we can always do. From Equation (3.7.35), the maximum value of m, $m^{\max}$ is

$$m^{\max} = m_1^{\max} + m_2^{\max} = j_1 + j_2. \tag{B.1.1}$$

There is only one ket that corresponds to the eigenvalue $m^{\max}$, whether the description is in terms of $|j_1 j_2; m_1 m_2\rangle$ or $|j_1 j_2; jm\rangle$. In other words, choosing the phase factor to be 1, we have

$$|j_1 j_2; j_1 j_2\rangle = |j_1 j_2; j_1 + j_2, j_1 + j_2\rangle. \tag{B.1.2}$$

In the $|j_1 j_2; m_1 m_2\rangle$ basis, there are two kets that correspond to the m eigenvalue $m^{\max} - 1$, namely, one ket with $m_1 = m_1^{\max} - 1$ and $m_2 = m_2^{\max}$ and one ket with $m_1 = m_1^{\max}$ and $m_2 = m_2^{\max} - 1$. There is thus a twofold degeneracy in this basis; therefore, there must be a twofold degeneracy in the $|j_1 j_2; jm\rangle$ basis as well. From where could this come? Clearly, $m^{\max} - 1$ is a possible m-value for $j = j_1 + j_2$. It is also a possible m-value for $j = j_1 + j_2 - 1$—in fact, the maximum m-value for this j. So j_1, j_2 can add to j's of $j_1 + j_2$ and $j_1 + j_2 - 1$.

We can continue in this way, but it is clear that the degeneracy cannot increase indefinitely. Indeed, for $m^{\min} = -j_1 - j_2$, there is once again a single ket. The maximum degeneracy is $(2 j_2 + 1)$-fold, as is apparent

456

TABLE B.1.   Special Examples of Values of m, m_1, and m_2 for the Two Cases $j_1 = 2$, $j_2 = 1$ and $j_1 = 2$, $j_2 = \frac{1}{2}$, Respectively

$j_1 = 2$, $j_2 = 1$ m	3	2	1	0	-1	-2	-3
(m_1, m_2)	(2,1)	(1,1)	(0,1)	(-1,1)	(-2,1)		
		(2,0)	(1,0)	(0,0)	(-1,0)	(-2,0)	
			(2,-1)	(1,-1)	(0,-1)	(-1,-1)	(-2,-1)
Numbers of States	1	2	3	3	3	2	1
$j_1 = 2$, $j_2 = \frac{1}{2}$ m	$\frac{5}{2}$	$\frac{3}{2}$	$\frac{1}{2}$	$-\frac{1}{2}$	$-\frac{3}{2}$	$-\frac{5}{2}$	
(m_1, m_2)	$(2,\frac{1}{2})$	$(1,\frac{1}{2})$	$(0,\frac{1}{2})$	$(-1,\frac{1}{2})$	$(-2,\frac{1}{2})$		
		$(2,-\frac{1}{2})$	$(1,-\frac{1}{2})$	$(0,-\frac{1}{2})$	$(-1,-\frac{1}{2})$	$(-2,-\frac{1}{2})$	
Numbers of States	1	2	2	2	2	1	

from Table B.1 constructed for two special examples: for $j_1 = 2$, $j_2 = 1$ and for $j_1 = 2$, $j_2 = \frac{1}{2}$. This $(2j_2 + 1)$-fold degeneracy must be associated with the $2j_2 + 1$ states j:

$$j_1 + j_2, j_1 + j_2 - 1, \ldots, j_1 - j_2. \qquad \text{(B.1.3)}$$

If we lift the restriction $j_1 \geq j_2$, we obtain (3.7.38).

APPENDIX C

Mathematical Details of Coulomb Scattering Formalism

C.1. THE COULOMB SCATTERING AMPLITUDE $f_c(k, \theta)$

Let us go back to the differential equation (7.13.7). The theory of differential equations tells us that the only singularity in the finite u-plane is at $u = 0$.* (We want the solution that is regular at $u = 0$.) We examine $\chi(u)$ in the Laplace transform space, t:

$$\chi(u) = \int_{t_1}^{t_2} e^{ut}f(t)\,dt, \tag{C.1.1}$$

where the path of integration $t_1 \to t_2$ in the complex t-plane will be decided later. If we substitute $\chi(u)$ given by (C.1.1) into (7.13.7), we obtain

$$\int_{t_1}^{t_2} [ut^2 + (1 - u)t - i\gamma] fe^{ut} dt$$

$$= \int_{t_1}^{t_2} f\left[(t - i\gamma) + t(t - 1)\frac{d}{dt}\right]e^{ut} dt$$

$$= t(t - 1)e^{ut}f|_{t_1}^{t_2} + \int_{t_1}^{t_2}\left\{(t - i\gamma)f - \frac{d}{dt}[t(t - 1)f(t)]\right\}e^{ut} dt = 0, \tag{C.1.2}$$

where we have integrated by parts. If we assume that surface terms vanish, evidently

$$(t - i\gamma)f(t) - \frac{d}{dt}[(t - 1)tf(t)] = 0, \tag{C.1.3}$$

and we can easily obtain the solution for $f(t)$ as

$$f = At^{i\gamma-1}(1 - t)^{-i\gamma}, \tag{C.1.4}$$

where A is some constant. As an interim summary we have [from (C.1.1)]

$$\chi(u) = A \int_C e^{ut}t^{i\gamma-1}(1 - t)^{-i\gamma}dt, \quad \int_{t_1}^{t_2} \to \int_C. \tag{C.1.5}$$

---

*For the mathematical background, see E. T. Whittaker and G. N. Watson, *A Course of Modern Analysis*, 4th ed. (Cambridge, London: 1935), Chapter XVI.

Now we must choose C. Note that the integrand in (C.1.5) has branch points at $t = 0, 1$ in the complex t-plane; see Figure C.1. For the surface term in (C.1.2) to vanish, we require that the t at the end points contain an imaginary part that goes to $+\infty$. This is because $u = ik(r - z) = ikr$ $(1 - \cos \theta) \equiv i\kappa$ and $\kappa > 0$. Hence,

$$e^{ut} \to e^{i\kappa t} \xrightarrow[t \to a + i\infty]{} 0.$$

and surface terms vanish. But there are lots of ways of reaching $t = a + i\infty$! The choice of C indicated in Figure C.1a will give the correct asymptotic forms, as the actual calculations show [see (C.1.10)], and we will adopt this specific contour.

Let $s = ut$. Then (C.1.5) becomes

$$\chi(u) = A \int_{\overline{C}} \frac{ds}{u} e^s \left(\frac{s}{u}\right)^{i\gamma - 1} \left(\frac{u - s}{u}\right)^{-i\gamma}$$

$$= A \int_{\overline{C}} ds\, e^s s^{i\gamma - 1} (u - s)^{-i\gamma}, \tag{C.1.6}$$

where $\overline{C}$ is the s-plane contour depicted in Figure C.2a. We require that $\chi(u)$ is regular at $u = 0$; in fact, it is because

$$\chi(0) = (-1)^{-i\gamma} A \int_{\overline{C}} \frac{e^s}{s} ds = (-1)^{-i\gamma} A 2\pi i. \tag{C.1.7}$$

We now evaluate (C.1.6) for $u \to \infty$—the asymptotic limit—and show that the correct form is obtained. For the curve C_1 in Figure C.2b and for a fixed s, $s = -(s_0 \pm i\varepsilon)$ and $s/u = -(s_0 \pm i\varepsilon)/i\kappa$, but this is small for $\kappa \to \infty$. So, we can expand $(u - s)$ in powers of s/u. For the curve C_2 in

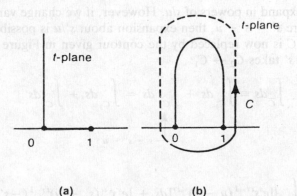

(a)   (b)

FIGURE C.1. (a) Branch point at $t = 0,1$ and simple straight-line branch cut between $(0, 1)$ in t-plane. (b) "Rubber-band distorted" branch cut between $(0, 1)$ and a possible contour C for (C.1.5)

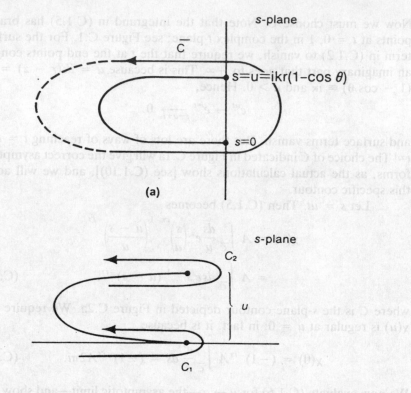

FIGURE C.2. (a) s-plane contour $\overline{C}$ for Equation (C.1.6). (b) Rubber-band distortion of $\overline{C}$ into C_1 plus C_2.

Figure C.2b, $s = -s_0 + i(\kappa \pm \varepsilon)$; hence, $s/u = 1 - (s_0 \pm i\varepsilon)/\kappa \underset{\kappa \to \infty}{\longrightarrow} 1$, so we can not expand in powers of s/u. However, if we change variables $s \to s'$ here, where $s' = s - u$, then expansion about s'/u is possible. Hence, the contour $\overline{C}$ is now replaced by the contour given in Figure C.2b and, further, $s \to s'$ takes $C_2 \to C_1$:

$$\int_{\overline{C}} ds \equiv \int_{C_1} ds + \int_{C_2} ds = \int_{C_1} ds + \int_{C_1} ds' \qquad (C.1.8)$$

$$\underset{s = s' + u}{\big\uparrow}$$

and

$$\chi(u) = A \int_{C_1} \{ [e^s s^{i\gamma - 1}(u - s)^{-i\gamma}] ds + [e^{s' + u}(s' + u)^{i\gamma - 1}(-s')^{-i\gamma}] ds' \}.$$

$$(C.1.9)$$

Here $(s' + u)^{i\gamma-1}$ is clearly expandable in s'/u, and—since s' is a dummy integration variable for the C_1-contour—we may write (C.1.9) more compactly as

$$\chi(u) = A\left\{u^{-i\gamma} \int_{C_1} e^s s^{i\gamma-1} \left(1 - \left(\frac{s}{u}\right)\right)^{-i\gamma} ds \right.$$

$$\left. + e^u u^{i\gamma-1}(-1)^{-i\gamma} \int_{C_1} e^s \left(1 + \left(\frac{s}{u}\right)\right)^{i\gamma-1} s^{-i\gamma} ds\right\}. \quad \text{(C.1.10)}$$

Note that the coefficients of the two integrals in (C.1.10), $u^{-i\gamma}$ and $e^u u^{i\gamma-1}(-1)^{-i\gamma}$, do have the correct asymptotic forms [see (7.13.9), (7.13.12), and (7.13.14)] for Coulomb scattering.

The leading terms in (C.1.10) are obtained when we let $s/u \to 0$; then

$$\chi(u) \sim 2\pi i A\left[u^{-i\gamma}g_1(\gamma) - (-u)^{i\gamma-1}e^u g_2(\gamma)\right]$$

$$2\pi i g_1(\gamma) = \int_{C_1} e^s s^{i\gamma-1} ds \quad \text{(C.1.11)}$$

$$2\pi i g_2(\gamma) = \int_{C_1} e^s s^{-i\gamma} ds.$$

Integrating the expression for $2\pi i g_2(\gamma)$ by parts, we have

$$2\pi i g_2(\gamma) = \int_{C_1} e^s s^{-i\gamma} ds = e^s s^{-i\gamma}\Big|_{-\infty-i\epsilon}^{-\infty+i\epsilon} - (-i\gamma)\int_{C_1} e^s s^{-i\gamma-1} ds$$

$$= + i\gamma g_1^*(\gamma) 2\pi i. \quad \text{(C.1.12)}$$

Noting that $-u = u^*$, we find

$$\chi(u) \cong 2\pi i A u^{-i\gamma}g_1(\gamma)\left[1 + \frac{(u^*)^{+i\gamma}}{u^{-i\gamma}}\frac{g_1^*(\gamma)}{g_1(\gamma)} i\gamma \frac{e^u}{u}\right]$$

$$= 2\pi i A u^{-i\gamma}g_1(\gamma)\left[1 + e^{i\phi(k,u,\gamma)} i\gamma \frac{e^u}{u}\right], \quad \text{(C.1.13)}$$

where we have noted that

$$\frac{(u^*)^{+i\gamma}}{u^{-i\gamma}}\frac{g_1^*(\gamma)}{g_1(\gamma)} = \frac{[u^{-i\gamma}g_1(\gamma)]^*}{[u^{-i\gamma}g_1(\gamma)]} = e^{i\phi(k,u,\gamma)}. \quad \text{(C.1.14)}$$

Using

$$(u^*)^{i\gamma} = (-i)^{i\gamma}[k(r-z)]^{i\gamma} = e^{+\gamma\pi/2}e^{i\gamma\ln k(r-z)}$$
$$(u)^{-i\gamma} = (i)^{-i\gamma}[k(r-z)]^{-i\gamma} = e^{+\gamma\pi/2}e^{-i\gamma\ln k(r-z)}. \quad \text{(C.1.15)}$$

in going from $\chi \rightarrow \psi$ [multiplication by e^{ikz} as in (7.13.4)], we obtain the normalized asymptotic $\psi_k(\mathbf{r})$, which is given by Eq. (7.13.15).

C.2. EVALUATION OF $A_l^{(1)}(kr)$ AND $A_l^{(2)}(kr)$ NECESSARY FOR THE PARTIAL WAVE ANALYSIS OF COULOMB SCATTERING

Let us note that

$$e^{ikrt} e^{ikr(1-t)} = e^{ikr},$$
$$e^{ikrt} e^{-ikr(1-t)} = e^{-ikr} e^{2ikrt}, \tag{C.2.1}$$

so that

$$A_l^{(1)}(kr) = \frac{Ae^{ikr}}{2kr} \int_C E_l[kr(1-t)]d(t, \gamma)\,dt. \tag{C.2.2}$$

Since $d(t, \gamma) \sim t^{-2}$ for large $|t|$ and $E_l \sim t^0 \sim 1$ and the only singularities in the t-plane are branch points $t = 0, 1$ and possible poles from E_l when its argument $kr(1 - t)$ vanishes, we close the contour C in the manner shown in Figure C.1b. This leads at once to

$$A_l^{(1)}(kr) = 0, \tag{C.2.3}$$

since—thinking of a stereographic projection of the complex plane on the unit sphere—the contour C can be viewed as surrounding the region exterior to it, where there are no poles.

For $A_l^{(2)}(kr)$, we have

$$A_l^{(2)}(kr) = \frac{Ae^{-ikr}}{2kr} \int_C E_l^* [kr(1-t)]e^{2ikrt}d(t, \gamma)\,dt. \tag{C.2.4}$$

We play the same game as we did between (C.1.5) and (C.1.6). Let $\bar{s} = \bar{u}t$, where $\bar{u} = 2ikr$; then $t = \bar{s}/\bar{u}$ and $1 - t = (\bar{u} - \bar{s})/\bar{u}$, so

$$A_l^{(2)}(kr) = \frac{iAe^{-\bar{u}/2}}{\bar{u}} \int_{\bar{C}} e^{\bar{s}}(\bar{s}/\bar{u})^{i\gamma-1} \left(\frac{\bar{u} - \bar{s}}{\bar{u}}\right)^{-i\gamma-1} E_l^* \left(\frac{\bar{u} - \bar{s}}{2i}\right) \frac{d\bar{s}}{\bar{u}}, \tag{C.2.5}$$

where $\bar{C}$ is like Figure C.2a except that now the ends of the branch point in the $\bar{s}$-plane are $\bar{s} = 0$ and $\bar{s} = 2ikr$. We recall that $\bar{u}^* = -\bar{u}$, and therefore

$$A_l^{(2)}(kr) = iAe^{-\bar{u}/2} \int_{\bar{C}} e^{\bar{s}} \bar{s}^{i\gamma-1}(\bar{u} - \bar{s})^{-i\gamma-1} E_l^* \left(\frac{\bar{u} - \bar{s}}{2i}\right) d\bar{s}$$

$$= iAe^{-\bar{u}/2} \int_{C_1} \left[e^s s^{i\gamma-1}(\bar{u} - s)^{-i\gamma-1} E_l^* \left(\frac{\bar{u} - s}{2i}\right)\right.$$

$$+ \ e^{s+\overline{u}}(s+\overline{u})^{i\gamma-1}(-s)^{-i\gamma-1} E_l^*\left(\frac{-s}{2i}\right)\Bigg]ds$$

$$\cong \frac{iA}{\overline{u}}\left[e^{-\overline{u}/2}\overline{u}^{-i\gamma}\int_{C_1} e^s s^{i\gamma-1} E_l^*\left(\frac{\overline{u}}{2i}\right)ds\right.$$

$$+ \ e^{\overline{u}/2}\overline{u}^{i\gamma}\int_{C_1} e^s(-s)^{-i\gamma-1} E_l^*\left(\frac{-s}{2i}\right)ds\Bigg]$$

$$\cong \frac{A}{2kr}\left[e^{-\overline{u}/2}\overline{u}^{-i\gamma}\int_{C_1} e^s s^{i\gamma-1}\frac{1}{(-i)^{l+1}}ds\right.$$

$$- \ (e^{-\overline{u}/2}\overline{u}^{-i\gamma})^*\int_{C_1} e^s s^{-i\gamma-1} E_l^*\left(\frac{-s}{2i}\right)ds\Bigg], \qquad \text{(C.2.6)}$$

where in the last equation we have used the asymptotic form in $\overline{u}$ for $E_l^*(\overline{u}/2i)$ as given in (7.13.24). Note next that $e^{-\overline{u}/2}\ \overline{u}^{-i\gamma} = e^{\pi\gamma/2}e^{-i(kr+\gamma\ln 2kr)}$; hence, (C.2.6) becomes

$$A_l^{(2)}(kr) \simeq -\frac{Ae^{\pi\gamma/2}}{2ikr}\ \{e^{-i[kr-(l\pi/2)+\gamma\ln 2kr]}2\pi ig_1(\gamma)$$

$$- e^{i[kr-(l\pi/2)+\gamma\ln 2kr]}2\pi ig_3(\gamma)\}, \qquad \text{(C.2.7)}$$

where

$$2\pi ig_1(\gamma) = \int_{C_1} e^s s^{i\gamma-1}ds = \frac{2\pi i}{\Gamma(1-i\gamma)}$$

$$2\pi ig_3(\gamma) = i^{l-1}\int_{C_1} e^s s^{-i\gamma-1} E_l^*\left(\frac{-s}{2i}\right)ds. \qquad \text{(C.2.8)}$$

Note $g_1(\gamma)$ and $g_3(\gamma)$ are used in Eq. (7.13.28), and indeed lead to a real phase $\eta_l(k)$.

SUPPLEMENT I

Adiabatic Change and Geometrical Phase

When the author died in 1982, this book was left in manuscript form; subsequently, there have been some new developments in quantum mechanics. The most important development is a definitive formulation of geometrical phases, introduced by M. V. Berry in 1983. The phase factors accompanying adiabatic changes are expressed in concise and elegant forms and have found universal applications in various fields of physics, thus giving a new viewpoint to quantum theory. We review here the physical consequences of these phases, which have in fact been used unconsciously in some cases already, by adding a supplement to the Japanese version of the text. (Here in the new English edition of *Modern Quantum Mechanics* we are providing a translation from Japanese of this supplement, prepared by Professor Akio Sakurai of Kyoto Sangyo University for the Japanese version of the book. The Editor deeply appreciates Professor Akio Sakurai's guidance on an initial translation provided by his student, Yasunaga Suzuki, as a term paper for the graduate quantum mechanics course here at the University of Hawaii—Manoa.)

ADIABATIC THEOREM

Let us first consider a spin with magnitude S in a uniform time-independent magnetic field. Due to the magnetic moment associated with the spin, the energy levels of this quantized system are split into $2S + 1$ levels. The state ket $|n\rangle$ with the nth energy eigenvalue E_n undergoes a change in phase factor as (for a Hamiltonian constant in time)

$$|n\rangle \to e^{-iE_n t/\hbar} |n\rangle \tag{S.1}$$

in time evolution, as we learned in Chapter 2. This is the time development of the stationary state. We next change the direction of the magnetic field very slowly. Following the slowly varying magnetic field, the direction of the spin changes also. We keep its component in the direction of the magnetic field constant in time, however. Thus the initial quantum number n does not change at all with the changing magnetic field. This is a typical example of the **adiabatic theorem** in quantum mechanics.

Generally speaking, the adiabatic theorem asserts that there should be mechanical invariants under the slow variation exerted externally on a mechanical system. The entropy in thermodynamic systems and action integral in classical mechanical systems are, like the quantum numbers in quantum mechanical systems, examples of *adiabatic invariants*. Here we simply regard an adiabatic change as a time change that is very slow compared with the time for proper motion in each system (such as periods of oscillation).[†] We do not discuss how slow change can be regarded as an **adiabatic change** (see A. Messiah, *Quantum Mechanics*, New York: Interscience, 1961, Chapter XVII). Our problem is to discuss how the state ket $|n\rangle$ of a quantum mechanical system changes under adiabatic changes. We find that apart from the simple extension of (S.1), there is another phase factor dependent upon the path of an adiabatic process. The general expression was clearly given by Berry (M. V. Berry, *Proceedings of the Royal Society of London*. Vol. **A392** (1984), p. 45) in his seminal paper.

BERRY'S PHASE

We consider the Hamiltonian of the system with an external time-dependent parameter $R(t)$ by denoting it as $H(R(t))$. The ket $|n(R(t))\rangle$ of the nth energy eigenstate corresponding to $R(t)$ satisfies the eigenvalue equation at time t,

$$H(R(t))\,|n(R(t))\rangle = E_n\,(R(t))\,|n(R(t))\rangle \qquad (S.2)$$

where the ket $|n(R(t))\rangle$ has already been normalized. Let us make R evolve in time from $R(0) = R_0$. Suppose that the state ket is $|n(R_0), t_0 = 0; t\rangle$ at time t. The time-dependent Schrödinger equation that the state ket obeys is

$$H(R(t))\,|n(R_0), t_0; t\rangle = i\hbar\,\frac{\partial}{\partial t}\,|n(R_0), t_0; t\rangle \qquad (S.3)$$

where $t_0 = 0$. When the change of $R(t)$ is slow enough, we expect from the adiabatic theorem that $|n(R_0), t_0; t\rangle$ would be proportional to the nth energy eigenket $|n(R(t))\rangle$ of $H(R(t))$ at time t. Thus we represent it as

$$|n(R_0), t_0; t\rangle = \exp\left\{-\frac{i}{\hbar}\int_0^t E_n\,(R(t'))dt'\right\} \exp(i\gamma_n(t))\,|n(R(t))\rangle. \qquad (S.4)$$

The first factor on the r.h.s. is the usual dynamical phase factor summing up all phase changes in stationary states [c.f. (2.6.7)]. On the other hand, by substituting (S.4) into (S.3), the second phase factor $\exp(i\gamma_n(t))$ is shown to be determined by

---

[†]For adiabatic invariants in classical periodic systems and Ehrenfest's adiabatic hypothesis, see S. Tomonaga, *Quantum Mechanics I*. (Amsterdam: North-Holland Press, 1962).

$$\frac{d}{dt} \gamma_n(t) = i \langle n(\boldsymbol{R}(t)) \, | \, \boldsymbol{\nabla_R} n(\boldsymbol{R}(t)) \, \rangle \, \frac{d}{dt} \boldsymbol{R}(t). \tag{S.5}$$

Therefore, $\gamma_n(t)$ is represented by a path integral in the parameter $(\boldsymbol{R}-)$ space:

$$\gamma_n(t) = i \int_{\boldsymbol{R}_0 \, C}^{\boldsymbol{R}(t)} \langle n(\boldsymbol{R}(t')) \, | \, \boldsymbol{\nabla_R} n(\boldsymbol{R}(t')) \, \rangle \, d\boldsymbol{R}(t') \tag{S.6}$$

where the path C of integration is that of the adiabatic process as the external parameter $\boldsymbol{R}$ changes from $\boldsymbol{R}_0$ to $\boldsymbol{R}(t)$. We can see that γ_n is a real number by differentiating with respect to $\boldsymbol{R}$ both sides of the normalization condition:

$$\langle n(\boldsymbol{R}(t)) \, | \, n(\boldsymbol{R}(t)) \rangle = 1 \tag{S.7}$$

($\langle n \, | \, \boldsymbol{\nabla_R} n \rangle$ is pure imaginary.) Since the integral (S.6) contains the derivative of the eigenstate $| \boldsymbol{\nabla_R} n \rangle$, the practical evaluation here might be expected to be complicated. However, if $\boldsymbol{R}$ describes a closed loop in parameter space returning to the starting point after time interval T (the periodicity), as is in the case of $\boldsymbol{R}(T) = \boldsymbol{R}_0$, the path integral becomes greatly simplified. First applying the Stoke's theorem, we transform the line integral along the closed loop C to a surface integral over the surface $S(C)$ enclosed by the closed loop C:

$$\gamma_n(C) = i \oint_C \langle n(\boldsymbol{R}) \, | \, \boldsymbol{\nabla_R} n(\boldsymbol{R}) \rangle d\boldsymbol{R} = - \iint_{S(C)} \boldsymbol{V}_n(\boldsymbol{R}) \cdot d\boldsymbol{S}, \tag{S.8}$$

$$\boldsymbol{V}_n(\boldsymbol{R}) = \mathrm{Im} \, \boldsymbol{\nabla_R} n \times \langle n(\boldsymbol{R}) \, | \, \boldsymbol{\nabla_R} n(\boldsymbol{R}) \rangle$$

$$= \mathrm{Im} \, \langle \boldsymbol{\nabla_R} n(\boldsymbol{R}) \, | \times | \, \boldsymbol{\nabla_R} n(\boldsymbol{R}) \rangle$$

$$= \mathrm{Im} \sum_{m \neq n} \langle \boldsymbol{\nabla_R} n(\boldsymbol{R}) \, | m(\boldsymbol{R}) \rangle \times \langle m(\boldsymbol{R}) \, | \, \boldsymbol{\nabla_R} n(\boldsymbol{R}) \rangle, \tag{S.9}$$

where we have used the vector identity:

$$\boldsymbol{\nabla} \times [f(\boldsymbol{x}) \boldsymbol{\nabla} g(\boldsymbol{x})] = (\boldsymbol{\nabla} f(\boldsymbol{x})) \times (\boldsymbol{\nabla} g(\boldsymbol{x})). \tag{S.10}$$

Suppose $| n(\boldsymbol{R}) \rangle$ is modified by some phase factor $\exp[i\chi(\boldsymbol{R})]$. Then, even if the integrand of line integral (S.8) changes as

$$\langle n(\boldsymbol{R}) \boldsymbol{\nabla_R} n(\boldsymbol{R}) \rangle \rightarrow \langle n(\boldsymbol{R}) \boldsymbol{\nabla_R} n(\boldsymbol{R}) \rangle + i \boldsymbol{\nabla_R} \chi(\boldsymbol{R}), \tag{S.11}$$

$\boldsymbol{V}_n(\boldsymbol{R})$ does not change because $\boldsymbol{\nabla} \times \boldsymbol{\nabla} \chi = 0$ (see Section 2.6 on gauge invariance). We have omitted the term $m = n$ in the last line of (S.9) because

$\langle n | \nabla_R n \rangle$ is purely imaginary. On the other hand, the off-diagonal matrix element $\langle m | \nabla_R n \rangle$ is represented as follows. Multiplying $\langle m |$ from the left to the equation

$$(\nabla_R H(R)) \, |n(R)\rangle + H(R) \, (\nabla_R \, |n(R)\rangle)$$
$$= (\nabla_R E(R)) \, |n(R)\rangle + E_n(R) \, |\nabla_R n(R)\rangle \quad \text{(S.12)}$$

obtained by differentiating the eigenvalue equation (S.2) with respect to the external parameter R, we get

$$\langle m(R) \, | \nabla_R n(R) \rangle = \frac{\langle m(R) \, | \nabla_R H(R) \, | n(R) \rangle}{E_n - E_m}, \quad m \neq n. \quad \text{(S.13)}$$

Therefore the integrand of the surface integral (S.8) is given by

$$V_n(R) = \text{Im} \sum_{m \neq n} \frac{\langle n(R) \, | \nabla_R H(R) \, | m(R) \rangle \times \langle m(R) \, | \nabla_R H(R) \, | n(R) \rangle}{(E_m(R) - E_n(R))^2}.$$

$$\text{(S.14)}$$

Here we notice that the vector $V_n(R)$ passing through the surface of the integral $S(C)$ is expressed by the differential form of degree 2 of the Hamiltonian $H(R)$. Knowledge of the state ket $|n(R)\rangle$ itself is usually not needed to calculate V_n as we shall see later. To sum up, the state ket after one complete turn is expressed as

$$|n(R_0), t_0 = 0; T\rangle$$
$$= \exp(i\gamma_n(C))\exp\left\{ -\frac{i}{\hbar} \int_0^T E_n \, (R(t'))dt' \right\} |n(R_0)\rangle, \quad \text{(S.15)}$$

$$\gamma_n(C) = - \iint_{S(C)} V_n(R) \cdot dS. \quad \text{(S.16)}$$

Here, $\gamma_n(C)$ is called the **Berry's phase**, and comes from the adiabatic change of the external parameter. We shall next show that this phase is determined by the *geometric properties* in parameter space.

DEGENERACY POINT AND SOLID ANGLE—GEOMETRICAL PHASE FACTOR

Suppose that the nth energy eigenstate $|n(R)\rangle$ is degenerate with the mth eigenstate $|m(R)\rangle$ for an external parameter R^*. Although the *degeneracy* *point R^** in the parameter space is by no means on the path of the actual adiabatic change, the existence of R^* is essential for the value of $\gamma_n(C)$. This is because the integrand $V_n(R)$ of $\gamma_n(C)$ is singular at R^*, as is evident from (S.14).

Let us continue our discussion by taking as an example, the problem of the spin in a magnetic field mentioned earlier (spin magnitude S, and magnetic moment $g\mu S/\hbar$.[†] When the magnetic field $B(t)$ slowly changes its direction while keeping its magnitude constant, we denote the spin component as $S_{z'} = m\hbar$ ($m = -S, \ldots, +S$) along the direction of the magnetic field at each instance (taking this to be the positive direction of the z'-axis). Writing the Hamiltonian of this system as

$$H(B) = -g\mu S \cdot B(t)/\hbar, \tag{S.17}$$

the energy eigenvalue is

$$E_m = -g\mu m B \tag{S.18}$$

and

$$\nabla_B H(B) = -g\mu S/\hbar. \tag{S.19}$$

The degeneracy point is at the origin of the parameter space, $B = 0$, where there are $2S+1$ fold degeneracies. When we rotate the direction of the magnetic field B keeping its magnitude constant and bring it back to the initial direction again, the vector B goes around the closed loop on a sphere of radius B. Then the vector $V_m(B)$ can be expressed from (S.14) as

$$V_m(B) = \text{Im} \sum_{m' \neq m} \frac{\langle m(B) | S/\hbar | m'(B) \rangle \times \langle m'(B) | S/\hbar | m(B) \rangle}{B^2 (m' - m)^2}. \tag{S.20}$$

In order to make the calculation easier, let us take the z-axis of spin space to be the direction of the magnetic field (z'-axis direction). Since only the terms with $m' = m \pm 1$ contribute to the intermediate states, we use the expression (3.5.41) for the matrix element of the spin operator:

$$\langle S, m \pm 1 | S_x/\hbar | S, m \rangle = \tfrac{1}{2}\sqrt{(S \mp m)(S \pm m + 1)}, \tag{S.21}$$

$$\langle S, m \pm 1 | S_y/\hbar | S, m \rangle = \frac{\mp i}{2}\sqrt{(S \mp m)(S \pm m + 1)}.$$

By substituting (S.21) into (S.20), we obtain the components of the vector $V_m(B)$ as follows:

$$(V_m(B))_{x'} = 0, \quad (V_m(B))_{y'} = 0, \quad (V_m(B))_{z'} = \frac{m}{B^2}. \tag{S.22}$$

[†]Here spin magnitude S is in unit of $\hbar$, while vector S has dimension of $\hbar$.

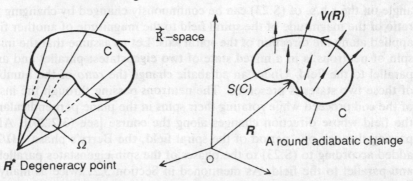

FIGURE S.1. External parameter R-space. For the adiabatic change of one turn along the closed loop C, the *geometrical phase* is given by the surface integral of the vector $V(R)$ penetrating through the surface S(C) surrounded by C (right). This is proportional to the solid angle that the closed loop C subtends at the degeneracy point R^* (left).

Thus the vector $V(B)$ is parallel to the magnetic field B and penetrates normally through the spherical surface of the B-space. Hence the phase $\gamma_m(C)$ is given by

$$\gamma_m(C) = -m \iint_{S(C)} \frac{\hat{\mathbf{B}}}{B^2} \cdot d\mathbf{B} = -m \int_C d\Omega = -m\Omega(C) \quad (S.23)$$

where $\Omega(C)$ is the *solid angle* which the closed circuit C subtends at the degeneracy point. This simple expression for $\gamma_m(C)$ is dependent neither on the magnitude of the magnetic field nor on the spin which determines the dynamics of the system, but exclusively on the dimensionless quantum number m and the solid angle $\Omega(C)$. The phase factor $\exp(i\gamma_m(C))$ accompanying the adiabatic change along the closed loop is regarded as a **geometrical phase factor** associated with the degeneracy point that is singular. Figure S.1 illustrates this integral for the geometrical phase in the parameter space.

According to (S.23), the state ket changes its sign if $m\Omega(C) = \pm\pi$ after one round trip of an adiabatic process. We notice that this is the case not only for fermions with m = half integer but also for bosons with m = integer.

EXPERIMENTAL VERIFICATION

The experiment to verify (S.23) has been performed by letting polarized neutrons pass through a coil which produces a spiral magnetic field inside. The neutrons, having passed through one complete period of the spiral field after time interval T, feel the same field as the initial ones. The solid angle on the r.h.s. of (S.23) can be continuously changed by changing the ratio of the magnitude of the spiral field to the magnitude of another field applied along the direction of the spiral axis. Let us assume that the initial spin of neutrons is in a mixed state of two eigenstates: parallel and anti-parallel to the field. Under an adiabatic change the *ratio* of the numbers of these two states is preserved. The neutrons passing through the inside of the coil proceed while rotating their spins in the plane perpendicular to the field whose direction changes along the course [see (3.2.20)]. After passing through one period of the spiral field, the Berry's phase $\mp\Omega/2$ is added according to (S.23) to the phases of the spin eigenstates parallel or anti-parallel to the field. As mentioned in Section 3.2, twice as many of them contribute to the rotational angle of the spin expectation value. Therefore, besides the dynamical phase, the contribution from geometrical phase is added in the total angle of spin rotation, ϕ, during one period of the field. To wit,

$$\phi = g\mu BT/\hbar + \Omega. \qquad (S.24)$$

The value of ϕ is obtained from the measurement of the neutron polarization. The measured value of $\Delta\phi = \phi - g\mu BT/\hbar$ closely agrees with Ω determined by the experimental condition (the ratio of the fields for two directions). Thus, the validity of (S.23) for the Berry's phase was confirmed (see Fig. S.2). This experiment was performed by T. Bitter and D. Dubbers in 1987.

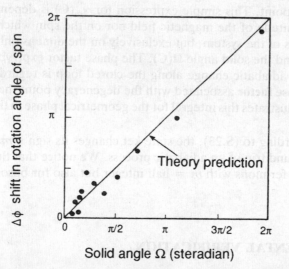

FIGURE S.2. Experimental data showing the existence of the geometrical phase. The shift $\Delta\phi$ in the rotation angle of the spin of neutrons that have passed the spiral magnetic field is almost equal to the solid angle Ω determined by the applied fields. The solid line is the prediction of the theory.

GENERAL CONSIDERATION OF TWO-LEVEL CROSSING

For general cases with external parameter $R = (x, y, z)$, the same situation as the above example of spin in the field can be realized around the degeneracy point R^* if there are some crossing levels. Choosing R^* as the origin of the parameter space, we suppose that the energy eigenstates $|+(R)\rangle$ and $|-(R)\rangle$ are degenerate at $R^* = 0$. Taking each eigenvalue to be such that $E_+(R) \geq E_-(R)$, we measure energy from the degeneracy point. We expand the Hamiltonian $H(R)$ around the origin up to the first order in R, and perform an appropriate linear transformation. Then the general Hamiltonian connecting the two levels is expressed by a 2×2 Hermitian matrix;

$$H(R) = \frac{1}{2} \begin{pmatrix} Z & X-iY \\ X+iY & -Z \end{pmatrix} = \frac{1}{2} R \cdot \sigma. \tag{S.25}$$

The energy eigenvalues are $E_\pm(R) = \pm\frac{1}{2}R$ and the two levels *conically* cross at the degeneracy point. $\nabla_R H(R)$ is equal to $\frac{1}{2}\sigma$. These expressions are the same as those of the case $m = \pm\frac{1}{2}$ for the spin in the field. Therefore, by integrating over surface S

$$V_\pm(R) = \pm\frac{\hat{R}}{2R^2}, \tag{S.26}$$

the geometrical factor for general two-level crossing is obtained as:

$$\exp(i\gamma_\pm(C)) = \exp\left\{-i \iint_{S(C)} V_\pm(R) \cdot dS\right\} = \exp\left(\mp\frac{i}{2}\Omega(C)\right). \tag{S.27}$$

As before, $\Omega(C)$ is the solid angle of the closed loop (adiabatic path) C, at the degeneracy point R^*.

We notice here that the expression (S.26) for the vector $V_\pm(R)$ is equivalent to the magnetic field (2.6.74) produced by a magnetic monopole placed at the origin. The singularity of the degeneracy point in the parameter space is structurally the same as that of a magnetic monopole, and the magnetic field by a magnetic monopole is regarded as determining the geometrical phase. We can exploit further the analogy to the magnetic field; for example, in comparing the two following relations

$$B(r) = \nabla \times A(r) \tag{S.28}$$

$$V(R) = \text{Im } \nabla_R \times \langle n(R) | \nabla_R n(R) \rangle, \tag{S.29}$$

we can interpret $\langle n(R) | \nabla_R n(R) \rangle$ as a kind of vector-potential caused by the singularity at the degeneracy point. As we have shown in (S.11), this quantity is gauge dependent, but $V(R)$, which corresponds to the magnetic flux density, B, is gauge-invariant.

AHARANOV-BOHM EFFECT REVISITED

In Section 2.6 we studied some examples where integrals along paths determine the phase factors. Among them the effect of electric as well as gravitational fields gives rise to dynamical phase factors. On the other hand, the Aharanov-Bohm effect due to the magnetic field can be shown to be just a consequence of a geometrical phase factor.

Let a small box confining an electron (charge $e < 0$) make one turn along a closed loop C, which surrounds a magnetic flux line Φ_B (see Fig. S.3). We take as R the vector connecting the origin fixed in the space and a reference point in the box. In this case the vector R is an external parameter in the real space itself. By using the vector-potential A to describe the magnetic field B, the nth wave function of the electron in the box (position vector r) is written as

$$\langle r | n(R) \rangle = \exp\left\{ \frac{ie}{\hbar c} \int_R^r A(r') \cdot dr' \right\} \psi_n (r - R) \qquad (S.30)$$

where $\psi_n(r')$ is the wave function of the electron at the r' position coordinates of the box in the absence of magnetic field. Then, in the presence

Magnetic flux line

FIGURE S.3. The Aharanov-Bohm Effect. Electron in a box takes one turn around a magnetic flux line.

of magnetic field, we can easily calculate the derivative of the wave function with respect to the external parameter to obtain

$$\langle n(\boldsymbol{R}) \mid \nabla_{\boldsymbol{R}} n(\boldsymbol{R})\rangle = \int d^3\, x \psi_n^*\, (\boldsymbol{r} - \boldsymbol{R})$$

$$\times \left\{ -\frac{ie}{\hbar c}\, \boldsymbol{A}(\boldsymbol{R})\, \psi_n(\boldsymbol{r} - \boldsymbol{R}) + \nabla_{\boldsymbol{R}} \psi_n(\boldsymbol{r} - \boldsymbol{R}) \right\} = -\frac{ie\boldsymbol{A}(\boldsymbol{R})}{\hbar c}. \quad (\text{S.31})$$

The second term under the integral vanishes for the electron in the box. From (S.6) and (S.31) we see that the geometrical phase is given by

$$\gamma_n(\text{C}) = \frac{e}{\hbar c} \oint_{\text{C}} \boldsymbol{A} \cdot d\boldsymbol{R} = \frac{e}{\hbar c} \iint_{S(\text{C})} \boldsymbol{B}(\boldsymbol{R}) \cdot d\boldsymbol{S} = \frac{e}{\hbar c}\, \Phi_B. \quad (\text{S.32})$$

This result is just the expression (2.6.70) of the Aharanov-Bohm effect obtained earlier in Chapter 2.

COMPLEX SYSTEM AND ADIABATIC POTENTIAL

Up to now, the quantity $\boldsymbol{R}$ that changes adiabatically is an external parameter. A more interesting question is to treat quantum mechanically some complex system made up of two constituent systems, where an adiabatically changing quantity is contained in the system as an internal dynamical variable. We shall discuss how the appearance of the Berry's phase in one of the constituent systems reversely influences the other constituent that moves slowly. The former can respond quickly to an adiabatic change caused by the latter. For background, let us first consider the problem of a polyatomic molecule which is composed of electrons and nuclei, a typical example of a complex system. When calculating the energy levels of rotation and vibration of a molecule, we shall apply a method that has been used for many years.

Consider the case of a diatomic molecule; we write the Hamiltonian of the complex system as

$$H_T = H_N(\boldsymbol{R}) + H_{el}\,(\boldsymbol{r}_1, \ldots, \boldsymbol{r}_N) + V(\boldsymbol{R}, \boldsymbol{r}_1, \ldots, \boldsymbol{r}_N), \quad (\text{S.33})$$

where $\boldsymbol{R}$ is the relative position coordinate between the two nuclei, $\boldsymbol{r}_1, \boldsymbol{r}_2,$ $\ldots, \boldsymbol{r}_N$ the N-electron coordinates, and the center of mass of the molecule is chosen at the origin. The first, second, and third terms of the Hamiltonian correspond to the kinetic energy of nuclei, the energy of the electron system, and the interaction energies among nuclei themselves and between nuclei and electrons respectively. Since the nuclei with heavy mass move relatively slowly and electrons with light mass move quickly, we can use an **adiabatic approximation** here. We first fix the position of the nuclei and determine the eigenstate of electrons $|n(\boldsymbol{R})\rangle$ corresponding to the fixed configuration of the nuclei

$$\{H_{el}\,(\boldsymbol{r}_1,\ldots,\boldsymbol{r}_N)\,+\,V(\boldsymbol{R},\boldsymbol{r}_1,\ldots,\boldsymbol{r}_N)\}\,|n(\boldsymbol{R})\rangle$$

$$= U_n(\boldsymbol{R})\,|n(\boldsymbol{R})\rangle, \quad \text{(S.34)}$$

where $U_n(\boldsymbol{R})$ is the energy of the nth eigenstate. We next approximate the state ket of the complex system in the form of a product of the nucleus ket $|A\rangle$ and the electron ket

$$\Psi = |A\rangle\,|n(\boldsymbol{R})\rangle. \quad \text{(S.35)}$$

Substituting this into the Schrödinger equation $H_T\Psi = E\Psi$ of the complex system, we obtain

$$(H_N(\boldsymbol{R})\,+\,U_n(\boldsymbol{R}))\,|A\rangle\,|n(\boldsymbol{R})\rangle = E_n\,|A\rangle\,|n(\boldsymbol{R})\rangle. \quad \text{(S.36)}$$

Since $H_N(\boldsymbol{R})$ is the differential operator with respect to coordinates of the nuclei $\boldsymbol{R}$, it will operate on both the nucleus state ket $|A\rangle$ and the electron state ket $|n(\boldsymbol{R})\rangle$. However, we can ignore the derivative term of electron state ket with respect to $\boldsymbol{R}$, as long as the amplitude of the relative motion of the two nuclei is small compared to the equilibrium distance between them. This approximation is the so-called **Born-Oppenheimer approximation**. Equation (S.36) then leads to a simple eigenvalue equation that involves only the coordinates of the nuclei, as follows:

$$(H_N(\boldsymbol{R})\,+\,U_n(\boldsymbol{R}))\,|A\rangle = E_n|A\rangle. \quad \text{(S.37)}$$

In the above equation the effective potential $U_n(\boldsymbol{R})$ that determines the motion of the nuclei is called **adiabatic potential**. It is the sum of the Coulomb repulsive force between nuclei and the energy of electrons for fixed $\boldsymbol{R}$. $U_n(R)$ is obtained for each level of the electron system. The minimum $U_n(R)$ gives approximately the equilibrium distance between nuclei about which the molecule vibrates and rotates. The corresponding energy levels are given approximately by

$$E_n \cong \hbar\omega_n(N + \tfrac{1}{2}) + \frac{\hbar^2 L(L + 1)}{2I_n}$$

$$N = 0,1,2,\ldots, L = 0,1,2,\ldots, \quad \text{(S.38)}$$

where ω_n stands for the angular frequency determined by the curvature at the minimum of $U_n(R)$ and I_n is the moment of inertia of the molecule. If the two nuclei are identical, L is further limited to be an even or odd number by permutation symmetry.

DYNAMICAL JAHN-TELLER EFFECT

Our object is to investigate the role of the geometrical phase in a complex system. To this end, let us consider the case in which the electronic states are degenerate for a certain space configuration R^* of the nuclei; that is, for a case such that the adiabatic potentials satisfy

$$U_n(R^*) = U_m(R^*) \tag{S.39}$$

and cross one another at R^*. Let us remember that an adiabatic change of one turn around the degeneracy point R^* in the R-space causes a geometrical phase. Thus for the case of the diatomic molecule where the distance associated with the nuclei is a single one-dimensional parameter in determining the electron state, this is not enough to discuss the Berry's phase. We need to consider tri-atomic molecules (ions) or a group of atoms in a crystal. Here we use the latter one as an example for discussion purpose. Generally in crystals the electronic states in the crystal fields (e.g., a pair of d-orbital states) are often degenerate in energy for certain atomic configurations of high symmetry. Then, in most cases, the crystal becomes slightly distorted to assume a lower symmetric configuration, and thus moves in a more stable state by lowering its electronic energy. This phenomenon is what is called the **Jahn-Teller effect**. To make the argument simpler, consider the electronic state of the central ion surrounded by four atoms in a plane. Suppose that the four atoms are placed in a square configuration, for which electronic states $|a\rangle$ and $|b\rangle$ extending their orbitals in different directions respectively are degenerate. The deformation of the lattice then removes the two-fold degeneracy. Displacements of atoms from the equilibrium position, taken on the square lattice points, are expressed in terms of the normal modes of vibration. Among the several possible normal modes, we look at the two independent modes A and B as shown in Fig. S.4, which couple with the degenerate electronic states. Suppose that A and B have the same eigen frequency, ω, and we denote their normal coordinates as Q_a and Q_b, respectively.[†] On the other hand, the

FIGURE S.4. Distortion of lattices causing dynamical Jahn-Teller effect. Two normal modes, Q_a and Q_b, are shown.

[†]Our explanation for the Jahn-Teller effect is not exact but conceptual.

electron system is described by a linear-combination of the two degenerate levels

$$|\alpha\rangle = C_a|a\rangle + C_b|b\rangle. \tag{S.40}$$

Then the effective Hamiltonian of the normal vibration, which couples with the electron system, can be written in the form of

$$\frac{P_a^2 + P_b^2}{2\mu} + \frac{\mu\omega^2}{2}(Q_a^2 + Q_b^2) - K\begin{pmatrix} -Q_a & Q_b \\ Q_b & Q_a \end{pmatrix} \tag{S.41}$$

where P_a and P_b are the conjugate momenta to Q_a and Q_b, respectively; μ is the effective mass of the normal vibration and K is the strength of the coupling between electrons and lattices. The matrix that represents the interaction operates on the electron state vector $\binom{C_a}{C_b}$. We have expressed the interaction by the first order terms of the normal coordinates, Q_a and Q_b, assuming that the vibration of the atomic displacement is small. For normal coordinates written as

$$Q_a = \rho \cos\theta, \quad Q_b = \rho \sin\theta, \tag{S.42}$$

the eigenenergy ε and the eigenket of the electron system are obtained by solving

$$-K\rho \begin{pmatrix} -\cos\theta & \sin\theta \\ -\sin\theta & \cos\theta \end{pmatrix} \begin{pmatrix} C_a \\ C_b \end{pmatrix} = \varepsilon \begin{pmatrix} C_a \\ C_b \end{pmatrix} \tag{S.43}$$

as

$$\varepsilon = \pm K\rho \tag{S.44}$$

$$|+(\theta)\rangle = \cos\frac{\theta}{2}|a\rangle - \sin\frac{\theta}{2}|b\rangle$$

$$|-(\theta)\rangle = \sin\frac{\theta}{2}|a\rangle + \cos\frac{\theta}{2}|b\rangle. \tag{S.45}$$

From (S.41) and (S.44) the adiabatic potential for the normal coordinates is given by the two-valued function

$$V_{ad}^{\pm}(\rho) = \tfrac{1}{2}\mu\omega^2\rho^2 \pm K\rho. \tag{S.46}$$

If one illustrates the surface of the adiabatic potential as a function of Q_a and Q_b, a "Mexican hat" shape like Fig. S.5 emerges. The potential consists of two axially-symmetric surfaces and assumes a minimum value at $\rho_0 = K/\mu\omega^2$.

FIGURE S.5. Adiabatic potential surface related to dynamical Jahn-Teller effect (S.46).

Here we notice that the electron state kets (S.45) change sign for rotation by 2π around the symmetry axis:

$$|\pm(\theta = 2\pi)\rangle = (-1)\,|\pm(\theta = 0)\rangle. \qquad (S.47)$$

Formally, this is the same as the rotation of the spin with $S = \frac{1}{2}$ discussed in Section 3.2, since the sinusoidal dependence of the ket on the rotation in (S.45) is given by just one half of the rotation angle, $\theta/2$. Naturally, in our case, it is the *orbital state* ket of the electron system that has changed sign and thus has nothing to do with spins. The factor (-1) on the r.h.s. of (S.47) is easily shown to be just the Berry's phase factor. Here the origin of the $Q_a Q_b$-plane is a degeneracy point of the electron system. When the vector (Q_a, Q_b) describing the state of the lattice deformation circulates once around this origin, the corresponding "solid angle" amounts to 2π. Therefore, from the general expression (S.27) the electron state ket is multiplied by the geometrical phase factor $\exp(\mp i2\pi/2) = -1$. It is to be noted that as early as in 1963, this kind of Berry's phase was already taken into account in a very natural way by G. Herzberg and H. C. Longuet-Higgins, when they solved the problem of a coupled system with degeneracy while studying poly-atomic molecules.

As shown here, for such an electron-lattice system in which degenerate electronic states couple to two lattice vibrational modes, a minimum of the adiabatic potential does not form a well but a continuous valley. Thus, the dynamical deformation of the lattice and the corresponding adiabatic state change of the electron system are both incorporated. This is the so-called **dynamical Jahn-Teller effect**. Now, let us consider the dynamical motion of the normal coordinates (Q_a, Q_b) (that is, (ρ, θ)) under the adiabatic potential (S.46) and find the influence of the Berry's phase on the dynamics. The two-dimensional Schrödinger's equation to be solved is

$$\left\{ -\frac{\hbar^2}{2\mu}\left(\frac{\partial^2}{\partial\rho^2} + \frac{1}{\rho}\frac{\partial}{\partial\rho} + \frac{1}{\rho^2}\frac{\partial^2}{\partial\theta^2}\right) + V_{ad}^{\pm}(\rho)\right\}\Psi(\rho,\theta) = E\Psi(\rho,\theta), \qquad (S.48)$$

where the wave function $\Psi(\rho,\theta)$ is expressed by the product of the nucleus piece $\phi_\pm(\rho,\theta)$ and the electron state ket

$$\Psi(\rho,\theta) = \phi_+(\rho,\theta) \, |+(\theta)\rangle + \phi_-(\rho,\theta) \, |-(\theta)\rangle. \qquad (S.49)$$

The adiabatic potential written as $V_{ad}^\pm$ in (S.48) is to be understood as acting on ϕ_+ in $\Psi(\rho,\theta)$ for V_{ad}^+ and on ϕ_- for V_{ad}^-. Since (S.48) is a differential equation with separable variables we can solve it by choosing the nucleus wave function as

$$\phi_\pm(\rho,\theta) = f_\pm(\rho) \, e^{ij\theta}. \qquad (S.50)$$

Here the most important point is that the state function $\Psi(\rho,\theta)$, which describes the whole coupled system consisting of electrons and lattices, must remain a single valued function. The state ket of the electron system changes sign when θ is rotated by 2π. Therefore, in order to cancel this sign change, $\phi_\pm(\rho,\theta)$ must change its sign as well to preserve the single-valued nature of $\Psi(\rho,\theta)$! From this requirement we conclude that $\exp(ij2\pi) = -1$, that is

$$j = (l + \tfrac{1}{2}) = \text{half integer}, \, (l = \text{integer}). \qquad (S.51)$$

The presence of the Berry's phase has changed the quantum number that characterizes the motion of atoms, from the usual integer number to *half integer* one.[†]

If two adiabatic levels are well separated, we are allowed to solve the equation (S.48) by ignoring the mixing between $\phi_+(\rho,\theta)|+(\theta)\rangle$ and $\phi_-(\rho,\theta)|-(\theta)\rangle$. Then the low energy excitations in the potential valley is approximately expressed by

$$E_{nj} \cong (n + \tfrac{1}{2})\hbar\omega + \frac{\hbar^2(j^2 + \tfrac{1}{4})}{2\mu\rho_o^2}. \qquad (S.52)$$

$$(n: \text{integer}, \, j: \text{half integer})$$

The result is just the sum of the energies of vibration along the radial direction and those of rotation in the plane of the normal mode coordinates. (The factor $\tfrac{1}{4}$ in the numerator of the second term comes from the electron system.) In the picture of lattice deformation they are the energies related to oscillation of the *magnitude* of the atomic displacement and transformation of the deformation *patterns*, respectively. These kinds of energy levels have been well analyzed experimentally through spectral measurements for ions in crystals and poly-atomic molecular gases and also through several physical measurements on matter. So scientists in these fields have

---

[†]A general discussion is given using path integral method and action in H. Kuratsuji and S. Iida, *Prog. Theor. Phys.* **74** (1985), p. 439 concerning how Berry's phase modifies the quantization condition of dynamical variables.

been familiar with the half-integer quantization which appears in rotational levels for sometime. After Berry's paper, the precise spectral experiment on a tri-atomic molecular gas, Na_3 was repeated again in 1986, and the half-integer quantization was reconfirmed by G. Delacretaz *et al*.

UNIVERSALITY OF GEOMETRICAL PHASE

So far we have discussed a geometrical phase called the Berry's phase by taking quantum-mechanical systems as example. However, let us notice that the Planck's constant is lost in the general expression giving the phase in (S.27). In this respect it is totally different from the dynamical factor (2.6.7) discussed in Chapter 2. Therefore, although the original derivation by Berry is based on quantum mechanics, the geometrical phase factor itself is expected to be universal, regardless of quantum-mechanical systems or classical-mechanical ones. The question is then, where can we find a geometrical phase in a classical system effected by an adiabatic change?

Detection of the Berry's phase has been done for light, which is on the one hand very quantum-mechanical and relativistic, but on the other hand also describable by classical electrodynamics. By letting linearly polarized light pass through the inside of a spirally-twisted optical fiber, one observes the rotation of its polarization plane. According to quantum theory a photon is a particle with spin one, and the spin in an eigenstate is either parallel to the direction of propagation or anti-parallel to it. (This leads to the *helicity* eigenvalue being $+1$ or -1 respectively.) Each eigenstate is a circularly polarized light with a rotational direction opposite to each other. When the linearly-polarized light, which is a combination of these two states, passes through the inside of a once-twisted optical fiber, the propagation vector (the relevant quantity for an adiabatic change here) describes a closed circuit. (At the same time the spin also rotates.) As a result the different Berry's phase is added to each component of the combination state, so that the polarization plane of light rotates. In the 1986 experiment performed by Chiao, Wu, and Tomita, the agreement between the rotational angle of the polarization plane and the solid angle determined by the degree of twist of the optical fiber was confirmed. On the other hand, the effect can also be explained by classical electrodynamics as a result of integration of continuous *parallel transformation* of the electric field vector inside the optical fiber. Although the directions of light at the entrance and the exit are parallel, a difference between the polarization planes is produced for the optical fiber which is twisted in the middle.

Furthermore, even for a classical-mechanical system a geometrical phase factor emerges when we oscillate a conical pendulum on the revolving earth. Seen from the rest coordinate system the time needed for change in the gravity direction at a certain place on the revolving earth is very much larger than the period of the conical pendulum. That is, the direction of the gravity acting on the pendulum *adiabatically* changes as the earth rotates. Let us take the rotational angular velocity of the pendulum in the orbital plane to be ω. In the total rotational angle θ of the conical pendulum after one day (earth period of revolution = T) a deviation by $\Delta\theta$ from the simply predicted value ωT, a dynamical angle, is realized. That is,

$$\theta = \omega T + \Delta\theta. \tag{S.53}$$

The shift $\Delta\theta$ is dependent on the latitude of the measurement point but is independent of the gravity and the length of the string which govern the motion of the pendulum. This is after all a geometrical phase and is generally called the **Hannay's angle**.

So the phenomenon is quite similar to the rotation of a quantum spin in a varying magnetic field. Let us compare the two expressions for the total rotational angles in these two cases, (S.24) and (S.53). We may speculate that $\Delta\theta = \Omega$. For the conical pendulum, *this is the case*. The Hannay's angle is equal to the solid angle subtended at the center of the earth by the closed circuit which the gravity vector acting on the pendulum draws following the rotation of the earth. This is a geometrical phase in classical mechanics corresponding to the Berry's phase in quantum mechanics.

In this way geometrical phases accompanying adiabatic changes appear in various systems such as oscillating systems, optical systems, spin systems, molecular systems, and so on, regardless of whether we are dealing with classical or quantum mechanics. In solid state physics, this kind of argument has also been used to explain the quantum Hall effect besides the dynamical Jahn–Teller effect discussed above. Last but not least Berry's phase has also impacted field theory. Without prior knowledge of the geometrical phase, it has nevertheless been possible to accommodate such a phase naturally into theories if one treats precisely Schrödinger's equation, Newton's equation, Maxwell's equations, and the path-integrals. However, we can conclude by saying that our understanding of quantum mechanics has been deepened since the existence of geometrical phases was explicitly revealed.

SUPPLEMENT II

Non-Exponential Decays

Radioactive nuclei furnish us with one of the best known examples of unstable, or decaying, systems. The assumption that the radioactive decay of any nucleus is a random process, and, furthermore, that even in a large sample each nucleus decays independently, leads to the familiar *exponential decay law*,

$$N(t) = N(t_0)e^{-\lambda(t-t_0)}, \tag{T.1a}$$

where $N(t)$ is the number of nuclei that have not decayed after a time t, and λ is a constant determined by the properties of the individual nucleus. Since the fluctuations in (T.1a) are small only when the number of nuclei is large, we can rephrase the radioactive decay law as a probabilistic statement: The probability that any particular nucleus will not undergo a decay in a time interval between t_0 and t is given by

$$P(t) = e^{-\lambda(t-t_0)}, \quad t > t_0 \tag{T.1b}$$

The quantity $P(t)$ may be called the survival probability. Notice that $P(t_0) = 1$; this is the statement of our knowledge that the nucleus under examination had not decayed at $t = t_0$. Here, we investigate the form of $P(t)$ for quantum mechanical systems. This is necessary because within the framework of quantum mechanics, probabilities are derived from fundamental probability amplitudes, so that it is not *a priori* obvious that the assumptions leading to (T.1) can be consistently incorporated.

In keeping with our intuitive notions, we will say that a quantum system is in an unstable state if the survival probability for that state reduces to zero monotonically with time.[†] If the state vector of the system at time t is given by $|q_i, t\rangle$ (here, q_i denote all quantum numbers necessary to specify the state), the survival probability $P(t)$ is given in terms of the survival amplitude (c.f. the analogous discussion in Chapter 2 of text),

$$a(t) \equiv \langle q_i, t_0 | q_i, t \rangle = \langle q_i, t_0 | U(t, t_0) | q_i, t_0 \rangle, \tag{T.2}$$

by

$$P(t) = |a(t)|^2. \tag{T.3}$$

[†]It is important to stress the requirement of monotonicity, since it is possible to find examples where the survival probability exhibits an oscillatory behavior (see, e.g., Rabi oscillations, Sec. 5.5 of text). Notice that the oscillatory behavior persists even when the external potential is time independent).

For an isolated system, the Hamiltonian is time independent, and the unitary operator $U(t, t_0)$ in (T.2) that evolves the states from an initial time t_0 to a later time t is given by $U(t, t_0) \equiv e^{-iH(t-t_0)/\hbar}$. We thus see that if $|q_i, t\rangle$ is a normalized *stationary state* so that it has a definite value of energy, $a(t)$ is a pure phase and $P(t) = 1$.

Although an unstable state of a quantum mechanical system cannot be represented as one of the energy eigenkets, the assumption of completeness of the eigenkets of the Hamiltonian tells us that we can represent the unstable state as a linear superposition over these eigenkets with time-independent complex coefficients; that is,

$$|q_i, t\rangle = S_\varepsilon |\varepsilon, t\rangle\langle\varepsilon|q_i, t_0\rangle. \tag{T.4}$$

Here, S denotes a summation (integration) over the discrete (continuous) part of the spectrum of H. We can thus write (T.2) as,

$$a(t) = S_\varepsilon e^{-i\varepsilon(t-t_0)/\hbar}|\langle\varepsilon|q_i, t_0\rangle|^2. \tag{T.5}$$

It is reasonable to suppose that the unstable states are orthogonal to the (normalizable) discrete eigenstates of the Hamiltonian which, as we argued above, cannot decay. We will, therefore, assume that unstable states are associated with the continuum states of the Hamiltonian. This is in keeping with our intuitive expectation from the fact that an unstable particle decays only to continuum states; that is, the unstable state has non-vanishing projections only on continuum states into which it can decay. In this case, the survival amplitude in (T.5) can be written as the Fourier transform,

$$a(t) = \int d\varepsilon\, e^{-i\varepsilon t/\hbar}\rho(\varepsilon), \tag{T.6}$$

of a real non-negative function

$$\rho(\varepsilon) \equiv |\langle\varepsilon|q_i, t_0\rangle|^2, \tag{T.7}$$

where (for later convenience) we have set $t_0 = 0$.

Notice that $\langle\varepsilon|q_i\rangle$ is just the wave-function for the decaying state in the energy representation, so that $\rho(\varepsilon)$ is just the probability density that an energy measurement of this state yields a value ε. If $\rho(\varepsilon)$ has the familiar Breit-Wigner form,

$$\rho_{BW}(\varepsilon) = (\Gamma/2\pi)/[(\varepsilon - \varepsilon_0)^2 + \Gamma^2/4], \tag{T.8a}$$

we leave it to the reader (c.f. the discussion (5.8.21) to (5.8.24) of text) to show that the corresponding survival probability has the form

$$P_{BW}(t) = e^{-\Gamma|t-t_0|/\hbar}, \tag{T.8b}$$

so that the decay of the state is indeed described by the exponential decay law.

We will now show that with some very reasonable assumptions, Eq. (T.1b) can *never be exact* regardless of the nature of the quantum system. In particular, we will show that for very long times, the survival probability must decrease at a rate that is slower than exponential. To see this, we first remark that any interacting quantum-mechanical system must have a ground state; that is, there is a state $|\varepsilon_0\rangle$, with $H|\varepsilon_0\rangle = \varepsilon_0|\varepsilon_0\rangle$ such that ε_0 is the smallest eigenvalue of H. If this was not the case, it would be possible to extract arbitrarily large amounts of energy from the system by interactions that send it to eigenstates of increasingly lower energy. The existence of the ground state obviously implies that the probability density function $\rho(\varepsilon)$ introduced via (T.7) above vanishes if $\varepsilon < \varepsilon_0$.

To proceed further, we introduce a theorem due to Paley and Wiener (R. Paley and N. Wiener, "Fourier Transforms in the Complex Domain," Am. Math. Soc. Pub. Vol. **XIX**, 1934), which can be stated as follows:

If $a(t)$ and $\rho(\varepsilon)$ are Fourier transforms of each other such that $\rho(\varepsilon) = 0$ for $\varepsilon < \varepsilon_0$ and $\int_{-\infty}^{\infty} dt |a(t)|^2$ is finite, then $\int_{-\infty}^{\infty} dt |\ln|a(t)||/(1 + t^2)$ is also finite.

We will see below (where we follow essentially the argument of L. A. Khalfin, Sov. Phys. JETP Vol. **6**, pg. 1053, 1958) that this remarkable result strongly constrains the long time behavior of the survival probability. First, we note that the fact that $\rho(\varepsilon)$ is real implies $a^*(t) = a(-t)$ so that if the survival probability decays sufficiently fast for large times, $\int_{-\infty}^{\infty} dt |a(t)|^2$ is finite, and the Fourier transform pair $a(t)$ and $\rho(\varepsilon)$ in (T.6) indeed satisfies the conditions for the Paley-Wiener theorem. Thus, for large times, $|\ln|a(t)||$ is required to increase slower than linearly, and hence the exponential behavior for $|a(t)|$ is precluded.

We point out that while our general argument implies that the long time behavior of the survival probability cannot be exactly exponential, it does not shed any light on when the non-exponential behavior sets in or on how much the survival probability deviates from the exponential form. The former requires the specification of a time scale other than the lifetime, and so is probably dependent on the details of the dynamics that causes the decay. We also remark that the Breit-Wigner form $\rho_{BW}(\varepsilon)$ in (T.8a) (which led to the exponential form for the survival probability (T.8b)) is non-vanishing for all values of ε, and so violates the conditions of applicability of the Paley-Wiener theorem. Physically this form of $\rho(\varepsilon)$ violates our assumption of the existence of a ground state, so that the resulting exponential behavior can be, at best, an approximation to the real situation. It will be left as an exercise for the reader to check that if we cut off the Breit-Wigner form of ρ, the survival probability $P(t)$ decays according to a power law for large times.

We stress here that the fact that we have not seen deviations from the exponential decay law at large times does not vitiate our general arguments that do not tell us when the non-exponential behavior sets in. It could be that non-exponential decay occurs only after many lifetimes in which case it would be very difficult to observe. There are, however, equally general arguments that imply deviations from the exponential decay law for very short times (defined precisely below) which we turn to now.

We begin by noting (our discussion essentially follows that of B. Misra and E. C. G. Sudarshan, J. Math. Phys. Vol. **18**, 756, 1977) that the time derivative of the survival amplitude (T.6),

$$da/dt = \int d\varepsilon(-i\varepsilon/\hbar)e^{-i\varepsilon t/\hbar}\rho(\varepsilon), \tag{T.9}$$

is a well defined, continuous function of t if we further assume (as is physically reasonable) that the decaying state has a finite energy expectation value. We can, therefore, evaluate the rate of change of the survival probability,

$$dP(t=\tau)/dt = [da^*(\tau)/dt]a(\tau) + a^*(\tau)[da(\tau)/dt]$$

$$= -\dot{a}(-\tau)a(\tau) + a(-\tau)\dot{a}(\tau) \tag{T.10}$$

where we have used $a^*(t) = a(-t)$ and the dot denotes differentiation with respect to the argument. We thus see that,

$$dP(t=0)/dt = 0, \tag{T.11}$$

which of course means that the survival probability cannot be an exponential at $t = 0$! We remind the reader that in (T.6), $t = 0$ was defined as the latest instant of time when we knew that the system had not yet decayed. This implies that $t = 0$ is also the time when the system was last observed or, in Dirac's terminology, the time of preparation of the state of the system. We remark that while our argument clearly precludes the possibility of exponential decay at $t = 0$, it sets no limitations on when exponential decay may set in.

Taking this analysis a step further, we can consider successive observations of a system. As discussed above, (T.11) must hold after each of these observations. The implications of this are schematically illustrated in Fig. T.1. The survival probability for a system prepared at $t = t_1$ is shown by the curve labeled 1 in Fig. T.1. Notice that, in keeping with (T.11), the slope of the curve is zero at $t = t_1$. If this system is allowed to evolve undisturbed, the survival probability will follow the first curve which may rapidly take an exponential form (of course, for very large values of t, not shown in the figure, we have seen that the decay will be slower than exponential). The size of the flat region at $t = t_1$ is not determined by our general arguments and must be dependent on dynamical details.

If, however, an observation is made on this system at $t = t_2$, our arguments above imply that (T.11) must hold at $t = t_2$, so that the system

FIGURE T.1. A schematic of the short time behavior of the survival probability $P(t)$ of a state of a quantum mechanical system prepared at $t = t_1$ is illustrated by the curve labeled 1. The curves labeled 2, 3, 4 show how $P(t)$ is modified by observations of the state at times t_2, t_3, t_4. Notice that each successive measurement increases the survival probability from what it would have been had the system not been disturbed by that measurement.

now follows the curve labeled 2. Successive observations at $t = t_3$, $t = t_4$, etc., would make the system evolve along the other curves in the figure. We see that the qualitative effect of these successive observations is to increase the survival probability of the system being observed from what it would have been if the system was allowed to evolve undisturbed after its preparation at $t = t_1$. This inhibition of the decay appears to be a feature of quantum mechanics, once we grant that each observation of the system corresponds to the preparation of the quantum mechanical state.

These arguments imply that it should be possible to slow down the decay of a quantum mechanical system by making successive rapid observations on it. In the limit of continuous observation (provided that this can be operationally defined), an unstable system would not decay. This has been referred to as the **quantum Zeno effect**.

Deviations from the exponential decay law have never been observed for radioactive nuclei or for the well measured K_L mesons of particle physics. W. M. Itano *et al.*, Phys. Rev. Vol. **A41**, 2295, 1990, have however recently demonstrated that the rate for transitions between two discrete levels of a quantum system is indeed inhibited by successive measurements of the state of the system. These authors have further shown that the amount of inhibition increases with the frequency with which the system is monitored. They argue that their results are completely consistent with the expectation from quantum mechanics assuming, as usual, that each measurement is effectively equivalent to preparing afresh the state of the system. This serves to bring home the fact that while this inhibition of transitions may be somewhat surprising, it is a consequence of the structure of quantum mechanics.

At this point, it is fair to warn the reader that we have only touched upon the basic question in our discussion of the quantum Zeno effect. There is considerable (and somewhat controversial) literature on the physical implications of this result. It is not our purpose here to discuss these in detail, nor is it our purpose to enter into various subtleties (both physical and philosophical) of the issues involved. For this, we refer the reader to the original literature.

To sum up, we have presented very general arguments to demonstrate that the decay of any quantum mechanical state must deviate from the familiar exponential decay law, both for very long and for very short times as measured from the instant of preparation of the state of the system. These deviations have not been experimentally observed for systems that exhibit (at least approximately) exponential decay. Since these arguments refer only to asymptotically long and short times, they do not preclude the possibility that a decaying quantum mechanical system may exhibit (essentially) exponential decay over most of its lifetime. Indeed by making suitable approximations, the exponential decay law has been derived (see, e.g., Merzbacher [1970], Chapter 18) for model systems whose decay can be described in perturbation theory. It is instructive to study these approximations and trace why they are invalid for very long and very short times (as they must be in view of our general considerations).

Bibliography

The literature in quantum mechanics is very large and very diverse. We present here a bibliography of those books to which we refer specifically in our text as well as a reference section of more-elementary texts in quantum mechanics (generally at the undergraduate level) that provide the background to our book (addressed primarily to the first-year graduate student). Since many books have been written about elementary quantum mechanics, the list in this reference section is, of course, not meant to be complete. The editor has studied some of the suggested books, read others, glanced at a few, and likely missed others. The editor apologizes in advance if, as is all too probable, there are glaring omissions. Throughout the book little attempt has been made to quote original papers; the few that have been quoted are noted in the footnotes or the text itself. This we believe to be appropriate in a book whose primary purpose is to serve as the textbook to a basic beginning graduate course.

Baym, G. *Lectures on Quantum Mechanics*, New York: W. A. Benjamin, 1969.

Bethe, H. A., and R. W. Jackiw. *Intermediate Quantum Mechanics*, 2nd ed., New York: W. A. Benjamin, 1968.

Biedenharn, L. C., and H. Van Dam. (eds) *Quantum Theory of Angular Momentum*, New York: Academic Press, 1965.

Bjorken, J. D., and S. D. Drell, *Relativistic Quantum Fields*, New York: McGraw-Hill, 1965.

Bohm, D. *Quantum Theory*, Englewood Cliffs, NJ: Prentice-Hall, 1951.

Dirac, P. A. M. *Quantum Mechanics*, 4th ed., London: Oxford Univ. Press, 1958.

487

Dirac, P. A. M. *Quantum Mechanics*, 4th ed., London: Oxford Univ. Press, 1958.

Edmonds, A. R. *Angular Momentum in Quantum Mechanics*, Princeton, NJ: Princeton University Press, 1960.

Fermi, E. *Nuclear Physics*, Chicago: University of Chicago Press, 1950.

Feynman, R. P., and A. R. Hibbs. *Quantum Mechanics and Path Integrals*, New York: McGraw-Hill, 1964.

Finkelstein, R. J. *Nonrelativistic Mechanics*, Reading, MA: W. A. Benjamin, 1973.

Frauenfelder, H., and E. M. Henley. *Subatomic Physics*, Englewood Cliffs, NJ: Prentice-Hall, 1974.

French, A. P., and E. F. Taylor. *An Introduction to Quantum Physics*, New York: W. W. Norton, 1978.

Goldberger, M. L., and K. M. Watson. *Collision Theory*, New York: Wiley, 1964.

Goldstein, H. *Classical Mechanics*, 2nd. ed., Reading, MA: Addison-Wesley, 1980.

Gottfried, K. *Quantum Mechanics*, vol. I, New York: W. A. Benjamin, 1966.

Jackson, J. D. *Classical Electrodynamics*, 2nd ed., New York: Wiley, 1975.

Landau, L. D.; and E. M. Lifschitz. *Quantum Mechanics*, Reading, MA: Addison-Wesley, 1958.

Merzbacher, E. *Quantum Mechanics*, 2nd ed., New York: Wiley, 1970.

Messiah, A. *Quantum Mechanics*, New York: Interscience, 1961.

Morse, P. M., and H. Feshbach. *Methods of Theoretical Physics*, (2 vols.), New York: McGraw-Hill, 1953.

Newton, R. G. *Scattering Theory of Waves and Particles*, 2nd. ed., New York: McGraw-Hill, 1982.

Preston, M. *Physics of the Nucleus*, Reading, MA: Addison-Wesley, 1962.

Sakurai, J. J. *Advanced Quantum Mechanics*, Reading, MA: Addison-Wesley, 1967.

Sargent III, M., M. O. Scully, and W. E. Lamb, Jr. *Laser Physics*, Reading, MA: Addison-Wesley, 1974.

Saxon, D. S. *Elementary Quantum Mechanics*. San Francisco: Holden-Day, 1968.

Schiff, L. *Quantum Mechanics*, 3rd. ed., New York: McGraw-Hill, 1968.

Tomanaga, S. *Quantum Mechanics I*, Amsterdam: North-Holland, 1962.

Whittaker, E. T., and G. N. Watson. *A Courst of Modern Analysis*, New York: Cambridge University Press, 1965.

REFERENCE SECTION

Dicke, R. H., and J. P. Wittke, *Introduction to Quantum Mechanics*, Reading, MA: Addison-Wesley, 1960.

A very readable but terse book at the junior or senior level. It discusses a few topics, notably quantum statistics, not usually treated in textbooks at this level.

Feynman, R. P., R. B. Leighton, and M. Sands, *The Feynman Lectures on Physics*, vol. 3, *Quantum Mechanics*, Reading, MA: Addison-Wesley, 1965.

This is an introduction to quantum mechanics that approaches the subject from the viewpoint of state vectors, an approach that—together with Dirac's classic —greatly stimulated the spirit and substance of the earlier chapters of our own book. The many fascinating examples (for example, the Stern-Gerlach experiment) discussed with a minimum of formalism are to be noted in particular.

Gasiorowicz, S. *Quantum Physics*, New York: Wiley 1974.

This book is at a level comparable to that of Dicke and Wittke 1960. Gasiorowicz is known to be a very effective teacher, who makes difficult concepts simple and clear even in advanced research areas of particle theory. Hence it is not surprising that his quantum physics book reflects that clarity of purpose that enhances the readability of the book.

Mandl, F. *Quantum Mechanics*, London: Butterworths Scientific Publications, 1957.

This book contains a clear and compact presentation of the foundation and mathematical principles of wave mechanics at a level comparable to Gasiorowicz's book.

Matthews, P. T. *Introduction to Quantum Mechanics*, 3rd ed., London: McGraw-Hill, 1974.

This third edition is lucid, concise, self-contained, and addressed to the undergraduate. It is a mathematically oriented introduction to development in wave and matrix mechanics, based on clearly defined postulates.

Mott, N. F. *Elements of Wave Mechanics*, London: Cambridge University Press, 1952.

A short but delightful treatment of wave mechanics at an elementary theoretical level by one of the pioneers.

Park, D. *Introduction to the Quantum Theory*, 2nd. ed., New York: McGraw-Hill, 1974.

Intended for advanced undergraduates, this attractive book by an outstanding pedagoguc has a general introduction to quantum theory, followed by selected applications to various branches of physics, illustrating different aspects of the theory. The applications appear to require little teaching, and hence students can use the book as a reference.

Pauling, L., and E. B. Wilson, *Introduction to Quantum Mechanics*, New York: McGraw-Hill, 1935.

Though one of the older texts, it is still well worth studying. There is a surprisingly complete treatment of the hydrogen atom and harmonic oscillator from the wave mechanics viewpoint.

Rojansky, V. *Introductory Quantum Mechanics*, Englewood Cliffs, NJ: Prentice-Hall, 1938.

Despite its vintage, this book remains a classical text, especially valuable for its detailed coverage of the fundamental principles of wave and matrix mechanics.

Index